Welcome to

SRA Real Math

Take your students farther than they've ever imagined.

Discover the Difference of Real Math

Discover *Real Math* to help meet today's standards

Let quality mathematics research support the daily challenges you face.

Great teachers need great tools to meet the demands of education today. Just as each teacher takes a different approach to teaching, each student has individual ways of understanding. *Real Math* offers you meaningful instruction specifically designed to reach each student.

Real Math's true-to-life applications, standards-based curriculum, and extensive teacher resources will help you open your students' eyes to all math has to offer. They learn essential math skills while understanding the important role of math in daily life.

The nuts and bolts.
Understanding is at the heart of every *Real Math* lesson. Success in basic computational skills is only the beginning. The difference with *Real Math* is that it elevates basic learning to a new level of engagement and application by connecting thinking and reasoning to learning.

Why settle for merely "Adequate" Yearly Progress?
More than ever before, teachers are accountable for the performance of their students. Your focus as a teacher is being directed toward meeting mandated goals like Adequate Yearly Progress (AYP) or student performance on mandated tests.

Real Math offers you **differentiated instruction** designed to help you make AYP and meet standards by offering **research-based, standards-based**, quality education for all students, including English language learners, high-achieving students, and those in need of intervention.

The test of time.
Incorporating over 30 years of research with the latest mathematical findings, *Real Math* helps you build and reinforce learning with proven lessons. *Real Math* is an all-inclusive tool for engaging your students while building their math competency.

Take five.
Just as Reading First has identified key elements for teaching children to read, the mathematics research community* has identified five key proficiencies that students need to achieve in math. Those strands are: understanding, computing, applying, reasoning, and engaging.

> *Real Math* is the first program to fully integrate all five strands of mathematical proficiency throughout every lesson.

"*The program has been very beneficial for teachers and students. Teachers have a variety of tools to help struggling students as well as those children doing an outstanding job who need enrichment. The teacher manual is so user-friendly that our teachers can pick it up on a daily basis and implement a successful lesson with ease.*"

–Kim Leitzke
Math Teacher Leader
Barton Elementary School
NCLB Blue Ribbon Award 2003
Milwaukee, WI

Use actual working tools to demonstrate mathematical thinking as it is applied outside of the classroom.

* Kilpatrick, J., Swafford, J. and Findell, B. eds. *Adding It Up: Helping Children Learn Mathematics.* Washington, D.C.: National Research Council/National Academy Press, 2001.

Kilpatrick, Jeremy, Martin, W. Gary, and Schifter, Deborah, eds. *A Research Companion to Principles and Standards for School Mathematics.* Reston, VA: National Council of Teachers of Mathematics, Inc. 2003.

Real Math is the first program to fully integrate all five strands of mathematical proficiency as defined by today's research*.

The five key proficiencies that students need to achieve in math are:

1 Understanding
Comprehending mathematical concepts, operations, and relations—knowing what mathematical symbols, diagrams, and procedures mean

2 Computing
Carrying out mathematical procedures, such as adding, subtracting, multiplying, and dividing numbers flexibly, accurately, efficiently, and appropriately

3 Applying
Being able to formulate problems mathematically and devise strategies for solving them using concepts and procedures appropriately

4 Reasoning
Using logic to explain and justify a solution to a problem or to extend from something known to something not yet known

5 Engaging
Seeing mathematics as sensible, useful, and doable

By incorporating all five strands, *Real Math* frees you from the daily challenge of gathering materials to meet state standards, allowing you to pursue your passion for doing what you love most—teaching.

Discover meaningful, true-to-life instruction

Reach each student with explicit instruction and conceptual development.

Engaging lessons that appeal to your students' personal interests go a long way toward maintaining their attention. Revisiting concepts in different contexts over time ensures understanding by making math personal. This personal understanding and appreciation of mathematical concepts helps you develop greater thinking and mastery in each student.

A dual approach.

Real Math's explicit lessons combine **skill-building** and **problem-solving instruction** that includes unique lesson ideas, the latest technology, and engaging games.

Thinking Stories, which are narratives interspersed with questions for students to answer, require students to consider problems in novel ways. As an integral part of *Real Math* lessons, games provide skill practice and stimulate critical thinking as students formulate strategies and solve true-to-life problems.

Everything you need.

Real Math's all-inclusive program gives you everything you need to face the diverse challenges of your classroom. The wealth of teacher resources includes easy-to-use lesson plans, teaching tips, activity ideas, reteaching strategies, practice sessions, professional development, technology, and assessment opportunities at every level.

Show students how math adds adventure in and out of the classroom.

Five-a-day.

All five math proficiencies are integrated and interwoven into every lesson so your students develop a full understanding of mathematics with every turn of the page. *Real Math* concepts are carefully developed using research-supported strategies, including features like *Teaching for Understanding* that emphasize concept development to build comprehension of mathematical concepts, operations, and relations.

Boost thinking power.

Some other math programs show a quick increase in test scores as students develop computational skills, then see scores drop off as students fail to develop critical thinking skills. However, every lesson in *Real Math* features questions and problems that require thinking, not just calculating. As you help students build math comprehension, they will excel on standardized tests, which require constructed responses and problem-solving skills.

Real Math doesn't just help you teach why math is important, but shows students how it can be applied in their after-school activities.

Real Math
Discover the Difference

Discover a versatile way to teach

All-inclusive, flexible lessons offer guided instruction, practice, and assessment for every task.

Step-by-step guide.

Explicit instruction walks you through the details of each *Real Math* lesson, offering everything you need to perform each task. Because *Real Math* is flexible to fit your teaching style, it reduces time spent planning so you can focus on what's most important: teaching.

Easy teaching. Easy learning.

Multiple opportunities for students to understand each exercise make preparing to meet state standards part of every lesson.

Game on.

Real Math activities, such as games and technology projects, ensure that students use key skills to absorb essential ideas and information.

Teaching Lesson 1.8

Mental Math 5

 Ask students to respond to exercises such as the following.

a. Six plus how many equals 13? 7
b. Eighteen minus how many equals 9? 9
c. What number minus 5 equals 8? 13
d. Four plus how many equals 12? 8
e. What number minus 7 equals 3? 10
f. Eleven minus how many equals 5? 6

1 Develop 20

Tell Students In Today's Lesson They Will
find the perimeters of rectangles and squares.

Guided Discussion UNDERSTANDING   Whole Group

Define perimeter as the length of the path around the boundary of a figure.
- Draw a square on the board and label each side 10 cm.
- Have students find the perimeter by adding the lengths of the sides of the square.

10 cm
10 cm   10 cm
10 cm

Next draw a rectangle and label its sides 10 cm and 15 cm.

Have students find its perimeter by adding the lengths of the sides together. Then ask the students questions such as the following:

15 cm
10 cm   10 cm
15 cm

■ **What are some realistic examples of situations that might require finding the perimeter?** Possible answers: determining the jogging distance around a field; building a fence around a garden; making a frame for a picture

Skill Building ENGAGING   Small Group

- Have students work in small groups or with partners to find the perimeter, of various items in the classroom, such as a rectangular table or desk tops.
- Ask students to explain how they found the perimeters, and compare the groups' results.
- Some students may be curious about finding the perimeter of curved objects. Although this concept is not formally addressed at the fourth-grade level, students might enjoy using yarn or string to find the length around the outside of round objects, such as tires, plates, and CDs.

2 Assign Student Pages 25

Pages 30–31 UNDERSTANDING

Have students complete pages 30–31 on their own.

Before students do the problems on student page 30, remind them that *cm* is the symbol for centimeter(s). Also encourage them to make diagrams to help them solve the word problems on page 31.

Problems 11–12 If the dimensions are whole numbers of centimeters, rectangles with a perimeter of 20 cm can have the following dimensions: 1×9, 2×8, 3×7, 4×6, and 5×5. Rectangles with a perimeter of 10 cm can be 1×4 or 2×3. Congruent rectangles (such as 1×9 and 9×1) are counted only once. If numbers other than whole numbers are allowed, for example, $1\frac{1}{2} \times 8\frac{1}{2}$ cm, there are an infinite number of such rectangles. As an extension to this problem, you can have students find the area of each rectangle by counting the squares. Ask them to find the rectangle that has the greatest area. The 5×5 rectangle has an area of 25 square centimeters.

Monitoring Student Progress

If . . . students have difficulty reading and understanding the word problems,	**Then . . .** have the students work in small groups with at least one good reader per group.

As Students Finish

 Game Roll a 15 Game or Roll 20 to 5 Game (introduced in Lesson 1.7)

e Games Roll a 15 Game or Roll 20 to 5 Game

30B Chapter 1 · Lesson 8

Leave a lasting impression.

Practice through games, realistic problem solving, interactive projects, and writing activities assures student engagement and piques interest.

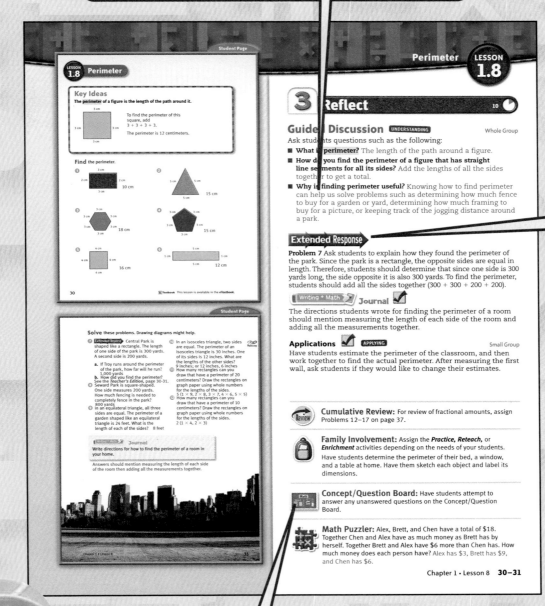

Make it personal.

Encouraging students to explain their thinking personalizes math and helps them internalize and apply concepts.

Fun materials maintain student interest and help reinforce computational thinking skills.

Teach them to think for themselves.

Real Math helps you promote realistic thinking and problem-solving skills. Your students learn to ask relevant questions while you help them learn to find answers by conducting their own research.

Discover the value of ongoing assessment

Use resources and strategies to differentiate instruction for each student.

Making progress.
Look for specific ongoing assessment and progress monitoring strategies in each lesson for a complete evaluation of student understanding. This ongoing assessment offers you strategic solutions for every learning situation and helps you make certain that your students fully grasp content. With enrich, practice, and reteach materials, you'll ensure no student is left behind.

Vital extras.
Valuable tools, such as the *English Learner Support Guide,* Extended Response, Guided Discussion, Writing + Math Journal prompts, projects, and **WebQuests,** provide opportunities for students to demonstrate understanding in real contexts, not just on tests.

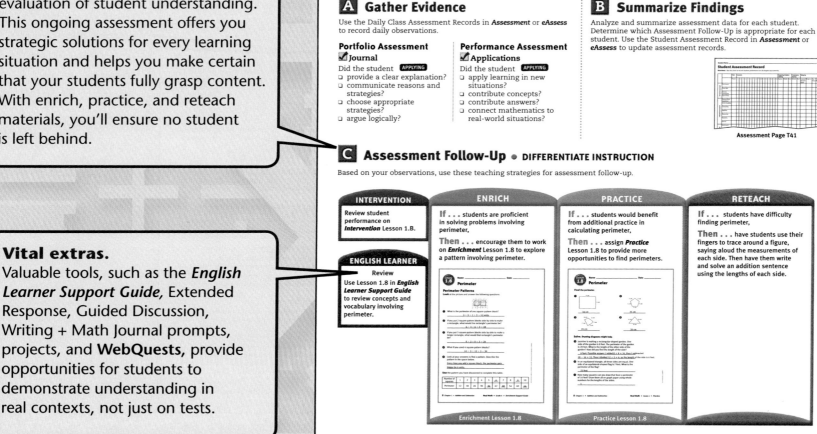

Discover how technology can take your lessons beyond the everyday

Prepare students for a lifetime of learning with interactive instruction.

Keeping up with technology.

Technology resources for teachers and students enrich instruction and expand learning. *Real Math* helps you build skills by offering the latest in technology to help take your classroom to the next level. *Real Math* features useful materials such as the following:

- **ePlanner** online lesson planning helps make your job easier by organizing daily, weekly, and monthly lesson plans and homework detail, linking to all technology components.

- **ePresentation** enables you to present each lesson electronically through an interactive presentation. It also provides lesson summaries and electronic lessons that can be accessed from home.

- **eAssess** online assessment tools allow you to create assessments that students can take online and view reports based on math topics, standards, and differentiated instruction.

- **eMathTools** are math technology resources including number lines and multiplication tables, geometric exploration tools, and probability simulations.

- **eGames** offer electronic versions of games from each grade level.

- **Building Blocks** activities are engaging, research-based computer activities that develop math understanding.

- **eTextbook** gives students access from home with an electronic version of the *Student Edition*.

For additional resources, visit **SRARealMath.com**.

Online Professional Development

Build confidence and expertise in delivering *Real Math* lessons using Online Professional Development. This series of six online courses includes video excerpts and demonstrates how *Real Math* lessons implement each of the following:

- Teaching Computational Fluency

- Teaching for Understanding

- Teaching Applications of Mathematics

- Teaching Mathematical Reasoning and Problem Solving

- Engaging Children in Mathematics

- Mathematics Classroom Management

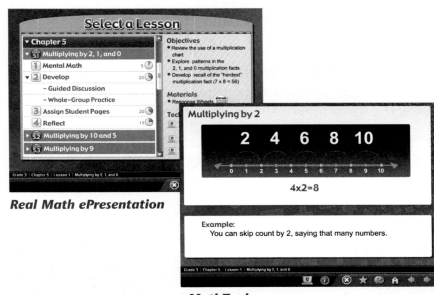

Real Math ePresentation

eMathTools

Discover the confidence of comprehensive teacher support

Extensive resources include empowering materials for you and your students.

TEACHER MATERIALS prepare you with great tools and resources.

- **Teacher's Edition, Grades PreK–6**
  A wealth of background information and strategies helps you provide quality instruction.

- **Manipulative Kits, Grades PreK–6**
  These complete Manipulative Kits support concept development and are available in individual, module, and teacher manipulative packages.

- **Assessment, Grades K–6**
  A variety of assessment options helps you evaluate student proficiency and inform instruction.

- **Game Mat Package, Grades K–6**
  Make learning enjoyable with these exciting math board games and manipulatives for the classroom.

- **Home Connection, Grades PreK–6**
  A collection of newsletters, surveys, and activities encourage school-to-home communications.

- **Home Connection Game Package, Grades K–6**
  Support learning at home with this math games kit.

STUDENT MATERIALS are unique and engaging, giving you a fresh approach to teaching mathematics.

- **Big Books, Grade PreK**
  These counting books include math concepts specifically chosen for preschoolers.

- **Student Edition, Grades K–6**
  Research-based lessons offer development and practice for all concepts.

- **Across the Curriculum Math Connections, Grades K–6**
  Engaging cross-curricular projects and **WebQuests** help develop mathematical proficiency.

- **Student Assessment Booklet, Grades K–6**
  This convenient assessment tool helps keep students on track.

- **Exercise Book, Grades 3–6**
  Build math skills using these exercises from the hardbound student books to help students record their answers and show their work.

Materials that offer hands-on learning go a long way in engaging conceptual thinking skills and problem solving.

With materials to DIFFERENTIATE INSTRUCTION, you meet the needs of all your students.

- **Intervention Support Guide**, Grades K–6
  Bring all students up-to-speed with alternative approaches, more intense instruction, and additional practice of prerequisite skills for every chapter.

- **English Learner Support Guide**, Grades K–6
  Take advantage of strategies for previewing and reviewing lesson concepts and vocabulary.

- **Enrichment Support Guide**, Grades K–6
  This guide includes activities for every lesson designed to expand lesson concepts.

- **Practice Workbook**, Grades K–6
  This workbook version offers extra practice for your convenience.

- **Practice Blackline Masters**, Grades K–6
  Reproducible pages offer extra practice for every lesson.

- **Reteach Support Guide**, Grades 1–6
  Use this tool to offer alternative strategies for presenting lesson concepts.

Professional development from SRA/McGraw-Hill provides you with an unparalleled level of support, resources, and partnership.

Real Math is based on a strong, standards-based philosophy of instruction. A key to successful implementation of the program within your school or district is to have an understanding of its background and how to apply its research-based principles in your classroom. You'll find that professional development opportunities for *Real Math* are hands-on, giving you the chance to gain valuable experience with each component of the program.

Because each school is different, your SRA/McGraw-Hill sales representative will customize a professional development plan to fit your needs. Here are some resources your school or district may utilize:

- On-site training upon implementation
- Weekend seminars and regional training
- Summer institutes
- Online professional development
- Workbooks and guides
- Classroom demonstrations
- After-school workshops with teachers and administrators
- Orientation sessions for the community, parents, and parent groups
- Mentor teachers and coaches
- Resources online at **SRAonline.com**

SRA Real Math
Discover the Difference

Discover the experience *Real Math* authors bring to every lesson

Steve Willoughby is Professor Emeritus at both New York University and the University of Arizona. He has taught all grades from first through twelfth. He has been a professor of both education and of mathematics at the University of Wisconsin and at New York University (where he also was the Head of the Division of Mathematics, Science, and Statistics Education), and a Professor of Mathematics at the University of Arizona. Dr. Willoughby served as President of NCTM from 1982 to 1984. Dr. Willoughby has published more than 200 books and articles on mathematics and mathematics education and is the principal author of *Real Math*. In 1995, he received the Lifetime Achievement Medal for Leadership in Mathematics Education from the Mathematics Education Trust.

Carl Bereiter is a Professor Emeritus of Educational Psychology and Special Advisor on Learning Technology at the Ontario Institute for Studies of the University of Toronto. He has published widely on a variety of topics in instruction, cognitive psychology, and educational policy. Honors include a Guggenheim Fellowship, fellowships at the Center for Advanced Study in the Behavioral Sciences, and election to the U.S. National Academy of Education.

Peter Hilton is Distinguished Professor of Mathematics Emeritus of the State University of New York, Binghamton, and Distinguished Professor of Mathematics at the University of Central Florida, Orlando. He is the author of eighteen books and over 500 research articles. His areas of special interest are algebraic topology, homological algebra, and group theory. Professor Hilton has served as Chairman of the United States Commission on Mathematical Instruction and Secretary/Treasurer of the International Commission on Mathematical Instruction.

Joseph H. Rubinstein is a Professor of Education at Coker College in Hartsville, South Carolina, where he teaches prospective teachers how to teach mathematics and science. He was chairperson of the education department at Coker for fifteen years. He received B.A., M.S., and Ph.D. degrees in biology from New York University. He served as Director of the Open Court Publishing Company's Mathematics and Science Curriculum Development Center for its first seven years, where he coauthored and directed a nationwide field-testing program for *Real Math*.

Douglas H. Clements, Professor of Early Childhood, Mathematics, and Computer Education at the University at Buffalo, State University of New York, has conducted research and published widely on the learning and teaching of geometry, computer applications in mathematics education, the early development of mathematical ideas, and the effects of social interactions on learning. Along with Julie

Sarama, Dr. Clements has directed several research projects funded by the National Science Foundation and the U.S. Department of Education's Institute of Educational Sciences, one of which resulted in much of the mathematics software and activities included in *Real Math*.

Joan Moss is an Associate Professor of Mathematics Education at the University of Toronto. She has more than twenty years experience as a classroom teacher, scholar, and researcher. Her extensive research has included studies of the development of children's understanding of rational numbers and the development of early algebraic reasoning. Dr. Moss has been widely published with research articles and chapters for the National Council of Teachers of Mathematics as well as the National Academy of Science. She is a member of the National Council of Teachers of Mathematics, American Educational Research Association, the North American Chapter of the Psychology of Mathematics Education, and the Canadian Mathematics Education Study Group.

Jean Pedersen is Professor of Mathematics and Computer Science at Santa Clara University, California. Along with Peter Hilton, she has published six books and over ninety research articles in mathematics. Her research interests include polyhedral geometry, combinatorics, and the teaching of mathematics, especially geometry, to precollege students.

Julie Sarama is an Associate Professor of Mathematics Education at the University at Buffalo, State University of New York. She conducts research on the implementation and effects of software and curricula in mathematics classrooms, young children's development of mathematical concepts and competencies, implementation and scale-up of educational reform, and professional development. Dr. Sarama has taught secondary mathematics and computer science, gifted math at the middle school level, preschool and kindergarten mathematics enrichment classes, and mathematics methods and content courses for elementary to secondary teachers.

Contributing Authors

Hortensia Soto-Johnson is Assistant Professor of Mathematics, University of Northern Colorado. B.S. Chadron State College (Mathematics); MS in Mathematics, University of Arizona; Ph.D. in Educational Mathematics, University of Northern Colorado.

Erica Walker is Assistant Professor of Mathematics and Education, Teachers College, Columbia University. B.S. cum laude, Birmingham-Southern College (Mathematics, Spanish minor); M.Ed., Wake Forest University (Mathematics Education); Ed.M., Ed.D., Harvard University (Administration, Planning, and Social Policy).

SRA
Real Math

Teacher's Edition

Grade 2 • Volume 1

Stephen S. Willoughby

•

Carl Bereiter

•

Peter Hilton

•

Joseph H. Rubinstein

•

Joan Moss

•

Jean Pedersen

SRA

Columbus, OH

The McGraw·Hill Companies

Authors

Stephen S. Willoughby
Professor Emeritus of Mathematics
University of Arizona
Tucson, AZ

Carl Bereiter
Professor Emeritus
Centre for Applied Cognitive Science
Ontario Institute for Studies in Education
University of Toronto, Canada

Peter Hilton
Distinguished Professor of
Mathematics Emeritus
State University of New York
Binghamton, NY

Joseph H. Rubinstein
Professor of Education
Coker College
Hartsville, SC

Joan Moss
Associate Professor, Department of Human
Development and Applied Psychology
Ontario Institute for Studies in Education
University of Toronto, Canada

Jean Pedersen
Professor, Department of
Mathematics and Computer Science
Santa Clara University, Santa Clara, CA

PreKindergarten and Building Blocks Authors

Douglas H. Clements
Professor of Early Childhood and Mathematics Education
University at Buffalo
State University of New York, NY

Julie Sarama
Associate Professor of Mathematics Education
University at Buffalo
State University of New York, NY

Contributing Authors

Hortensia Soto-Johnson
Assistant Professor of Mathematics
University of Northern Colorado, CO

Erika Walker
Assistant Professor of Mathematics and Education
Teachers College, Columbia University, NY

Research Consultants

Jeremy Kilpatrick
Regents Professor of Mathematics Education
University of Georgia, GA

Alfinio Flores
Professor of Mathematics Education
Arizona State University, AZ

Gilbert J. Cuevas
Professor of Mathematics Education
University of Miami, Coral Gables, FL

Contributing Writers

Holly MacLean, Ed.D., Supervisor Principal, Treasure Valley
Mathematics and Science Center, Boise, ID
Edward Manfre, Mathematics Education Consultant, Albuquerque, NM
Elizabeth Jimenez, English Language Learner Consultant, Pomona, CA

Kim L. Pettig, Ed.D., Instructional Challenge Coordinator
Pittsford Central School District, Pittsford, NY
Rosemary Tolliver, M.Ed., Gifted Coordinator/Curriculum Director, Columbus, OH

National Advisory Board

Justin Anderson, Teacher, Robey Elementary School, Indianapolis, IN
David S. Bradley, Administrator, Granite, UT
Donna M. Bradley, Head of the Lower School, St. Marks Episcopal
Palm Beach Gardens, FL
Grace Dublin, Teacher, Laurelhurst Elementary, Seattle, WA
Leisha W. Fordham, Teacher, Bolton Academy, Atlanta, GA

Ebony Frierson, Teacher, Eastminister Day School, Columbia, SC
Flavia Gunter, Teacher, Morningside Elementary School, Atlanta, GA
Audrey Marie Jacobs, Teacher, Lewis & Clark Elementary, St. Louis, MO
Florencetine Jasmin, Elementary Math Curriculum Specialist, Baltimore, MD
Kim Leitzke, Teacher, Clara Barton Elementary School, Milwaukee, WI
Nick Restivo, Principal, Long Beach High School, Long Island, NY

SRAonline.com

SRA

Printed in the United States of America.

Send all inquiries to:
SRA/McGraw-Hill
4400 Easton Commons
Columbus, OH 43219

ISBN 0-07-603712-6

3 4 5 6 7 8 9 WEB 12 11 10 09 08 07

The **McGraw·Hill** Companies

Exploring 💡 Problem Solving Theme: Teamwork—Library

CHAPTER 2

Addition Facts

Exploring  Problem Solving Theme: Pets

Subtraction Facts

CHAPTER 3

Exploring 💡 Problem Solving · Theme: Origami

Exploring Problem Solving · Introducing Strategies

Exploring Problem Solving · Comparing Strategies

Exploring Problem Solving · Using Strategies

Measurement, Graphing, and Probability

Exploring 💡 Problem Solving   Theme: Toy Factory

Two-Digit Addition

CHAPTER 5

Exploring 💡Problem Solving **Theme: Parks and Picnics**

CHAPTER 6

Two-Digit Subtraction

Exploring  Problem Solving **Theme: Zoo**

Fractions

CHAPTER 7

Exploring 🔍 Problem Solving Theme: Museums

Exploring 💡 Problem Solving Theme: Dinosaurs

Three-Digit Addition and Subtraction

CHAPTER 9

Exploring 💡Problem Solving **Theme: Mail Delivery and The Pony Express**

CHAPTER 10

Measurement

Exploring 💡 Problem Solving Theme: Growing Plants

Introducing Multiplication and Division

CHAPTER
11

Exploring 💡 **Problem Solving** Theme: Ethnic Food

CHAPTER 12
Patterns and Algebra

Exploring 💡 **Problem Solving** Theme: Frontier and Native American Homes

Back Matter

Getting Started

*This section provides an overview of classroom management issues and explanations of the **Real Math** program elements and how to use them.*

Real Math is a comprehensive program designed to achieve these goals:

Teach basic skills with understanding so students can use them fluently to solve real problems and help understand the real world

•

Teach students to think mathematically so they can reason, understand, and apply mathematics meaningfully in order to identify, solve, and communicate about real problems

•

Teach students to reason so that they have sufficient confidence and understanding to reconstruct or even construct mathematical methods that they have forgotten or never learned

•

Engage students in mathematics so they enjoy math, see it as understandable and useful, and willingly use it to help them understand their environment

Real Math is a program that acknowledges the critical role teachers play in math education. The program is designed to provide thorough background, teaching strategies, and resources to support teacher delivery of a coherent mathematics curriculum that will develop student understanding and enjoyment of mathematics.

The following pages are designed to help you get started with **Real Math.**

A variety of program materials are designed to help teachers provide a quality mathematics curriculum. The first step in getting started is to familiarize yourself with the program resources.

Core Materials

Teacher's Edition

The **Teacher's Edition** is the heart of the **Real Math** curriculum. It provides background for teachers and complete lesson plans with explicit suggestions on how to develop math concepts. It explains when and how to use the program resources.

Student Edition

The **Student Edition** includes developmental activities, practice exercises, games to help develop higher-order thinking skills and practice traditional basic skills, as well as problem-solving explorations, and cumulative reviews.

Essential Materials

The key materials beyond the textbook that students must have to complete the program activities are **Number Cubes** and **Number Strips** at Grades K–2, and **Response Wheels, Equivalence Cards,** and **Number Cubes** at Grades 3–6. The materials are in the **Individual Manipulative Kits** or the **Essential Materials Module.**

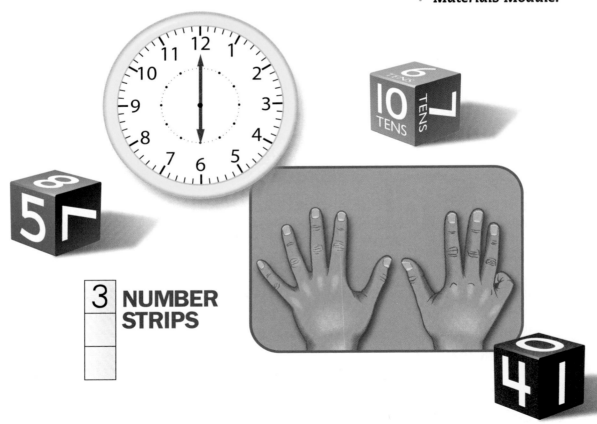

NUMBER STRIPS

In addition to these core components of the program, the following materials provide specific resources to facilitate instruction.

Component	Grades	Purpose
Practice Blackline Masters	K–6	Extra practice for every lesson
Practice Workbook	K–6	Workbook version of extra practice for teacher convenience
Enrichment Support Guide	K–6	Activities for every lesson designed to expand lesson concepts
Reteach Support Guide	K–6	Alternative strategies for presenting lesson concepts
Intervention Support Guide	K–6	Instruction and practice of prerequisite skills for every chapter to bring all students up to speed
English Learner Support Guide	K–6	Strategies for previewing and reviewing lesson concepts and vocabulary for students learning English
Assessment	K–6	Variety of assessment options to evaluate student proficiency and inform instruction
Student Assessment Booklet	K–6	Assessment booklets for teacher convenience
Home Connection	PreK–6	Newsletters, surveys, and activities to encourage home and school communications
Across the Curriculum Math Connections	K–6	Cross-curricular projects and **WebQuests** that develop math proficiency and provide interesting math applications
Exercise Book	3–6	A duplication of the **Student Edition** exercises in a workbook format
Big Book	PreK	Counting book specifically chosen for preschoolers
Game Mat Kit	K–6	Contains 15 copies of each of the Game Mats at each grade level and enough playing pieces, **Number Cubes,** and play money for an entire class; includes a **Guide for Using the Game Mats** and a set of color transparencies of the basic version of each game
Home Connection Game Kit	K–6	Math games kit for home use that includes the game mats and cube games
Manipulative Kits	PreK–6	Available in Topic Modules or Individual Kits to support concept development; available in convenient packaging options
Professional Development • Online/CD • Books		Six professional development courses that offer school districts complete staff development in math education
Calculator Package		Calculators available for classroom convenience

Real Math Technology Resources

Math resources designed to facilitate instruction and record keeping and to expand student learning

For Teachers		For Students	
Planner	A tool to help teachers plan daily lessons, plot year-long goals, view program components, and assign homework	Building Blocks	**Activities** (PreK–6) Engaging research-based activities designed to reinforce levels of mathematical development in different strands of mathematics
Presentation	An online presentation tool to enable teachers to present each lesson electronically and links to *eGames, eMathTools,* and *eTextbook* for easy demonstration purposes	Textbook	An electronic version of the **Student Edition** that students can access from home
Assess	An assessment tool to grade, track, and report electronic versions of assessments • View reports of assessments taken online • Create assessments from a database of items correlated to standards • Enter scores from paper assessments	Games	(K–6) Electronic versions of twelve games from each grade level of **Real Math;** competitive games that involve luck, skill, and strategy to help practice skills and develop mathematical thinking
Professional Development A series of six online courses that teach different aspects of mathematics		MathTools	Electronic math tools to help students solve problems and explore math concepts

Chapter Organization

The first few pages of each chapter help you understand the chapter focus and see how concepts are developed.

Chapter Overview

- **Teaching for Understanding** provides the big ideas of the chapter.

- **Skills Trace** shows where concepts were previously introduced and how they will be followed up.

- **Prerequisite Skills** help determine if students are ready for the chapter.

- **Games** and **Problem Solving** provide an overview of key chapter experiences.

- **Math Background** provides mathematical and pedagogical information relevant to the chapter.

- **What Research Says** offers insights into children's learning and research-based teaching strategies.

- **Planning Guide** includes objectives that explain how the key concepts are developed lesson by lesson and which resources can be used in each lesson.

- **Technology Resources** list resources that are available to help with planning or to support instruction.

Chapter Introduction

Each Chapter Introduction introduces concepts and provides ways to assess prior knowledge.

- **Pretest** helps evaluate what students know and do not know about the chapter concepts in order to determine what to reteach, emphasize, or skip.

- **Access Prior Knowledge** offers preliminary discussion about chapter concepts to determine what students know.

- **Exploring Problem Solving** introduces the chapter theme and concepts by exploring the ways in which students solve real-world problems.

- **Concept/Question Board** establishes connections and applications of the chapter concepts to students' thinking and lives outside the classroom.

- **Assess and Differentiate** uses assessments to summarize and analyze evidence of student understanding and to plan for differentiating instruction.

- **Project Overview** outlines two projects that students can work on during the course of the chapter that apply chapter concepts across the curriculum.

Lessons

Lessons provide overview, ideas for differentiating instruction, complete lesson plans, teaching strategies, and assessments that inform instruction.

Exploring Problem Solving

These lessons introduce, compare, and use problem-solving strategies and appear in the beginning, middle, and end of each chapter.

Cumulative Review

Cumulative Review exercises provide practice for standardized-test formats in the middle and end of the chapter and allow you to evaluate if students are retaining previously developed concepts and skills.

Individual Oral Assessment

These individual assessment interviews in the middle of each chapter provide an opportunity to individually evaluate student understanding.

Thinking Stories (K–3) and Exploring Problem Solving

These activities at the end of each chapter offer applications of lesson concepts and development of students' mathematical thinking and problem-solving abilities.

Chapter Wrap-Up

The Chapter Wrap-up provides ways to review chapter concepts and assess student understanding.

- **Key Ideas Review** refreshes student knowledge of the key concepts.

- **Chapter Review** provides a review of chapter concepts.

- **Practice Test** is in the same format as the Chapter Test and gives students a chance for self-assessment before taking the Chapter Test.

Once you understand how a chapter is organized, survey the resources in each lesson.

Lesson Planning

The first page of each lesson helps teachers prepare to teach each lesson.

- **Context of the Lesson** explains how the lesson is developed in the context of the chapter and includes information about how concepts were previously developed, as well as specific information about expectations of student performance.

- **Planning for Learning: Differentiate Instruction** provides ideas for planning how to adapt the lesson depending on assessments of student understanding.

- **Lesson Planner** includes Objectives, Materials lists, and Looking Ahead tips to prepare for upcoming lessons.

Lesson Plans

Every lesson throughout *Real Math* is structured in the same way.

Mental Math

- **Mental Math** is a five-minute warm-up at the beginning of each lesson that provides cumulative review.

Develop

- **Develop** is the heart of the lesson instruction. Here are suggestions for how to introduce lesson concepts, ideas for Guided Discussion, Skill Building, and Strategy Building activities to develop student understanding.

Assign Student Pages

- **Assign Student Pages** explains when to have students complete the lesson pages and ideas for what they can do when they finish.

Reflect

- **Reflect** is a vital part of the lesson that offers ways to help students summarize, reflect, and expand on their understanding of the lesson concepts.

Assess and Differentiate

- **Assess and Differentiate** uses informal and formal assessments to summarize and analyze evidence of student understanding and plan for differentiating instruction.

*In **Real Math** there are activities that will occur again and again. Establishing rules or routines for these activities with students will facilitate instruction.*

Mental Math

Mental Math exercises provide cumulative review and computation practice for students and provide opportunities to assess students' skills quickly. Mental Math is an essential component of **Real Math** because it helps students review skills they have already learned that are prerequisite skills for upcoming lessons.

Most Mental Math exercises are done in the following four steps, which include the **Find, Hide,** and **Show** routine. The pace should be lively enough to keep things moving, yet not so fast that students do not have time to think.

Step 1

Present a problem orally, by writing it on the board, or by using *ePresentation.*

Step 2

Students **find** the answer and arrange their *Response Wheels, Number Cubes,* or other response device to display it.

Step 3

Students **hide** the answer while you provide enough time for most students to find the answer.

Step 4

Students **show** the answer to you, while you show and say the answer to the class.

This four-step process allows students to participate in a nonthreatening way. You can tell instantly whether all students are participating and whether they have the right answer. If a student gets a wrong answer, only that student and you know it. You can make note of students who are struggling and give them extra help later on.

Tips

- Occasionally add a "peek-to-be-sure" step to the Find, Hide, and Show procedure. Some students will have found an answer and hidden it while waiting for others in the class to do the same. This is the time to give the "Peek" command, which asks the students who have found answers to check them. This keeps them involved during the few seconds of waiting for the "Show" command.

- Use judgment to decide when to give the "Show" command. You do not have to wait for every student to find and hide an answer. But you should wait long enough so that students who are making progress toward a solution have time to finish. Remember, too, that students who cannot answer in time will know they are having difficulty, and you will also know they are having difficulty. The rest of the class need not know. Prolonged waiting only calls attention to the slower students. Furthermore, after you say "Show," a few more seconds will pass while you are checking answers, and during this time students still have time to find and show their responses.

- Encourage students. Because response exercises are active exchanges between you and the students, use these opportunities to let them know you are pleased with their efforts and that you have confidence in them.

- If it is difficult for you to see all the response-card answers when students are at their seats, have them sit on the floor closer to you. Or you might walk around the room, but do this quickly so you do not slow the lively pace of the exercise.

Guided Discussion

"Teachers must make judgments about when to tell, when to question, and when to correct. They must decide when to guide with prompting and when to let students grapple with a mathematical issue.... The point of classroom discourse is to develop students' understanding of key ideas. But it also provides opportunities to emphasize and model mathematical reasoning and problem solving and to enhance students' disposition toward mathematics."

—Kilpatrick, J., Swafford, J. and Findell, B. eds. *Adding It Up: Helping Children Learn Mathematics.* Washington, D.C.: National Research Council/National Academy Press, 2001, p. 346.

Guided Discussion is expected in almost all **Real Math** lessons. In Guided Discussion students speak the language of mathematics, communicate mathematically, explain their thinking, and demonstrate understanding.

Routines or rules for Guided Discussion established at the beginning of the year can make discussions more productive and promote listening and speaking skills.

1. **Pay attention to others.** Give full attention to the person who is speaking. This includes looking at the speaker and nodding to show that you understand.

2. **Wait for speakers to answer and complete their thoughts.** Sometimes teachers and other students get impatient and move on, ask someone else, or give the answer before someone has a chance to think and speak. Giving students time to answer is a vital part of teaching for understanding.

3. **Listen.** Let yourself finish listening before you begin to speak. You cannot listen if you are busy thinking about what you want to say next.

4. **Respect speakers** by taking turns and making sure that everyone gets a chance to speak and that no one dominates the conversation.

5. **Build on others' ideas** by making connections, drawing analogies, or expanding on the idea.

6. **Ask questions.** Asking questions of another speaker shows that you were listening. Ask if you are not sure you understand what the speaker has said, or ask for clarification or explanation. It is a good idea to repeat in your own words what the speaker said so you can be sure your understanding is correct.

 **RESEARCH IN ACTION**

"One of the most striking aspects of Japanese classrooms, especially at the first-grade level, was the amount of verbal explanation that occurred during mathematics class. We were able to identify segments that contained explanations by either the teacher, a student, or both the teacher and a student.... Nearly 50 percent of all Japanese first-grade segments contained verbal explanations, compared with only about 20 percent of the American segments....Whereas the American teachers were more likely to stress participation in nonverbal activities or the asking of short-answer questions to lead students into a new topic, Japanese teachers would give, and ask students to give, lengthy verbal explanations of mathematical concepts and algorithms."

—Stigler, James W. *"The Use of Verbal Explanation in Japanese and American Classrooms,"* Arithmetic Teacher, October 1988.

Questions to Ask

Questions help teachers learn about student thinking and consider instructional implications of that knowledge. Teachers should be prepared for unexpected answers and probe further with questions to understand student thought processes. Sometimes the unexpected answer demonstrates true insight.

Not all questions are the same. Questions have different purposes.

- **Engaging Questions** invite students into a discussion, keep them engaged in conversation, and invite them to share their work. Engaging questions are typically open-ended and encourage different ways of responding.

- **Exploring Questions** ask students to provide explanations, make analogies, or identify problems and solutions.

- **Synthesizing Questions** ask students to identify patterns, make generalizations or rules, or argue, prove, or demonstrate their assumptions.

- **Clarifying Questions** help students explain their thinking or help you understand their thinking.

- **Refocusing Questions** help students get back on track or move away from a dead-end strategy.

See Appendix A for more information about Guided Discussion.

Games

Games are a vital part of **Real Math.** They have been written specifically for the program to support the concepts and skills being taught. Students enjoying the friendly competition may not even realize how much math they are learning and practicing.

Purposes of Games

- Games provide practice to reinforce new skills and review previously covered topics.

- Most **Real Math** games place students in an environment in which they are expected to recognize situations that can be analyzed by mathematical thought, to formulate their own problems, to solve those problems, to use their solutions to improve their game-playing strategies, and to communicate with other players about their strategies.

- Games give students a chance to work out important mathematical ideas and problem-solving strategies.

- Games give you an opportunity to informally monitor student progress by watching students as they play.

- Games allow students of all ability levels to compete fairly. Winning games requires a mix of chance, skills, and thinking strategies.

Types of Games

Game Mats are found in the **Game Mat Kit** and are reproduced in Appendix D. The **Game Mat Kit** contains fifteen copies of each of the different **Game Mats** in a grade level, which should accommodate a class of thirty because most games are played by two or more players. The package also contains enough playing pieces, **Number Cubes,** and play money for an entire class, along with a **Guide for Using the Game Mats** and a set of color transparencies of the basic version of each game. Reduced-size copies of the **Game Mats** can also be found in the back of this **Teacher's Edition.**

Many of the **Game Mats** have both a basic and a harder version for differentiating instruction.

Cube and Other Games

Directions for **Cube Games** that require only **Number Cubes** are in the **Teacher's Edition** or **Student Edition** of appropriate lessons. Directions for all **Cube Games** are reproduced in the **Home Connection Support Guide** and in the **Home Connection Game Kit.**

Many of the **Cube Games** have variations that extend the mathematics or provide applications for new thinking strategies. Variations can be learned quickly, making the **Cube Games** even more practical and useful in the classroom.

eGames are electronic versions of some of the **Game Mats** and **Cube Games.**

Building Blocks electronic activities and games are referenced in appropriate lessons. These activities provide additional opportunities for practice and exploration.

Routines for Introducing Games

1. Familiarize yourself with the rules of each game by playing it before showing students how to play it.

2. Demonstrate, do not just tell, how a game is played. Overhead projector versions of the **Game Mats** are provided for demonstrating games in front of the class. The **ePresentation** or **eGames** can be displayed for the class to see how to play those games.

3. Let students who already know the game rules (perhaps from a previous grade) help students who are new to the games.

4. Do not teach strategies to students. Rather, encourage students to develop their own game-playing strategies and discuss their strategies in small groups or as a class.

Tips for Using Games

- Stress enjoyment and learning rather than competition. Emphasize sportsmanship, fair play, and taking turns.

- Change the composition of the game-playing groups from day to day. Students can learn different things by playing with different partners. From time to time, use groups of both similar and mixed ability levels.

- Assign a referee to each group. The referee makes sure that rules are followed, reminds players when it is their turn, keeps track of the score, and in some games acts as banker. Referees are especially helpful in the lower grades.

- Encourage students to play games during their free time in school and at home. Make the games easily accessible, perhaps in a math center.

See Appendix A for more information about **Real Math** Games.

Thinking Stories and Exploring Problem Solving

"Problem solving is a complex endeavor that requires critical thinking and therefore, on a logical basis, more development than most other types of lessons."

—Grouws, Douglas A. and Thomas L. Good. "Issues in Problem-Solving Instruction," *Arithmetic Teacher*, April 1989.

Real Math includes problems solving in every lesson. **Real Math** Exploring Problem Solving lessons and Thinking Stories are designed to provide further opportunities to explore and discuss problem-solving strategies and alternative approaches to solving problems.

What are Thinking Stories?

Thinking Stories are an essential component of **Real Math** Grades K–3 that help develop students' problem-solving skills. The stories describe people using mathematics and logic in correct and incorrect ways. The stories are designed to be read to students. Interspersed throughout the stories are questions that ask students to solve problems, make predictions, and analyze the characters' thinking. The same Thinking Story characters appear in all grade levels, so they "grow" with the students. Each character has peculiar thinking patterns that students come to know. For example, Mr. Muddle takes things too literally, Ferdie jumps to conclusions, Ms. Eng does not provide enough information, and Mr. Breezy provides too much information.

use zone

Routines for Thinking Stories

1. Read each story aloud.

2. Stop for each question, and discuss possible answers after you ask it. Some questions have brief answers and should be handled quickly. Others call for deeper thinking or have a range of possible answers and will require several minutes of discussion. Encourage and discuss answers.

Wait for students to respond. A minute or two of silence while students think is a good idea.

Problem Solving

3. If your students enjoy a particular story, consider reading it again another day.

What are Exploring Problem Solving Lessons?

The Exploring Problem Solving lessons at the beginning, middle, and end of each chapter in Grades K–6 also promote development of reasoning and problem-solving abilities. These lessons provide real problems that can be solved in a variety of ways. The lessons model different problem-solving strategies and provide opportunities for students to solve rich problems and discuss their problem-solving strategies. In Grades 4–6, Exploring Problem Solving includes nonfiction articles from which interesting problems are derived and explored.

Routines for Exploring Problem Solving

1. Read the lessons with students.

2. Discuss the problems and any sample solutions so that everyone understands what the problem is asking.

3. Allow students to solve problems on their own or in small groups. Showing students how to do a problem robs them of valuable thinking and their investment and confidence in their own solutions.

4. Facilitate a discussion of alternative problem solutions, and have students discuss advantages, limitations, unique features, and generalizable features of different solutions.

See Appendix A for more information about Thinking Stories and Exploring Problem Solving.

Assign Student Pages, As Students Finish, and Reflect

In almost every lesson, teachers will assign student pages to complete during class. Students will finish at different times and should know what they can do to use their extra time productively until the Reflect part of the lesson. Students should not feel penalized for finishing early and should do something that is mathematically rewarding.

Assign Student Pages

Assign Student Pages Routines

Student book exercises in **Real Math** are primarily nonmechanical. Student book pages help students learn to think about the problems. For example, addition and subtraction problems are mixed earlier than in traditional programs so students learn to pay attention to what a problem says, rather than to add unthinkingly whenever they see two numbers. This early mixing of problems also helps establish the relationship between addition and subtraction.

Because student book exercises are nonmechanical, they sometimes require your active participation.

1. Make sure students know what pages to work on and any special requirements of those pages.

2. Tell students whether they should work independently or in small groups as they complete the pages.

3. Tell students how long they have to work on the student pages before you plan to begin the Reflect part of the lesson.

4. Tell students what their options are if they finish early. Suggested options are listed under the Assign Student Pages heading in each lesson. These include

   a. suggested **eMathTools** to use.

   b. **Game Mats, Cube Games, eGames,** and **Building Blocks** activities to play.

   c. Writing+Math Journal suggestions.

5. As students work on the student pages, circulate around the room to monitor their progress. Use the Monitoring Student Progress suggestions for ideas on what to look for. Comment positively on student work, and stop to ask exploring, synthesizing, clarifying, or refocusing questions.

6. You may also use this time to work with English learners or students who need intervention.

7. You may want to complete the Informal Assessment checklists on the last page of each lesson.

8. Since games are an important and integral part of the program that provide necessary practice in traditional basic skills as well as higher-order thinking skills, when games are included in a lesson, be sure to stop work on student pages early enough to leave enough time to play the game.

Reflect

Reflect Routines

1. At the designated time, have students stop their activity and direct their attention to reflecting on the lesson.

2. Use the suggested questions in Reflect, or ask students to consider these ideas:

   a. Think about related matters that go beyond the scope of the lesson

   b. Summarize ideas about the lesson concepts

   c. Compare how the lesson concept or skill is similar to or different from other skills

   d. Identify ways to apply the lesson in other curricular areas, other strands of mathematics, or in the world outside of school

   e. Discuss solutions to Extended Response questions

Assess and Differentiate

Assessment Follow-Up: Differentiate Instruction

Based on your informal assessments and observations, choose from the following to differentiate for homework:

   a. Complete the student pages

   b. Family Involvement suggestions, such as playing a **Real Math** game

   c. Enrichment ideas

   d. Practice

   e. Reteach

Differentiate Instruction

"Classrooms grounded in best-practice education, and modified to be responsive to student differences, benefit virtually all students. Differentiation addresses the needs of struggling and advanced learners. It addresses the needs of students for whom English is a second language and students who have strong learning style preferences. It addresses gender differences and cultural differences."

—Tomlinson, Carol Ann, *The Differentiated Classroom: Responding to the Needs of All Learners*. 1999, p.24

Instruction can be differentiated in three key ways:

- **Content** is what the teacher wants students to learn and the materials or mechanisms through which that is accomplished. Differentiating the content may be teaching prerequisite concepts to students who need intervention, or by asking questions that cause students to think beyond concepts covered in the lesson.

- **Process** is how or which activities the students do to ensure they use key skills to make sense of the content. Differentiating the process may include alternating the pace of the lesson.

- **Product** is how the student demonstrates what he or she has come to know. Differentiating the product may include assigning Enrichment, Practice, or Reteach activities to complete.

Real Math provides a wealth of support for differentiating instruction, but teachers must make decisions based on their assessments of student understanding and performance.

Routines for Differentiating Instruction

1. Plan for differentiation

a. To prepare for a lesson, scan the suggestions in Planning for All Learners for differentiating instruction on the first page of each lesson. Be prepared to differentiate the content or process depending on your estimation of student understanding.

b. English Learner strategies **differentiate the process** for introducing the lesson by previewing key concepts and vocabulary.

c. Intervention lessons **differentiate content** for those students who have not yet mastered prerequisite skills.

d. Enrich strategies **differentiate the process** if students already understand the content.

e. Practice strategies **differentiate the process** if students need practice.

f. Reteach strategies **differentiate the process** if students are not understanding lesson material.

2. Monitor student progress
As students participate in Mental Math, Guided Discussion, Skill Building, Strategy Building, Games, and other lesson activities, be alert to signs of understanding and misunderstanding. The Informal Assessment Checklists include rubrics to help gather evidence about students' math proficiency.

3. Follow-Up
Summarize your formal assessments and informal observations, and consider how to differentiate student products in the lesson follow-up assignments. Program resources include

a. **Enrichment** activities for students who have a secure understanding.

b. **Practice** activities for students who have adequate understanding.

c. **Reteach** activities for student who have an emerging understanding.

4. Adjust tomorrow's lesson
Based on student understanding and performance, consider how the next lesson should be adjusted for different learners.

"Differentiating instruction does not mean just having students do different things. When a teacher lacks clarity about what a student should know, understand, and be able to do as a result of a lesson, the learning tasks she creates may or may not be engaging and we can almost be certain the tasks won't help students understand essential ideas or principles. A fuzzy sense of the essentials results in fuzzy activities, which in turn results in fuzzy student understanding. That's a barrier to high-quality teaching and learning."

—Tomlinson, Carol Ann, *The Differentiated Classroom: Responding to the Needs of All Learners*. 1999, p. 4

See Appendix A for more information about Differentiating Instruction.

Using Technology

Technology Resources for Teachers

Real Math includes several pieces of integrated technology for teachers designed to increase efficiency and effectiveness of instruction and assessment.

Suggested Procedures for Using Technology

[e] Planner

- **Yearly Planning** Use the *ePlanner* before school begins to plan out the mathematics course for the year. Plot out school events, holidays, and testing periods, and then organize lessons to ensure that key topics are addressed.

- **Weekly Planning** Use the *ePlanner* to adjust daily lesson plans and pacing based on your assessment of student understanding.

[e] Assess

- **Daily Records** Use *eAssess* to record daily formal and informal assessments.

- **Report Cards** Use *eAssess* to print student and class reports to determine grades.

- **Parent-Teacher Conferences** Use *eAssess* to print student reports to discuss with parents.

[e] Presentation

- **Planning** Use *ePresentation* to preview lesson concepts and activities before class.

- **Presentation** Use *ePresentation* to present multimedia lessons to students. *ePresentation* includes the complete lesson, including Guided Discussion questions, *eGame* demonstrations, and *eMathTools.*

Technology Resources for Students

Real Math provides engaging technology resources to enrich, apply, and extend learning.

[e] **Games** are electronic versions of appropriate cube and mat games to extend practice and skill- and strategy-building activities in engaging contexts.

[e] **MathTools** are electronic tools that students can use to solve problems, test solutions, explore concepts, or demonstrate understanding.

Building Blocks activities are designed to reinforce key concepts and develop mathematics understanding.

[e] **Textbook** is the complete *Student Edition* in electronic format.

Routines for Using Technology

1. Determine rules for computer use, and communicate them to students. Rules should include

   a. sharing available computers. Some teachers have a computer sign-up chart for each computer. Some teachers have the students track this themselves.

   b. computer time. You might limit the amount of time students can be at the computer or allow students to work in pairs. Some teachers have students work until they complete an activity. Others allow students to continue on with additional activities.

2. Familiarize students with your rules for proper use of computers, including how to turn computers on, load programs, and shut down the computers. Some teachers manage computers themselves; others have an aide or student in charge of computer management.

3. Using the suggestions for As Students Finish under **Assign Student Pages** in each lesson, make sure the computers are on, the programs are loaded, and that students know how to access the software.

4. Make sure students know what to do once they complete the computer activity.

See Appendix A for more information about using *Real Math* Technology.

Managing Materials

Managing Materials

Real Math provides a wealth of resources. Establishing procedures for use of materials will simplify management issues and allow students to spend more time developing mathematical understanding.

Books

Teacher's Edition and **Support Guides** should be at your fingertips.

Student Editions may be kept at student desks or on a shelf in the classroom.

Response Wheels*

Each student in Grades 3–6 gets one **Response Wheel.** Because they are used daily, **Response Wheels** should be kept in students' desks, notebooks, or mathematics books. They should be stored in such a way that they are not likely to become bent or lost. You may wish to number or otherwise identify each card so that each student can be responsible for his or her card.

Number Cubes*

Each student in Grades 1 and 2 gets four **Number Cubes.** Because they are used frequently, it may be best to have the students keep the cubes in their desks, perhaps with their play money (see next column). In Grades 3–6, students have two cubes that are used to generate random numbers.

> * **Response Wheels** and **Number Cubes** are packaged in the **Essential Materials Module** and as part of the **Individual Student Manipulative Kit,** for your convenience.

Game Mat Kits

The **Game Mat Kit** includes fifteen copies of each **Game Mat** and game kit playing pieces packaged in individual bags. There is storage space for the **Game Mat** and the playing pieces in the **Game Mat Kit** box. Students will benefit from a demonstration of how you want to have students put pieces back in bags and return them and the **Game Mats** to the kit.

Manipulatives

Real Math manipulatives come in three configurations.

- **Individual Manipulative Kits** These kits include **Number Cubes,** money, clock faces, rulers, interlocking cubes, counters, pattern blocks, tape measures, and spinners. A kit appropriate for Grades K–2 and another kit for 3–6 are available. These kits can be stored at student desks or in a designated tub or shelf in the classroom.

- **Manipulative Modules** Manipulatives are also available in modules for specific topics: Counting, Base-Ten, Fractions, Geometry, Measurement, Money, and Time. These kits contain enough materials for class use.

- **Teacher Manipulative Kit** This kit provides presentation-style manipulatives and overhead-projector manipulatives for demonstration purposes.

See Appendix A for more information about Materials.

It is important to keep parents informed about what their children are doing in mathematics so they can support students' mathematical understanding and development at home.

Family Involvement

Family members can play a critical role in students' success in mathematics if they understand how to help. For example, the games, Thinking Stories, and other activities in **Real Math** may be unfamiliar to parents. Parents need to be assured that these are important activities designed to develop a solid understanding of mathematical concepts and provide essential practice with arithmetic skills.

Real Math has several elements built into the program that can enable family-school communications.

Home Connection

This book includes ready-made Parent and Student Surveys, Newsletters, and Games that teachers can use to communicate with student families. Newsletters are available for every chapter.

Home Connection Game Kit

This kit includes all the **Game Mats** and **Cube Games** for a grade level, packaged in a game box along with the pieces needed to play the games. Families can purchase the kit, or you can establish a "lending game library."

Assessment Resources

Assessment includes several resources to communicate with families.

- **Student Assessment Record** is a convenient form to record all student assessments on a daily or weekly basis. These forms are handy to use at parent-teacher conferences.

- **Parent-Teacher Conference Checklist** provides a helpful way to organize thoughts about students in preparation for parent-teacher conferences.

Parent Aides

Often parents are willing to volunteer to help out in the classroom. There are many ways they can help.

- Computer Management—Make sure computers are on and loaded with appropriate software. Be available to troubleshoot and answer questions while students use the computers.

- Intervention Aide—Use the **Intervention Support Guide** to work with students to build prerequisite skills.

- English Learner Aide—Use the **English Learner Support Guide** to work with English Learners to preview and review lesson concepts.

- Manipulatives Manager—Make sure manipulatives are available for student use, when appropriate.

Family Participation

There are many ways that families can assist students in learning math.

Playing Games

Playing games with students is an enjoyable way to help them practice their math skills. **Home Connection** contains reproducible directions for each of the **Cube Games.** Reproductions of the **Game Mats** are in the back of this **Teacher's Edition.** The **Home Connection Game Kit** is also available.

Practicing Basic Facts

Home Connection contains reproducible flash cards for basic facts and directions for games using the cards. Make sure parents and helpers understand how best to use flash cards.

- Never ridicule students for incorrect answers.

- Stop practice when the student becomes disinterested.

Using Math in Everyday Life

Encourage parents to show students how they use mathematics throughout the day and to ask for students' help. For example, families can estimate the total cost of a shopping trip, measure ingredients and adjust recipes for new quantities when cooking, and estimate when to leave on a trip to arrive by a certain time.

The lessons are designed to be taught at a lively pace. Students should move quickly from activity to activity. In this way, they will remain alert and interested in what they are learning.

Pacing

Here are some tips for proper pacing:

- Be prepared. Materials must be ready, and you must be ready. Sections in the lesson plans titled Looking Ahead and Materials will help you prepare the items you will need in time for when they are needed. Also, read the lesson plan in advance or preview the *ePresentation* so you will not lose time figuring out what to do while the lesson is in progress.

- Use the time estimates. To help you manage time, lesson plans suggest a number of minutes for each activity. These times cannot be precise for every teacher and for every lesson. Some activities will take you more time and some will take less. Even so, the suggested times will help you to plan in advance how you will carry out each activity.

- Watch the clock. Use it as an ally. The clock can tell you when you have concentrated on an activity too long, even before students show signs of restlessness. It can tell you when you have lapsed into too much talking or when you are shifting too slowly from one activity to another.

Using Lessons over Two Days

Most lessons can be completed in one day (about 45–60 minutes of class time). However, you may find that you occasionally need to spend an extra day on some lessons. Refer to the Lesson Plans chart at the beginning of each unit for pacing suggestions. When you decide to take two days for a lesson, try dividing it as follows:

Day 1

- Review skills that students will need for the lesson.

- Do all suggested Teach activities, but not the **Student Edition** pages.

Day 2

- Review and/or adapt the Mental Math exercises from the previous day.

- Provide additional teaching and practice on related skills.

- Allow plenty of time for students to work on the **Student Edition** pages.

- Devote time to a related **Cube Game** or **Game Mat.**

- Extend the Reflect discussion.

Adjusting Instruction for Longer or Shorter Math Sessions

Most teachers have about 45–60 minutes each day to devote to mathematics. If your schedule varies greatly from that consider the following tips for adjusting instruction.

If you have more than 60 minutes for math...

- Lengthen Guided Discussion and game times by five minutes each (more when new games are introduced).

- Repeat whole-group activities when you feel that students will remain interested.

- Use the **Reteach, Practice,** and **Enrichment Masters** and the **Cross-Curricular Connections** provided throughout the **Teacher's Edition.**

If you have fewer than 45 minutes for math...

- Do not eliminate the Games or Thinking Stories. These help develop mathematical intelligence and are essential portions of the curriculum.

- Do the Thinking Story and Exploring Problem Solving activities outside the regular mathematics period (e.g., first thing in the morning, right after lunch, or at read-aloud time).

- Play games that reinforce previous lessons outside the regular class period, such as every Friday, perhaps.

- Conduct Mental Math on basic facts outside the regular mathematics period.

- Reduce time spent on a few lesson components by a minute or two.

- Have students spend more time working on student pages outside of class.

Real Math is rich in opportunities and resources to conduct comprehensive assessments that inform instruction. The *Real Math* Assessments are designed to evaluate all math proficiencies.

Assessment

Goals of Assessment

1. To improve instruction by informing teachers about the effectiveness of their lessons

2. To promote growth of students by identifying where they need additional instruction and support

3. To recognize accomplishments

Phases of Assessment

Planning As you develop lesson plans, you can consider how you might assess the instruction, determining how you will tell if students have grasped the material.

Gather Evidence Throughout the instructional phase, you can informally and formally gather evidence of student understanding. The Informal Assessment Checklists and Student Assessment Records are provided to help you record data.

Summarize Findings Taking time to reflect on the assessments to summarize findings and make plans for follow-up is a critical part of any lesson.

Use Results Use the results of your findings to differentiate instruction or to adjust or confirm future lessons.

Real Math is rich in opportunities to monitor student progress to accomplish these goals.

Informal Daily Assessment

Informal Daily Assessments evaluate students' math proficiencies in computational fluency, reasoning, understanding, applying, and engaging. Mental Math exercises, Games, Thinking Stories, and *Student Edition* pages can be used for day-to-day observation and assessment of how well each student is learning skills and grasping concepts. Because of their special nature, these activities are an effective and convenient means of monitoring students. Games, for example, allow you to watch students practice particular skills under conditions more natural to them than most classroom activities. Mental Math exercises allow you to provide adequate work and time to see individual responses, give immediate feedback, and involve the entire class.

Simple rubrics enable teachers to record and track their observations. These can later be recorded by hand in the Student Assessment Record or in *eAssess* to help provide a more complete view of student proficiency.

Formal Assessments

The *Student Edition* and *Assessment* provide formal assessments for each chapter. Included are Pretests, Speed Tests, Daily Quizzes, Practice Tests, and Chapter Tests to evaluate students' understanding of chapter concepts. Cumulative Review, Key Ideas Review, and Chapter Review are available to prepare students for formal assessments.

Mastery Checkpoints provide periodic progress checks.

Individual Oral Assessment

Oral Assessment, which is in the middle of the chapter, provides an opportunity for teachers to interview students and get a first-hand assessment of student reasoning and understanding.

Individual Portfolio Assessment

Journals and Chapter Projects can be used for Portfolio Assessment.

See Appendix A for more information about Assessment.

 Assessment

The Mastery Checkpoints are key Grade 2 skills for which students are expected to demonstrate mastery. **Assessment** contains a blackline master for each Mastery Checkpoint.

Grade 2 includes key skills that are important for students' future progress. To help monitor progress for each student, corresponding Mastery Checkpoints appear throughout the Grade 2 **Teacher's Edition.** Each Mastery Checkpoint appears in the lesson where most students are expected to have achieved proficiency. The table to the right provides a list of the Grade 2 skills and corresponding lessons that include the Mastery Checkpoints.

Do not delay the progress of the entire class while waiting for all students to demonstrate success with a particular skill. More teaching and practice on that skill are always given in a later lesson, usually the following lesson. At that time, you can focus on students who need extra help.

Mastery Checkpoints

The Mastery Checkpoint Chart in **Assessment** provides a convenient way to keep track of your students' progress.

- Fill in the names of all the students in the class.

- When a Mastery Checkpoint is encountered in the **Teacher's Edition,** follow the suggestions for observing each student. Then record students' progress, as follows:

Place an **R** in the appropriate column beside the name of each student who demonstrates success on the skill in question.

Pencil in a *P* in the appropriate column for each student who grasps the concept but still needs further practice to sharpen his or her skill. Assign extra practice to these students.

Pencil in a *T* for each student who has not yet grasped the idea and needs further teaching. Give extra teaching to these students.

Change *T*s (needs teaching) to *P*s (needs practice) and *P*s to *R*s (just needs refreshing) as students demonstrate success on the skill.

Grade 2 Checkpoints		
Number	Lesson	Topic
1	1.2	Odd and Even Numbers
2	1.5	Writing Numbers through 100
3	1.7	Numerical Sequence through 100
4	2.8	Addition Facts
5	3.6	Subtraction Facts
6	4.5	Measuring Length
7	5.1	Two-Digit Addition
8	6.7	Two-Digit Subtraction
9	6.8	Inequalities and Equalities
10	6.10	Addition and Subtraction Applications
11	7.8	Simple Fractions
12	7.10	Telling Time After and Before the Hour
13	8.6	Congruency
14	9.2	Numerical Sequence (0–100)
15	9.9	Familiarity with Money (Coins and Bills)
16	9.10	Three-Digit Addition and Subtraction
17	11.6	Multiplication Facts
18	12.5	Column Addition

See Appendix A for more about Assessment.

Number Sense

Teaching for Understanding

In this chapter students focus on number basics and properties of numbers. The goal of these lessons is to provide a basic review and to reintroduce students to number concepts they might have forgotten. These lessons also serve as a reminder for where students might encounter numbers in everyday situations, for example, the calendar and money. Many students will already be proficient in the concepts covered in this chapter.

Prerequisite Skills and Concepts
● Counting Objects ● Reading and Writing Numbers to 20 ● Identifying Coins

Number Sense Skills Trace

Before Grade 2	Grade 2	After Grade 2
Grades K–1 Informally and formally introduced number basics and properties of numbers, such as recognizing and writing numbers	**This chapter** reviews number concepts that are encountered in everyday situations.	**Grade 3** Review number concepts for greater numbers extending the place value to 10,000

Problem Solving

Problem solving is in every lesson. This chapter includes the following:

CHAPTER INTRODUCTION Students review counting and writing numbers, making and using estimates, and using numbers for different applications, such as money and calendars. (pp. 1I–2C)

EXPLORING PROBLEM SOLVING Lessons provide a specific focus on problem-solving strategies. (pp. 15–16, 16A and 27–28, 28A)

THINKING STORY In "Mr. Muddle Takes a Test" students help a character answer questions based on numbers in a set. (pp. 39A–39E, 39–40)

Games

Develop reasoning skills, and provide extensive practice.

• **Tracing and Writing Numbers Game** (Lesson 1.1)
• **Odds-Evens Game** (Lesson 1.2)
• **Counting and Writing Numbers Game** (Lesson 1.3)
• **Yard Sale Game** (Lesson 1.5)
• **Calendar Game** (Lesson 1.6)

Math Background

Number Sense

The Value of Number Sense

Number sense is understanding the relative sizes of numbers and how to use them, whether doing arithmetic, classification, estimation, or measurement. Understanding number sense allows students to build their understanding of number systems and computation.

Counting On and Back

This chapter begins with a review of the mathematical concepts of counting on and counting back.

- Counting on involves saying numbers forward beginning at 1 or a number other than 1.

- Counting back involves saying numbers in reverse order (for example, "10, 9, 8").

- Counting on is a more efficient procedure for solving addition problems than counting up from 1. For example, to find how many fruits there are in all if there are 15 apples and 3 pears, students can count from 1 to 15 then on to 18 or can start at 15 and count "16, 17, 18."

- Counting on can also be used to solve subtraction problems. For example, if there are 16 oranges and 23 bananas, to find how many more bananas than oranges, students can start at 16, count "17, 18, 19, 20, 21, 22, 23" and notice they named 7 numbers, so there are 7 more bananas than oranges.

The Number Line

- A number line shows numbers in order. In this chapter students work only with whole numbers, but in later grades students will use number lines for fractions, decimals, and negative numbers as well.

- The number line is useful for showing the inverse relationship between addition and subtraction. Students can see, for example, that if you start at 23 and count on 2 spaces to 25, then count back 2 spaces from 25 to 23, you end up at your starting point.

- Using a number line also prepares students for coordinate graphing (introduced in Chapter 4), because a number line is a one-dimensional graph, and the axes of a coordinate graph are two number lines.

Counting and Writing Numbers Game

The **Counting and Writing Numbers Game** is a simple variation of Nim, a game that can be exceedingly complex and that is often studied and played by students of mathematics. Several other games in **Real Math** are also based on Nim, including **Count to 20 by 1 or 2** and **Don't Take Them All** from Grade 1. The basic rules usually involve having a starting number, an increment, and an ending number. Other conditions are imposed in more advanced variations. Whatever the conditions, it is usually possible to find a winning strategy. As students play the **Counting and Writing Numbers Game,** they may discover winning strategies using working backward, knowing that their choice of counting on one, two, or three numbers affects who will say the ending number. Do not teach winning strategies or use a winning strategy consistently when demonstrating the game so students can discover on their own whether there is an optimal strategy and what it is.

Basic Facts

Although we expect students to commit basic addition and subtraction facts to memory if they have not already done so, fluency will be developed in Chapters 2 and 3. In this chapter we focus on having students understand the relation between addition and subtraction. Such understanding will help develop the fluency we expect later. Also by mixing addition and subtraction problems, we start teaching students to watch the signs.

What Research Says

About Number Sense

How Children Develop Counting and Organizational Knowledge for Numbers

The act of counting involves much more than the simple reciting of number words. While learning to count, the child develops the awareness that words and symbols can be used to represent objects and the awareness that each object will have its own unique corresponding word or symbol. Counting involves one-to-one correspondence and the meaningful use of sequences of number words. The child will develop procedures for organizing or coordinating his or her counting actions along with an understanding of a purpose for these actions. Strategies associated with counting include the use of counting-all, counting-on, counting-up, and counting-back techniques.

Key steps from the learning trajectory for counting for children in Grades 1–2 are described below. For the complete trajectory, see Appendix B.

Level Name	Description
Counting from N (N + 1, N − 1)	Around six years of age, children begin to count on, counting verbally and with objects from numbers other than 1. Another noticeable accomplishment is that children can determine immediately the number just before or just after another number without having to start back at 1.
Skip Counting by Tens to 100	A child at this level can count by tens to 100. He or she can count through decades knowing, for example, that 40 comes after 39.
Counting to 100	A child at this level can count by ones through 100, including the decade transitions from 19 to 20, 29 to 30, and so on.

Clements, Douglas and J. Sarama, eds. *Engaging Young Children in Mathematics: Standards for Early Childhood Mathematics Education.* Mahwah, New Jersey: Lawrence Erlbaum Associates, Publishers, 2004.

Research-Based Teaching Strategies

"Number sense develops as students understand the size of numbers, develop multiple ways of thinking about and representing numbers, use numbers as referents, and develop accurate perceptions about the effects of operations on numbers."

National Council of Teachers of Mathematics. *Principles and Standards for School Mathematics.* Reston, VA: NCTM, 2000, p. 80.

As children work with numbers, they gradually develop a complex network of ideas associated with counting and numbers. This number sense develops as children acquire increasingly complex understandings of the language, symbols, skills, and actions relating to their work with numbers. For the child, number sense is evidenced in how he or she describes the value or quantity of a number, in the ways he or she is able to compose or decompose a number, or even in the symbols that he or she uses to represent the number.

To support the learner in developing a richer, experience-based understanding of new concepts or relationships in mathematics, a variety of strategies to model or represent these concepts can be employed. These representations might be made through the use of pictures, manipulative models, real-world situations, number lines, collections of objects, oral language, and written symbols.

RESEARCH IN ACTION

Counting Chapter 1 continues to reinforce the development of effective and efficient procedures for counting and symbolically representing collections of objects. Counting-on, counting-up, and counting-back strategies will be a particular focus in the chapter.

Data Analysis Throughout Chapter 1, students will explore processes and procedures for describing, organizing, representing, and analyzing quantities or collections.

Communication Effective communication of strategies and conceptual understandings to support the learner's developing number sense will be reinforced throughout Chapter 1.

Vocabulary

add (Lesson 1.8) to find the amount made by combining two or more numbers

count back (Lesson 1.1) to count in descending order

count on (Lesson 1.1) to count in ascending order

equal sign (Lesson 1.9) =, shows the two values are the same

estimate (Lesson 1.3) a judgment of a number or other quantity that may not be exactly correct

even numbers (Lesson 1.2) numbers that can be divided equally into two groups

greater than sign (Lesson 1.9) >, shows the value on the left is larger than the value on the right

inverse operations (Lesson 1.10) operations that undo each other

less than sign (Lesson 1.9) <, shows the value on the left is smaller than the value on the right

number line (Lesson 1.7) a line on which points are identified with real numbers

odd numbers (Lesson 1.2) numbers that cannot be divided equally into two groups

ones place (Lesson 1.5) the right digit in a two-digit number

subtract (Lesson 1.8) to take away or deduct a number from another number

tens place (Lesson 1.5) the left digit in a two-digit number

English Learner

Cognates

For English learners, a quick way to acquire new English vocabulary is to build on what is known in the primary language.

English	Spanish
count	contar
pair	par
rounds	rondas
digit	dígito
signs	signos
application	aplicación
relation signs	signos de relación
inverse	inverso

Access Vocabulary

English learners might understand words in different contexts, or they might not understand idioms. Review chapter vocabulary for this concern. For example:

missing numbers	spaces that are blank where numbers need to be filled in to complete the counting sequence
ring the number	draw a circle around the number
pair off	When students each select a partner, they pair off.
bundle	a bunch of items grouped together with a band or tie
watch the signs	pay attention to the operational signs to know if you should count on or count back
two years from now	two years in the future
greater numbers	larger quantities
easier than it looks	not difficult

CHAPTER 1 Overview

Chapter Planner

Lessons	Objectives	NCTM Standards	State Standards
1.1 Counting and Writing Numbers pages 3A–4A 45–60 minutes	To review counting and writing numerals from 0 to 100	Number and Operations, Data Analysis and Probability	
1.2 Odds and Evens pages 5A–6A 45–60 minutes	To present the concept of odd and even numbers and informally introduce the concept of half	Number and Operations, Algebra	
1.3 Counting and Estimating pages 7A–8A 45–60 minutes	To practice counting and writing numbers and introduce the concept of estimation	Number and Operations, Data Analysis and Probability, Problem Solving	
1.4 Making Estimates pages 9A–10A 45–60 minutes	To practice estimating and measuring length, weight, and capacity using nonstandard units	Measurement	
1.5 Place Value and Money pages 11A–12A 45–60 minutes	To formally introduce place value and to count and use money	Number and Operations, Problem Solving	
1.6 The Calendar pages 13A–14A 45–60 minutes	To introduce the use and meaning of a calendar and to introduce and use ordinal numbers	Number and Operations, Algebra, Measurement	
1.7 Counting on a Number Line pages 19A–20A 45–60 minutes	To introduce using a number line, focusing on adding and subtracting 0, 1, 2, and 3 in the 0–100 range	Number and Operations	
1.8 Counting Applications pages 21A–22A 45–60 minutes	To continue using a number line to solve simple word problems involving adding and subtracting 0, 1, 2, and 3	Number and Operations, Problem Solving	
1.9 Comparing Numbers pages 23A–24A 45–60 minutes	To introduce the use of equality and inequality signs, focusing on the relationship between two numbers and between sums or differences	Number and Operations, Algebra	
1.10 Relating Addition and Subtraction pages 25A–26A 45–60 minutes	To demonstrate the relationship between addition and subtraction with a focus on fact families	Number and Operations, Algebra	

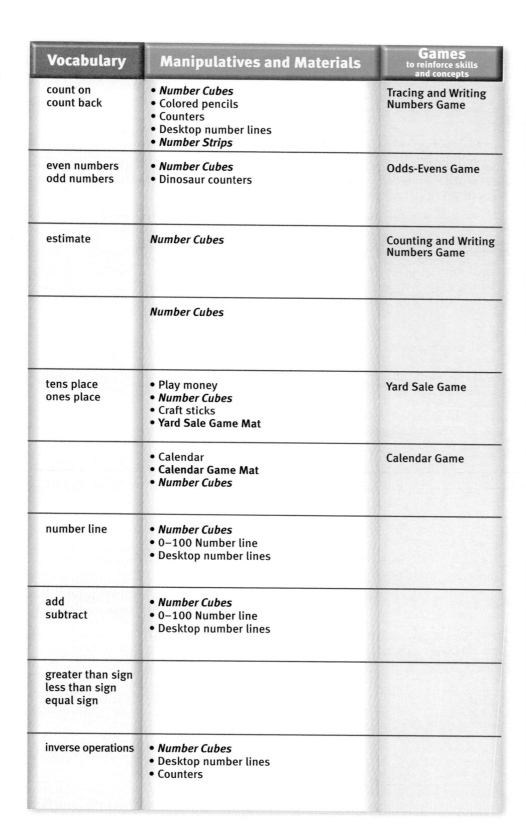

Vocabulary	Manipulatives and Materials	Games to reinforce skills and concepts
count on count back	• *Number Cubes* • Colored pencils • Counters • Desktop number lines • *Number Strips*	Tracing and Writing Numbers Game
even numbers odd numbers	• *Number Cubes* • Dinosaur counters	Odds-Evens Game
estimate	*Number Cubes*	Counting and Writing Numbers Game
	Number Cubes	
tens place ones place	• Play money • *Number Cubes* • Craft sticks • **Yard Sale Game Mat**	Yard Sale Game
	• Calendar • **Calendar Game Mat** • *Number Cubes*	Calendar Game
number line	• *Number Cubes* • 0–100 Number line • Desktop number lines	
add subtract	• *Number Cubes* • 0–100 Number line • Desktop number lines	
greater than sign less than sign equal sign		
inverse operations	• *Number Cubes* • Desktop number lines • Counters	

Additional Resources

Differentiated Instruction

Intervention Support Guide Provides instruction for prerequisite skills:

- Lesson 1.A Counting and Coins–1
- Lesson 1.B Counting and Coins–2
- Lesson 1.C Counting and Coins–3

Enrichment Support Guide Extends lesson concepts

Practice Reinforces lesson skills and concepts

Reteach Support Guide Provides alternate instruction for lesson concepts

English Learner Support Guide Previews and reviews lesson concepts and vocabulary for English learners

Technology

The following electronic resources are available:

Planner Lessons 1.1–1.10

Presentation Lessons 1.1–1.10

Textbook Lessons 1.1–1.10

Assess Lessons 1.1–1.10

MathTools *Sets Former* Lessons 1.1, 1.2
Base Ten Lesson 1.5
Coins and Money Lesson 1.5
Calendar Lesson 1.6
Number Line Lessons 1.7, 1.8, 1.10
100 Table Lesson 1.9

Games *Calendar Game* Lesson 1.6

Building Blocks *Book Stacks* Lesson 1.1
Build Stairs 3 Lesson 1.2
Rocket Blast 2 Lesson 1.3
Workin' on the Railroad Lesson 1.4
Number Compare 3 Lesson 1.5
Ordinal Construction Company Lesson 1.6
Pizza Pizzazz 5 Lesson 1.7
Sea to Shore Lesson 1.8
Number Compare 4 Lesson 1.9

Assessment
Informal Assessment rubrics at the end of each lesson provide daily evaluation of student math proficiency.

Chapter Planner, continued

Problem Solving	When to Use	Objectives	NCTM Standards	Skills Covered
Chapter Introduction (pp. 1I–2C) 15–30 minutes	Use before beginning Chapter 1	To introduce chapter concepts in a problem-solving setting	Problem Solving, Communication	Number sense
Exploring Problem Solving (pp. 15–16, 16A) 30–45 minutes	Use anytime during the chapter	To explore methods of solving nonroutine problems	Problem Solving, Communication	Number sense
Exploring Problem Solving (pp. 27–28, 28A) 45–60 minutes	Use anytime during the chapter	To explore methods of solving nonroutine problems	Problem Solving, Communication	Number sense
Thinking Story–Mr. Muddle Takes a Test (pp. 39A–39E, 39–40) 20–30 minutes	Use anytime during the chapter	To develop logical reasoning while integrating reading skills with mathematics	Number and Operations, Problem Solving	Number sense

Review	When to Use	Objectives	NCTM Standards	Skills Covered
Cumulative Review (p. 17–18) 15–30 minutes	Use anytime after Lesson 1.6	To review concepts and skills taught earlier in the year	Number and Operations	Reading and Writing Numbers, Odds and Evens, Place Value
Cumulative Review (p. 29–30) 15–30 minutes	Use anytime during the chapter	To review concepts and skills taught earlier in the year	Number and Operations	Reading and Writing Numbers, Equalities and inequalities
Chapter 1 Review (pp. 33A, 33–34) 30–45 minutes	Use after Lesson 1.10	To review concepts and skills taught in the chapter	Number and Operations, Data Analysis and Probability	Patterns, Counting, Using a clock, Using a calendar

Assessment	When to Use	Objectives	NCTM Standards	Skills Covered
Informal Assessment Rubrics (pp. 4A–26A) 5 minutes per student	Use at the end of each lesson	To provide daily evaluation of math proficiency	Problem Solving, Number and Operations, Communication	Computing, Understanding, Reasoning, Applying, Engaging
Pretest (*Assessment* pp. 22–23) 15–30 minutes	Use prior to Chapter 1	To provide assessment of prerequisite and chapter topics	Number and Operations, Problem Solving	Computing, Understanding, Reasoning, Applying, Engaging
Individual Oral Assessment (p. 18A) 5 minutes per student	Begin use after Lesson 1.6	To provide alternate means of assessing students' progress	Number and Operations, Problem Solving	Counting using **Number Cubes**, Counting to share, Patterns, Telling time
Mastery Checkpoint (*Assessment* pp. T50–T52) 5 minutes per student	Use after Lessons 1.2, 1.5, 1.7 or in place of the Chapter 1 Review	To provide assessment of mastery of key skills	Number and Operations	Odd and even numbers, Writing numbers through 100, Numerical sequence through 100
Chapter 1 Practice Test (pp. 35–36, 37–38) 30–45 minutes	Use after or in place of the Chapter 1 Review	To provide assessment or additional practice of the chapter concepts	Data Analysis and Probability, Number and Operations	Counting, Finger sets, Patterns, Telling time, Using a calendar
Chapter 1 Test (*Assessment* pp. 29–32) 30–45 minutes	Use after or in place of the Chapter 1 Review	To provide assessment on the chapter concepts	Geometry, Data Analysis and Probability, Number and Operations	Classifying, Patterns, Telling time, Finger sets, Counting to share

Technology Resources and Support

Visit SRAonline.com for online versions of the *Real Math* eSuite.

Technology for Teachers

e Presentation	**Lessons 1.1–1.10** Use the *ePresentation* to interactively present chapter content.	
e Planner	Use the Chapter and Lesson Planners to outline activities and time frames for Chapter 1.	
e Assess	Students can take the following assessments in *eAssess:* • Chapter Pretest • Mastery Checkpoint **Lessons 1.2, 1.5, and 1.7** • Chapter Test Teachers can record results and print reports for all assessments in this chapter.	
e MathTools	**Sets Former** Lessons 1.1, 1.2; **Base Ten** Lesson 1.5; **Coins and Money** Lesson 1.5; **Calendar** Lesson 1.6; **Number Line** Lessons 1.7, 1.8, 1.10; **100 Table** Lesson 1.9	

Technology for Students

e Textbook	An electronic, interactive version of the *Student Edition* is available for all lessons in Chapter 1.
e MathTools	**Sets Former** Lessons 1.1, 1.2 **Base Ten** Lesson 1.5 **Coins and Money** Lesson 1.5 **Calendar** Lesson 1.6 **Number Line** Lessons 1.7, 1.8, 1.10 **100 Table** Lesson 1.9
e Games	**Calendar Game** Lesson 1.6
TECH KNOWLEDGE	*TechKnowledge* Level 2 provides lessons that specifically teach the Unit 10 Internet and Unit 7 Spreadsheet applications that students can use in this chapter's projects.
Building Blocks	**Book Stacks** Lesson 1.1 **Build Stairs 3** Lesson 1.2 **Rocket Blast 2** Lesson 1.3 **Workin' on the Railroad** Lesson 1.4 **Number Compare 3** Lesson 1.5 **Ordinal Construction Company** Lesson 1.6 **Pizza Pizzazz 5** Lesson 1.7 **Sea to Shore** Lesson 1.8 **Number Compare 4** Lesson 1.9

CHAPTER 1

Introduction

Number Sense

1   Introduce Chapter 1   10

Chapter Objectives

This opener helps students prepare for the work with number sense in this chapter by providing an activity in which they can identify and classify numbers. Explain to students that in this chapter they will build on what they already know about numbers. They will

- count and write numbers.
- estimate.
- apply counting to real-world situations.
- compare numbers.

Pretest COMPUTING

Administer the Pretest on **Assessment** pages 22–23.

The Pretest covers the following prerequisite skills:

- Counting (Problems 1–4)
- Number sequence (Problems 5–8, 13, and 14)
- Addition and subtraction (Problems 9–12 and 19–22)
- Even numbers (Problem 15)
- Estimation (Problem 16)
- Place value (Problems 17 and 18)

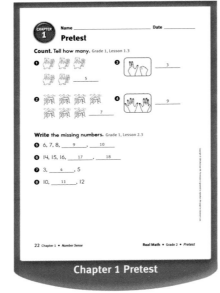

Chapter 1 Pretest

Access Prior Knowledge UNDERSTANDING

Guided Discussion

Initiate a discussion about numbers. Have students brainstorm about numbers and the different ways they are used in daily life.

2   Exploring Problem Solving   15

Tell Students In Today's Lesson They Will

- find numbers in a picture of a library.
- talk about the different purposes those numbers serve.
- talk about the strategies used to find all the numbers.

Materials

None

Guided Discussion   UNDERSTANDING

Have students discuss their trips to the library. Ask questions such as the following:

- **What are some of the different things people can do at a library?** read, look for books to check out, study, find information in books, magazines, or on the computer
- **How does the library keep track of who has which books?** When someone uses a library card to check out a book, a computer keeps a record of who has the book.
- **How does the librarian know one library card from another?** Each library card has a long number that tells to whom that card belongs.

Using Student Pages   APPLYING

Have students look at the illustration on page 2. If students do not comment on the numbers in the picture, ask them to find numbers that help people know what time it is or the quantity of something. Explain that numbers can show many things and that people see numbers in many settings, including the library.

Have students work on their own or with a partner to find and ring as many numbers as they can. Remind them that some of the numbers will be large and easy to see, but others will be harder to find. They will have to look closely at the entire illustration.

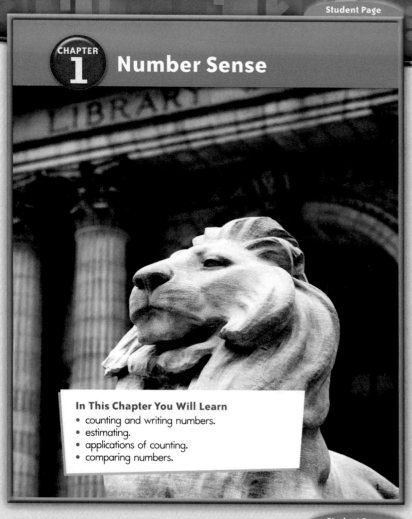

CHAPTER 1 Number Sense

In This Chapter You Will Learn
- counting and writing numbers.
- estimating.
- applications of counting.
- comparing numbers.

1

Problem Solving

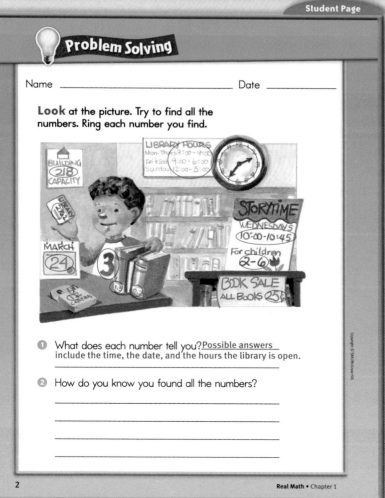

Name _____ Date _____

Look at the picture. Try to find all the numbers. Ring each number you find.

❶ What does each number tell you? <u>Possible answers</u> include the time, the date, and the hours the library is open.
_____

❷ How do you know you found all the numbers?
_____
_____
_____
_____

2

Real Math • Chapter 1

Concept/Question Board APPLYING

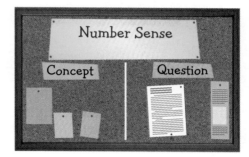

Questions
Have students think of and write three questions they have about numbers and how they can be used. Then have them select one question to post on the Question side of the Board.

Concepts
As students work through the chapter, have them collect examples of how numbers are used in everyday situations. For each example, have them write a problem that relates to the item(s). Have them display their examples on the Concept side of the Board. Suggest the following:

- time
- height and weight

Answers
Throughout the chapter, have students post answers to the questions and solutions to the problems on the Board.

3 Reflect 20

Effective Communication After students have had sufficient time to look for numbers, have them bring their books with them to a group area in front of a board. First, discuss the methods students used to make sure they found all the numbers. In discussion, bring out these points:

- Some numbers were harder to find than others because they were smaller or in less obvious places.
- Using a system can make it easier to ensure you haven't missed something.

Next have students share the numbers they found and where they found them. Record the information on the board in a table such as the one below:

Where are the numbers?
on the calendar
on the poster

When you have listed all the places, remind students that numbers give different types of information. Ask students what each number they found communicates. Add a second column to the table, and use it to record student responses.

Where are the numbers?	What do the numbers show?
on the calendar	what day it is
on the poster	how many people are allowed in the library
on the book spine	where the book belongs
on the crayon box	how many crayons are in the box

Help students notice that some of these uses of numbers are similar. Then guide students in classifying the uses by listing categories such as the following:

- telling when
- telling how many
- telling how much
- telling where
- telling who

Help students expand on this idea by asking them to think about other settings in which they see numbers and what purposes those numbers serve. Possible settings include highway signs, stores, room numbers, games, restaurants, telephones, license plates, and mail.

Sample Solutions Strategies

To make sure they have found all the numbers in the picture, students might use one or more of the following strategies:

Use a System

Students might scan from top to bottom and left to right in the same way they would read. Or they might break up the picture into sections and examine each section.

Use Common Knowledge

Students might recall what they know about libraries to predict where numbers are likely to be found and then search those places carefully.

Extension

Have students search their after-school environments for ways numbers are used. Remind them to look for numbers when they are in the car, when they are walking in their neighborhoods, at the store, at soccer practice, and anywhere else they might be after school. They should record at least ten places where they saw numbers and bring in their records to share and discuss.

Home Connection

At this time, you may want to send home the letter on pages 2–5 of **Home Connection.** This letter describes what students will be learning and what activities they can do at home to support their work in school.

Home Connection
Page 2

Assess and Differentiate

 Assess Use *eAssess* to record and analyze evidence of student understanding.

Gather Evidence

Use the Daily Class Assessment Records in **Assessment** or *eAssess* to record Informal and Formal Assessments.

Informal Assessment
☑ **Access Prior Knowledge**
Did the student **UNDERSTANDING**
- ❏ make important observations?
- ❏ extend or generalize learning?
- ❏ provide insightful answers?
- ❏ pose insightful questions?

Informal Assessment
☑ **Concept/Question Board**
Did the student **APPLYING**
- ❏ apply learning in new situations?
- ❏ contribute concepts?
- ❏ contribute answers?
- ❏ connect mathematics to real-world situations?

Formal Assessment
☑ **Pretest**  **COMPUTING**
Review student answers in each problem set.
- ❏ Counting (Problems 1–4)
- ❏ Number sequence (Problems 5–8, 13, and 14)
- ❏ Addition and subtraction (Problems 9–12 and 19–22)
- ❏ Even numbers (Problem 15)
- ❏ Estimation (Problem 16)
- ❏ Place value (Problems 17 and 18)

Summarize Findings

Analyze and summarize assessment data for each student. Determine which Assessment Follow-Up is appropriate for each student. Use the Student Assessment Record in **Assessment** or *eAssess* to update assessment records.

C Assessment Follow-Up ● DIFFERENTIATE INSTRUCTION

Based on your observations of each student, use these teaching strategies for a general approach to the chapter. Look for specific Differentiate Instruction and Monitoring Student Progress strategies in each lesson that relate specifically to the lesson content.

ENRICH	PRACTICE	RETEACH	INTERVENTION	ENGLISH LEARNER
If . . . students demonstrate a **secure understanding** of chapter concepts, **Then . . .** move quickly through the chapter or use *Enrichment* Lessons 1.1–1.10 as assessment follow-up to extend and apply understanding.	**If . . .** students grasp chapter concepts with **competent understanding**, **Then . . .** use *Practice* Lessons 1.1–1.10 as lesson follow-up to develop fluency.	**If . . .** students have prerequisite understanding but demonstrate **emerging understanding** of chapter concepts, **Then . . .** use *Reteach* Lesson 1.2 to reteach lesson concepts.	**If . . .** students are not competent with prerequisite skills, **Then . . .** use *Intervention* Lessons 1.A–1.C before each lesson to develop fluency with prerequisite skills.	Use *English Learner Support Guide* Lessons 1.1–1.10 for strategies to preteach lesson vocabulary and concepts.

Math Across the Curriculum

Preview the chapter projects with students. Assign projects or have students choose from the projects to extend and enrich concepts in this chapter.

Analyze Primary Sources 3–4 weeks

SOCIAL STUDIES WebQuest

MATH OBJECTIVE
To reinforce studies of counting by writing numbers of historical documents found

SOCIAL STUDIES OBJECTIVE
To reinforce studies of historical materials as primary source documents

TECHNOLOGY OBJECTIVE
To use a spreadsheet program to track use of historical documents

Have students use technology to

- view and listen to historical documents.
- record the number of items viewed.

For this project, students use the Internet to investigate the following types of documents:

- historical manuscripts such as letters and government papers
- historical photos
- historical interviews

For specific step-by-step instructions for this project, see **Across the Curriculum Math Connections** pages 12–17.

Knowledge Age Skills

High-Level Responsibility Students take on decision-making roles.

Problem Formulation, Planning, and Strategizing Students organize types of historical documents.

TechKnowledge Level 2 provides lessons that specifically teach the Unit 10 Internet and Unit 7 Spreadsheet applications that students can use in this project.

Create a Reading Log

LANGUAGE ARTS

1–2 weeks

MATH OBJECTIVE
To reinforce studies of the calendar by recording dates in a reading log

LANGUAGE ARTS OBJECTIVE
To reinforce studies of journal writing by recording entries in a reading log

TECHNOLOGY OBJECTIVE
To use a database program to create a reading log

Have students use mathematics to record dates in a reading log. To broaden the language arts concept, have them use their logs to record reading time for works which you are currently studying.

As part of the project, students should consider the following issues:

- how to create a reading log
- what information is recorded in a reading log
- how to create a database
- how to enter information in a database
- how dates are important in keeping a reading log

For specific step-by-step instructions for this project, see **Across the Curriculum Math Connections** pages 18–21.

Knowledge Age Skills

Problem Formulation, Planning, and Strategizing Students create reading logs by using a database program.

Self-Monitoring and Self- and Group Assessment Students monitor themselves by keeping a log of the time they spend reading each day.

Lesson Planner

OBJECTIVES
- To review counting and writing numerals from 0 to 100
- To informally introduce probability by using the **Tracing and Writing Numbers Game**

NCTM STANDARDS

Number and Operations
- Counting with understanding and recognizing "how many" in sets of objects
- Developing understanding of the relative position and magnitude of whole numbers
- Connecting number words and numerals to the quantities they represent

Data Analysis and Probability
- Discussing events related to students' experiences as likely or unlikely
- Understanding and applying basic concepts of probability

MATERIALS
- *Number Cubes
- Colored pencils (two colors per pair of students)
- *Number Strips
- *Counters
- *Desktop number lines

TECHNOLOGY
- **Presentation** Lesson 1.1
- **MathTools** Set Formers
- **Building Blocks** Book Stacks

TEST PREP
None

Counting and Writing Numbers

Context of the Lesson This lesson reviews counting and writing numbers. Many students will already be proficient in the information presented in this lesson and subsequent lessons of the chapter.

See page 1B for Math Background for teachers for this lesson.

Planning for Learning ● DIFFERENTIATE INSTRUCTION

INTERVENTION

If . . . students lack the prerequisite skill of counting objects,

Then . . . teach **Intervention** Lesson 1.B.

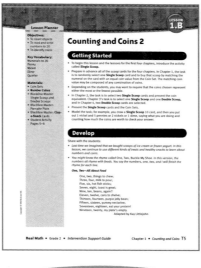

Intervention Lesson 1.B

ENGLISH LEARNER

Preview

If . . . students need language support,

Then . . . use Lesson 1.1 in **English Learner Support Guide** to preview lesson concepts and vocabulary.

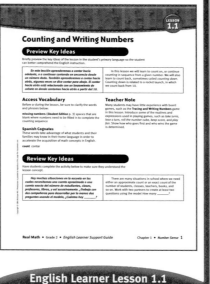

English Learner Lesson 1.1

ENRICH

If . . . students are proficient in the lesson concepts,

Then . . . emphasize the game variations.

PRACTICE

If . . . students would benefit from additional practice,

Then . . . extend Skill Building before assigning the student pages.

RETEACH

If . . . students are having difficulty understanding number sequence,

Then . . . extend Guided Discussion before assigning the student pages.

Vocabulary
count on v. to count in ascending order

count back v. to count in descending order

Access Vocabulary
missing numbers spaces that are blank where numbers need to be filled in to complete the counting sequence

Spanish Cognates
count contar

Mental Math 5

  Show students how to find, hide, and show answers on their **Number Cubes** by using the steps described on page T32. Then have them use these techniques to show what number comes next when given a number. For example:

a. 4 5   **b.** 10 11   **c.** 12 13

d. 15 16   **e.** 52 53   **f.** 38 39

1 Develop 20

Tell Students In Today's Lesson They Will

count and write numbers to 100.

Whole Group

Guided Discussion MathTools UNDERSTANDING

Counting Review

Discuss and review counting and the sequence of numbers from 0 to 100 with students. Use counters or **eMathTools: Set Formers** to demonstrate.

Skill Building COMPUTING

Whole Group

Counting Activity

Counting On

Starting at 1, have students count on in unison. Stop them after they get to 10, and have them start again at a greater number. You may have individual students start, and then have others join in.

Counting Back

Have students count back from a number. Stop students intermittently, and let different students start at a new number and count back, with others joining in.

At this time, the counting should be with numbers through 100. If students are having trouble, allow them to use a number line, but encourage them not to depend on it.

Giving a Stopping Point

If students are having little or no trouble with counting, increase the level of difficulty by having them count in unison within a set span. They must keep the stopping point in mind as they count so they don't continue past it. You may want to write the last number on the board. Give at least one series of numbers that ends with 100.

Skill and Strategy Building

Whole Group

 Tracing and Writing Numbers Game

Principal Skills: counting from 1 to 10, writing and recognizing numbers from 0 to 10, basic probability

There are three games on student page 4, one in which students trace numerals and two in which students write the numerals.

- The tracing version can be skipped if the reinforcement is not needed.
- Demonstrate the game by playing it with a student in front of the class.
- Make sure students understand that they can select to roll either cube before each turn. Choosing which cube to roll encourages students to think about probability, even though the concept is not explained at this time.

Game Variations

- Instead of counting the numbers in each color to determine the winner, add their values. The player with the higher sum is the winner. This variation encourages students to consider number magnitude.
- Students can also keep score using **Number Strips** laid end to end. The player with the longest row is the winner.

2 Assign Student Pages 15

Pages 3–4 ENGAGING

Have students complete page 3 independently.

> **Monitoring Student Progress**
>
> **If . . .** students demonstrate poor familiarity with numbers in the 0 to 100 range,
>
> **Then . . .** provide individual tutoring by counting with them using a number line. Try to remove the number line as a counting tool as soon as feasible.

As Students Finish

 Have students play the **Tracing and Writing Numbers Game** in pairs.

 Have students use **Book Stacks** to reinforce counting to a specific number.

Student Page

Name _____ Date _____

LESSON 1.1 **Counting and Writing Numbers**

Key Ideas

You can count on.   You can count back.

| 4 | 5 | 6 | | 6 | 5 | 4 |

Count on, or count back.
Fill in the missing numbers.

1

| 5 | 6 | 7 | 8 | 9 | 10 | 11 | 12 |

2

| 76 | 77 | 78 | 79 | 80 | 81 | 82 | 83 |

3

| 39 | 38 | 37 | 36 | 35 | 34 | 33 | 32 |

4

| 63 | 62 | 61 | 60 | 59 | 58 | 57 | 56 |

Textbook This lesson is available in the *eTextbook*.   3

Guided Discussion   **APPLYING**

Ask students to make up and discuss problems that have solutions that can be found by counting. Possible problems include the following:

- **How many students are there in the classroom?**
- **How many students drink milk at lunch?**
- **How many teachers are there in the school?**

Ask students to think about why someone would want to know these answers. For example, to know how many desks need to be in the room, someone would need to know how many students there are in a classroom.

Encourage students to see that counting helps people figure out how resources should be distributed.

 Cumulative Review: For cumulative review of previously learned skills, see page 17–18.

 Family Involvement: Assign the *Practice, Reteach,* or *Enrichment* activities depending on the needs of your students. Have students play the **Tracing and Writing Numbers Game** with family members.

 Concept/Question Board: Have students look for additional examples that use counting and numbers and post them on the Concept/Question Board.

 Math Puzzler: Complete the pattern: 87, 86, 84, 83, 81, 80, _____, _____ 78, 77

Student Page

Number Sequence and Strategies Practice

Tracing and Writing Numbers Game

Players: Two

Materials:

- 0–5 and 5–10 **Number Cubes**
- Different-colored pencil for each player

HOW TO PLAY

1 Players take turns rolling the 0–5 or the 5–10 **Number Cube** and then tracing or writing the number rolled. Each player uses a different color to write with.

2 If a player rolls a number that has already been traced or written, the player loses a turn.

3 When a complete row of numbers has been traced or written, each player counts how many numbers he or she entered.

4 The player who entered more numbers is the winner.

Tracing Game

| 0 | 1 | 2 | 3 | 4 | 5 | 6 | 7 | 8 | 9 | 10 |

Writing Game

| | | | | | | | | | | |

| | | | | | | | | | | |

4   **Real Math** • Chapter 1 • Lesson 1

4 Assess and Differentiate

 Assess Use *eAssess* to record and analyze evidence of student understanding.

A Gather Evidence

Use the Daily Class Assessment Records in *Assessment* or *eAssess* to record daily observations.

Informal Assessment
☑ **Skill Building**

Did the student **COMPUTING**
- ❑ respond accurately?
- ❑ respond quickly?
- ❑ respond with confidence?
- ❑ self-correct?

Performance Assessment
☑ **Guided Discussion**

Did the student **APPLYING**
- ❑ apply learning in new situations?
- ❑ contribute concepts?
- ❑ contribute answers?
- ❑ connect mathematics to real-world situations?

B Summarize Findings

Analyze and summarize assessment data for each student. Determine which Assessment Follow-Up is appropriate for each student. Use the Student Assessment Record in *Assessment* or *eAssess* to update assessment records.

Assessment page T41

C Assessment Follow-Up • DIFFERENTIATE INSTRUCTION

Based on your observations, use these teaching strategies for assessment follow-up.

INTERVENTION

Review student performance on *Intervention* Lesson 1.B to see if students have mastered prerequisite skills for this lesson.

ENGLISH LEARNER

Review

Use Lesson 1.1 in *English Learner Support Guide* to review lesson concepts and vocabulary.

ENRICH

If . . . students are proficient in the lesson concepts,

Then . . . encourage them to work on the chapter projects or *Enrichment* Lesson 1.1.

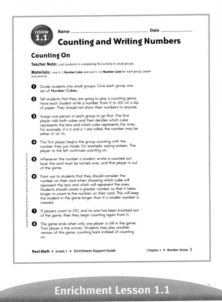

Enrichment Lesson 1.1

PRACTICE

If . . . students would benefit from additional practice,

Then . . . assign *Practice* Lesson 1.1.

Practice Lesson 1.1

RETEACH

If . . . students are having difficulty understanding counting,

Then . . . have them practice counting with manipulatives or have them count objects in the classroom.

OBJECTIVES
- To present the concept of odd and even numbers
- To informally introduce the concept of half

NCTM STANDARDS
Number and Operations
- Developing understanding of the relative position and magnitude of whole numbers
- Understanding and representing commonly used fractions
- Developing a sense of whole numbers and representing and using them in flexible ways

Algebra
- Sorting, classifying, and ordering objects by properties
- Recognizing, describing, and extending patterns

MATERIALS
- *Number Cubes
- *Dinosaur Counters

TECHNOLOGY
 Presentation Lesson 1.2
 MathTools Set Formers
Building Blocks Build Stairs 3

TEST PREP
Cumulative Review
Mental Math reviews counting in sequence (Lesson 1.1).

Extended Response
Problem 16

Writing + Math
Journal

Odds and Evens

Context of the Lesson This is the second lesson on number basics and the first lesson on odd and even numbers. Students will learn how to find halves and a formal definition of *half* in Chapter 7.
See page 1B for Math Background for teachers for this lesson.

Planning for Learning ● DIFFERENTIATE INSTRUCTION

INTERVENTION
If . . . students lack the prerequisite skill of reading and writing numbers to 20,

Then . . . teach **Intervention** Lesson 1.A.

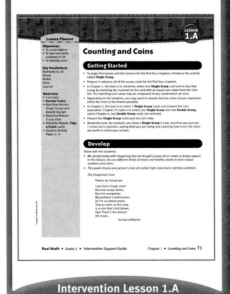

Intervention Lesson 1.A

ENGLISH LEARNER
Preview
If . . . students need language support,

Then . . . use Lesson 1.2 in **English Learner Support Guide** to preview lesson concepts and vocabulary.

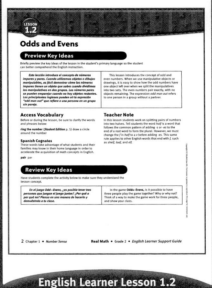

English Learner Lesson 1.2

ENRICH
If . . . students are proficient in the lesson concepts,

Then . . . extend the time allotted to play the **Odds-Evens Game.**

PRACTICE
If . . . students would benefit from additional practice,

Then . . . extend Guided Discussion before assigning the student pages.

RETEACH
If . . . students are having difficulty understanding odd and even numbers,

Then . . . extend Guided Discussion before assigning the student pages.

Vocabulary
even numbers *n.* numbers that can be divided equally into two groups

odd numbers *n.* numbers that cannot be divided equally into two groups

Access Vocabulary
ring the number draw a circle around the number

Spanish Cognates
pair par

Mental Math 5

 Have students use their **Number Cubes** to complete number sequences. Possible examples include the following:

a. 32, 33, 34, __35__
b. 68, 69, 70, __71__
c. 5, 6, 7, __8__
d. 55, 56, 57, __58__

1 Develop 20

Tell Students In Today's Lesson They Will

learn about odd and even numbers and strategies for determining whether a number is odd or even.

Guided Discussion  MathTools   Whole Group

Dividing into Halves REASONING

Using manipulatives, show students how to divide a specific number in half. Use ten **Dinosaur Counters** or the **eMathTools: Set Formers.** Have students count the dinosaurs aloud to see that you have ten. Then divide them into two equal piles, counting as you place each dinosaur in its separate pile.

■ **How many dinosaurs are in each pile?** five

Repeat the above procedure using sixteen dinosaurs. Explain that when you split a number into two equal piles with none left over, the number is even.

Repeat the above procedure using nine dinosaurs.

■ **Do we have an extra dinosaur?** yes

If a student suggests breaking the dinosaur in half, praise the student, but explain that for now, only whole dinosaurs will be used. Tell students that if a number cannot be split into two equal piles without breaking objects, the number is odd.

Hold up various odd and even numbers of dinosaurs, and have students tell whether the numbers are odd or even. When the number is even, have students tell what half of the number is.

Skill and Strategy Building COMPUTING   Whole Group

 Odds-Evens Game

Demonstrate and play a round of the **Odds-Evens** game with students.

Principal Skills: identifying odd and even numbers through ten

2 Assign Student Pages 20

Pages 5–6 UNDERSTANDING

Have students complete page 5 independently. Allow students to use manipulatives if needed.

Monitoring Student Progress

If . . . students are having difficulty identifying odd and even numbers on student page 5,	**Then . . .** use manipulatives to demonstrate the single-digit even and odd numbers. Then remind students of the last-digit rule. Demonstrate that any number of tens is always even. Whether any number of sticks is odd or even depends on the number in the ones place. Let the students practice, using dinosaur counters to verify answers.

As Students Finish

 When students finish, have them play the **Odds-Evens Game** in pairs.

Building Blocks Have students use **Build Stairs 3** to review number sequence.

Name _____ Date _____

 LESSON 1.2 Odds and Evens

Key Ideas

Even numbers can be split into two equal parts. Odd numbers cannot.

Ring the odd numbers.

Write how many sticks would be in each pile if you split the even numbers.

1. 10 **5**   2. ⑪   3. 12 **6**

4. ⑬   5. 14 **7**   6. ⑮

7. 16 **8**   8. ⑰   9. 18 **9**

10. ⑲   11. 20 **10**   12. ㉑

13. 2 **1**   14. ①   15. 4 **2**

16. **Extended Response** The house numbers on one side of Franklin Street are 542, 544, and 546.
   a. What are the likely house numbers on the other side of the street? **541, 543, 545, 547**
   b. If you were delivering the mail on Franklin Street, how would you sort it before starting to make deliveries? Explain why. **by odds and evens to avoid crossing the street for every house**

📖 Textbook This lesson is available in the *eTextbook*.   5

Game

Number Properties and Sequence Strategies Practice

Odds–Evens Game

Players: Two
Materials: None

HOW TO PLAY

1. Player One is the even player. Player Two is the odd player.
2. Each player secretly chooses a number between 0 and 5 and hides one hand behind his or her back with that many fingers showing.
3. Both players count aloud to 3 together and then bring their hidden fingers to the front.
4. If the total number of fingers showing is even, the even player wins. If the total number of fingers showing is odd, the odd player wins.

Writing + Math Journal

How many even numbers do you count if you start at 1 and count on by ones to 10? How many odd numbers?

6   Real Math • Chapter 1 • Lesson 2

---

3 Reflect   10

Guided Discussion UNDERSTANDING   Whole Group

Ask students to give definitions of odd and even numbers in their own words. Students should realize that even numbers can be divided equally into two groups and odd numbers cannot.

- Have students write a rule for identifying odd and even numbers for their portfolios.
- **Is 1,348,296,578,924 odd or even? How can you tell without using *Dinosaur Counters* and making piles?** even; The number in the ones place determines if a number is odd or even.

Writing + Math Journal

Discuss students' answers. Students may notice that the number of digits counted (whether even or odd) is 5, or half of 10. When counting to an even number, there will always be the same number of even or odd numbers. When counting to an odd number, there will always be one more odd number than even number.

✓ Use Mastery Checkpoint 1 found in *Assessment* to evaluate student mastery of odd and even numbers. By this time, students should be able to correctly answer eighty percent of the Mastery Checkpoint items.

Review **Cumulative Review:** For cumulative review of previously learned skills, see page 17–18.

🎒 **Family Involvement:** Assign the *Practice, Reteach,* or *Enrichment* activities depending on the needs of your students. Have students play the **Odds-Evens Game** with a family member.

Concept/Question Board: Have students look for additional examples that use number properties and post them on the Concept/Question Board.

🧩 **Math Puzzler:** Write the following pattern on the board, and ask students to fill in the missing numbers: 73, 73, 72, 72, 71, _____, _____, _____, _____ 71, 70, 70, 69

Chapter 1 • Lesson 2   **5–6**

Assess and Differentiate

 Assess Use *eAssess* to record and analyze evidence of student understanding.

A Gather Evidence

Use the Daily Class Assessment Records in *Assessment* or *eAssess* to record daily observations.

Formal Assessment

☑ **Mastery Checkpoint**

Did the student
- ❏ use correct procedures?
- ❏ respond with at least 80% accuracy?

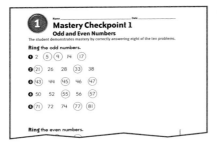

Assessment page T50

B Summarize Findings

Analyze and summarize assessment data for each student. Determine which Assessment Follow-Up is appropriate for each student. Use the Student Assessment Record in *Assessment* or *eAssess* to update assessment records.

Assessment page T41

C Assessment Follow-Up ● DIFFERENTIATE INSTRUCTION

Based on your observations, use these teaching strategies for assessment follow-up.

INTERVENTION	ENRICH	PRACTICE	RETEACH
Review student performance on *Intervention* Lesson 1.A to see if students have mastered prerequisite skills for this lesson.	**If . . .** students are proficient in the lesson concepts, **Then . . .** encourage them to work on the chapter projects or *Enrichment* Lesson 1.2.	**If . . .** students would benefit from additional practice, **Then . . .** assign *Practice* Lesson 1.2.	**If . . .** students are having difficulty understanding odd and even numbers, **Then . . .** reteach the concept using *Reteach* Lesson 1.2.

ENGLISH LEARNER

Review

Use Lesson 1.2 in *English Learner Support Guide* to review lesson concepts and vocabulary.

Enrichment Lesson 1.2

Practice Lesson 1.2

Reteach Lesson 1.2

Lesson Planner

OBJECTIVES
- To practice counting and writing numbers
- To introduce the concept of estimation

NCTM STANDARDS

Number and Operations
- Counting with understanding and recognizing "how many" in sets of objects
- Developing understanding of the relative position and magnitude of whole numbers

Data Analysis and Probability
- Posing questions and gathering data about students and surroundings
- Sorting and classifying objects according to their attributes and organizing data about the objects
- Discussing events as likely or unlikely

Problem Solving
Applying appropriate strategies to solve problems

MATERIALS
*Number Cubes

TECHNOLOGY
e**Presentation** Lesson 1.3
Building Blocks Rocket Blast 2

TEST PREP
Cumulative Review
Mental Math reviews odd and even numbers (Lesson 1.2).

Writing + Math
Journal

*Manipulative Kit Item

Counting and Estimating

Context of the Lesson This lesson introduces the concept of estimation. Estimation is also taught in Lesson 1.4.

See page 1B for Math Background for teachers for this lesson.

Planning for Learning ● DIFFERENTIATE INSTRUCTION

INTERVENTION	ENGLISH LEARNER	ENRICH
If . . . students lack the prerequisite skill of counting objects, **Then . . .** teach *Intervention* Lesson 1.C.	Preview **If . . .** students need language support, **Then . . .** use Lesson 1.3 in *English Learner Support Guide* to preview lesson concepts and vocabulary.	**If . . .** students are proficient in the lesson concepts, **Then . . .** emphasize estimating objects in more complex ratios while doing the student pages.

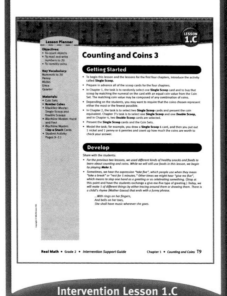

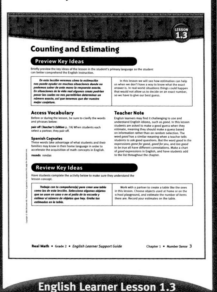

Intervention Lesson 1.C

English Learner Lesson 1.3

PRACTICE
If . . . students would benefit from additional practice, **Then . . .** extend Guided Discussion before assigning the student pages.

RETEACH
If . . . students are having difficulty understanding estimating, **Then . . .** extend Guided Discussion before assigning the student pages.

Vocabulary
estimate \es´tə māt´\ *n.* a judgment of a number or other quantity that may not be exactly correct

Access Vocabulary
pair off When students each select a partner, they pair off.

Spanish Cognates
rounds rondas

Mental Math 5

  Have students find, hide, and then show the answers to the following questions on their **Number Cubes:**

a. I am an odd number between 6 and 9. Who am I? 7

b. I am an even number between 45 and 48. Who am I? 46

c. I am the first odd number after 57. Who am I? 59

1 Develop 5

Tell Students In Today's Lesson They Will

learn about and make estimations.

Guided Discussion REASONING   Whole Group

Discuss estimation and its uses with students. Ask students questions that introduce the concept of estimation, such as the following:

■ **How would you figure out how many muffins to make for a party for 15 people?**

Explain that estimates are not exact but are close guesses based on the information you have. For example, if you are going to a party for fifteen people, you can guess that each person will eat one muffin. Ask students if they can think of reasons that this estimate would be inaccurate. *Would a person ever eat more than one muffin? Would a person ever not eat any muffins?*

■ **If you and four friends were going to the beach, how many towels would you need to take?**

Can you think of situations in which someone might use more than one towel?

Skill and Strategy Building ENGAGING

 Counting and Writing Numbers Game

Introduce and demonstrate the **Counting and Writing Numbers Game** on page 8 by playing a few rounds with a student in front of the class.

Although the rules do not specify, encourage students to choose a range of approximately twenty numbers so that a game can be played quickly. This will allow more time for game repetitions.

Principal Skills: counting and writing numbers in the 0 to 100 range

Game Variations

If students playing the game need an additional challenge, have them play the game counting back.

2 Assign Student Pages 35

Pages 7–8 APPLYING

Have students complete page 7 as a class. This activity is designed to provide practice in counting and making estimates.

● For the first two charts, ask students to count the number of designated objects and then, without counting, estimate the number of related objects.

● Then have them count to check their estimates.

● Select your own related objects to complete the third chart.

> #### Monitoring Student Progress
>
> | **If . . .** students are counting exact numbers instead of estimating, | **Then . . .** remind students what estimation is, and ask them to quickly estimate something that would be difficult to count, such as a pile of sticks. |

As Students Finish

Game As students finish, have them play additional rounds of the **Counting and Writing Numbers Game.**

Building Blocks Have students use *Rocket Blast 2* to reinforce estimating the position of numbers on a number line.

RESEARCH IN ACTION

"Counting a set of objects is a complex task involving thinking, perception, and movement, with much of its complexity obscured by familiarity…Counting is not simply reciting the number word sequence. There must be items to count; and there must be a procedure to make each utterance of a number word correspond with one of the items to be counted."

"Early research on children's understanding of the mathematical basis for counting focused on five principles their thinking must follow if their counting is to be mathematically useful:

1. *One-to-one:* there must be a one-to-one relation between counting words and objects;

2. *Stable order* (of the counting words): these counting words must be recited in a consistent, reproducible order;

3. *Cardinal:* the last counting word spoken indicates how many objects are in the set as a whole (rather than being a property of a particular object in the set);

4. *Abstraction:* any kinds of objects can be collected together for purposes of a count; and

5. *Order irrelevance* (for the objects counted): objects can be counted in any sequence without altering the outcome."

Kilpatrick, J., J. Swafford, and B. Findell, eds. *Adding It Up: Helping Children Learn Mathematics.* Washington, D.C.: National Research Council/ National Academy Press, 2001, pp. 159–160.

Key Ideas

When you **estimate**, you make a good guess about what you think the answer will be using information you know. If you count the desks in a classroom, you can estimate how many students are in the class.

Complete the estimating activity.

Count Objects	Students	
Estimate Related Objects	Desks	

Count to Check Estimate _____

Count Objects	Shoes	
Estimate Related Objects	Students	

Count to Check Estimate _____

Count Objects		
Estimate Related Objects		

Count to Check Estimate _____

Textbook This lesson is available in the **eTextbook**.

7

Game

Number Sequence and Strategies Practice

Counting and Writing Numbers Game

Players: Two

Materials: Pencil and paper for each player

HOW TO PLAY

❶ Player One chooses a starting number and an ending number between 0 and 100.

❷ Starting with Player One, players take turns counting, saying, and writing the next one, two, or three numbers. Each player can advance up to three numbers a turn.

❸ Each player must advance at least one number per turn.

❹ The player who says and writes the ending number wins the game.

Sample Game
Start at 27. Stop at 40.

Allison: 27
Geoff: 28, 29

Allison: 30, 31, 32
Geoff: 33

Allison: 34, 35, 36
Geoff: 37

Allison: 38, 39, 40

 Writing + Math Journal

If you were playing this game to 40, what number less than 40 would you have to say and write to be sure you would win?

---

3 Reflect   10

Guided Discussion UNDERSTANDING   Whole Group

Encourage students to discuss why estimating is often difficult. Allow students to express their thoughts.

■ **Why is it easier to estimate the number of students in a classroom if the number of desks is known?** because you can use that information to assume that every student will need one desk

Writing + Math Journal

Discuss students' answers. In this version of the game, whoever says 36 first can always win the game. Can students figure out what number they would have to say to get to say 36? 32

Review Cumulative Review: For cumulative review of previously learned skills, see page 17–18.

Family Involvement: Assign the *Practice, Reteach,* or *Enrichment* activities depending on the needs of your students. Have students play the **Counting and Writing Numbers Game** with a family member.

Concept/Question Board: Have students look for additional examples that use counting and numbers and post them on the Concept/Question Board.

Math Puzzler: Morgan is third in line. Rishi is 7 places behind Morgan. Sharice is 4 places in front of Rishi. The teacher told students standing in odd-numbered places to sit. Should Morgan sit? Rishi? Sharice? yes; no; no

4 Assess and Differentiate

 Assess Use *eAssess* to record and analyze evidence of student understanding.

A Gather Evidence

Use the Daily Class Assessment Records in *Assessment* or *eAssess* to record daily observations.

Informal Assessment
☑ **Guided Discussion**
Did the student **REASONING**
- ❏ provide a clear explanation?
- ❏ communicate reasons and strategies?
- ❏ choose appropriate strategies?
- ❏ argue logically?

Performance Assessment
☑ **Student Pages**
Did the student **APPLYING**
- ❏ apply learning in new situations?
- ❏ contribute concepts?
- ❏ contribute answers?
- ❏ connect mathematics to real-world situations?

B Summarize Findings

Analyze and summarize assessment data for each student. Determine which Assessment Follow-Up is appropriate for each student. Use the Student Assessment Record in *Assessment* or *eAssess* to update assessment records.

Assessment page T41

C Assessment Follow-Up ● DIFFERENTIATE INSTRUCTION

Based on your observations, use these teaching strategies for assessment follow-up.

INTERVENTION
Review student performance on *Intervention* Lesson 1.C to see if students have mastered prerequisite skills for this lesson.

ENGLISH LEARNER
Review
Use Lesson 1.3 in *English Learner Support Guide* to review lesson concepts and vocabulary.

ENRICH
If . . . students are proficient in the lesson concepts,
Then . . . encourage them to work on the chapter projects or *Enrichment* Lesson 1.3.

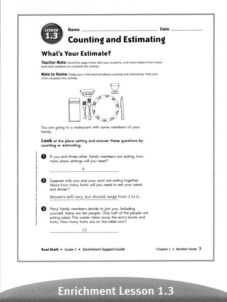

Enrichment Lesson 1.3

PRACTICE
If . . . students would benefit from additional practice,
Then . . . assign *Practice* Lesson 1.3.

Practice Lesson 1.3

RETEACH
If . . . students are having difficulty understanding estimating,
Then . . . have them count the number of students in the class and then estimate the number of noses, eyes, or fingers the group has. Discuss how they arrived at their answers.

OBJECTIVES
To practice estimating and measuring length, weight, and capacity using nonstandard units

NCTM STANDARDS
Measurement
- Recognizing the attributes of length, volume, weight, and capacity
- Comparing objects according to attributes of length, volume, weight, and capacity
- Understanding how to measure using nonstandard units
- Developing common referents for measure to make comparisons and estimates

MATERIALS
*Number Cubes

TECHNOLOGY
ⓔ **Presentation** Lesson 1.4
Building Blocks Workin' on the Railroad

TEST PREP
Cumulative Review
Mental Math reviews numbers and sequencing facts (Lessons 1.1–1.3).

Writing + Math
Journal

Making Estimates

Context of the Lesson The lesson reviews measurement concepts introduced in Grade 1. Standard metric and customary units are reintroduced in Chapters 4 and 10.

See page 1B for Math Background for teachers for this lesson.

Planning for Learning ● DIFFERENTIATE INSTRUCTION

INTERVENTION

If . . . students lack the prerequisite skill of reading and writing numbers to 20,

Then . . . teach *Intervention* Lesson 1.B.

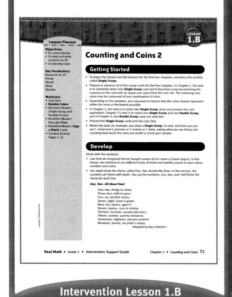

Intervention Lesson 1.B

ENGLISH LEARNER

Preview

If . . . students need language support,

Then . . . use Lesson 1.4 in *English Learner Support Guide* to preview lesson concepts and vocabulary.

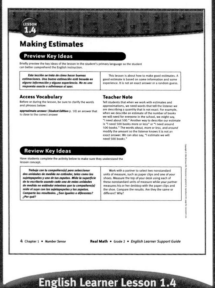

English Learner Lesson 1.4

ENRICH

If . . . students are proficient in the lesson concepts,

Then . . . emphasize the chapter projects.

PRACTICE

If . . . students would benefit from additional practice,

Then . . . extend Strategy Building before starting the Books to the Top of the Door Activity.

RETEACH

If . . . students are having difficulty understanding estimating,

Then . . . extend Strategy Building discussion while completing the student pages.

*Manipulative Kit Item

Mental Math   5

 Review Ask students a series of questions about number sequence. Have students show their answers using **Number Cubes.** Possible exercises include the following:

a. I am the number before 18. Who am I? 17

b. I am the number following 25. Who am I? 26

c. I am the number following 49. Who am I? 50

d. I am the number before 50. Who am I? 49

e. I am a number between 38 and 40. Who am I? 39

f. I am a number between 75 and 77. Who am I? 76

1 Develop   20

Tell Students In Today's Lesson They Will

complete activities using measurement and estimation.

Strategy Building ENGAGING

Whole Group

Have students complete the illustrated problems as a class.

Illustration Set One

Ask students to estimate the number of steps on the third ladder. Point out that the first ladder has six steps, and the second, taller ladder has twenty steps. Accept answers roughly halfway between six and twenty. Ask students to explain how they made their estimates.

Illustration Set Two

Ask students to estimate the number of books on the third bookcase. Point out that the first bookcase contains about twenty books, and the second bookcase has about forty books. Accept answers that indicate about twenty books per shelf. Ask students to explain their reasoning.

Illustration Set Three

Point out that the pitcher holds eight glasses of juice.

■ **How many glasses of juice will the second pitcher have?**
Establish that because the pitcher has about one-half the juice as the full pitcher, it should have juice for half the number of glasses.

■ **How many glasses of juice does the third pitcher contain?**
Because it has about one-half the juice of the second pitcher, it should have enough juice for one-half the number of glasses.

2 Assign Student Pages   20

Pages 9–10 APPLYING

Have students complete the activity illustrated on page 10 as a class.

Books to the Top of the Door

Have students stack their math books on the floor. When ten books have been stacked, ask the class to estimate how many books it would take to reach the top of the door. Focus discussion on how students made their estimates and how they might use guides, such as tiles, to sharpen their estimates. Students might suggest that if it takes ten books to reach one tile and there are twenty tiles, it must take 10 + 10 + 10 and so on. At this time, simply pose the problem, and have students think about possible solutions. This is a good opportunity to practice estimation because most students will not know how to calculate the exact answer.

Monitoring Student Progress

If . . . students' estimates are grossly wrong, especially if they estimate the measure of a small object to be more than a related larger object,

Then . . . students will require one-on-one coaching and discussion as they continue to make estimates. Present problems that involve estimating capacity and number, and have students physically check their estimates.

As Students Finish

Building Blocks Have students use **Workin' on the Railroad** to reinforce measuring using nonstandard units.

RESEARCH IN ACTION

"Computational estimation is a higher-order thinking skill, requiring many decisions by the estimator. A rule-based approach may handicap the learner more than a slower approach that develops understanding and the ability to make an on-the-spot choice (or invention) of an appropriate algorithm for obtaining an estimate."

Sowder, Judith. "Developing Understanding of Computational Estimation." *Arithmetic Teacher,* January 1989.

Name _____ Date _____

LESSON 1.4 Making Estimates

Key Ideas
Estimating means using information you have to make good guesses about answers to problems.

Six steps   Twenty steps   About how many steps? __about 13__

About twenty books   About forty books   About how many books? __about 60__

■ Textbook This lesson is available in the *eTextbook*.

9

LESSON 1.4 • Making Estimates

The pitcher holds eight glasses of juice.   About how many glasses of juice are in the pitcher? __about 4__   About how many glasses of juice are in the pitcher? __about 2__

Complete the Books to the Top of the Door Activity.

Writing + Math Journal
Can you explain why estimating works when you want to find an approximate answer?

---

3 Reflect   10

Guided Discussion   UNDERSTANDING   Whole Group

Briefly discuss the Books to the Top of the Door Activity. Ask students how they would report the height of the door in their classroom if they were exchanging information with another classroom.

■ **Would reporting that the door is 120 math books high be helpful to another class?** Unless the other class knows the size of their math books, this information would have little meaning.

● Talk about the importance of standard units of measure. For example, if the class reported the height of their door as 12 feet, would that be meaningful to another class? It would be because unlike a math book, a foot is always the same length and is widely known.

Writing + Math Journal
Discuss students' answers. Why does estimating work for some problems but not others?

Cumulative Review: For cumulative review of previously learned skills, see page 17–18.

Family Involvement: Assign the *Practice, Reteach,* or *Enrichment* activities depending on the needs of your students. Have students estimate the height of objects in their homes using nonstandard units of measure and report their results to the class.

Concept/Question Board: Encourage students to continue to post questions, answers, and examples on the Concept/Question Board.

Math Puzzler: John and Laura bought a pizza. The pizza maker cut it into eight pieces. "Would you cut it into sixteen pieces for us, please?" asked John. "We're really hungry." Will cutting it into sixteen pieces help? Why or why not? No, they will still have the same amount of pizza; it will just be in smaller pieces.

Assess and Differentiate

 Assess Use *eAssess* to record and analyze evidence of student understanding.

A Gather Evidence

Use the Daily Class Assessment Records in *Assessment* or *eAssess* to record daily observations.

Performance Assessment
☑ **Strategy Building**

Did the student **ENGAGING**
- ❏ pay attention to others' contributions?
- ❏ contribute information and ideas?
- ❏ improve on a strategy?
- ❏ reflect on and check the accuracy of his or her work?

Formal Assessment
☑ **Student Pages**

Did the student **APPLYING**
- ❏ apply learning in new situations?
- ❏ contribute concepts?
- ❏ contribute answers?
- ❏ connect mathematics to real-world situations?

B Summarize Findings

Analyze and summarize assessment data for each student. Determine which Assessment Follow-Up is appropriate for each student. Use the Student Assessment Record in *Assessment* or *eAssess* to update assessment records.

Assessment page T41

C Assessment Follow-Up ● DIFFERENTIATE INSTRUCTION

Based on your observations, use these teaching strategies for assessment follow-up.

INTERVENTION
Review student performance on *Intervention* Lesson 1.B to see if students have mastered prerequisite skills for this lesson.

ENGLISH LEARNER
Review

Use Lesson 1.4 in *English Learner Support Guide* to review lesson concepts and vocabulary.

ENRICH
If . . . students are proficient in the lesson concepts,

Then . . . encourage them to work on the chapter projects or *Enrichment* Lesson 1.4.

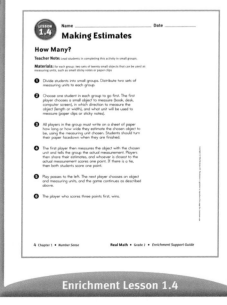

Enrichment Lesson 1.4

PRACTICE
If . . . students would benefit from additional practice,

Then . . . assign *Practice* Lesson 1.4.

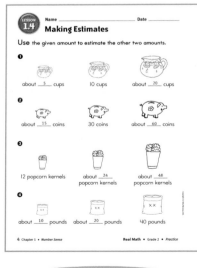

Practice Lesson 1.4

RETEACH
If . . . students are having difficulty understanding estimating,

Then . . . have them work in groups to estimate numbers of objects. Have each student estimate and compare estimates with other students.

Lesson Planner

OBJECTIVES
- To formally introduce place value
- To introduce counting and using money

NCTM STANDARDS

Number and Operations
- Using multiple models to develop an understanding of place value
- Connecting numerals to the quantities they represent
- Developing a sense of whole numbers and representing them in flexible ways

Problem Solving
Solving problems that arise in mathematics and other contexts

MATERIALS
- *Play money
- *Number Cubes
- *Craft sticks
- Yard Sale Game Mat

TECHNOLOGY
- ⒺPresentation Lesson 1.5
- ⒺMathTools Base-Ten Blocks
  Coins and Money
- Building Blocks Number Compare 3

TEST PREP
Cumulative Review (Review)
Mental Math reviews counting on and counting back (Lessons 1.1–1.3).

Writing + Math
Journal

Place Value and Money

Context of the Lesson This lesson gives students an explanation of place value for two-digit numbers. Although most students are probably already comfortable with place value and use it instinctually, terms and place organization are redefined for students. In this lesson, money is used as a way to represent numbers.

See page 1B for Math Background for teachers for this lesson.

Planning for Learning ● DIFFERENTIATE INSTRUCTION

INTERVENTION
If . . . students lack the prerequisite skill of identifying coins,

Then . . . teach **Intervention** Lesson 1.C.

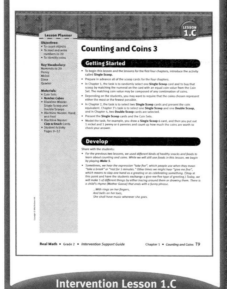

Intervention Lesson 1.C

ENGLISH LEARNER
Preview

If . . . students need language support,

Then . . . use Lesson 1.5 in **English Learner Support Guide** to preview lesson concepts and vocabulary.

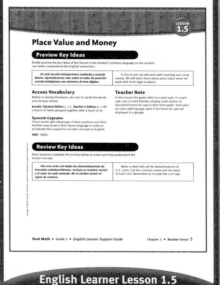

English Learner Lesson 1.5

ENRICH
If . . . students are proficient in the lesson concepts,

Then . . . emphasize Strategy Building.

PRACTICE
If . . . students would benefit from additional practice,

Then . . . extend Skill Building before assigning the student pages.

RETEACH
If . . . students are having difficulty understanding place value,

Then . . . extend Guided Discussion before assigning the student pages.

Vocabulary
tens place *n.* the left digit in a two-digit number

ones place *n.* the right digit in a two-digit number

Access Vocabulary
bundle a bunch of items grouped together with a band or tie

Spanish Cognates
digit dígito

Mental Math 5

 Present counting problems, and have students use their **Number Cubes.** Possible exercises include the following:

a. Show the number that is 1 more than 80. 81

b. Show the number that is 1 less than 80. 79

c. Show the number that is 3 more than 49. 52

d. Show the number that is 1 less than 51. 50

e. Show the number that is 11 more than 10. 21

f. Show the number that is 1 less than 19. 18

1 Develop 30

Tell Students In Today's Lesson They Will

learn about place value, two-digit numbers, and money.

Guided Discussion MathTools Whole Group

Place Value

 Display single sticks, and have the class count aloud and display the number on their **Number Cubes** as you hold up the sticks. When you reach ten, ask students how they made that number with their cubes. Discuss how ten individual ones is the same as one in the tens place. Bundle the ten sticks together. Explain that ten can be shown using the blue cube, but also teach students how to display the number using the yellow and red cubes. Then repeat the process through nineteen. Stop, and ask students what adjustments they will have to make to their cubes if you add another stick. You can also use the **eMathTools: Base-Ten Blocks** as the base-ten material.

Skill Building APPLYING Whole Group

- Explain to students that there are ten digits: 0, 1, 2, 3, 4, 5, 6, 7, 8, and 9.
- These digits can be combined in any order to create any number.
- Write the number 38 on the board. Show which column is the tens place and which is the ones place. Then go through the expanded counting with students, explaining that this is three tens and eight ones.
- Have students create this number with concrete objects, such as sticks.
- Repeat this procedure for several other numbers, but do not use numbers greater than 100.

Strategy Building Whole Group

Complete a brief strategy-building response exercise with students. Select two digits between 0 and 9. Have students tell you what the greatest number is that could be created using those

two digits. For example, if you select 4 and 9, the greatest number would be 94. After students have become comfortable creating the greatest number, have them create the least number using two selected digits. Alternate the questions between greatest and least possible numbers for the remainder of the activity.

Guided Discussion MathTools  Whole Group REASONING

Money and Value

Discuss how money is used to purchase products, and allow students to relate their own experiences with the use of money. Go through each denomination of bill and coin by using play money or **eMathTools: Coins and Money.** Have students show you the value of the coin or bill with their **Number Cubes** as you explain the different denominations. Demonstrate how to count money. Count aloud as you place the coins or bills on a desk. Then have individual students do the same, counting aloud for the whole class. Demonstrate how ten $1 bills equal one $10 bill. Have students discuss why we have different denominations of money.

Skill and Strategy Building

Game Yard Sale Game Whole Group

Demonstrate the **Yard Sale Game** by playing a round with students. Complete directions are on the game mat in the **Teacher's Edition.**

2 Assign Student Pages 20

Pages 11–12 UNDERSTANDING

Have students complete pages 11–12 independently or in small groups.

Monitoring Student Progress

If . . . students appear to be less familiar with money and the value of common items,

Then . . . students will benefit from playing the **Yard Sale Game,** especially the harder version.

As Students Finish

 Game As students finish, have them play the **Yard Sale Game.**

 Building Blocks Have students use **Number Compare 3** to reinforce place value and number value.

LESSON 1.5 — Place Value and Money

Name _____ Date _____

Key Ideas

When you count 10 or more of an object, you can make a two-digit number by using the **tens place**. The other number stays in the **ones place**.

There are ten sticks in each bundle.

tens place → ← ones place

5 tens and 7 = 57

You can count money to find out how much you have. Different kinds of money are worth different amounts.

How many? Write your answers.

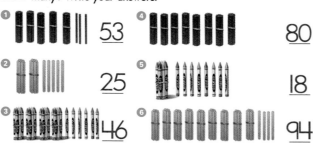

① 53   ④ 80

② 25   ⑤ 18

③ 46   ⑥ 94

Textbook This lesson is available in the **eTextbook.**   11

LESSON 1.5 • Place Value and Money

How much money?

⑦ $34

⑧ $42

⑨ $57

⑩ $32

⑪ 32¢

⑫ 21¢

⑬ $22

⑭ $33

 Play the **Yard Sale Game.**

Writing + Math Journal

How many ways could you make a dollar using only one kind of coin?

12   **Real Math • Chapter 1 • Lesson 5**

 Reflect LESSON 1.5   10

Guided Discussion APPLYING   Whole Group

Lead a discussion about what might be purchased for the classroom if $50 or $100 were available. What would be most useful? Focus discussion on the approximate value of items students mention.

Writing + Math Journal

Discuss students' answers. There are six ways to make a dollar using only one kind of coin. Ask students how many pennies make up a dollar. What about dimes?

☑ Use Mastery Checkpoint 2 found in **Assessment** to evaluate student mastery of writing numbers through 100. By this time, students should be able to correctly answer eighty percent of the Mastery Checkpoint items.

Cumulative Review: For cumulative review of previously learned skills, see page 17–18.

Family Involvement: Assign the **Practice, Reteach,** or **Enrichment** activities depending on the needs of your students. Have students play the **Yard Sale Game** with a family member.

Concept/Question Board: Encourage students to continue to post questions, answers, and examples on the Concept/Question Board.

Math Puzzler: I have 3 aquariums. I have 40 fish in one aquarium and 30 fish in another. Can you tell how many I have in all 3? Why or why not? no; You need to know how many fish are in the third aquarium.

4 # Assess and Differentiate

 Assess Use *eAssess* to record and analyze evidence of student understanding.

A Gather Evidence

Use the Daily Class Assessment Records in **Assessment** or *eAssess* to record daily observations.

Formal Assessment
☑ **Mastery Checkpoint**

Did the student
❑ use correct procedures?
❑ respond with at least 80% accuracy?

2 Name ___ Date ___
Mastery Checkpoint 2
Writing Numbers through 100
The student demonstrates mastery by writing well-formed numbers for all the items.

Count on or count back. Fill in the missing numbers.

❶ 63 | 64 | 65 | 66 | 67 | 68 | 69

❷ 35 | 34 | 33 | 32 | 31 | 30 | 29

❸ 48 | 49 | 50 | 51 | 52 | 53 | 54

❹ 76 | 77 | 78 | 79 | 80 | 81 | 82

❺ 84 | 83 | 82 | 81 | 80 | 79 | 78

Assessment page T51

B Summarize Findings

Analyze and summarize assessment data for each student. Determine which Assessment Follow-Up is appropriate for each student. Use the Student Assessment Record in **Assessment** or *eAssess* to update assessment records.

Assessment page T41

C Assessment Follow-Up • DIFFERENTIATE INSTRUCTION

Based on your observations, use these teaching strategies for assessment follow-up.

INTERVENTION

Review student performance on **Intervention** Lesson 1.C to see if students have mastered prerequisite skills for this lesson.

ENGLISH LEARNER
Review

Use Lesson 1.5 in **English Learner Support Guide** to review lesson concepts and vocabulary.

ENRICH

If . . . students are proficient in the lesson concepts,

Then . . . encourage them to work on the chapter projects or **Enrichment** Lesson 1.5.

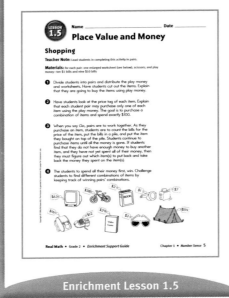

Enrichment Lesson 1.5

PRACTICE

If . . . students would benefit from additional practice,

Then . . . assign **Practice** Lesson 1.5.

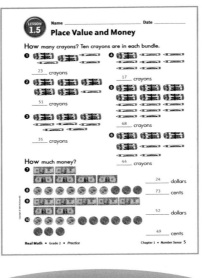

Practice Lesson 1.5

RETEACH

If . . . students are having difficulty counting money,

Then . . . have them keep a written running total as they count each bill or coin.

OBJECTIVES
- To introduce the use and meaning of a calendar
- To introduce the use of ordinal numbers

NCTM STANDARDS

Number and Operations
- Developing understanding of the relative position and magnitude of whole, ordinal, and cardinal numbers, and their connections
- Connecting number words to the quantities they represent using various models and representations

Algebra
- Recognizing and describing patterns
- Modeling situations that involve the addition of whole numbers
- Describing quantitative change

Measurement
Recognizing attributes of time

MATERIALS
- Calendar
- Calendar Game Mat
- *Number Cubes

TECHNOLOGY
- Ⓔ **Presentation** Lesson 1.6
- Ⓔ **Games** Calendar Game
- Ⓔ **MathTools** Electronic Calendar
- **Building Blocks** Ordinal Construction Company

TEST PREP

Cumulative Review
Mental Math reviews place value (Lesson 1.5).

Multistep Problems
Problem 12

Writing + Math
Journal

*Manipulative Kit Item

The Calendar

Context of the Lesson This lesson on calendars is presented early in the school year because it provides an interesting application for counting and writing numbers and also because the students' understanding of the monthly calendar will grow during the year.

See page 1B for Math Background for teachers for this lesson.

Planning for Learning ● DIFFERENTIATE INSTRUCTION

INTERVENTION

If . . . students lack the prerequisite skill of reading and writing numbers to 20,

Then . . . teach *Intervention* Lesson 1.B.

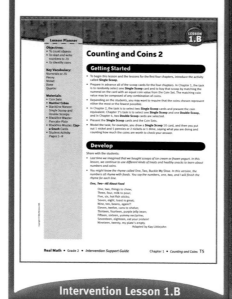

Intervention Lesson 1.B

ENGLISH LEARNER

Preview

If . . . students need language support,

Then . . . use Lesson 1.6 in *English Learner Support Guide* to preview lesson concepts and vocabulary.

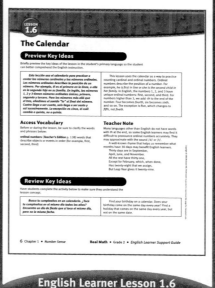

English Learner Lesson 1.6

ENRICH

If . . . students are proficient in the lesson concepts,

Then . . . emphasize Guided Discussion in Reflect.

PRACTICE

If . . . students would benefit from additional practice,

Then . . . extend Strategy Building before assigning the student pages.

RETEACH

If . . . students are having difficulty understanding ordinal numbers,

Then . . . extend Guided Discussion before assigning the student pages.

Mental Math

 Present place value problems orally, and have students use **Number Cubes** to respond. Possible exercises include the following:

a. What number is in the tens place in 62? 6

b. What number is in the ones place in 31? 1

c. What number is in the ones place in 33? 3

d. What number is in the tens place in 51? 5

e. What number is in the ones place in 78? 8

f. What number is in the tens place in 11? 1

1 Develop 20

Tell Students In Today's Lesson They Will

learn how to use a calendar and how to use ordinal numbers.

Guided Discussion UNDERSTANDING   Whole Group

Using a calendar for the current month, ask and discuss questions such as the following:

- **Which day of the week is the first day of this month?**
- **Which day of the week is the eighth day of this month?**
- **Which day of the week is the fifteenth day of the month?**
- **What date was a week before the tenth?**
- **What date is two weeks after the tenth?**
- **Which day of the week will be the first day of the next month?**
- **Which day of the week was the last day of the last month?**

Some students may notice that they can get some of these answers by adding or subtracting 7.

Ordinal Numbers

Numbers can be used to describe where objects fall in a sequence. For example, if you were watching cars on a racetrack, the fastest car would cross the finish line first, the next car would be second, and so on. Discuss and count ordinal numbers from first to twentieth with students.

- **Do you see any pattern in the names of ordinal numbers?** After first, second, and third, most ordinal number names can be made by adding *th* to the number.

Skill and Strategy Building ENGAGING

 Calendar Game **Games**

Demonstrate the **Calendar Game** by playing a round with students. Complete directions are on the game mat, and in the **Teacher's Edition.** This game is also available as an **eGame.**

Strategy Building

To maintain focus on and interest in the calendar throughout the year, complete the following activities:

- Allow each student to select one day on the classroom monthly calendar as his or her special day. Make sure they do not select days that your school is not in session.
- Have students post their names on their special day.
- Allow each student to do something special on his or her day. For example, the student may bring something from home to show the class, demonstrate a hobby, play a musical instrument, or select a math game for the class to play.
- Refer to each student's day when appropriate. For example: Tomorrow is Tuesday, November 4th, Heidi's special day. She will be bringing her violin to class.
- As special days approach, encourage students to figure out how many days are remaining until their special days. Encourage thinking in time equivalencies, for example: It is seven days, or one week, until Joe's special day.

2 Assign Student Pages 25

Pages 13–14 APPLYING

Have students complete pages 13 and 14 independently.

Monitoring Student Progress

If . . . students have difficulty answering questions about the calendar,

Then . . . provide extra practice, and refer to the calendar during routine classroom activities.

As Students Finish

 As students finish, have them play the **Calendar Game.**

 Games *Calendar Game*

 Have students use **Ordinal Construction Company** to practice using ordinal numbers.

Name _____ Date _____

LESSON 1.6 The Calendar

Key Ideas
You can use a calendar to keep track of special days.

December has 31 days.

Fill in the missing numbers.

December

Sunday	Monday	Tuesday	Wednesday	Thursday	Friday	Saturday
			1	2	3	4
5	6	7	8	9	10	11
12	13	14	15	16	17	18
19	20	21	22	23	24	25
26	27	28	29	30	31	

Write the answers.

1. What day is December 5? __Sunday__
2. What day is December 12? __Sunday__
3. What day is December 23? __Thursday__
4. What day is December 17? __Friday__

Textbook This lesson is available in the *eTextbook*.

13

LESSON 1.6 • The Calendar

September has thirty days.
Fill in the missing numbers.

September

Sunday	Monday	Tuesday	Wednesday	Thursday	Friday	Saturday
				1	2	3
4	5	6	7	8	9	10
11	12	13	14	15	16	17
18	19	20	21	22	23	24
25	26	27	28	29	30	

Write the day of the week.

5. September 1 __Thursday__
6. September 2 __Friday__
7. September 14 __Wednesday__
8. September 9 __Friday__

9. What is the twenty-first day of this month? __Wednesday__
10. Saturday, September 3, is the __third__ day of the month.

11. On September 7, Sam found out that he would have a test on September 14. How much time does Sam have to prepare? __seven days, or a week__

12. Samir's family is going to visit his aunt for a week. They leave on September 2. While they are there, they decide to stay for an extra two days. What day will they come home? __Sunday, September 11__

Game Play the **Calendar Game.**

Writing + Math / Journal
Do all weeks have the same number of days? Do all months have the same number of days? Do all years have the same number of months?

14

Real Math • Chapter 1 • Lesson 6

---

3 Reflect

10

Guided Discussion APPLYING

Whole Group

Have students create a bulletin board calendar for the class where they can keep track of and post special days such as field trips, school breaks, or school assemblies. Point to upcoming events, and have students count the number of days until that event.

Have students make a list of the events using ordinal numbers. Which event will be first? Which will be second?

Writing + Math Journal REASONING

Discuss students' answers. A week is always seven days long, and all years have twelve months. However, the number of days in a month varies.

Curriculum Connection: Students may be interested in researching how the modern calendar was created and the different calendars that cultures have used.

Cumulative Review: For cumulative review of previously learned skills, see page 17–18.

Family Involvement: Assign the *Practice, Reteach,* or *Enrichment* activities depending on the needs of your students. Have students play the **Calendar Game** with a family member.

Concept/Question Board: Encourage students to continue to post questions, answers, and examples on the Concept/Question Board.

Math Puzzler: If you started at 23 and skip counted aloud by threes, what would be the sixth number you would say? 38

Assess and Differentiate

 Assess Use **eAssess** to record and analyze evidence of student understanding.

A Gather Evidence

Use the Daily Class Assessment Records in **Assessment** or **eAssess** to record daily observations.

Informal Assessment
☑ Guided Discussion

Did the student **UNDERSTANDING**
- ❏ make important observations?
- ❏ extend or generalize learning?
- ❏ provide insightful answers?
- ❏ pose insightful questions?

Informal Assessment
☑ Student Pages

Did the student **APPLYING**
- ❏ apply learning to new situations?
- ❏ contribute concepts?
- ❏ contribute answers?
- ❏ connect mathematics to real-world situations?

B Summarize Findings

Analyze and summarize assessment data for each student. Determine which Assessment Follow-Up is appropriate for each student. Use the Student Assessment Record in **Assessment** or **eAssess** to update assessment records.

Assessment page T41

C Assessment Follow-Up ● DIFFERENTIATE INSTRUCTION

Based on your observations, use these teaching strategies for assessment follow-up.

INTERVENTION

Review student performance on **Intervention** Lesson 1.B to see if students have mastered prerequisite skills for this lesson.

ENGLISH LEARNER

Review

Use Lesson 1.6 in **English Learner Support Guide** to review lesson concepts and vocabulary.

ENRICH

If . . . students are proficient in the lesson concepts,

Then . . . encourage them to work on the chapter projects or **Enrichment** Lesson 1.6.

Enrichment Lesson 1.6

PRACTICE

If . . . students would benefit from additional practice,

Then . . . assign **Practice** Lesson 1.6.

Practice Lesson 1.6

RETEACH

If . . . students are having difficulty understanding ordinal numbers,

Then . . . have them get in a line. Then ask them who is first, second, third, and so on.

Exploring Problem Solving

Objectives
- To explore the Use Counters and Use a Pattern strategies
- To develop an understanding that problems may have multiple solutions
- To explore ways to present solutions clearly

Materials
Counters (a few for each pair or group of students)

Context of the Lesson Reasoning and problem solving are prevalent in every **Real Math** lesson. This lesson and other special problem-solving lessons allow more time for students to share and compare the methods they use to solve problems. In this lesson, students look at the value of using a pattern to make an organized list of possibilities.

1 Develop · 5

Tell Students In Today's Lesson They Will
- listen to a problem about arranging toy dinosaurs on a shelf.
- look at two different ways that other students used to solve the problem.
- work on the problem alone and share their work.

Guided Discussion

Present the following problem to students:

Mrs. García, the librarian, is going to feature books about dinosaurs for two weeks. So she wants to display her two stuffed dinosaurs on a shelf in the library. To add interest, she wants to change the arrangement of the dinosaurs each day. She wonders if she can make a different arrangement each day for ten days. Can she?

2 Exploring Problem Solving · 25

Using Student Pages

Have students look at the illustration on top of page 15, and ask the following questions:

- **How many cubbies do you see in this shelf?** six
- **How many stuffed dinosaurs does Mrs. García have?** two

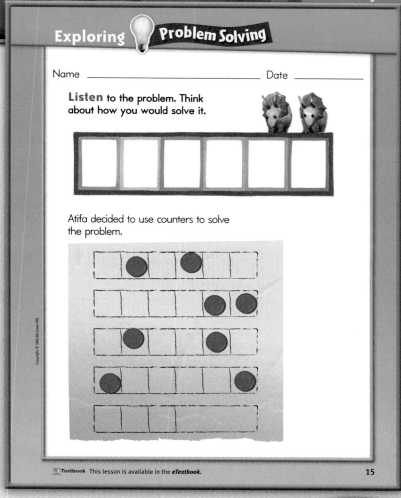

Exploring Problem Solving

Name _____ Date _____

Listen to the problem. Think about how you would solve it.

Atifa decided to use counters to solve the problem.

Textbook This lesson is available in the *eTextbook*. 15

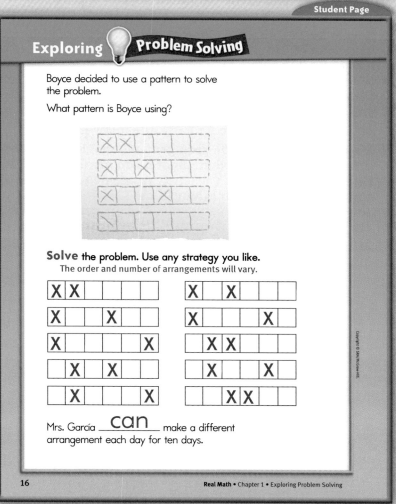

Exploring Problem Solving

Boyce decided to use a pattern to solve the problem.

What pattern is Boyce using?

Solve the problem. Use any strategy you like.
The order and number of arrangements will vary.

Mrs. García ___can___ make a different arrangement each day for ten days.

16 **Real Math** • Chapter 1 • Exploring Problem Solving

Draw a shelf on the board with a single row of six cubbies, and ask for a volunteer to show one way to arrange the dinosaurs. Then ask the following:

- **Are there other ways the dinosaurs can be arranged?** Have students show one or two other arrangements until students understand what constitutes a different arrangement.

Analyzing Sample Solution 1: Using Counters

Have students look at the illustration of Atifa's strategy on page 15. Ask the following:

- **How is Atifa approaching this problem?** She is putting counters in different squares.
- **What does each counter stand for?** a stuffed dinosaur
- **What is the same about each of Atifa's arrangements?** Each of them has two counters.
- **What is different about the arrangements?** Each arrangement shows the two counters in a different pair of boxes.
- **How many ways has Atifa found so far?** four
- **Is that enough for ten days?** no
- **Do you think there are more ways to arrange the dinosaurs?** yes

Have students share what they like about Atifa's strategy and what they might do differently.

Analyzing Sample Solution 2: Using a Pattern (to Make an Organized List)

Have students look at the picture of Boyce's approach to solving the problem. Ask the following:

- **How is Boyce's strategy different from Atifa's?** He is drawing Xs instead of placing counters. Students might not yet see that Boyce is using a pattern.
- **Where do you think Boyce will draw Xs next?** If he continues the pattern, he will put them in the first and fifth cubbies.
- **What will Boyce draw after that?** Xs in the first and last cubbies

Draw a 1 × 6 grid on the board. Ask the following:

- **After Boyce shows all the arrangements that have a dinosaur in the first cubbyhole, what might he do next?** Help students see that it would make sense for him to now do all the arrangements with a dinosaur in the second cubby.
- **How will you work on the problem?** Allow students to share strategies.

Have students share what they like about Boyce's strategy and what they might do differently.

Have students work individually or in pairs on the problem. When students find ten different arrangements, encourage them to try to find more. It is not necessary that they find all fifteen ways. The purpose of this lesson is to help students understand that there are different ways to approach a problem and that there are often many answers to a single problem.

Explain to students that they may combine Atifa's and Boyce's strategies, for example, by using counters to try an arrangement and then drawing it. Remind students that you will be asking them to share their work.

 **Reflect** 10

 **Knowledge Age Skills**

Problem Formulation, Planning, and Strategizing Draw ten or more 1 × 6 grids on the board. Ask for a student volunteer to show one way of arranging the dinosaurs on the shelf. Continue to have students share arrangements that are different from those already shown. Each time, ask students how their arrangements are different from what has already been demonstrated.

Ask students to explain their methods. Some of them may have used a pattern to systematically change the arrangements. Some of them may have simply tried arrangements at random.

	X				X
		X		X	
			X	X	

In discussion, bring out these points:

- A pattern can help you organize possibilities. That way you can keep track so you do not repeat or miss any possibilities.
- Using objects makes it easier to try different arrangements. Making a diagram can be a useful way to keep track of things you try.

 Assess 15

When evaluating student work, focus not only on the correctness of the answer but also on whether students thought rationally about the problem. Questions to consider include the following:

- Did the student understand the problem?
- Did the student realize there are many ways to arrange the dinosaurs?
- Could the student keep a reasonably clear record of arrangements?
- Could the student find, use, and explain a pattern?
- Could the student describe the method he or she used to solve the problem?

Cumulative Review

Assign Pages 17–18

Use the Cumulative Review as a review of concepts and skills that students have previously learned.

Here are different ways that you can assign these problems to your students as they work through the chapter:

- With some of the lessons in the chapter, assign a set of cumulative review problems to be completed as practice or for homework.
  Lesson 1.1—Problems 1–3
  Lesson 1.2—Problems 4–9
  Lesson 1.3—Problems 10–11
  Lesson 1.4—Problem 12
  Lesson 1.5—Problems 13–14
  Lesson 1.6—Problems 15–16
- At any point during the chapter, assign part or all of the cumulative review problems to be completed as practice or for homework.

Cumulative Review

Problems 1–3 review telling time on a clock, Grade 1 Lesson 1.11

Problems 4–9 review odd and even numbers, Lesson 1.2

Problems 10–11 review patterns, Grade 1 Lesson 1.2

Problem 12 reviews counting on, counting back, and writing numbers, Lesson 1.1

Problems 13–14 review estimating numbers and amounts, Lesson 1.4

Problems 15–16 review tally marks and counting by tens, Grade 1 Lesson 8.6

Monitoring Student Progress

If . . . students miss more than one problem in a section,

Then . . . refer to the indicated lesson for remediation suggestions.

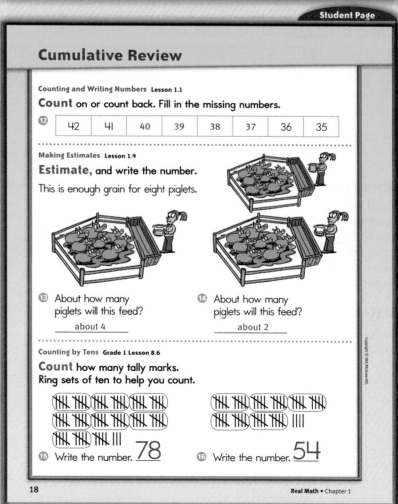

Individual Oral Assessment

Purpose of the Test

The Individual Oral Assessment is designed to measure students' growing knowledge of chapter concepts. It is administered individually to each student, and it requires oral responses from each student. The test takes about five minutes to complete. See **Assessment** for detailed instructions for administering and interpreting the test, and record students' answers on the Student Assessment Recording Sheet.

Assessment page T27

Directions

Read each question to the student, and record his or her oral response. If the student answers correctly, go to the next question. Stop when the student misses two questions at the same level. Students should not use scrap paper.

Materials

Base-ten blocks, two 6-ounce cups, water, calendar of November, number line (14–25)

Questions

Level 1: Prerequisite

1. What number comes right after 5? 6
2. What number comes right before 17? 16
3. Count on from 5 to 12. 5, 6, 7, 8, 9, 10, 11, 12
4. Count back from 9. 9, 8, 7, 6, 5, 4, 3, 2, 1

Level 2: Basic

5. What number is between 9 and 11? 10
6. What number is between 16 and 18? 17
7. Count on from 4 to 11. 4, 5, 6, 7, 8, 9, 10, 11
8. Is 4 even or odd? even

Level 3: At Level

9. Count back from 77 to 66. 77, 76, 75, 74, 73, 72, 71, 70, 69, 68, 67, 66
10. (Show 5 two-digit numbers less than 50.) Which numbers are odd?
11. Can you make two equal groups from 24? yes How many are in each group? 12
12. About how many girls are in our class? Accept reasonable estimates.

Level 4: Challenge Application

13. (Show 5 three-digit numbers.) Which numbers are even?
14. Can you make two equal groups from 75? no
15. (Show two cups—one half filled; the second completely filled.) This cup (point to the half-filled cup) has 3 ounces of water. About how many ounces of water is in this cup (point to the full cup)? 6 ounces
16. (Show 25 cubes.) How many groups of tens can you make? 2

Level 5: Content Beyond Mid-Chapter

17. (Show a calendar of November of any year.) What day is November 11?
18. (Show a number line from 14 to 25.) What is 23 − 2? 21
19. Which is greater, 35 or 44? 44
20. (Show 20 − 3 ___ 12 + 6.) Which symbol makes this number sentence true? < or less than

Lesson Planner

OBJECTIVES

To introduce using a number line to add and subtract 0, 1, 2, and 3 in the 0 to 100 range

NCTM STANDARDS

Number and Operations

- Developing understanding of the relative position and magnitude of whole numbers
- Developing a sense of whole numbers and representing and using them in flexible ways
- Understanding the meaning of addition and subtraction of whole numbers and the relationship between the operations
- Using strategies for whole-number computations
- Using a variety of tools to compute

MATERIALS

- *Number Cubes
- 0–100 Number line
- *Desktop Number Lines

TECHNOLOGY

- **Presentation** Lesson 1.7
- **MathTools** Number Line
- **Building Blocks** Pizza Pizzazz 5

TEST PREP

Cumulative Review

Mental Math reviews ordinal numbers and number order (Lessons 1.1–1.3, 1.6).

Counting on a Number Line

Context of the Lesson In this lesson students add and subtract within three places using a number line. In Chapter 2 students will commit the basic addition facts to memory. At that time you should no longer have number lines available for general use. If they are available, students will rely on them rather than commit the facts to memory. Students learn subtraction facts in Chapter 3.

See page 1B for Math Background for teachers for this lesson.

Planning for Learning ● DIFFERENTIATE INSTRUCTION

INTERVENTION

If . . . students lack the prerequisite skill of identifying coins,

Then . . . teach **Intervention** Lesson 1.A.

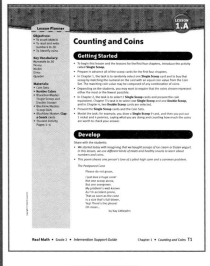

Intervention Lesson 1.A

ENGLISH LEARNER

Preview

If . . . students need language support,

Then . . . use Lesson 1.7 in **English Learner Support Guide** to preview lesson concepts and vocabulary.

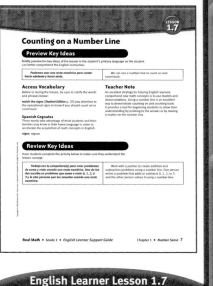

English Learner Lesson 1.7

ENRICH

If . . . students are proficient in the lesson concepts,

Then . . . allow students to explore **eMathTools: Number Line.**

PRACTICE

If . . . students would benefit from additional practice,

Then . . . extend Skill Building before assigning the student pages.

RETEACH

If . . . students are having difficulty understanding using a number line,

Then . . . extend Guided Discussion before assigning the student pages.

Vocabulary
number line n. a line on which points are identified with real numbers

Access Vocabulary
watch the signs pay attention to the operational signs to know if you should count on or count back

Spanish Cognates
signs signos

---

*Manipulative Kit Item

Teaching Lesson 1.7

Mental Math · 5

  Write the following number sequence on the board: 2, 4, 6, 8, 10, 12, 14, 16.

Ask questions such as the following, and ask students to reply using their **Number Cubes.**

a. What is the first number? 2

b. What is the sixth number? 12

c. What is the third number? 6

d. What is the last number? 16

e. What is the eighth number? 16

f. What is the second number? 4

1 Develop · 10

Tell Students In Today's Lesson They Will

add and subtract 0, 1, 2, and 3 using a number line.

Whole Group

Guided Discussion MathTools UNDERSTANDING

Introduce the addition and subtraction signs to students. Remind them that when using addition they count on, and when using subtraction they count back.

Put a large 0 to 100 number line on the board, or use the **eMathTools: Number Line.** Present and discuss problems in which the number to be added or subtracted is 0, 1, 2, or 3. Possible problems include the following:

■ **What's 3 more than 89?** 92
■ **What's 2 less than 71?** 69

Emphasize that instead of counting numbers, students should count the number of skips, or the spaces between the numbers. Students should think in terms of the steps between numbers rather than counting the numbers themselves. In doing subtraction problems, start with a given number, and count back. Encourage students to think of the sequences in their heads as they solve these problems.

Skill Building

What is 1 less than 96? 95
What is 3 more than 21? 24
What is 0 more than 85? 85
What is 2 more than 39? 41
What is 2 less than 57? 55
What is 1 more than 88? 89
What is 3 less than 40? 37
What is 0 less than 9? 9
What is 1 less than 62? 61
What is 3 more than 89? 92

2 Assign Student Pages · 30

Pages 19–20

Have students complete pages 19 and 20 independently.

Monitoring Student Progress

If . . . students are getting wrong answers that are one number from the correct answer,

Then . . . show students the correct way to use a number line by counting spaces and not points.

As Students Finish

Building Blocks Have students use **Pizza Pizzazz 5** to practice counting on to a number.

RESEARCH IN ACTION

"The number line has potential for organizing thinking about numbers and making connections with geometry. The number line is a line with points labeled by numbers. The potential of the number line does not stop at providing a simple way to picture all rational numbers geometrically. It also lets you form geometric models for the operations of arithmetic. Numbers on the number line have a dual nature: they are simultaneously points and oriented segments. A deep understanding of number and operations on the number line requires flexibility in using each interpretation."

Kilpatrick, J., J. Swafford, and B. Findell, eds. *Adding It Up: Helping Children Learn Mathematics.* Washington, D.C.: National Research Council/ National Academy Press, 2001, pp. 87–92.

LESSON 1.7 Counting on a Number Line

Name _____ Date _____

Key Ideas

You can use a number line to count on and to count back.

What is 18 + 2?

Find 18, and then move on 2 steps.
18 + 2 is 20.

What is 20 − 2?

Find 20, and then move back 2 steps. 20 − 2 is 18.

Draw a ring around the answers.

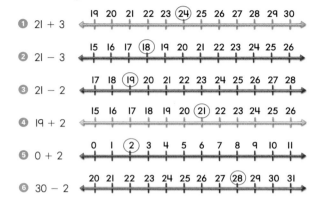

① 21 + 3   19 20 21 22 23 ㉔ 25 26 27 28 29 30

② 21 − 3   15 16 17 ⑱ 19 20 21 22 23 24 25 26

③ 21 − 2   17 18 ⑲ 20 21 22 23 24 25 26 27 28

④ 19 + 2   15 16 17 18 19 20 ㉑ 22 23 24 25 26

⑤ 0 + 2   0 1 ② 3 4 5 6 7 8 9 10 11

⑥ 30 − 2   20 21 22 23 24 25 26 27 ㉘ 29 30 31

Textbook This lesson is available in the *eTextbook*.   19

LESSON 1.7 · Counting on a Number Line

Find the answers. Watch the signs.

0 1 2 3 4 5 6 7 8 9 10 11 12 13 14 15 16 17 18 19 20 21 22 23 24 25 26 27 28 29 30 31 32 33 34 35

⑦ 31 + 2 = 33

⑧ 10 − 1 = 9

⑨ 30 − 1 = 29

⑩ 2 + 2 = 4

⑪ 35 − 2 = 33

⑫ 7 − 1 = 6

⑬ 27 − 2 = 25

⑭ 34 + 1 = 35

⑮ 9 + 3 = 12

⑯ 36 − 3 = 33

⑰ 4 + 1 = 5

⑱ 32 − 3 = 29

20   **Real Math · Chapter 1 · Lesson 7**

---

③ Reflect   10

Guided Discussion APPLYING

Write the following incorrect number sentences on the board:

73 + 3 = 75

29 + 2 = 30

51 − 3 = 49

Tell students that a second grader in another school made these mistakes when solving the exercises. Ask the class how they would help this student correct the errors.

Through discussion and by giving plenty of time, help students see that this student was making a common error by counting numbers rather than spaces. Let students explain how they would help this student.

Use Mastery Checkpoint 3 found in **Assessment** to evaluate students' mastery of numerical sequence through 100. By this time, students should be able to correctly answer eighty percent of the Mastery Checkpoint items.

Cumulative Review: For cumulative review of previously learned skills, see page 29–30.

Family Involvement: Assign the **Practice, Reteach,** or **Enrichment** activities depending on the needs of your students. Have students practice creating and using a number line with a family member.

Concept/Question Board: Encourage students to continue to post questions, answers, and examples on the Concept/Question Board.

Math Puzzler: If you wrote all the even numbers from 1 to 50, how many times would you write the number 2? The number 3? 10, 5

Assess and Differentiate

 Assess Use *eAssess* to record and analyze evidence of student understanding.

A Gather Evidence

Use the Daily Class Assessment Records in *Assessment* or *eAssess* to record daily observations.

Formal Assessment

☑ **Mastery Checkpoint**

Did the student
- ❑ use correct procedures?
- ❑ respond with at least 80% accuracy?

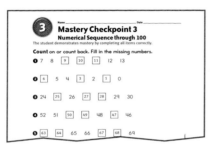

Assessment page T52

B Summarize Findings

Analyze and summarize assessment data for each student. Determine which Assessment Follow-Up is appropriate for each student. Use the Student Assessment Record in *Assessment* or *eAssess* to update assessment records.

Assessment page T41

C Assessment Follow-Up ● DIFFERENTIATE INSTRUCTION

Based on your observations, use these teaching strategies for assessment follow-up.

INTERVENTION	ENRICH	PRACTICE	RETEACH
Review student performance on *Intervention* Lesson 1.A to see if students have mastered prerequisite skills for this lesson.	**If . . .** students are proficient in the lesson concepts, **Then . . .** encourage them to work on the chapter projects or *Enrichment* Lesson 1.7.	**If . . .** students would benefit from additional practice, **Then . . .** assign *Practice* Lesson 1.7.	**If . . .** students are having difficulty understanding using a number line, **Then . . .** have them use counters on a large number line to physically move the number of indicated spaces.

ENGLISH LEARNER

Review

Use Lesson 1.7 in *English Learner Support Guide* to review lesson concepts and vocabulary.

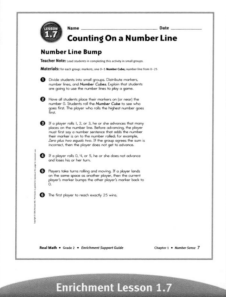

Enrichment Lesson 1.7

Practice Lesson 1.7

OBJECTIVES

- To continue to review using a number line to add and subtract 0, 1, 2, and 3 in the 0 to 100 range
- To solve simple word problems involving adding and subtracting 0, 1, 2, and 3

NCTM STANDARDS

Number and Operations

- Developing understanding of the relative position and magnitude of whole numbers
- Understanding the meaning of addition and subtraction of whole numbers
- Using strategies for whole-number computations
- Using a variety of tools to compute
- Understanding the effect of adding and subtracting whole numbers

Problem Solving

- Solving problems in mathematics and other contexts
- Applying and adapting strategies to solve problems

MATERIALS

- *Number Cubes
- 0–100 Number line
- *Desktop Number Lines

TECHNOLOGY

- ⓔ **Presentation** Lesson 1.8
- ⓔ **MathTools** Number Line
- **Building Blocks** Sea to Shore

TEST PREP

Cumulative Review

Mental Math reviews adding and subtracting using a number line (Lesson 1.7).

Extended Response
Problem 20

Multistep Problems
Problem 19

Writing + Math
Journal

*Manipulative Kit Item

Counting Applications

Context of the Lesson This lesson is largely a continuation of Lesson 7. In this lesson students will do simple addition and subtraction exercises using a number line. They will also solve word problems.

See page 1B for Math Background for teachers for this lesson.

Planning for Learning ● DIFFERENTIATE INSTRUCTION

INTERVENTION

If . . . students lack the prerequisite skill of counting objects,

Then . . . teach *Intervention* Lesson 1.C.

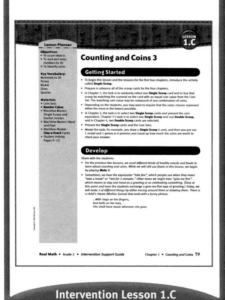

Intervention Lesson 1.C

ENGLISH LEARNER

Preview

If . . . students need language support,

Then . . . use Lesson 1.8 in *English Learner Support Guide* to preview lesson concepts and vocabulary.

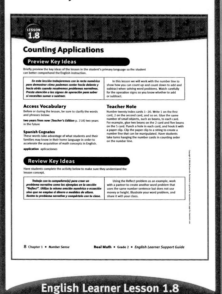

English Learner Lesson 1.8

ENRICH

If . . . students are proficient in the lesson concepts,

Then . . . emphasize Guided Discussion in Reflect.

PRACTICE

If . . . students would benefit from additional practice,

Then . . . extend Strategy Building before assigning the student pages.

RETEACH

If . . . students are having difficulty understanding adding and subtracting with a number line,

Then . . . extend Guided Discussion before assigning the student pages.

Vocabulary
add \ad\ *v.* to find the amount made by combining two or more numbers

subtract \səb trakt´\ *v.* to take away or deduct a number from another number

Access Vocabulary
two years from now two years in the future

Spanish Cognates
application aplicación

Mental Math 5

 Review

Display a number line, or use **eMathTools: Number Line.** Present problems orally and on the board and have students use their **Number Cubes** to respond. Possible problems include the following:

a. $96 - 0 = 96$

b. $85 + 1 = 86$

c. $55 - 0 = 55$

d. $37 - 1 = 36$

e. $76 + 3 = 79$

f. $27 - 1 = 26$

g. $17 - 0 = 17$

h. $21 - 3 = 18$

1 Develop 15

Tell Students In Today's Lesson They Will

solve word problems related to addition and subtraction.

Guided Discussion REASONING

Review the terms *add* and *subtract* with students.

- Write the following word problem on the board: Padma started with 12 comic books. She gave away 3 to her friends at school. How many comic books does she have now? 9

Go through the problem with students, and show them how to create a number sentence.

- ■ **Do you need to add or subtract to find the answer?** subtract, because she is giving away comic books

Have students solve the problem by counting back using **Desktop Number Lines** or **eMathTools: Number Line.**

- Now write the following word problem on the board: Samatar has 5 books. His uncle gave him 2 more books. How many books does he have now? 7

- Repeat the same process to have students solve this problem.

Strategy Building

1. Jamal is 12 years old. Two years ago he won a spelling bee. How old was he then? 10

2. Two years ago Jill was 48 inches tall. How tall is she today? can't tell based on given information

3. The Ace football team was losing to the Hornets by a score of 21 to 19. At the last minute, the Ace team scored a field goal worth 3 points. Who won the game, and by how much? What was the final score? The Ace team won by 1 point. The score was 22 to 21.

4. James is 31 years old. He has been married for 3 years. How old was he when he got married? 28

5. Grady got a score of 88 on a spelling test. His teacher told him he was two points away from earning an A in spelling. How many points are needed to earn an A in spelling? 90

Monitoring Student Progress

If . . . students are having difficulty adding and using a number line,

Then . . . have them play **Building Blocks: Sea to Shore** to reinforce adding on a number line.

2 Assign Student Pages 30

Pages 21–22 UNDERSTANDING

Have students complete page 21 independently. Provide help only to those who ask for it.

Do the problems on page 22 together with the class. Read the problems aloud so that you are certain all students understand. Have individual students explain how they solved each problem.

Monitoring Student Progress

If . . . students have difficulty understanding the word problems on page 22,

Then . . . students should get individual or small-group attention in which they are asked to act out similar problems.

As Students Finish

 Game

Have students play any of the games previously introduced, or you can assign games based on students' needs.

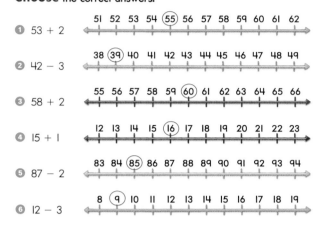

Name _____ Date _____

LESSON 1.8 Counting Applications

Key Ideas
You can count on and count back to add and to subtract.

Choose the correct answers.

1. 53 + 2   51 52 53 54 (55) 56 57 58 59 60 61 62

2. 42 − 3   38 (39) 40 41 42 43 44 45 46 47 48 49

3. 58 + 2   55 56 57 58 59 (60) 61 62 63 64 65 66

4. 15 + 1   12 13 14 15 (16) 17 18 19 20 21 22 23

5. 87 − 2   83 84 (85) 86 87 88 89 90 91 92 93 94

6. 12 − 3   8 (9) 10 11 12 13 14 15 16 17 18 19

Complete these exercises. Watch the signs.

7. 87 + 2 = **89**   8. 88 + 3 = **91**   9. 38 − 3 = **35**

10. 32 − 3 = **29**   11. 48 + 0 = **48**   12. 11 − 2 = **9**

📙 **Textbook** This lesson is available in the *eTextbook*.

21

LESSON 1.8 · Counting Applications

Solve these problems.

13. I have $43. If I pay $2 for a library fine, how much money will I have left? **$41**

14. Mr. González is 34 years old.
    a. How old will he be two years from now? **36**
    b. How old will he be three years from now? **37**

15. James had $89. He bought 2 presents for his sister. Now how much money does he have? **can't answer because there is insufficient information**

16. Mahala is 7 years old. She earned $2 today. Now she has $85. How many dollars did she have yesterday? **$83**

17. I have $19. If my aunt gives me $3, how much money will I have? **$22**

18. An airplane holds 67 passengers, 2 pilots, and 1 attendant. How many people does it hold? **70**

19. *Multistep* Sara had $39. She bought a present for her brother for $2. Then she earned $2 by running errands. How much money does she have now? **$39**

20. **Extended Response** Choose a problem that could not be solved. Tell what information is missing. _____ **In Problem 15, we need to know how much his sister's present costs or how much he has left.**

Writing + Math Journal
Create a problem in which you would have to use addition or subtraction to solve. Then write a number sentence to go with your problem.

22   **Real Math** • Chapter 1 • Lesson 8

---

③ Reflect
10 ⏱

Guided Discussion   **UNDERSTANDING**
Whole Group

Read the following two problems aloud, and allow students to discuss their solutions.

- ■ **Mark was 43 inches tall, and then he grew 2 more inches. Now how tall is he?** 45 inches
- ■ **Jamal had $43, and then he earned 2 more dollars. Now how much money does he have?** $45
- ■ **How are these problems the same?** Both problems are about a change of 2 from the number 43.
- ■ **How are they different?** One is about money, and the other is about height.
- ■ **If you write a number sentence for the first problem, does the same sentence solve the second problem?** yes

With these questions, help students see that the same number sentence can sometimes be used to solve two very different problems.

Writing + Math Journal ✓ **APPLYING**

Discuss students' answers. Have students share the problems they created with each other and discuss the strategies they used. How could the problems be improved?

Review **Cumulative Review:** For cumulative review of previously learned skills, see page 29–30.

Family Involvement: Assign the *Practice, Reteach,* or *Enrichment* activities depending on the needs of your students. Have students practice making word problems and their corresponding number sentences with their family members.

Concept/Question Board: Have students attempt to answer any unanswered questions on the Concept/Question Board.

Math Puzzler: Vanna is not older than Rudy. Ladonna is younger than Vanna. Write their names from youngest to oldest. Ladonna, Vanna, Rudy

4 Assess and Differentiate

 Assess Use *eAssess* to record and analyze evidence of student understanding.

A Gather Evidence

Use the Daily Class Assessment Records in *Assessment* or *eAssess* to record daily observations.

Informal Assessment
✔ **Guided Discussion**

Did the student **REASONING**
- ❑ provide a clear explanation?
- ❑ communicate reasons and strategies?
- ❑ choose appropriate strategies?
- ❑ argue logically?

Portfolio Assessment
✔ **Journal**

Did the student **APPLYING**
- ❑ apply learning in new situations?
- ❑ contribute concepts?
- ❑ contribute answers?
- ❑ connect mathematics to real-world situations?

B Summarize Findings

Analyze and summarize assessment data for each student. Determine which Assessment Follow-Up is appropriate for each student. Use the Student Assessment Record in *Assessment* or *eAssess* to update assessment records.

Assessment page T41

C Assessment Follow-Up • DIFFERENTIATE INSTRUCTION

Based on your observations, use these teaching strategies for assessment follow-up.

INTERVENTION

Review student performance on *Intervention* Lesson 1.C to see if students have mastered prerequisite skills for this lesson.

ENGLISH LEARNER

Review

Use Lesson 1.8 in *English Learner Support Guide* to review lesson concepts and vocabulary.

ENRICH

If . . . students are proficient in the lesson concepts,

Then . . . encourage them to work on the chapter projects or *Enrichment* Lesson 1.8.

Enrichment Lesson 1.8

PRACTICE

If . . . students would benefit from additional practice,

Then . . . assign *Practice* Lesson 1.8.

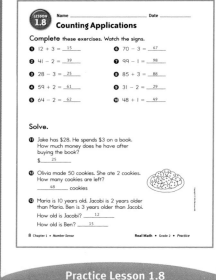

Practice Lesson 1.8

RETEACH

If . . . students are having difficulty deciding whether to add or subtract,

Then . . . teach them key words that indicate addition and subtraction.

Lesson Planner

OBJECTIVES
To introduce the use of equality and inequality signs to show the relation between two numbers and between sums or differences

NCTM STANDARDS
Number and Operations
- Using models to develop initial understandings of place value and the base-ten number system
- Developing understanding of the relative position of whole numbers
- Understanding the meanings of addition and subtraction of whole numbers and the relationship between the operations
- Understanding the effects of adding and subtracting whole numbers
- Developing and using strategies for whole-number computations

Algebra
Using concrete and verbal representations to develop understanding of symbolic notation

MATERIALS
None

TECHNOLOGY
e **Presentation** Lesson 1.9
e **MathTools** 100 Table
Building Blocks Number Compare 4

TEST PREP
Cumulative Review
Mental Math reviews number order (Lessons 1.1–1.2, 1.5).

Comparing Numbers

Context of the Lesson Students used relation signs in the first-grade program, but this is the first time they are introduced to them in the second grade. The use of equalities and inequalities appears often and will be used in later chapters.

See page 1B for Math Background for teachers for this lesson.

Planning for Learning ● DIFFERENTIATE INSTRUCTION

INTERVENTION
If . . . students lack the prerequisite skill of identifying coins,

Then . . . teach **Intervention** Lesson 1.A.

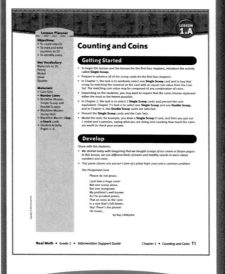

Intervention Lesson 1.A

ENGLISH LEARNER
Preview
If . . . students need language support,

Then . . . use Lesson 1.9 in **English Learner Support Guide** to preview lesson concepts and vocabulary.

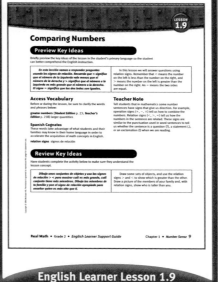

English Learner Lesson 1.9

ENRICH
If . . . students are proficient in the lesson concepts,

Then . . . emphasize Guided Discussion in Reflect.

PRACTICE
If . . . students would benefit from additional practice,

Then . . . have students use **Building Blocks** before assigning the student pages.

RETEACH
If . . . students are having difficulty understanding equalities and inequalities,

Then . . . extend Guided Discussion before assigning the student pages.

Vocabulary
greater than sign *n.* >, shows the value on the left is larger than the value on the right

less than sign *n.* <, shows the value on the left is smaller than the value on the right

equal sign *n.* =, shows the two values are the same

Access Vocabulary
greater numbers larger quantities

Spanish Cognates
relation signs signos de relación

Mental Math 5

  Write pairs of numbers on the board. Have students respond by showing thumbs-up if the number on the left comes before the number on the right when counting up and thumbs-down if it comes after. Possible exercises include the following:

a. 18, 20 up

b. 92, 29 down

c. 37, 27 down

d. 15, 18 up

e. 27, 1 down

f. 58, 24 down

1 Develop 20

Tell Students In Today's Lesson They Will

use the correct symbols to express equalities and inequalities.

Guided Discussion REASONING   Whole Group

Introduce students to the relation signs ($<$, $>$, and $=$). Use the board to demonstrate that the larger end of either inequality sign should point to the larger number and that the smaller end should point to the smaller number. Relate this to the illustration on student page 23, which compares the mouth of an alligator to the relation signs—the open mouth always tries to eat the greater number. Write pairs of numbers with a circle between them on the board. Have students come to the board and write the correct relation sign in the circle. Give several examples with a single number on each side. Possible examples include the following:

31 23   24 15   89 91

Then give some problems with sums or differences on each side. Possible examples include the following:

7 + 8 7 + 9   26 − 5 38 − 5

Students do not need to solve the addition and subtraction problems. At this time, students should decide which side is less without determining the sums and differences. Ask for explanations, and encourage those students who are able to do so to show a way to get the answer without doing the calculation. For example, 26 is less than 38, and if you take away 5 from both, 26 − 5 must be less than 38 − 5.

2 Assign Student Pages 20

Pages 23–24   **e MathTools** UNDERSTANDING

Have students fill in the **100 Table** on page 23 independently and look for patterns. Have students complete page 24 independently. Provide help only to those who ask for it.

Monitoring Student Progress

| **If . . .** students are taking a long time to complete page 24, | **Then . . .** remind students not to try to do the actual calculations but to try to figure out which answer must be greater based on the relationships between the numbers. However, do not penalize students who insist on doing the calculations. |

As Students Finish

e MathTools Have students experiment with **eMathTools: 100 Table** and look for patterns.

Building Blocks Have students use **Number Compare 4** to reinforce place value and number value.

Name _____ Date _____

LESSON 1.9 Comparing Numbers

Key Ideas

The greater-than sign and less-than sign show which amount is greater.

The wider end always points to the greater amount. Use an **equal sign** if both sides are the same.

63 > 37

Fill in the blanks on this table.

0	1	2	3	4	5	6	7	8	9
10	11	12	13	14	15	16	17	18	19
20	21	22	23	24	25	26	27	28	29
30	31	32	33	34	35	36	37	38	39
40	41	42	43	44	45	46	47	48	49
50	51	52	53	54	55	56	57	58	59
60	61	62	63	64	65	66	67	68	69
70	71	72	73	74	75	76	77	78	79
80	81	82	83	84	85	86	87	88	89
90	91	92	93	94	95	96	97	98	99
100									

Textbook This lesson is available in the *eTextbook*.

23

LESSON 1.9 · Comparing Numbers

Draw the correct sign: <, >, or =.
Use a number line if you need to.

1. 35 < 37
2. 45 < 62
3. 77 < 82
4. 83 + 1 < 83 + 2
5. 83 − 1 > 83 − 2
6. 83 + 1 > 83 − 1
7. 75 + 3 < 75 + 4
8. 75 + 23 < 75 + 24
9. 12 + 12 = 11 + 13

10. 25 + 3 < 25 + 6
11. 25 + 4 < 25 + 5
12. 25 + 5 > 25 + 4
13. 25 + 6 > 25 + 3
14. 65 − 3 > 65 − 4
15. 66 − 3 = 65 − 2
16. 39 + 2 < 39 + 3
17. 99 + 0 = 98 + 1
18. 87 + 87 > 86 + 86

24

Real Math • Chapter 1 • Lesson 9

---

3 Reflect
10

Guided Discussion [UNDERSTANDING]
Whole Group

Put the following problem on the board, and ask students if they can place the relation sign correctly.

5,785 + 3 ◯ 5,785 + 2

As students choose the correct sign, praise them for being able to calculate with such very large numbers. Students will probably point out that calculations were not necessary; only the ability to reason was necessary. Conclude by showing students that with a bit of thinking, many problems that look difficult are really not that difficult.

Cumulative Review: For cumulative review of previously learned skills, see page 29–30.

Family Involvement: Assign the *Practice, Reteach,* or *Enrichment* activities depending on the needs of your students.

Concept/Question Board: Have students attempt to answer any unanswered questions on the Concept/Question Board.

Math Puzzler: What is the fewest number of coins you can use to make 43¢? What are they? six; 1 quarter, 1 dime, 1 nickel, and 3 pennies

4 Assess and Differentiate

 Assess Use *eAssess* to record and analyze evidence of student understanding.

A Gather Evidence

Use the Daily Class Assessment Records in *Assessment* or *eAssess* to record daily observations.

Informal Assessment
☑ **Guided Discussion**

Did the student **REASONING**
- ❏ provide a clear explanation?
- ❏ communicate reasons and strategies?
- ❏ choose appropriate strategies?
- ❏ argue logically?

Informal Assessment
☑ **Student Pages**

Did the student **UNDERSTANDING**
- ❏ make important observations?
- ❏ extend or generalize learning?
- ❏ provide insightful answers?
- ❏ pose insightful questions?

B Summarize Findings

Analyze and summarize assessment data for each student. Determine which Assessment Follow-Up is appropriate for each student. Use the Student Assessment Record in *Assessment* or *eAssess* to update assessment records.

Assessment page T41

C Assessment Follow-Up ● DIFFERENTIATE INSTRUCTION

Based on your observations, use these teaching strategies for assessment follow-up.

INTERVENTION	ENRICH	PRACTICE	RETEACH
Review student performance on *Intervention* Lesson 1.A to see if students have mastered prerequisite skills for this lesson.	**If . . .** students are proficient in the lesson concepts, **Then . . .** encourage them to work on the chapter projects or *Enrichment* Lesson 1.9.	**If . . .** students would benefit from additional practice, **Then . . .** assign *Practice* Lesson 1.9.	**If . . .** students are having difficulty understanding equalities and inequalities, **Then . . .** have them relate less than or greater than to other comparisons such as shorter than or longer than.

ENGLISH LEARNER

Review

Use Lesson 1.9 in *English Learner Support Guide* to review lesson concepts and vocabulary.

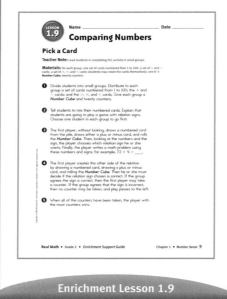

Enrichment Lesson 1.9

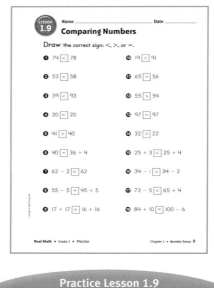

Practice Lesson 1.9

Lesson Planner

OBJECTIVES
- To demonstrate the relationship between addition and subtraction
- To introduce students to fact families

NCTM STANDARDS
Number and Operations
- Understanding the meanings of addition and subtraction of whole numbers and the relationship between the operations
- Understanding the effects of adding and subtracting whole numbers
- Developing and using strategies for whole-number computations

Algebra
- Sorting and classifying objects by number
- Using concrete and verbal representations to develop understanding of symbolic notation

MATERIALS
- *Number Cubes
- *Desktop Number Lines
- *Counters

TECHNOLOGY
- ⒠ **Presentation** Lesson 1.10
- ⒠ **MathTools** Number Line

TEST PREP
Cumulative Review
Mental Math reviews adding and subtracting 0, 1, 2, and 3 (Lesson 1.7).

Writing + Math
Journal

Relating Addition and Subtraction

Context of the Lesson This lesson focuses on the inverse relationship between addition and subtraction. Some students may be intimidated by the addition and subtraction problems. Explain that they should feel free to use their number lines and that memorization of facts is not expected at this time. The purpose of this lesson is only to highlight the inverse relationship between addition and subtraction.

See page 1B for Math Background for teachers for this lesson.

Planning for Learning ● DIFFERENTIATE INSTRUCTION

INTERVENTION
If . . . students lack the prerequisite skill of reading and writing numbers to 20,

Then . . . teach **Intervention** Lesson 1.B.

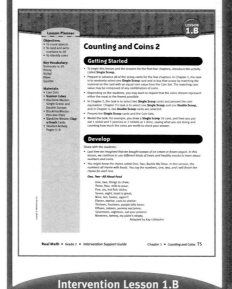

Intervention Lesson 1.B

ENGLISH LEARNER
Preview

If . . . students need language support,

Then . . . use Lesson 1.10 in **English Learner Support Guide** to preview lesson concepts and vocabulary.

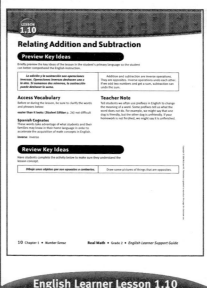

English Learner Lesson 1.10

ENRICH
If . . . students are proficient in the lesson concepts,

Then . . . emphasize Guided Discussion in Reflect and the Journal activity.

PRACTICE
If . . . students would benefit from additional practice,

Then . . . extend Skill Practice before assigning the student pages.

RETEACH
If . . . students are having difficulty understanding addition and subtraction,

Then . . . extend Guided Discussion before assigning the student pages.

Vocabulary
inverse operations *n.* operations that undo each other

Access Vocabulary
easier than it looks not difficult

Spanish Cognates
inverse inverso

---

*Manipulative Kit Item

Mental Math 5

Present problems in which students must add or subtract by 0, 1, 2, or 3. Focus attention on the problems in which 0 is added to or subtracted from large numbers. Students find, hide, and show answers using **Number Cubes.** Possible problems include the following:

a. $88 + 3 = 91$ **b.** $88 + 2 = 90$

c. $88 + 1 = 89$ **d.** $88 + 0 = 88$

e. $45 + 3 = 48$ **f.** $48 - 3 = 45$

1 Develop 25

Tell Students In Today's Lesson They Will

learn how addition and subtraction undo each other.

Guided Discussion ☑ REASONING

Whole Group

Inverse Operations

Discuss inverse operations with students. Explain to them that *inverse* means that the two operations undo each other. Illustrate how this works by showing students six counters.

For example, say to students, *Now I will subtract two from six.*

Remove two counters.

- **How many counters do I have now?** 4
- **What would I need to do to have six counters again?** add 2

Discuss what would happen if you were to add and subtract 0. Would that change the original number? Encourage students to realize that adding or subtracting 0 does not change the original number.

Fact Families UNDERSTANDING

Demonstrate how fact families can be created from an addition problem. For example, show problems such as the following:

$3 + 2 = 5$

$2 + 3 = 5$

$5 - 2 = 3$

$5 - 3 = 2$

If students are able to solve one of the problems, then they can solve and create the remaining problems by correctly rearranging the signs and digits.

Skill Practice MathTools COMPUTING

Whole Group

Adding and Subtracting on a Number Line

Use a 0 to 20 number line or **eMathTools: Number Line** to present addition and subtraction exercises.

First demonstrate and then have students come to the front of the room and show how to count on or count back to find the sums or differences. Create problems that use the same number

ranges as on student page 25. Possible problems include the following:

$7 + 3 = 10$	$8 + 1 = 9$	$9 + 2 = 11$	$2 + 3 = 5$
$10 - 2 = 8$	$12 - 3 = 9$	$8 - 2 = 6$	$7 - 1 = 6$

As students become more comfortable, encourage them to try to complete the exercises without using the number line. Remove the number line when appropriate so students do not become dependent on it.

2 Assign Student Pages 15

Pages 25–26 UNDERSTANDING

Have students complete pages 25 and 26 independently.

Monitoring Student Progress

If . . . students have difficulty starting the student pages,

Then . . . check with students individually to be sure that they understand the format. If not, model the thinking involved in the first two or three exercises.

As Students Finish

Game Have students play any of the games previously introduced or assign games based on their needs.

RESEARCH IN ACTION

"It is very important for teachers to provide children with opportunities to recognize the meaning of mathematical symbols, mathematical operations, and the patterns or relationships represented in the child's work with numbers. For example, the number sense that a child acquires should be based upon an understanding that inverse operations, such as addition and subtraction, undo the operations of the other. Instructionally, teachers must encourage their students to think beyond simply finding the answer and to actually have them think about the numerical relationships that are being represented or modeled by the symbols, words, or materials being used in the lesson."

Kilpatrick, J., J. Swafford, and B. Findell, eds. *Adding It Up: Helping Children Learn Mathematics.* Washington, D.C.: National Research Council/National Academy Press, 2001, pp. 270–271.

Name _____ Date _____

LESSON
1.10

Relating Addition and Subtraction

Key Ideas

Addition and subtraction are **inverse operations**.

They undo each other.

$5 + 3 = 8$ $8 - 3 = 5$

Use the number line to find the answers.

`0 1 2 3 4 5 6 7 8 9 10 11 12 13 14 15 16 17 18 19 20 21`

① $6 + 3 = 9$

② $3 + 1 = 4$

③ $8 + 2 = 10$

④ $6 + 1 = 7$

⑤ $4 - 1 = 3$

⑥ $10 - 2 = 8$

⑦ $7 - 1 = 6$

⑧ $5 - 2 = 3$

⑨ $2 + 3 = 5$

⑩ $9 - 3 = 6$

⑪ $6 + 2 + 1 + 1 = 10$

⑫ $10 - 1 - 1 - 2 = 6$

⑬ $2 + 1 + 2 + 1 = 6$

⑭ $6 - 1 - 2 - 1 = 2$

⑮ $5 + 2 + 2 + 1 = 10$

⑯ $10 - 1 - 2 - 2 = 5$

Textbook This lesson is available in the *eTextbook*.

25

LESSON 1.10 · Relating Addition and Subtraction

Complete the following statements.
Some are easier than they look.

⑰ $5 + 3 = 8$

$3 + 5 = 8$

$8 - 5 = 3$

$8 - 3 = 5$

⑱ $5 - 3 = 2$

$3 + 2 = 5$

$5 - 2 = 3$

$2 + 3 = 5$

⑲ $9 + 5 = 14$

$5 + 9 = 14$

$14 - 5 = 9$

$14 - 9 = 5$

⑳ $13 - 6 = 7$

$6 + 7 = 13$

$13 - 7 = 6$

$7 + 6 = 13$

㉑ $3 + 8 = 11$

$11 - 3 = 8$

$11 - 8 = 3$

$8 + 3 = 11$

㉒ $234 + 175 = 409$

$175 + 234 = 409$

$409 - 175 = 234$

$409 - 234 = 175$

Writing + Math **Journal**

Using the numbers 9 and 2, create as many fact family problems as you can.

---

3 Reflect

10

Guided Discussion **UNDERSTANDING**

Call attention to the last group of problems on student page 26, and ask students to explain how they were able to find the sums and differences. Accept answers that indicate an understanding that addition and subtraction undo each other.

■ **Does the order of numbers make a difference when you are adding?** no

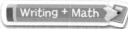 **Journal**

Have students use number lines to check their fact families. Encourage students to create other fact families that they can solve by using number lines. You may wish to give students a large sum, such as in Problem 22, and have them create fact families from that sum.

Cumulative Review: For cumulative review of previously learned skills, see page 29–30.

Family Involvement: Assign the *Practice, Reteach,* or *Enrichment* activities depending on the needs of your students. Encourage students to create fact families with their family members.

Concept/Question Board: Have students attempt to answer any unanswered questions on the Concept/Question Board.

Math Puzzler: How can you make 45¢ by using exactly five coins? 1 quarter and 4 nickels, or 4 dimes and 1 nickel

4 Assess and Differentiate

 Assess Use *eAssess* to record and analyze evidence of student understanding.

A Gather Evidence

Use the Daily Class Assessment Records in *Assessment* or *eAssess* to record daily observations.

Informal Assessment
☑ **Guided Discussion**

Did the student **REASONING**
- ❏ provide a clear explanation?
- ❏ communicate reasons and strategies?
- ❏ choose appropriate strategies?
- ❏ argue logically?

Informal Assessment
☑ **Guided Discussion**

Did the student **UNDERSTANDING**
- ❏ make important observations?
- ❏ extend or generalize learning?
- ❏ provide insightful answers?
- ❏ pose insightful questions?

B Summarize Findings

Analyze and summarize assessment data for each student. Determine which Assessment Follow-Up is appropriate for each student. Use the Student Assessment Record in *Assessment* or *eAssess* to update assessment records.

Assessment page T41

C Assessment Follow-Up ● DIFFERENTIATE INSTRUCTION

Based on your observations, use these teaching strategies for assessment follow-up.

INTERVENTION
Review student performance on *Intervention* Lesson 1.B to see if students have mastered prerequisite skills for this lesson.

ENGLISH LEARNER
Review
Use Lesson 1.10 in *English Learner Support Guide* to review lesson concepts and vocabulary.

ENRICH
If . . . students are proficient in the lesson concepts,
Then . . . encourage them to work on the chapter projects or *Enrichment* Lesson 1.10.

PRACTICE
If . . . students would benefit from additional practice,
Then . . . assign *Practice* Lesson 1.10.

RETEACH
If . . . students are having difficulty understanding the relationship between addition and subtraction,
Then . . . have them write inverse number sentences that use fact families as they solve sentences with counters.

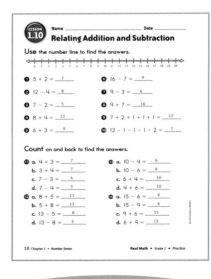

Enrichment Lesson 1.10

Practice Lesson 1.10

Exploring Problem Solving

Objectives
- To explore methods of solving nonroutine problems
- To discuss strategies and solutions
- To generalize how to make two groups equal when you do not know how many are in each group

Materials
- Counters (about 30 for each pair of students)
- Scratch paper

Context of the Lesson This lesson continues the work with number sense while providing the opportunity for students to spend extra time solving and discussing nonroutine problems. The lesson helps develop algebraic thinking by encouraging students to make generalizations about how numbers work.

1 Develop 5

Tell Students In Today's Lesson They Will
- solve an interesting problem about numbers of library books on a shelf.
- develop a rule that will help people know how to solve this type of problem.

Guided Discussion

Have students look at the picture on page 27. Help them interpret the picture by asking questions such as the following:

■ **Look at the first bookcase. How many more books are on the top shelf than are on the bottom shelf?** four
■ **Look at the second bookcase. How many more books are on the top shelf than are on the bottom shelf?** four
■ **Now look at the third bookcase. Which shelf has more books? How many more books?** The bottom shelf has four more books than the top shelf.

Present this problem:

Suppose you want to move books from one shelf to another so both shelves have the same number of books. How many books do you need to move from the top shelf to the bottom shelf in the first bookcase? In the other bookcases, how many books do you need to move?

Have counters and scratch paper available. Have students work with a partner to determine the number of books that have to be moved in each bookcase.

Afterward, ask students if they were surprised that the answer was two for each of the bookcases.

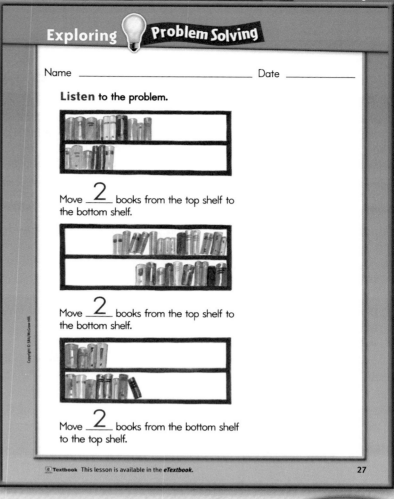

Exploring Problem Solving

Name _____ Date _____

Listen to the problem.

Move __2__ books from the top shelf to the bottom shelf.

Move __2__ books from the top shelf to the bottom shelf.

Move __2__ books from the bottom shelf to the top shelf.

Textbook This lesson is available in the *eTextbook*.   27

Exploring Problem Solving

Listen to the problem. Solve it with a partner.

Move __3__ books from one shelf to the other shelf.

Show how you solved the problem.

28   Real Math · Chapter 1 · Exploring Problem Solving

Have students look at the pictures on page 28. Read this problem:

Matthew and Addison are helping Mrs. García, the librarian, put library books back on the shelf after students have returned them. Mrs. García asked them to be sure to put the same number of books on each shelf. They have put away all the books she gave them, but there are six more books on one shelf than on the other shelf. They need to figure out what to do to make the number of books on each shelf the same. Your job is to decide how many books need to be moved from one shelf to the other shelf so the two shelves have the same number of books.

To make sure students understand the problem, ask questions such as the following:

- **Can you tell how many books are on each shelf?** no
- **Which shelf has more books?** It is impossible to tell from this picture.
- **Do you know how many more books are on one of the shelves than the other?** yes, six
- **What is the problem asking?** How many books need to be moved from one shelf to the other so the two shelves have an equal number of books?

 Exploring Problem Solving 25

Using Student Pages

Have students work in pairs or small groups, but have each group work with a different number. For example, tell one group to suppose the top shelf has eight books on it. Tell another group to suppose the top shelf has twelve books on it, and so on.

Circulate as students are working, and give help as needed.

- If students do not seem to know how to proceed, ask guiding but nondirected questions, such as: *Do you think using counters could help? How? Could you draw a math picture to help you? What would be in the picture?*
- Make note of the different strategies students use to help you decide which groups to call on to share their methods.

Sample Solutions Strategies

Students might use one or more of the following strategies:

Act It Out with Objects

Students might use counters to show how many books are on the top shelf and then move counters to the bottom shelf until they have an equal number.

Draw a Picture

Students might draw the number of books on one shelf and cross them out as they draw additional books on the other shelf.

Guess, Check, and Adjust

Students might start with pictures or counters on the shelf, move some to the bottom shelf and compare. If they do not have an equal number, they can try again, this time moving a different number of marks or counters.

Use Number Sense

Students might focus on the extra books on the shelf that has more. Then they might realize that they need to move half of those to the other shelf.

 **Reflect** 10

 **Knowledge Age Skills**

Problem Formulation, Planning, and Strategizing Ask each group to share their strategies and their solutions to the problem. Help students understand the following points:

- Different people might prefer different strategies.
- A strategy might be appropriate even if the answer is not correct.

As you discuss the results, ask questions such as the following:

- **What was different about the problems that each group worked on?** Each group used a different number of books on the shelves.
- **What was the same?** In each case, there were six more books on one shelf than on the other. Help students see that except for the beginning numbers they worked on the same problem.
- **What do you notice about everyone's answer?** Everyone got an answer of three.
- **If there are always six more books on one shelf, do you think the answer will always be three? Why do you think so?** Students might have a sense of why it is always true but have difficulty explaining it.

Extension

If interest warrants, have groups of students work on similar problems with different numbers. For example, one group works on a problem in which there are ten more books on one shelf than on the other. Another group solves the problem for eight more books.

 **Assess** 15

When evaluating student work, focus on whether students thought rationally about the problem. Questions to consider include the following:

- Did the student understand the problem?
- Did the student have a strategy for solving the problem?
- Did the student continue to work on trying to solve the problem even though he or she might have encountered difficulty?
- Did the student ask for help immediately, or did he or she try different strategies?
- Did the student notice the consistent pattern?
- Was the student able to explain his or her thinking?

Cumulative Review

Assign Pages 29–30

Use the Cumulative Review as a review of concepts and skills that students have previously learned.

Here are different ways that you can assign these problems to your students as they work through the chapter:

- With some of the lessons in the chapter, assign a set of cumulative review problems to be completed as practice or for homework.
  Lesson 1.7—Problems 1–3
  Lesson 1.8—Problems 4–5
  Lesson 1.9—Problems 6–11
  Lesson 1.10—Problems 12–18
- At any point during the chapter, assign part or all of the cumulative review problems to be completed as practice or for homework.

Cumulative Review

Problems 1–3 review addition using finger sets, Grade 1 Lesson 1.6

Problems 4–5 review place value and money, Lesson 1.5

Problems 6–11 review comparing numbers in number statements, Lesson 1.9

Problems 12–18 review adding and subtracting on a number line, Lesson 1.10

Monitoring Student Progress

If . . . students miss more than one problem in a section,

Then . . . refer to the indicated lesson for remediation suggestions.

Student Page

Cumulative Review

Name _____ Date _____

Finger Sets Grade 1 Lesson 1.6
Write the number shown (number on finger set + number of counters).

1. + = 5
2. + = 5
3. + = 11

Place Value and Money Lesson 1.5
Count, and write the amount shown.

4. ____44____ ¢

5. $____22____

ⓒ **Textbook** This lesson is available in the *eTextbook*. 29

Student Page

Cumulative Review

Comparing Numbers Lesson 1.9
Draw the correct sign: <, >, or =.

6. 38 − 1 ⊝ 38 − 2
7. 38 + 1 ⊝ 38 − 1
8. 67 + 3 ⊜ 66 + 4
9. 82 + 3 ⊝ 82 + 2
10. 44 − 1 ⊝ 43 − 1
11. 67 − 3 ⊝ 66 − 4

Relating Addition and Subtraction Lesson 1.10
Use the number line to find the answers.
Some are easier than they look.

0 1 2 3 4 5 6 7 8 9 10 11 12 13 14 15 16 17 18 19 20

12. 5 + 2 = __7__
13. 8 + 1 = __9__
14. 9 + 1 = __10__
15. 5 − 1 − 1 − 2 = __1__
16. 7 + 3 = __10__
17. 1 + 2 + 2 + 1 = __6__

Solve.

18. 234 + 175 = __409__   409 − 175 = __234__

175 + 234 = __409__   409 − 234 = __175__

30 **Real Math** • Chapter 1

Wrap-Up

1 Discuss 5

Concept/Question Board

Review the Concept/Question Board with students.

- Discuss students' contributions to the Concept side of the Board.
- Have students repose their questions, and lead a discussion to find satisfactory answers.

Chapter Projects ☑ APPLYING

Provide an opportunity for students who have worked on one or more of the projects outlined on page 2C to share their work with the class. Allow each student or student group five minutes to present or discuss their projects. For formal assessment, use the rubrics found in *Across the Curriculum Math Connections;* the rubric for **Analyze Primary Sources** is on page 17, and the rubric for **Create a Reading Log** is on page 21. For informal assessment, use the following rubric and questions.

	Exceeds Expectations	Meets Expectations	Minimally Meets Expectations
Applies mathematics in real-world situations:	❑	❑	❑
Demonstrates strong engagement in the activity:	❑	❑	❑

Analyze Primary Sources

- Why is it important to study historical documents?
- How many photos did you view? How many narratives did you listen to?
- How did you record the numbers of items you viewed or listened to?
- Was a spreadsheet a good way to record your information? Why or why not?
- Which historical documents did you like best? Why?
- How did the historical documents help you see how life was in the past?

Create a Reading Log

- What types of books did you read? How long did you read?
- What information did you include in your reading log?
- Is a database a good way to create a reading log? Why or why not?
- What other fields could you add to your reading log?
- How did using a calendar help you with your reading log?

2 Assign Student Pages 25

Key Ideas Review UNDERSTANDING

Have students complete the Review questions independently or in small groups. Then discuss each question as a class.

Possible Answers

Problem ❶ Problems 1–4 review terms used for describing numbers and digits. The answer is 53 with the 5 highlighted. Students should remember that the first digit of a two-digit number is in the tens place.

Problem ❷ The answer is 47 with the 7 highlighted. Students should remember that the second digit of a two-digit number is in the ones place.

Problem ❸ The answer is 18. Students should remember that a two-digit number is even if the digit in the ones place is even.

Problem ❹ The answer is 21. Students should remember that a two-digit number is odd if the digit in the ones place is odd.

Problem ❺ Problem 5 reviews making estimates. Students should recognize that the blue book has a thickness that is about halfway between that of the red book and the green book, so the number of pages will likely be about halfway between the number of pages in the red book (100) and the number of pages in the green book (500). The answer is 300.

Extended Response

Problem ❻ Problem 6 reviews the characteristics of odd and even numbers. Students' drawings should show that an even number of objects can be divided into two equal groups, while an odd number of objects cannot.

Problem ❼ Problems 7–8 review adding and subtracting on a number line. Students should remember that counting on with a number line represents addition and that the number of jumps, not the points, should be counted. The answer is $17 + 4 = 21$.

Problem ❽ Students should remember that counting back with a number line represents subtraction. The answer is $14 - 2 = 12$.

Problem ❾ Problems 9–10 review comparing numbers and number expressions. Possible answers for this problem are 3, 2, 1, or 0.

Problem ❿ Possible answers for this problem are 3 and any number greater than 3.

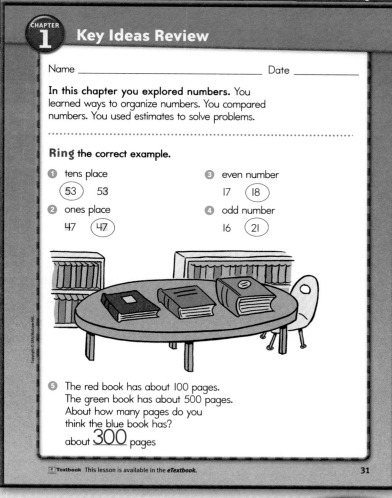

Chapter Review

Use the Chapter 1 Review to indicate areas in which each student is having difficulty or in which the class may need help. If students do well on the Chapter 1 Review, you may wish to skip directly to the Chapter Test; if not, you may spend a day or so helping students overcome their individual difficulties before taking the Practice Test.

Next to each set of problems is a list of the lessons in the chapter that covered those concepts. If they need help, students can refer to a specific lesson for additional instruction. You can also use this information to make additional assignments based on the previous lesson concepts.

Have students complete pages 33–34 on their own.

Monitoring Student Progress

Problems 1–4 Lessons 1.5 and 1.7

If . . . students write an incorrect answer,

Then . . . determine whether counting or counting by groups of ten is the difficulty, and then review accordingly.

Problems 5–8 Lesson 1.2

If . . . students have difficulty with these problems,

Then . . . have them use counters to illustrate each problem.

Problem 9 Lesson 1.4

If . . . students have difficulty with this problem,

Then . . . review estimating. Have students copy windows on the empty building to check their estimates.

Problems 10–12 Lessons 1.1 and 1.8

If . . . students miss both problems,

Then . . . reteach the process of counting on and counting back with smaller numbers.

Problems 13–14 Lesson 1.9

If . . . students miss both problems,

Then . . . review the greater than and less than symbols using the alligator mouth concept.

Name _____ Date _____

Lesson 1.5 **Count**, and then write the number.

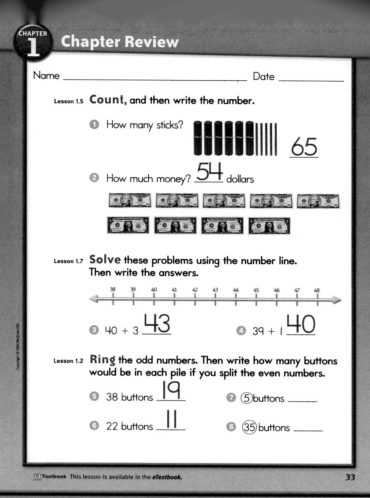

1 How many sticks? **65**

2 How much money? **54** dollars

Lesson 1.7 **Solve** these problems using the number line. Then write the answers.

3 40 + 3 **43**

4 39 + 1 **40**

Lesson 1.2 **Ring** the odd numbers. Then write how many buttons would be in each pile if you split the even numbers.

5 38 buttons **19**

6 22 buttons **11**

7 ⑤ buttons _____

8 ㉟ buttons _____

Lesson 1.4 **Estimate** the number of floors in the first building.

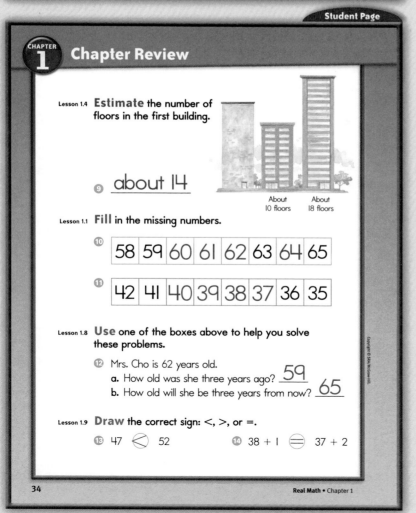

9 **about 14**

About 10 floors   About 18 floors

Lesson 1.1 **Fill** in the missing numbers.

10 | 58 | 59 | 60 | 61 | 62 | 63 | 64 | 65 |

11 | 42 | 41 | 40 | 39 | 38 | 37 | 36 | 35 |

Lesson 1.8 **Use** one of the boxes above to help you solve these problems.

12 Mrs. Cho is 62 years old.
a. How old was she three years ago? **59**
b. How old will she be three years from now? **65**

Lesson 1.9 **Draw** the correct sign: <, >, or =.

13 47 ⟨ 52

14 38 + 1 ⊜ 37 + 2

 Chapter Tests 40

Practice Test

Student Pages 35–38

- The Chapter 1 Practice Test on **Student Edition** pages 35–38 provides an opportunity to formally evaluate students' proficiency with concepts developed in this chapter.
- The content is similar to the Chapter 1 Review, in standardized format.

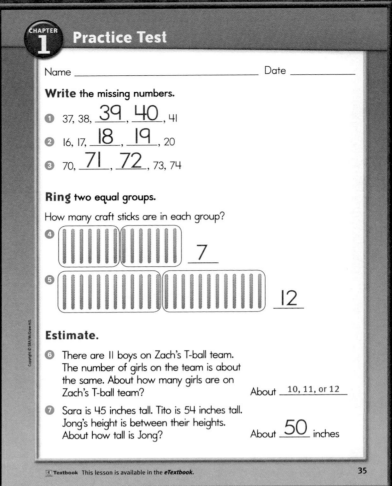

CHAPTER 1 Practice Test

Name _____ Date _____

Write the missing numbers.

1. 37, 38, __39__, __40__, 41
2. 16, 17, __18__, __19__, 20
3. 70, __71__, __72__, 73, 74

Ring two equal groups.

How many craft sticks are in each group?

4. __7__
5. __12__

Estimate.

6. There are 11 boys on Zach's T-ball team. The number of girls on the team is about the same. About how many girls are on Zach's T-ball team?   About __10, 11, or 12__

7. Sara is 45 inches tall. Tito is 54 inches tall. Jong's height is between their heights. About how tall is Jong?   About __50__ inches

Textbook This lesson is available in the *eTextbook*.   35

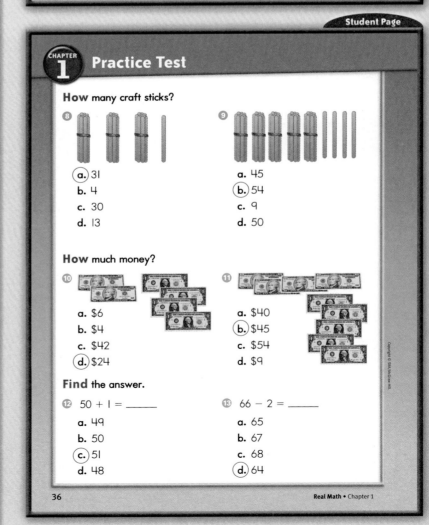

CHAPTER 1 Practice Test

How many craft sticks?

8.
a. 31
b. 4
c. 30
d. 13

9.
a. 45
b. 54
c. 9
d. 50

How much money?

10.
a. $6
b. $4
c. $42
d. $24

11.
a. $40
b. $45
c. $54
d. $9

Find the answer.

12. 50 + 1 = _____
a. 49
b. 50
c. 51
d. 48

13. 66 − 2 = _____
a. 65
b. 67
c. 68
d. 64

36   **Real Math** • Chapter 1

CHAPTER 1 Practice Test

Name _____ Date _____

Ring the letter of the answer that makes the sentence true.

⑭ _____ > 37

  a. 35
  (b.) 39
  c. 33
  d. 37

⑮ 45 < _____

  a. 40
  b. 45
  (c.) 46
  d. 43

Ring the letter of the answer that shows how many.

⑯

  a. 10
  b. 14
  c. 12
  (d.) 11

⑱

  a. 10
  b. 11
  (c.) 20
  d. 18

⑰

  a. 26
  (b.) 15
  c. 13
  d. 12

⑲

  (a.) 18
  b. 17
  c. 20
  d. 19

Textbook This lesson is available in the *eTextbook*.

37

CHAPTER 1 Practice Test

Solve.

⑳ 250 + 125 = 375

Use this math fact to write one more addition fact and two related subtraction facts.

    125 + 250 = 375

    375 − 125 = 250

    375 − 250 = 125

Use the calendar to solve.

June						
SUN	MON	TUE	WED	THU	FRI	SAT
			1	2	3	4
5	6	7	8	9	10	11
12	13	14	15	16	17	18
19	20	21	22	23	24	25
26	27	28	29	30		

㉑ What is the sixth day of this month? _____ Monday

㉒ How many Wednesdays are in the month? _____ 5

㉓ What day is June 25? _____ Saturday

㉔ Tamara and her dad went fishing on June 19. On what day did they go fishing? _____ Sunday

38   **Real Math • Chapter 1**

Chapter Test ✔ COMPUTING

For further evaluation instead of or in addition to this test, you may wish to have students take the Chapter 1 Test provided in **Assessment**.

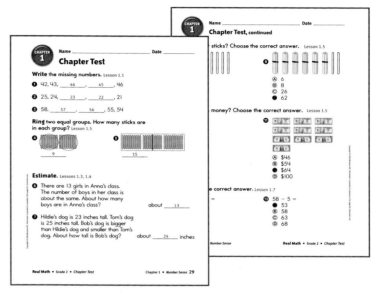

Assessment, pages 29–30

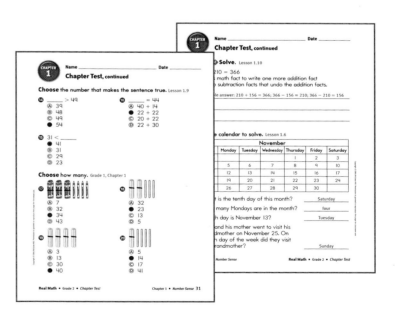

Assessment, pages 31–32

4 Assess and Differentiate

 Assess Use *eAssess* to record and analyze evidence of student understanding.

A Gather Evidence

Use the Daily Class Assessment Records in **Assessment** or *eAssess* to record Informal and Formal Assessments.

Informal Assessment
✓ **Key Ideas Review** UNDERSTANDING

Did the student
- ❑ make important observations?
- ❑ extend or generalize learning?
- ❑ provide insightful answers?
- ❑ pose insightful questions?

Informal Assessment
✓ **Project** APPLYING

Did the student
- ❑ meet the project objectives?
- ❑ communicate clearly?
- ❑ complete the project accurately?
- ❑ connect mathematics to real-world situations?

Formal Assessment
✓ **Chapter Test** COMPUTING

Score the test, and record the results.

B Summarize Findings

Analyze and summarize assessment data for each student. Determine which Chapter Follow-Up is appropriate for each student. Use the Student Assessment Record in **Assessment** or *eAssess* to update assessment records.

C Chapter Follow-Up • DIFFERENTIATE INSTRUCTION

Based on your observations, use these teaching strategies for chapter follow-up.

ENRICH	PRACTICE	RETEACH	INTERVENTION
If . . . students demonstrate a **secure understanding** of chapter concepts,	**If . . .** students demonstrate **competent understanding** of chapter concepts,	**If . . .** students demonstrate **emerging understanding** of chapter concepts,	**If . . .** students demonstrate **minimal understanding** of chapter concepts,
Then . . . move on to the next chapter.	**Then . . .** move on to the next chapter.	**Then . . .** move on to the next chapter, but continue to provide cumulative review.	**Then . . .** intensive intervention is still needed before they start the next chapter.

Mr. Muddle Takes a Test

Context of the Thinking Story Mr. Muddle wants to find a job as a librarian in order to earn money. He takes a test to see what kind of work at which he is good.

Lesson Planner

OBJECTIVES
To develop logical thinking while integrating reading skills with mathematics

NCTM STANDARDS
Number and Operations
- Connecting number words to the quantities they represent
- Subtracting small numbers

Measurement
Recognizing the attributes of time

Communication
Communicating mathematical thinking clearly

READING STANDARDS
- Listening for details
- Drawing conclusions
- Evaluating information
- Making inferences

Using the Thinking Story

The Thinking Story may be used at any time throughout the chapter. Read the Thinking Story "Mr. Muddle Takes a Test" to your class. As you read the story, give students time to think about each question, but not so much that they forget the point being made.

Mr. Muddle Takes a Test

"I can't understand it," Mr. Muddle said. "I'm not spending any more than I used to, yet I seem to be running out of money."

"Are you still earning as much money as you used to?" Mr. Eng asked him.

"Well, no," said Mr. Muddle. "As a matter of fact, ever since I stopped working, I haven't been earning any money at all. I wonder if that could have anything to do with my problem."

What does not working have to do with Mr. Muddle's problem? **He's still spending the same amount he used to, but he is not earning any money.**

"From the sound of it, you won't have any money at all in a little while unless you get a job and start earning some more," Mr. Eng told him. "Mrs. Breezy works for an employment agency. Maybe she could help you find a job."

The next time he thought of it, Mr. Muddle went down to the office where Mrs. Breezy worked.

"What kind of job are you looking for?" Mrs. Breezy asked.

"I want to be a librarian," Mr. Muddle said. "I find that I am running out of money, so I would like to earn some more by working in the library."

"Many people have that problem," Mrs. Breezy said, "but I was wondering what particular kind of work you are good at. Have you worked as a librarian in the past?"

"Oh, I'm good at all kinds of work," Mr. Muddle said, "but I can't remember exactly if I've worked as a librarian."

"Well," said Mrs. Breezy, "I think the thing to do would be to give you some tests to find out what you do best."

"Good," said Mr. Muddle. "I like tests."

"First we'll see how you are at arithmetic," Mrs. Breezy said. "If I have five apples and eat two of them, how many apples do I have left?"

"That's easy," said Mr. Muddle. "Five apples."

What do you think the answer was supposed to be?   **three**

"Perhaps you didn't hear the question," Mrs. Breezy said. "I said I have five apples and eat two of them."

"Exactly," said Mr. Muddle. "Then you have five apples—three on the outside and two on the inside."

"I think that's enough arithmetic," Mrs. Breezy said. "Let's try some different questions. How many days are in one week?"

"Which week?" Mr. Muddle asked.

Does it matter which week?   **no**

Why not?   **There are seven days in every week.**

"Any week," Mrs. Breezy said. "They all have the same number of days."

"I want to make sure I get this one right," Mr. Muddle said. "Do you mean a week starting on Sunday or on Monday?"

Does it make a difference?   **no**

Why not?   **No matter where you start counting, there are seven days in a week.**

"You can start on any day you like," Mrs. Breezy said. "The question is how many days will it take to make a whole week?"

"Then I would estimate, more or less, about seven," Mr. Muddle answered.

Is there anything wrong with Mr. Muddle's answer? **The answer, seven days, is an exact number, not an estimation or an approximation.**

"Actually," said Mrs. Breezy, "a week is always seven days, but we'll count your answer right. Now for a harder question: How many eggs are in a dozen?"

"How many eggs…in a dozen?"

"You're going to ask what kind of eggs, right?" Mrs. Breezy said.

"You've read my mind exactly," Mr. Muddle said.

"Well," she said, "the answer is any kind of eggs. It doesn't matter."

Why doesn't it matter? **A dozen is another name for 12. It relates to the number of items, not the kind of items.**

"You mean I can have any kind of eggs I want?" said Mr. Muddle. "Good. How about pigeon eggs?"

"That's just fine," Mrs. Breezy said.

"The only trouble is," Mr. Muddle said, "I don't think I've ever seen a dozen pigeon eggs. So you can't expect me to know how many pigeon eggs are in a dozen."

Have you ever seen a dozen pigeon eggs? **Allow several students to answer.**

Do you know how many pigeon eggs there are in a dozen? **12**

How can you know even if you've never seen a dozen pigeon eggs? **A dozen is another name for 12. It doesn't matter what items are being counted.**

"A dozen is a dozen, no matter what it is a dozen of," Mrs. Breezy said. "Do you know how many that is?"

"Give me a hint," said Mr. Muddle.

"All right. It's the same as the number of fingers on your hands, plus two."

"Two what?"

"Two fingers!"

"You mean to say that a dozen pigeon eggs is 12 fingers?" said Mr. Muddle. "I find that hard to believe."

What does Mrs. Breezy really mean? She means that the number 12, or one dozen, is the same quantity as 10 plus 2.

Mrs. Breezy explained patiently, "I mean that the number of pigeon eggs in a dozen is the same as the number of fingers on your hands, plus 2. That number is 12. I guess there isn't any point in asking you more questions."

"Did I pass the test?" Mr. Muddle asked.

"Let's put it this way," Mrs. Breezy said. "I don't think the test is going to help us much in finding you a job that's right for you, but I'll let you know."

"Thank you very much," said Mr. Muddle. "I've learned a lot from you. I've learned that there are 12 days in a week and seven eggs in a dozen. I won't forget it."

What's wrong with what Mr. Muddle said? He reversed the numbers. He should have said that there are seven days in a week and twelve eggs in a dozen.

The End

Guided Discussion

As students answer the questions in the story, ask them to communicate how they chose their answers. Allow students to debate the answers if necessary.

Using Student Pages 39–40

Have students follow the instructions and complete the **Student Edition** activities. Read the instructions aloud if students are having difficulty.

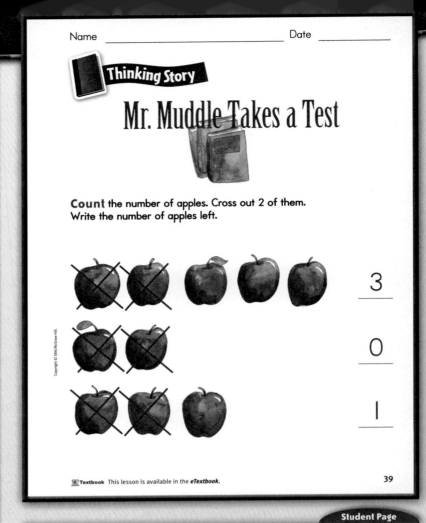

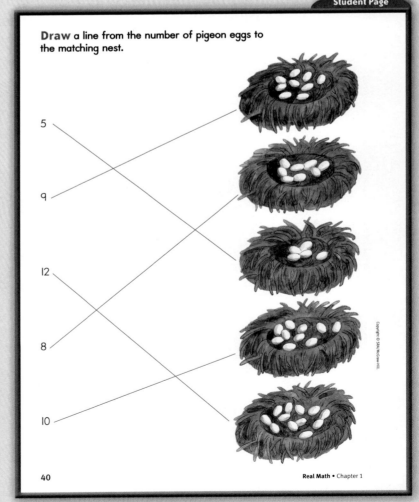

Lesson Study

Reflect on each of the lessons you taught in this chapter. Rate each one on the following scale, and then consider ways to maintain or improve positive teaching experiences in the future.

Lessons	Very Effective	Effective	Less Effective	What Worked	Ways to Improve
1.1 Counting and Writing Numbers					
1.2 Odds and Evens					
1.3 Counting and Estimating					
1.4 Making Estimates					
1.5 Place Value and Money					
1.6 The Calendar					
1.7 Counting on a Number Line					
1.8 Counting Applications					
1.9 Comparing Numbers					
1.10 Relating Addition and Subtraction					

Lessons

Addition Facts

Teaching for Understanding

This chapter focuses on developing automatic and quick recall of the basic addition facts. The objective is to begin a review of addition facts through +10 and to develop understanding of the effects of adding whole numbers. Students will use representations to develop and use strategies of whole-number addition computations.

Prerequisite Skills and Concepts

- Comparing Numbers ● Writing Numbers in Sequence ● Using a Function Table

Addition Facts Skills Trace

Before Grade 2	Grade 2	After Grade 2
Grades K–1 Informally and formally introduced addition to 100	**Chapter 1** reviewed number basics and properties of numbers. **This chapter** develops fluency with computational strategies for addition facts.	Review and mastery of the meaning of addition and basic facts. Formal introduction to addition of larger numbers

Problem Solving

Problem solving is in every lesson. This chapter includes the following:

CHAPTER INTRODUCTION Students determine how much food is needed to feed a dog a set amount of food (pp. 41I–42C).

EXPLORING PROBLEM SOLVING The first lesson provides addition-fact practice as students determine the cost of supplies for a pet hamster (pp. 53–54, 54A). The second lesson continues to provide practice with addition facts and money, as students figure out how to fairly share a pet-show prize between two winners (pp. 65–66, 66A).

THINKING STORY In "Plenty of Time" students help approximate lengths of time for a character to complete certain tasks (pp. 77A–77E, 77–78).

Games

Develop reasoning skills, and provide extensive practice.

- **Addition Table Game** (Lesson 2.1)
- **Addition Crossing Game** (Lesson 2.3)
- **Doubles Game** (Lesson 2.4)
- **Frog Pond Game** (Lesson 2.5)
- **Roll a 15 Game** (Lesson 2.7)

Math Background

Addition Facts

Learning Addition Facts

- The addition-fact review in these lessons focuses special attention on the relationships among facts so students can use these relationships to remember the facts, rather than viewing them as isolated bits of information to be memorized. For example, in Lesson 2.3 we focus on the relationships between the +10 facts, which are easy to find because of our base-ten number system, and the related +9 facts, which are one less than the +10 facts.

- The doubles facts are relatively easy to memorize because students have to remember only one addend. Once memorized, they can be used to recall other facts. For example, a student who memorizes 5 + 5 = 10 also has a strategy for knowing that 5 + 6 is one more than 10, or 11.

- The Addition Table is used to show clearly which facts have been covered and which facts are yet to be learned and to demonstrate patterns. By studying this table students can easily see that if they know the facts on one side of the diagonal formed by the doubles of numbers (for example, 7 + 4), they automatically know the facts on the other side of the diagonal (for example, 4 + 7). This illustrates the Commutative Law of Addition.

Fact Helpers

These strategies can help with many of the addition facts.

To add:	Think of:
0	No change
1	Counting on 1
2	Counting on 2
4	One less than adding 5
5	Finger sets
6	One more than adding 5
9	One less than adding 10
10	Write 1 in the tens place.

Function Basics

FUNCTION MACHINES

A function machine shows the input, output, and rule for a function. The same rule is used to find the output for every input.

FUNCTION RULES

A function rule tells how the input of a function is related to the output of a function. This chapter uses one-step function rules that perform a single operation. Chapter 12 introduces composite functions, which perform more than one operation on each input.

FINDING INPUTS

Knowing function rules and outputs, students can work backward to find inputs. This can involve using subtraction to reverse an addition function or addition to reverse a subtraction function.

The Paper Explorer

- Lesson 2.9 introduces the Paper Explorer as a way to better understand addition concepts. The Paper Explorer will also be used in later chapters to model multidigit addition and subtraction. It is not a calculator, but rather an exploration tool.

- Manipulating counters on the Paper Explorer allows students to notice relationships between many of the basic addition facts while practicing the facts with visual, auditory, and kinesthetic reinforcement.

- As students use the Paper Explorer, place emphasis on having them move the counters so they match the already given sums rather than having students determine the sums. Students will get frustrated if they are asked to determine sums, and then make a wrong move and get the wrong answer. This is especially true if students already know the correct sum. The idea here is to explore the relationships rather than calculate sums.

What Research Says

About Development of Addition Strategies

How Children Strengthen Addition Strategies

Learning single-digit addition and subtraction is generally characterized as "learning math facts." It is assumed that children must memorize these facts, yet research has shown that addition and subtraction have their roots in counting, counting on, number sense, the ability to compose and decompose numbers, and place value. Research has shown that learning methods for adding and subtracting with understanding is much more effective than rote memorization of seemingly isolated facts.

Fuson, Karen. "Pre-K to Grade 2 Goals and Standards: Achieving 21st Century Mastery for All" in Clements, Douglas and J. Sarama, eds. *Engaging Young Children in Mathematics: Standards for Early Childhood Mathematics Education.* Mahwah, New Jersey: Lawrence Erlbaum Associates, Publishers, 2004, p. 121.

The ability to add and subtract fluently develops over the course of several years. Over time, the child gains counting strategies and greater understanding of part/whole relationships. The child recognizes that larger numbers can be decomposed, or broken into smaller parts. The child develops greater flexibility in using strategies for finding sums and differences.

Learning Trajectories for Developing Concepts for Addition

Key steps from the learning trajectory for addition and subtraction for children in Grades 1 and 2 are described below. For the complete trajectory, see Appendix B.

Part-Whole +/−	Development in addition and subtraction has occurred when the child has part-whole understanding. This child can solve all problem types using flexible strategies and some derived facts (for example, "5 + 5 is 10, so 5 + 6 is 11"), and sometimes can do start unknown (_ + 6 = 11), but only by trial and error.
Numbers-in-Numbers +/−	Evidence of the next level is when a child recognizes that a number is part of a whole and can solve problems when the start is unknown (_ + 4 = 9) with counting strategies.
Deriver +/−	At the next level a child can use flexible strategies and derived combinations (for example, "7 + 7 is 14, so 7 + 8 is 15") to solve all types of problems.

Clements, Douglas and J. Sarama, eds. *Engaging Young Children in Mathematics: Standards for Early Childhood Mathematics Education.* Mahwah, New Jersey: Lawrence Erlbaum Associates, Publishers, 2004.

Research-Based Teaching Strategies

Second-grade students should become fluent when computing with whole numbers. *Computational fluency* refers to having and using efficient and accurate methods for computing. Fluency with whole-number computation depends in large part on fluency with basic number combinations. Fluency with the basic number combinations develops from well-understood meanings for the four operations and from a focus on thinking strategies.

Research shows that learners benefit when the new concepts being introduced in mathematics are brought to life using multiple representations of the new concept including oral language, written symbols, pictures, models, and real-world contexts in order to develop deeper understanding of the new concepts with children.

For example, "a growing body of research indicates that children from all over the world move through a progression of different procedures to find the sum of single digit numbers. This progression moves from counting all objects in a collection, to counting on from a known amount. Children may then employ procedures for counting using finger or auditory patterns, or for using doubles or by recomposing numbers to facilitate more abstract procedures for arriving at the sum."

Kilpatrick, J., J. Swafford, and B. Findell, eds. *Adding It Up: Helping Children Learn Mathematics.* Washington, D.C.: National Research Council/National Academy Press, 2001, pp. 187–190.

RESEARCH IN ACTION

Addition Table—Chapter 2 reinforces the development of effective and efficient procedures for performing addition. To facilitate this development, the chapter utilizes the Addition Table, which will be used to reinforce and model some patterns and strategies for learning the basic addition facts.

Addition Strategies—In Chapter 2 students will explore and focus on the use of a variety of effective addition strategies such as doubles, near doubles, and friendly "ten" or "near ten" numbers.

Vocabulary

addend (Lesson 2.7) a number to be added

Commutative Law (Lesson 2.2) a law in mathematics that states that the order of addition does not change the sum

function machine (Lesson 2.6) a machine that supplies one output for each input, according to a rule

perimeter (Lesson 2.8) the distance around a figure

sum (Lesson 2.1) a result obtained from addition

English Learner

Cognates

For English learners, a quick way to acquire new English vocabulary is to build on what is known in the primary language.

English	Spanish
sum	suma
order	orden
addition	adicíon
doubles	dobles
function	funcíon
machine	máquina
multiple	múltiple
apply	aplicar
perimeter	perímetro
explorer	explorador

Access Vocabulary

English learners may understand words in different contexts or not understand idioms. Review chapter vocabulary for this concern. For example:

table	a graphic display of organized information
diagonal	a slanted direction
sum	the answer to an addition problem; not the word *some*
add a number to itself	This means to add a number to the same number.
near	close to
input	a number put into a function machine
output	what an input becomes after the function rule has been applied to it
round	one complete turn for all the players in a game
garden	a part of the yard set aside for growing plants
thumbs-up	a signal given by holding out a fist with the thumb pointing up

Chapter Planner

Lessons	Objectives	NCTM Standards	State Standards
2.1 Basic Addition Facts and Table pages 43A–44A 45–60 minutes	To begin a review of basic addition facts using the Addition Table, focusing on automatic recall and fluency	Number and Operations, Representation	
2.2 The Commutative Law pages 45A–46A 45–60 minutes	To continue reviewing the addition facts, paying close attention to the Commutative Law of Addition	Number and Operations, Algebra, Representation	
2.3 +10 and +9 Addition Facts pages 47A–48A 45–60 minutes	To continue reviewing the addition facts, focusing on the +10 and the corresponding +9 facts	Number and Operations, Representation, Problem Solving	
2.4 Doubles pages 49A–50A 45–60 minutes	To continue reviewing the addition facts, paying special attention to the doubles facts	Number and Operations, Representation, Communication	
2.5 Near Doubles pages 51A–52A 45–60 minutes	To continue reviewing the addition facts, paying special attention to the facts that are 1 more than the doubles facts	Number and Operations, Representation, Problem Solving	
2.6 Remaining Facts and Function Machines pages 57A–58A 45–60 minutes	To apply addition facts through the reintroduction of function machines from Grade 1	Number and Operations, Representation, Algebra	
2.7 Using Multiple Addends pages 59A–60A 45–60 minutes	To continue reviewing the addition facts, focusing on exercises in which there are more than two addends	Number and Operations, Communication	
2.8 Applying Addition pages 61A–62A 45–60 minutes	To apply addition facts by finding the perimeter of polygons	Number and Operations, Geometry, Measurement	
2.9 The Paper Explorer– Single-Digit Addition pages 63A–64A 45–60 minutes	To introduce the Paper Explorer as a model to add single-digit numbers	Number and Operations, Representation	

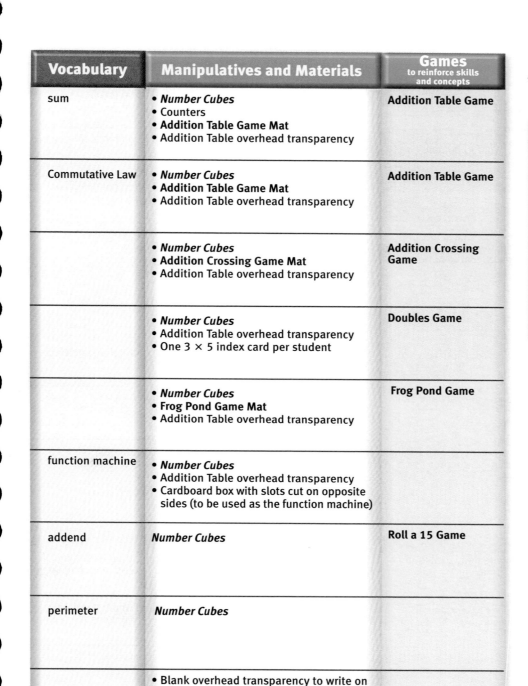

Vocabulary	Manipulatives and Materials	Games to reinforce skills and concepts
sum	• *Number Cubes* • Counters • **Addition Table Game Mat** • Addition Table overhead transparency	**Addition Table Game**
Commutative Law	• *Number Cubes* • **Addition Table Game Mat** • Addition Table overhead transparency	**Addition Table Game**
	• *Number Cubes* • **Addition Crossing Game Mat** • Addition Table overhead transparency	**Addition Crossing Game**
	• *Number Cubes* • Addition Table overhead transparency • One 3 × 5 index card per student	**Doubles Game**
	• *Number Cubes* • **Frog Pond Game Mat** • Addition Table overhead transparency	**Frog Pond Game**
function machine	• *Number Cubes* • Addition Table overhead transparency • Cardboard box with slots cut on opposite sides (to be used as the function machine)	
addend	*Number Cubes*	**Roll a 15 Game**
perimeter	*Number Cubes*	
	• Blank overhead transparency to write on • Overhead transparency of the Paper Explorer on *Practice* page 121 • Counters	

Additional Resources

Differentiated Instruction

Intervention Support Guide Provides instruction for the following prerequisite skills:

- Lesson 2.A Numbers and Functions–1
- Lesson 2.B Numbers and Functions–2
- Lesson 2.C Numbers and Functions–3

Enrichment Support Guide Extends lesson concepts

Practice Reinforces lesson skills and concepts

Reteach Support Guide Provides alternate instruction for lesson concepts

English Learner Support Guide Previews and reviews lesson concepts and vocabulary for English learners

Technology

The following electronic resources are available:

e **Planner** Lessons 2.1–2.9

e **Presentation** Lessons 2.1–2.9

e **Textbook** Lessons 2.1–2.9

e **Assess** Lessons 2.1–2.9

e **MathTools** *Addition Table* Lessons 2.1–2.5
      Function Machine Lesson 2.6

e **Games** *Addition Table Game* Lessons 2.1 and 2.2
      Roll a 15 Game Lesson 2.7

Building Blocks *Number Snapshots 8* Lesson 2.4
      Eggcellent: Addition Choice Lesson 2.5
      Function Machine 1 Lesson 2.6
      Shape Parts 3 Lesson 2.7
      Barkley's Bones 1–20 Lesson 2.8
      Double Compare 1–20 Lesson 2.9

Assessment
Informal Assessment rubrics at the end of each lesson provide daily evaluation of student math proficiency.

Chapter Planner, continued

Problem Solving	When to Use	Objectives	NCTM Standards	Skills Covered
Chapter Introduction (pp. 41I–42C) 15–30 minutes	Use before beginning Chapter 2.	To introduce chapter concepts in a problem-solving setting	Problem Solving, Communication	Basic addition facts, Measurement
Exploring Problem Solving (pp. 53–54, 54A) 30–45 minutes	Use anytime during the chapter.	To explore methods of solving nonroutine problems	Problem Solving, Communication	Basic addition facts, Money
Exploring Problem Solving (pp. 65–66, 66A) 45–60 minutes	Use anytime during the chapter.	To explore methods of solving nonroutine problems	Problem Solving, Communication	Basic addition facts, Money, Sharing fairly
Thinking Story–Plenty of Time (pp. 77A–77E, 77–78) 20–30 minutes	Use anytime during the chapter.	To develop logical reasoning while integrating reading skills with mathematics	Number and Operations, Problem Solving, Communication	Measurement of time

Review	When to Use	Objectives	NCTM Standards	Skills Covered
Cumulative Review (p. 55–56) 15–30 minutes	Use anytime after Lesson 2.5.	To review concepts and skills taught earlier in the year	Number and Operations	Addition strategies, Addition fact table
Cumulative Review (p. 67–68) 15–30 minutes	Use anytime after Lesson 2.9.	To review concepts and skills taught earlier in the year	Number and Operations	Addition strategies, Applications of addition
Chapter 2 Review (pp. 71A, 71–72) 30–45 minutes	Use after Lesson 2.9.	To review concepts and skills taught in the chapter	Number and Operations	Addition strategies, Applications of addition

Assessment	When to Use	Objectives	NCTM Standards	Skills Covered
Informal Assessment Rubrics (pp. 44A–64A) 5 minutes per student	Use at the end of each lesson.	To provide daily evaluation of math proficiency	Number and Operations, Communication	Computing, Understanding, Reasoning, Applying, Engaging
Pretest (*Assessment* pp. 34–35) 15–30 minutes	Use prior to Chapter 2.	To provide assessment of prerequisite and chapter topics	Number and Operations, Problem Solving	Computing, Understanding, Reasoning, Applying, Engaging
Individual Oral Assessment (p. 56A) 5 minutes per student	Begin use after Lesson 2.4.	To provide alternate means of assessing students' progress	Number and Operations	Addition facts
Mastery Checkpoint (*Assessment* pp. T53–T54) 5 minutes per student	Use after Lesson 2.9.	To provide assessment of mastery of key skills	Number and Operations	Addition facts
Speed Test (*Assessment* p. T44) 10–15 minutes	Use after Lesson 2.8.	To provide assessment of addition fact fluency	Number and Operations	Addition facts
Chapter 2 Practice Test (pp. 73–74, 75–76) 30–45 minutes	Use after or in place of the Chapter 2 Review.	To provide assessment of the chapter concepts	Number and Operations	Addition facts
Chapter 2 Test (*Assessment* pp. 41–44) 30–45 minutes	Use after or in place of the Chapter 2 Review.	To provide assessment of the chapter concepts	Number and Operations	Addition facts

Technology Resources and Support

Visit SRAonline.com for online versions of the **Real Math** eSuite.

Technology for Teachers

e Presentation	**Lessons 2.1–2.9** Use the *ePresentation* to interactively present chapter content.
e Planner	Use the Chapter and Lesson Planners to outline activities and time frames for Chapter 2.
e Assess	Students can take the following assessments in *eAssess*: • Chapter Pretest • Mastery Checkpoint **Lesson 2.9** • Speed Test **Lesson 2.8** • Chapter Test Teachers can record results and print reports for all assessments in this chapter.
e MathTools	**Addition Table** Lessons 2.1–2.5 **Function Machine** Lesson 2.6

Technology for Students

e Textbook	An electronic, interactive version of the **Student Edition** is available for all lessons in Chapter 2.
e MathTools	**Addition Table** Lessons 2.1–2.5 **Function Machine** Lesson 2.6
e Games	**Addition Table Game** Lessons 2.1 and 2.2 **Roll a 15 Game** Lesson 2.7
TECH KNOWLEDGE	*TechKnowledge* Level 2 provides lessons that specifically teach the Unit 10 Internet applications that students can use in this chapter's project.
Building Blocks	**Number Snapshots 8** Lesson 2.4 **Eggcellent: Addition Choice** Lesson 2.5 **Function Machine 1** Lesson 2.6 **Shape Parts 3** Lesson 2.7 **Barkley's Bones 1–20** Lesson 2.8 **Double Compare 1–20** Lesson 2.9

Addition Facts

1 Introduce Chapter 2   10

Chapter Objectives

Explain to students that in this chapter they will build on what they already know about addition. They will

- review and practice addition facts.
- learn more about addition in everyday situations.
- learn how to add more than two numbers.

Pretest COMPUTING

Administer the Pretest on **Assessment** pages 34 and 35.

The Pretest covers the following skills and topics from the chapter:

- Even and odd numbers (Problems 1 and 2)
- Equal groups (Problems 3 and 4)
- Count on or count back (Problems 5–8)
- Counting applications (Problems 9 and 10)
- Addition strategies: adding doubles and near doubles (Problems 11–18)
- Applying addition strategies: doubles, near doubles, multiple addends (Problems 19–22)

Chapter 2 Pretest

Access Prior Knowledge UNDERSTANDING

Talk about experiences with addition. Ask questions such as the following:

- **When do you use addition outside of school?** Possible answers: figuring out how much several things cost; figuring out how many items you have

Guided Discussion

Have students who own a pet share something about their pets. Then talk about pets in general, using questions such as the following:

- **Where do people get pets?** Possible answers: animal shelters, pet stores, people give them away
- **What kinds of things do pets need?** Possible answers: food, shelter, exercise, affection

2 Exploring Problem Solving   15

Tell Students In Today's Lesson They Will

- solve a problem about feeding a dog.
- explain how they solved the problem.
- show different ways to make a certain number.

Materials

None

Using Student Pages   APPLYING

Have students look at the picture on student page 42. Then present the following problem:

A neighbor is going away for the day and has asked you to take care of his dog, Beaker. One of your jobs is to feed Beaker exactly 16 ounces of dog food. That's one pound. Your neighbor has left some samples of dog food for you to use. As you can see in the picture, the samples are in small bags of different weights. You need to decide which bags to use so Beaker gets exactly 16 ounces of food. After you open a bag, you should use the whole bag so the food doesn't get stale.

Students are expected to use problem-solving skills to solve this problem.

Skill Building   UNDERSTANDING

Make sure students understand the problem by asking questions such as the following:

- **How much do you have to feed Beaker?** 16 ounces of dog food
- **What did your neighbor leave you to feed Beaker?** different weights of dog food samples
- **Is it okay to use part of a bag?** no
- **How many sample bags did your neighbor leave?** 6
- **What do the numbers on the bags tell you?** how many ounces each bag weighs

Have students work with a partner to find bags that can be combined to make 16 ounces. Have them record their answers in any form they like on the page. Later you can discuss these different ways, including number sentences.

Provide support as needed. If students are struggling, let them know that they can solve the problem if they keep trying. Suggest things they can do, for example, trying out any combination of numbers just to see if it will work and then trying another combination.

CHAPTER 2
Addition Facts

In This Chapter You Will Learn
- basic addition facts.
- about doubles.
- about function machines.

41

Problem Solving

Name _____ Date _____

Listen to the problem.

Which bags can you put together to make 16 ounces?

Show as many answers as you can.

Students may show one or more of these answers in this form or some other form:
10 + 6; 10 + 3 + 3; 8 + 6 + 2; 8 + 3 + 3 + 2

42   **Real Math • Chapter 2**

Concept/Question Board APPLYING

Questions
Have students think of and write three questions they have about addition and how it can be used. Then have them select one question to post on the Question side of the Board.

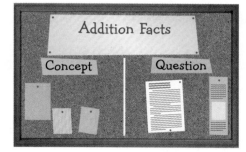

Concepts
As students work through the chapter, have them collect examples of how addition is used in everyday situations. For each example, have them write a problem that relates to the item(s). Have them display their examples on the Concept side of the Board. Suggest the following:
- grocery shopping
- banking

Answers
Throughout the chapter, have students post answers to the questions and solutions to the problems on the Board.

3 Reflect 15

 **Knowledge Age Skills**

Effective Communication Have students share their answers and explain how they found them and how they recorded them. Encourage students to ask for clarification if they do not understand what is being presented. As students present answers that have not been given before, record them on the board with number sentences. Help students understand the following points:

- A problem may have more than one correct answer.
- People may use different strategies to find the same answer.
- Sometimes a strategy may be appropriate even if the answer is wrong.
- Different people may use different ways to show the same answer. Whatever way you use should be clear enough for others to understand it easily.

Sample Solutions Strategies

Students might use one or more of the following strategies.

Act It Out with Objects/Guess, Check, and Adjust

Students may use **Number Strips** or counters (possibly in stacks or bags) to represent the various weights of the bags. Then they may combine different groups until they find a combination that equals 16.

Make a Diagram/Guess, Check, and Adjust

Students may write numbers or draw pictures to represent the different weights. Then they may combine different numbers until they find a combination that equals 16.

Using Number Sense

If students know that $10 + 6 = 16$, they might start with the 10-ounce bag and then look for ways to make 6. Or they may combine bags to make 10 and then look for ways to make 6.

Use a Pattern/Make an Organized List

Students might look first for all possible solutions that include the 10-ounce bag, the 8-ounce bag, and so on.

Home Connection

At this time, you may want to send home the letter on pages 6–9 of **Home Connection.** This letter describes what students will be learning and what activities they can do at home to support their work in school.

**Home Connection
Page 6**

Assess and Differentiate

 Assess Use *eAssess* to record and analyze evidence of student understanding.

A Gather Evidence

Use the Daily Class Assessment Records in **Assessment** or *eAssess* to record Informal and Formal Assessments.

Informal Assessment
☑ **Access Prior Knowledge**
Did the student `UNDERSTANDING`
- ❑ make important observations?
- ❑ extend or generalize learning?
- ❑ provide insightful answers?
- ❑ pose insightful questions?

Informal Assessment
☑ **Concept/Question Board**
Did the student `APPLYING`
- ❑ apply learning in new situations?
- ❑ contribute concepts?
- ❑ contribute answers?
- ❑ connect mathematics to real-world situations?

Formal Assessment
☑ **Pretest**  `COMPUTING`
- ❑ Even and odd numbers (Problems 1 and 2)
- ❑ Equal groups (Problems 3 and 4)
- ❑ Count on or count back (Problems 5–8)
- ❑ Counting applications (Problems 9 and 10)
- ❑ Addition strategies: adding doubles and near doubles (Problems 11–18)
- ❑ Applying addition strategies: doubles, near doubles, multiple addends (Problems 19 and 22)

B Summarize Findings

Analyze and summarize assessment data for each student. Determine which Assessment Follow-Up is appropriate for each student. Use the Student Assessment Record in **Assessment** or *eAssess* to update assessment records.

C Assessment Follow-Up ● DIFFERENTIATE INSTRUCTION

Based on your observations of each student, use these teaching strategies for a general approach to the chapter. Look for specific Differentiate Instruction and Monitoring Student Progress strategies in each lesson that relate specifically to the lesson content.

ENRICH	PRACTICE	RETEACH	INTERVENTION	ENGLISH LEARNER
If . . . students demonstrate a **secure understanding** of chapter concepts, **Then . . .** move quickly through the chapter or use **Enrichment** Lessons 2.1–2.9 as assessment follow-up to extend and apply understanding.	**If . . .** students grasp chapter concepts with **competent understanding, Then . . .** use **Practice** Lessons 2.1–2.9 as lesson follow-up to develop fluency.	**If . . .** students have prerequisite understanding but demonstrate **emerging understanding** of chapter concepts, **Then . . .** use **Reteach** Lesson 2.5 to reteach lesson concepts.	**If . . .** students are not competent with prerequisite skills, **Then . . .** use **Intervention** Lessons 2.A–2.C before each lesson to develop fluency with prerequisite skills.	Use **English Learner Support Guide** Lessons 2.1–2.9 for strategies to preteach lesson vocabulary and concepts.

Math Across the Curriculum

Preview the chapter projects with students. Assign projects or have students choose from the projects to extend and enrich concepts in this chapter.

Illustrate a Book about Pet Care 2–3 weeks

MATH OBJECTIVE
To reinforce studies of addition by adding numbers of minutes needed to perform tasks

SCIENCE OBJECTIVE
To reinforce studies of animals by identifying their basic needs

TECHNOLOGY OBJECTIVE
To use a drawing and graphics program to create drawings for a book

Have students use mathematics to create a book about pet care. To broaden the science concept, have them choose an animal from categories of animals you are currently studying.

As part of the project, students should consider the following issues:

- animal nutrition
- environmental needs of animals
- animal exercise and grooming
- attention needs of animals

For specific step-by-step instructions for this project, see **Across the Curriculum Math Connections** pages 22–25.

Creative Work with Ideas Students create books that illustrate how to take care of pets.

Problem Formulation, Planning, and Strategizing Students plan the sequence of pages in their books and create addition problems.

Communicate Needs as a Pet 2–3 weeks

MATH OBJECTIVE
To reinforce studies of basic addition facts by using an addition table for a presentation

FINE ARTS OBJECTIVE
To reinforce studies of theatre by communicating needs as a pet

TECHNOLOGY OBJECTIVE
To use the Internet to research pet needs and behavior

Have students use technology to

- gather information about caring for pets and pet communication.
- create presentations showing pet communication related to needs.

For this project, students use the Internet to investigate the following information:

- daily care of pets
- general pet behavior
- dog behavior and its causes
- cat behavior and its causes

For specific step-by-step instructions for this project, see **Across the Curriculum Math Connections** pages 26–31.

Teamwork Students work together to create effective presentations.

Effective Communication Students use their bodies and voices to communicate as pets.

TechKnowledge Level 2 provides lessons that specifically teach the Unit 10 Internet applications that students can use in this project.

Lesson Planner

OBJECTIVES
- To begin a review of addition facts, focusing on automatic recall and fluency
- To review the use of the addition table

NCTM STANDARDS
Number and Operations
- Developing and using strategies for addition
- Developing fluency with basic number combinations for addition
- Understanding the effects of adding whole numbers

Representation
Creating and using representations to organize, record, and communicate mathematical ideas

MATERIALS
- *Number Cubes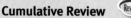
- *Counters
- **Addition Table Game Mat**
- Overhead transparency of the completed 10 + 10 Addition Table

TECHNOLOGY
- Ⓔ **Presentation** Lesson 2.1
- Ⓔ **Games** Addition Table Game
- Ⓔ **MathTools** Addition Table

TEST PREP
Cumulative Review
Mental Math reviews addition (Lesson 1.10).

Basic Addition Facts and Table

Context of the Lesson This chapter reviews the basic addition facts introduced in Grade 1 and focuses on developing automatic and quick recall. In this lesson students review the use of the Addition Table and the +0, +1, and +2 addition facts. The following lessons focus on relationships among facts so that students can use these relationships to remember the facts, rather than viewing them as isolated bits of information to be memorized. Depending on the addition skills of your class, these lessons may take extra time or may require only a quick review.

See page 41B for Math Background for teachers for this lesson.

Planning for Learning ● DIFFERENTIATE INSTRUCTION

INTERVENTION
If . . . students lack the prerequisite skill of comparing numbers,

Then . . . teach *Intervention* Lesson 2.A.

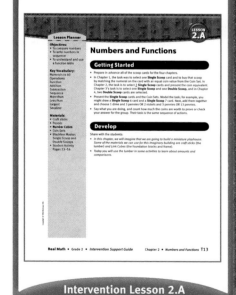

Intervention Lesson 2.A

ENGLISH LEARNER
Preview

If . . . students need language support,

Then . . . use Lesson 2.1 in *English Learner Support Guide* to preview lesson concepts and vocabulary.

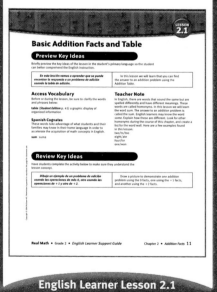

English Learner Lesson 2.1

ENRICH
If . . . students are proficient in the lesson concepts,

Then . . . have students play variations of the **Addition Table Game.**

PRACTICE
If . . . students would benefit from additional practice,

Then . . . extend game play before assigning the student pages.

RETEACH
If . . . students are having difficulty understanding the Addition Table,

Then . . . extend Guided Discussion before assigning the student pages.

Vocabulary
sum \sum\ *n.* a result obtained from addition

Access Vocabulary
table a graphic display of organized information

Spanish Cognates
sum suma

*Manipulative Kit Item

Mental Math 5

Do an addition-fact drill concentrating on +0, +1, and +2 facts, and have students show their answers with **Number Cubes.** Give exercises such as the following:

a. $3 + 1 = 4$ **b.** $3 + 0 = 3$ **c.** $3 + 2 = 5$
d. $5 + 0 = 5$ **e.** $5 + 2 = 7$ **f.** $1 + 1 = 2$
g. $1 + 0 = 1$ **h.** $8 + 2 = 10$ **i.** $2 + 1 = 3$

1 Develop 20

Tell Students In Today's Lesson They Will
review addition facts on the Addition Table.

Guided Discussion  MathTools REASONING
Whole Group

Ask students the following:

■ **What is 8 + 6?** 14

Encourage students to discuss how they can figure out the answer, or *sum,* if they do not know it. Be sure one suggestion is to count out a set of eight objects and then a set of six objects and then to count the number of objects in the combined set. Demonstrate this method with counters.

Next, ask students,

■ **What is 6 + 8?** 14

Many students will get this answer quickly. Ask students how they got their answers. Someone will likely point out that 6 + 8 is the same as 8 + 6 because the order of addition does not make a difference. Show the class the counters you used to solve the previous problem, and demonstrate how the order of the counters makes no difference. (This property of addition, known as the Commutative Law, will be covered in more depth in the next lesson.)

Discuss the method of counting groups of objects and then combining them and counting the total. Ask students,

■ **Why would it be hard to count the total every time you wanted to find a sum?** Possible answer: because you might be using very great numbers that would take a long time to count

Discuss that a faster way to find sums is to learn the addition facts. Display the completed 10 + 10 Addition Table overhead transparency, or use the *eMathTools: Addition Table.* Demonstrate how to use the Addition Table to find sums. Show students how to find the sum of 8 + 6 by finding where the 8 row meets the 6 column.

Skill and Strategy Building ENGAGING
Whole Group

 Games **Addition Table Game**

Demonstrate the **Addition Table Game** by playing at the overhead projector with a volunteer student. Rules for play are on the game mat. Students will play in small groups as they finish the student pages. You might also wish to assign one of the following game variations based on the ability of students.

Addition Table Game Variation 1: Each student uses a different color of counter and places counters on the mat as each sum is stated rather than removing them. The player with the most counters on the board is the winner.

Addition Table Game Variation 2: Instead of covering the Addition Table with counters, use play coins of different denominations. The winner is the player who wins the most money. This variation introduces the additional skill of counting money, and it also introduces an additional element of luck because a player who is losing may get lucky and win a quarter instead of a penny, nickel, or dime.

2 Assign Student Pages 25

Pages 43–44 UNDERSTANDING

On page 43, have students fill in the facts they know and can recall without counting on the Addition Table. Review each student's work to see where he or she is and to better plan the next several lessons.

Have students complete page 44 independently.

Monitoring Student Progress

If . . . students have difficulty with addition that appears to be related to a poor understanding of the meaning of addition,	**Then . . .** provide individual instruction on combining sets, followed by hidden-counter problems. Put out several counters, and have students count them. Then cover the counters, and put out more. Have students calculate how many total counters there are. Reverse roles and have students give you a hidden counter problem.
If . . . students have difficulty using the Addition Table,	**Then . . .** have them play Variation 1 of the **Addition Table Game.**

As Students Finish

  Addition Table Game

Games *Addition Table Game*

MathTools *Addition Table*

LESSON 2.1 — Basic Addition Facts and Table

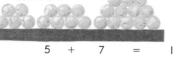

Key Ideas

You can use addition to combine two numbers. Addition tells how many there are after two sets are combined.

5   +   7   =   12

The answer to an addition problem is called the **sum**.

1 Fill in the sums you know on this Addition Table.

+	0	1	2	3	4	5	6	7	8	9	10
0	0	1	2	3	4	5	6	7	8	9	10
1	1	2	3	4	5	6	7	8	9	10	11
2	2	3	4	5	6	7	8	9	10	11	12
3	3	4	5	6	7	8	9	10	11	12	13
4	4	5	6	7	8	9	10	11	12	13	14
5	5	6	7	8	9	10	11	12	13	14	15
6	6	7	8	9	10	11	12	13	14	15	16
7	7	8	9	10	11	12	13	14	15	16	17
8	8	9	10	11	12	13	14	15	16	17	18
9	9	10	11	12	13	14	15	16	17	18	19
10	10	11	12	13	14	15	16	17	18	19	20

Textbook This lesson is available in the *eTextbook*.

43

LESSON 2.1 • Basic Addition Facts and Table

Complete the following addition exercises.

2 $5 + 1 = 6$ **7** $6 + 2 = 8$

3 $2 + 1 = 3$ **8** $6 + 3 = 9$

4 $8 + 2 = 10$ **9** $4 + 1 = 5$

5 $5 + 2 = 7$ **10** $9 + 0 = 9$

6 $7 + 1 = 8$ **11** $3 + 0 = 3$

12 $\begin{array}{r} 4 \\ +3 \\ \hline 7 \end{array}$ **13** $\begin{array}{r} 3 \\ +2 \\ \hline 5 \end{array}$ **14** $\begin{array}{r} 10 \\ +2 \\ \hline 12 \end{array}$

15 $\begin{array}{r} 8 \\ +1 \\ \hline 9 \end{array}$ **16** $\begin{array}{r} 7 \\ +3 \\ \hline 10 \end{array}$ **17** $\begin{array}{r} 8 \\ +3 \\ \hline 11 \end{array}$

18 $\begin{array}{r} 6 \\ +2 \\ \hline 8 \end{array}$ **19** $\begin{array}{r} 9 \\ +3 \\ \hline 12 \end{array}$ **20** $\begin{array}{r} 9 \\ +2 \\ \hline 11 \end{array}$

Game Play the **Addition Table Game.**

44   **Real Math • Chapter 2 • Lesson 1**

---

3 Reflect

10

Guided Discussion   UNDERSTANDING   Whole Group

Display the completed Addition Table on the overhead projector. Remind students that there are 121 facts but that they already know many of them. Remind students that in this lesson they have already covered 8 + 6 and 6 + 8. Tell students that many people have a hard time remembering that 8 + 6 = 14. Tell them you will expect them to remind you from time to time. Then be sure to include this fact in many of your Mental Math drills.

Elicit through discussion that students also know the +0 facts. Demonstrate this knowledge with a quick drill. Then shade the +0 facts on the Addition Table. Using the same procedure, quiz students on the +1 and +2 facts. If most students are proficient, shade those columns and rows. The table should now look like this:

+	0	1	2	3	4	5	6	7	8	9	10
0	0	1	2	3	4	5	6	7	8	9	10
1	1	2	3	4	5	6	7	8	9	10	11
2	2	3	4	5	6	7	8	9	10	11	12
3	3	4	5	6	7	8	9	10	11	12	13
4	4	5	6	7	8	9	10	11	12	13	14
5	5	6	7	8	9	10	11	12	13	14	15
6	6	7	8	9	10	11	12	13	14	15	16
7	7	8	9	10	11	12	13	14	15	16	17
8	8	9	10	11	12	13	14	15	16	17	18
9	9	10	11	12	13	14	15	16	17	18	19
10	10	11	12	13	14	15	16	17	18	19	20

 Cumulative Review: For cumulative review of previously learned skills, see page 55–56.

 Family Involvement: Assign the **Practice, Reteach,** or **Enrichment** activities depending on the needs of your students.

Have students play the **Addition Table Game** with a helper or play **eGames: Addition Table.**

 Concept/Question Board: Have students look for additional examples using addition and post them on the Concept/Question Board.

 Math Puzzler: Mark is 2 years younger than Brad. Brad is 1 year older than Jose. Jose is 8 years old. How old is Mark?
7 years old

4 Assess and Differentiate

 Assess Use **eAssess** to record and analyze evidence of student understanding.

A Gather Evidence

Use the Daily Class Assessment Records in **Assessment** or **eAssess** to record daily observations.

Informal Assessment

✓ Student Pages

Did the student [UNDERSTANDING]

☐ make important observations?
☐ extend or generalize learning?
☐ provide insightful answers?
☐ pose insightful questions?

Performance Assessment

✓ Game

Did the student [ENGAGING]

☐ pay attention to others' contributions?
☐ contribute information and ideas?
☐ improve on a strategy?
☐ reflect on and check the accuracy of his or her work?

B Summarize Findings

Analyze and summarize assessment data for each student. Determine which Assessment Follow-Up is appropriate for each student. Use the Student Assessment Record in **Assessment** or **eAssess** to update assessment records.

Assessment page T41

C Assessment Follow-Up ● DIFFERENTIATE INSTRUCTION

Based on your observations, use these teaching strategies for assessment follow-up.

INTERVENTION

Review student performance on **Intervention** Lesson 2.A to see if students have mastered prerequisite skills for this lesson.

ENGLISH LEARNER

Review

Use Lesson 2.1 in **English Learner Support Guide** to review lesson concepts and vocabulary.

ENRICH

If . . . students are proficient in the lesson concepts,

Then . . . encourage them to work on the chapter projects or **Enrichment** Lesson 2.1.

Enrichment Lesson 2.1

PRACTICE

If . . . students would benefit from additional practice,

Then . . . assign **Practice** Lesson 2.1.

Practice Lesson 2.1

RETEACH

If . . . students are having difficulty using an Addition Table,

Then . . . have them use a ruler horizontally or vertically to find the correct location.

LESSON 2.2

Lesson Planner

OBJECTIVES
To continue reviewing the addition facts, paying special attention to the Commutative Law of Addition

NCTM STANDARDS

Number and Operations
- Developing and using strategies for addition
- Developing fluency with basic number combinations for addition
- Understanding the effects of adding whole numbers

Algebra
Illustrating general principles and properties of operations, such as commutative, using specific numbers

Representation
Creating and using representations to organize, record, and communicate mathematical ideas

MATERIALS
- *Number Cubes
- Addition Table Game Mat
- Overhead transparency of the completed 10 + 10 Addition Table

TECHNOLOGY
- e **Presentation** Lesson 2.2
- e **MathTools** Addition Table
- e **Games** Addition Table Game

TEST PREP

Cumulative Review
Mental Math reviews +0, +1, and +2 addition facts (Lesson 2.1).

The Commutative Law

Context of the Lesson This lesson integrates addition fact practice with an understanding of the Commutative Law, also known as the Order Law or the Commutative or Order Property. The Commutative Law will be helpful for students as they study the Addition Table because students can see that if they know a fact on one side of the diagonal, for instance, 7 + 4, they also know the corresponding fact on the other side of the diagonal, such as 4 + 7.

See page 41B for Math Background for teachers for this lesson.

Planning for Learning ● DIFFERENTIATE INSTRUCTION

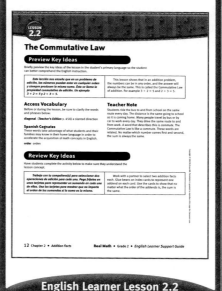

INTERVENTION	ENGLISH LEARNER	ENRICH
If . . . students lack the prerequisite skill of comparing numbers,	Preview	**If . . .** students are proficient in the lesson concepts,
Then . . . teach Intervention Lesson 2.A.	**If . . .** students need language support,	**Then . . .** have students play variations of the **Addition Table Game.**
	Then . . . use Lesson 2.2 in *English Learner Support Guide* to preview lesson concepts and vocabulary.	

PRACTICE

If . . . students would benefit from additional practice,

Then . . . extend game play before assigning the student pages.

RETEACH

If . . . students are having difficulty understanding the Commutative Law,

Then . . . extend Guided Discussion before assigning the student pages.

Intervention Lesson 2.A — **English Learner Lesson 2.2**

Vocabulary
Commutative Law *n.* a law in mathematics that states that the order of addition does not change the sum

Access Vocabulary
diagonal a slanted direction

Spanish Cognates
order orden

Mental Math 5

 Review

Do an addition-fact drill, concentrating on +0, +1, and +2 facts. Have students use **Number Cubes** to show their answers. Give exercises such as the following:

a. 5 + 1 = 6   **b.** 10 + 0 = 10   **c.** 1 + 9 = 10
d. 6 + 0 = 6   **e.** 10 + 2 = 12   **f.** 6 + 2 = 8
g. 7 + 2 = 9   **h.** 8 + 6 = 14   **i.** 6 + 8 = 14

1 Develop 20

Tell Students In Today's Lesson They Will
learn about the Commutative Law.

Guided Discussion REASONING   Whole Group

Using the overhead transparency of the Addition Table that was shaded during Reflect in the previous lesson, initiate a discussion in which you point out that if students know the facts on one side of the diagonal, then they also know the facts on the other side. Thus, if students know that 6 + 2 = 8, then they also know that 2 + 6 = 8. Call on students to verbalize why these facts are related. If necessary, explain the thinking for the students. For example, *If I have 6 apples in a bag in my left hand and 2 apples in a bag in my right hand, then I have 6 + 2, or 8 apples. If I switch the bags between hands so I have 2 apples in a bag in my left hand and 6 apples in a bag in my right hand, I have 2 + 6, or 8 apples. The number of apples I have is the same; they are just in a different order.* Repeat with other examples. Demonstrate by acting out with concrete objects if necessary.

Skill Practice COMPUTING   Whole Group

To reinforce fluency with the +0, +1, and +2 facts and to demonstrate the Commutative Law, present exercises, orally and in writing, as students show the sums with their **Number Cubes.** Give exercises such as the following:

a. 2 + 1 = 3   **b.** 1 + 2 = 3   **c.** 2 + 2 = 4
d. 6 + 8 = 14   **e.** 8 + 6 = 14   **f.** 6 + 2 = 8
g. 2 + 6 = 8   **h.** 1 + 4 = 5   **i.** 4 + 1 = 5

2 Assign Student Pages 25

Pages 45–46 COMPUTING

Have students complete page 45 and the top of page 46 independently. Use the pages to assess whether students have mastered the facts reviewed in the previous lesson. Consider doing the word problems on page 46 through group discussion, acting out the problems if necessary.

As Students Finish

 Game   Have students play one of the **Addition Table Game** variations introduced in Lesson 2.1.

e Games *Addition Table Game*

e MathTools Have students use the **Addition Table** to explore the Commutative Law.

RESEARCH IN ACTION

"Children's tools for beginning understandings of addition and subtraction are the counting word list ("one, two, three, four, etc."), the ability to count objects, some indicating act (e.g., pointing, moving objects) tying words said and objects counted together (one at a time) and the count-cardinal knowledge that the last count word said tells how many objects there are in all. These tools are learned in the preschool years by many but not all children. . ."

Fuson, Karen. "Pre-K to Grade 2 Goals and Standards: Achieving 21st Century Mastery for All" in Clements, Douglas and J. Sarama eds. *Engaging Young Children in Mathematics: Standards for Early Childhood Mathematics Education.* Mahwah, New Jersey: Lawrence Erlbaum Associates, Publishers, 2004, pp. 122–123.

LESSON 2.2 The Commutative Law

Key Ideas

The Commutative Law states that numbers can be added in any order and the sum will always be the same. For example:

$5 + 2 = 7$ and $2 + 5 = 7$

Add.

1. $2 + 6 = 8$
2. $6 + 2 = 8$
3. $0 + 5 = 5$
4. $5 + 0 = 5$
5. $1 + 9 = 10$
6. $9 + 1 = 10$
7. $2 + 8 = 10$
8. $8 + 2 = 10$

9. $1 + 7 = 8$
10. $7 + 1 = 8$
11. $2 + 1 = 3$
12. $1 + 2 = 3$
13. $6 + 1 = 7$
14. $1 + 6 = 7$
15. $0 + 0 = 0$
16. $0 + 1 = 1$

Textbook This lesson is available in the *eTextbook*.

45

LESSON 2.2 • The Commutative Law

Add.

17. 5
    $+ 2$
    $\overline{7}$

18. 2
    $+ 5$
    $\overline{7}$

19. 2
    $+ 3$
    $\overline{5}$

20. 3
    $+ 2$
    $\overline{5}$

21. 7
    $+ 2$
    $\overline{9}$

22. 2
    $+ 7$
    $\overline{9}$

23. 2
    $+ 9$
    $\overline{11}$

24. 9
    $+ 2$
    $\overline{11}$

Solve. Be sure you understand what each problem asks.

25. Priya has 8 yellow fish and 2 red fish. How many fish does she have? __10__

26. Max has 8 blue fish and 2 yellow fish. How many blue fish does he have? __8__

27. DeShawn had 8 yellow fish in his large tank and 2 red fish in his small tank. Then he moved the 2 red fish to his large tank. Now how many fish does DeShawn have in his large tank? __10__

46   **Real Math** • Chapter 2 • Lesson 2

---

3 Reflect   10

Guided Discussion UNDERSTANDING   Whole Group

Display on the overhead projector the shaded Addition Table used in the previous lesson. Review the progress the class is making toward knowing all the facts with quick recall. Discuss that in Lesson 2.1 students agreed they know the +0, +1, and +2 facts, so then they were left with only 64 facts to learn. Because students now know the Commutative Law, the number of remaining facts has been reduced to 36 (8 doubles facts and $\frac{1}{2}$ of the remaining facts).

Cumulative Review: For cumulative review of previously learned skills, see page 55–56.

Family Involvement: Assign the *Practice, Reteach,* or *Enrichment* activities depending on the needs of your students.

Have students play an appropriate variation of the **Addition Table Game** with a helper.

Concept/Question Board: Have students look for additional examples using addition and post them on the Concept/Question Board.

Math Puzzler: Juan, Tara, and Chen are standing in a line. In what different ways can they line up? six different ways—Juan, Tara, Chen; Juan, Chen, Tara; Tara, Juan, Chen; Tara, Chen, Juan; Chen, Juan, Tara; Chen, Tara, Juan

4 Assess and Differentiate

 Assess Use *eAssess* to record and analyze evidence of student understanding.

A Gather Evidence

Use the Daily Class Assessment Records in *Assessment* or *eAssess* to record daily observations.

Informal Assessment
☑ **Guided Discussion**

Did the student **REASONING**
- ☐ provide a clear explanation?
- ☐ communicate reasons and strategies?
- ☐ choose appropriate strategies?
- ☐ argue logically?

Performance Assessment
☑ **Game**

Did the student **ENGAGING**
- ☐ pay attention to others' contributions?
- ☐ contribute information and ideas?
- ☐ improve on a strategy?
- ☐ reflect on and check the accuracy of his or her work?

B Summarize Findings

Analyze and summarize assessment data for each student. Determine which Assessment Follow-Up is appropriate for each student. Use the Student Assessment Record in *Assessment* or *eAssess* to update assessment records.

Assessment page T41

C Assessment Follow-Up • DIFFERENTIATE INSTRUCTION

Based on your observations, use these teaching strategies for assessment follow-up.

INTERVENTION

Review student performance on *Intervention* Lesson 2.A to see if students have mastered prerequisite skills for this lesson.

ENGLISH LEARNER

Review

Use Lesson 2.2 in *English Learner Support Guide* to review lesson concepts and vocabulary.

ENRICH

If . . . students are proficient in the lesson concepts,

Then . . . encourage them to work on the chapter projects or *Enrichment* Lesson 2.2.

Enrichment Lesson 2.2

PRACTICE

If . . . students would benefit from additional practice,

Then . . . assign *Practice* Lesson 2.2.

Practice Lesson 2.2

RETEACH

If . . . students are having difficulty understanding the Commutative Law,

Then . . . remind them that it is adding forward and backward to get the same sum.

Lesson Planner

OBJECTIVES
To continue reviewing the addition facts, focusing on the +10 and the corresponding +9 facts

NCTM STANDARDS

Number and Operations
- Developing and using strategies for addition
- Developing fluency with basic number combinations for addition
- Understanding the effects of adding whole numbers

Representation
Creating and using representations to organize, record, and communicate mathematical ideas

Problem Solving
- Solving problems that arise in mathematics and other contexts
- Applying and adapting a variety of appropriate strategies to solve problems

MATERIALS
- *Number Cubes
- Addition Crossing Game Mat
- Overhead transparency of the completed 10 + 10 Addition Table

TECHNOLOGY
- Ⓔ Presentation Lesson 2.3
- Ⓔ MathTools Addition Table

TEST PREP

Cumulative Review (Review)
Mental Math reviews the Commutative Law (Lesson 2.2).

+10 and +9 Addition Facts

Context of the Lesson This lesson reviews the +10 and +9 addition facts. Students often find the +10 facts easy to memorize, and the +9 facts can be remembered because their sums are 1 less than the related +10 facts. Students continue to use the Addition Table to monitor their progress in memorizing the addition facts. By using the Addition Table, students see relationships among the facts. Thus, if students forget a fact, they are likely to be able to recall it by relating the forgotten fact to a known fact.

See page 41B for Math Background for teachers for this lesson.

Planning for Learning ● DIFFERENTIATE INSTRUCTION

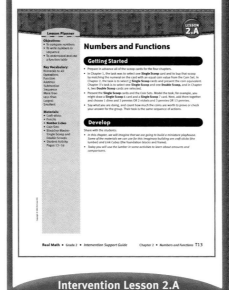

INTERVENTION
If . . . students lack the prerequisite skill of comparing numbers,

Then . . . teach *Intervention* Lesson 2.A.

Intervention Lesson 2.A

ENGLISH LEARNER
Preview

If . . . students need language support,

Then . . . use Lesson 2.3 in *English Learner Support Guide* to preview lesson concepts and vocabulary.

English Learner Lesson 2.3

ENRICH
If . . . students are proficient in the lesson concepts,

Then . . . emphasize exploring *eMathTools.*

PRACTICE
If . . . students would benefit from additional practice,

Then . . . extend Guided Discussion before assigning the student pages.

RETEACH
If . . . students are having difficulty understanding the +10 and +9 addition facts,

Then . . . extend Guided Discussion before assigning student pages.

Access Vocabulary
sum the answer to an addition problem; not the word *some*

Spanish Cognates
addition adición

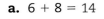

Mental Math 5

 Do an addition-fact drill focusing on the +0, +1, and +2 facts and demonstrating the Commutative Law. Students show answers with **Number Cubes.** Give exercises such as the following:

a. 6 + 8 = 14   **b.** 8 + 6 = 14   **c.** 3 + 1 = 4
d. 1 + 3 = 4   **e.** 5 + 1 = 6   **f.** 1 + 5 = 6
g. 4 + 2 = 6   **h.** 2 + 4 = 6   **i.** 8 + 2 = 10
j. 2 + 8 = 10   **k.** 8 + 0 = 8   **l.** 0 + 8 = 8

1 Develop 20

Tell Students In Today's Lesson They Will
learn the +10 and +9 facts.

Guided Discussion REASONING   Whole Group

Using the overhead transparency of the Addition Table that was shaded during the previous lessons, initiate a discussion on the facts students already know and have shaded on the table. Then tell students that they will soon be able to shade more facts—the +10 and +9 facts.

Explain to students that to add a number to 10, all they need to do is remember that numbers such as 17 simply mean 10 and 7, so 10 + 7 = 10 and 7, or 17. Point out that the +10 facts are easy to remember and that if students know the +10 facts, they can figure out the +9 facts as well. Allow students to explain why this is so. Possible answer: The +9 facts are 1 less than the corresponding +10 facts.

Remind students of the Commutative Law. For example, if students know 9 + 5, then they also know 5 + 9.

Skill Practice COMPUTING   Whole Group

 To reinforce fluency with the +10 and +9 facts and to evaluate student fluency, present exercises, orally and in writing, as students show the sums with their **Number Cubes.** Write the exercises one under the other so students are continually reminded of the relationships between the facts. Give exercises such as the following:

a. 3 + 10 = 13   **b.** 3 + 9 = 12
c. 10 + 5 = 15   **d.** 9 + 5 = 14
e. 7 + 10 = 17   **f.** 7 + 9 = 16
g. 10 + 6 = 16   **h.** 9 + 6 = 15

Skill and Strategy Building ENGAGING   Whole Group

Game   Addition Crossing Game

Demonstrate the **Addition Crossing Game** on page 48. Students will play as they finish page 47. Rules for play are on page 48 or on the game mat.

2 Assign Student Pages 25

Pages 47–48 UNDERSTANDING

Have students complete page 47 independently. Then have students play the **Addition Crossing Game** on page 48. Students may also use the game mat to play the game multiple times.

Monitoring Student Progress

If . . . students have difficulty with the +9 facts,	**Then . . .** work through several examples in which you combine a set of 10 objects with a set of fewer objects and determine the sum, and then remove one object from the set of 10 and determine the sum.

As Students Finish

Game   **Addition Crossing Game** Have students play the game in pairs.

 MathTools   Have students use the **Addition Table** tool to visualize the relationships between the +10 and +9 facts.

LESSON 2.3 +10 and +9 Addition Facts

Key Ideas

When you add 10 and a number, the sum is 10 and that number.

$10 + 7 = 17$

The sum of 9 and a number is 1 less than the sum of 10 and that number.

$9 + 7 = 16$

Add to find the sums.

1. $2 + 10 = 12$
2. $2 + 9 = 11$
3. $4 + 10 = 14$
4. $5 + 9 = 14$
5. $6 + 10 = 16$
6. $10 + 6 = 16$

7. $9 + 6 = 15$
8. $9 + 1 = 10$
9. $8 + 2 = 10$
10. $6 + 2 = 8$
11. $9 + 0 = 9$
12. $6 + 1 = 7$

13. $\begin{array}{r} 9 \\ + 10 \\ \hline 19 \end{array}$
14. $\begin{array}{r} 9 \\ + 9 \\ \hline 18 \end{array}$
15. $\begin{array}{r} 8 \\ + 10 \\ \hline 18 \end{array}$
16. $\begin{array}{r} 8 \\ + 9 \\ \hline 17 \end{array}$

eTextbook This lesson is available in the *eTextbook.*   47

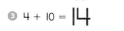 **Game**

Addition and Strategies Practice

Addition Crossing

Players: Two

Materials:
- *Number Cubes:* two 0–5 (red) and two 5–10 (blue)
- A different color of crayon for each player

HOW TO PLAY

❶ Players roll a 0–5 *Number Cube.* The person who rolls the greater number chooses his or her color of crayon and is followed by the second player.

❷ Take turns rolling any two cubes. Color either square that shows the sum of the addition fact you rolled. (For example, if you roll 3 and 8, you can color the square showing the sum of $3 + 8$ or $8 + 3$.)

❸ The first player to make a continuous path from one side to the opposite side is the winner. Your path can go up, down, forward, backward, or diagonally as long as all the squares are touching each other.

+	0	1	2	3	4	5	6	7	8	9	10
0	0	1	2	3	4	5	6	7	8	9	10
1	1	2	3	4	5	6	7	8	9	10	11
2	2	3	4	5	6	7	8	9	10	11	12
3	3	4	5	6	7	8	9	10	11	12	13
4	4	5	6	7	8	9	10	11	12	13	14
5	5	6	7	8	9	10	11	12	13	14	15
6	6	7	8	9	10	11	12	13	14	15	16
7	7	8	9	10	11	12	13	14	15	16	17
8	8	9	10	11	12	13	14	15	16	17	18
9	9	10	11	12	13	14	15	16	17	18	19
10	10	11	12	13	14	15	16	17	18	19	20

48   **Real Math • Chapter 2 • Lesson 3**

---

③ Reflect   10

Guided Discussion UNDERSTANDING   Whole Group

As in the previous lessons, display on the overhead projector the shaded Addition Table. Ask students if they feel the class knows the +10 and the corresponding +9 facts. If students feel confident, give a brief quiz on these facts. If most students show proficiency, shade the +10 and +9 facts. The table should now look like this:

+	0	1	2	3	4	5	6	7	8	9	10
0	0	1	2	3	4	5	6	7	8	9	10
1	1	2	3	4	5	6	7	8	9	10	11
2	2	3	4	5	6	7	8	9	10	11	12
3	3	4	5	6	7	8	9	10	11	12	13
4	4	5	6	7	8	9	10	11	12	13	14
5	5	6	7	8	9	10	11	12	13	14	15
6	6	7	8	9	10	11	12	13	14	15	16
7	7	8	9	10	11	12	13	14	15	16	17
8	8	9	10	11	12	13	14	15	16	17	18
9	9	10	11	12	13	14	15	16	17	18	19
10	10	11	12	13	14	15	16	17	18	19	20

 Cumulative Review: For cumulative review of previously learned skills, see page 55–56.

 Family Involvement: Assign the *Practice, Reteach,* or *Enrichment* activities depending on the needs of your students.

Have students play the **Addition Crossing Game** with a helper.

 Concept/Question Board: Have students look for additional examples using addition and post them on the Concept/Question Board.

 Math Puzzler: Mr. Ito's cat weighs 11 pounds. The cat used to weigh 9 pounds. How much weight did the cat gain?
2 pounds

Assess and Differentiate

 Assess Use **eAssess** to record and analyze evidence of student understanding.

A Gather Evidence

Use the Daily Class Assessment Records in **Assessment** or **eAssess** to record daily observations.

Informal Assessment
☑ **Mental Math**

Did the student **COMPUTING**
❑ respond accurately?
❑ respond quickly?
❑ respond with confidence?
❑ self-correct?

Informal Assessment
☑ **Concept/Question Board**

Did the student **APPLYING**
❑ apply learning in new situations?
❑ contribute concepts?
❑ contribute answers?
❑ connect mathematics to real-world situations?

B Summarize Findings

Analyze and summarize assessment data for each student. Determine which Assessment Follow-Up is appropriate for each student. Use the Student Assessment Record in **Assessment** or **eAssess** to update assessment records.

Assessment page T41

C Assessment Follow-Up • DIFFERENTIATE INSTRUCTION

Based on your observations, use these teaching strategies for assessment follow-up.

INTERVENTION	**ENRICH**	**PRACTICE**	**RETEACH**
Review student performance on **Intervention** Lesson 2.A to see if students have mastered prerequisite skills for this lesson.	**If . . .** students are proficient in the lesson concepts,	**If . . .** students would benefit from additional practice,	**If . . .** students are having difficulty understanding the +10 and +9 facts,
	Then . . . encourage them to work on the chapter projects or **Enrichment** Lesson 2.3.	**Then . . .** assign **Practice** Lesson 2.3.	**Then . . .** have them make an Addition Table with rows from 1 to 10 but columns for only 9 and 10.

ENGLISH LEARNER

Review

Use Lesson 2.3 in **English Learner Support Guide** to review lesson concepts and vocabulary.

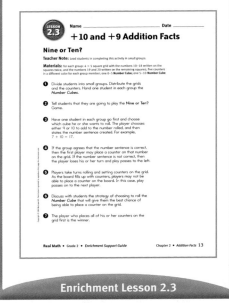

Enrichment Lesson 2.3

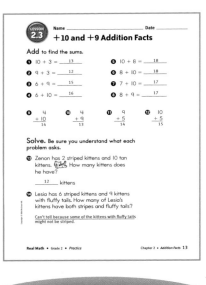

Practice Lesson 2.3

Lesson Planner

OBJECTIVES
To continue reviewing the addition facts, paying special attention to the doubles facts

NCTM STANDARDS
Number and Operations
- Developing and using strategies for addition
- Developing fluency with basic number combinations for addition
- Understanding the effects of adding whole numbers

Representation
Creating and using representations to organize, record, and communicate mathematical ideas

Communication
Communicating mathematical thinking coherently and clearly to peers, teachers, and others

MATERIALS
- *Number Cubes
- Overhead transparency of the completed 10 + 10 Addition Table
- One 3 × 5 index card per student

TECHNOLOGY
- e Presentation Lesson 2.4
- e MathTools Addition Table
- Building Blocks Number Snapshots 8

TEST PREP
Cumulative Review
Mental Math reviews the +10 and +9 facts (Lesson 2.3).

Writing + Math
Journal

Doubles

Context of the Lesson This lesson reviews the doubles facts, which are important because they are relatively easy for students to memorize because they each have only one addend to remember. After they are memorized, they can be used to recall the near-doubles facts, which will be covered in the next lesson.

See page 41B for Math Background for teachers for this lesson.

Planning for Learning ● DIFFERENTIATE INSTRUCTION

INTERVENTION
If . . . students lack the prerequisite skill of writing numbers in sequence,

Then . . . teach *Intervention* Lesson 2.B.

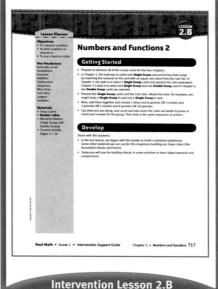

Intervention Lesson 2.B

ENGLISH LEARNER
Preview
If . . . students need language support,

Then . . . use Lesson 2.4 in *English Learner Support Guide* to preview lesson concepts and vocabulary.

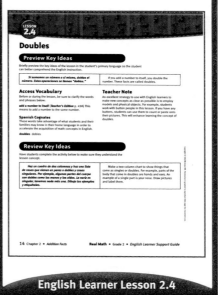

English Learner Lesson 2.4

ENRICH
If . . . students are proficient in the lesson concepts,

Then . . . emphasize additional game time.

PRACTICE
If . . . students would benefit from additional practice,

Then . . . extend Skill Building before assigning the student pages.

RETEACH
If . . . students are having difficulty understanding the doubles facts,

Then . . . extend Guided Discussion before assigning the student pages.

Access Vocabulary
add a number to itself This means to add a number to the same number.

Spanish Cognates
doubles dobles

---

*Manipulative Kit Item

Mental Math 5

Do a basic addition-fact drill focusing on the +10 and related +9 facts. Students show answers with **Number Cubes.** Give exercises such as the following:

a. 5 + 10 = 15   **b.** 5 + 9 = 14   **c.** 10 + 5 = 15
d. 9 + 5 = 14   **e.** 3 + 10 = 13 **f.** 3 + 9 = 12
g. 9 + 3 = 12   **h.** 6 + 10 = 16 **i.** 10 + 6 = 16
j. 9 + 6 = 15   **k.** 6 + 8 = 14   **l.** 8 + 6 = 14

1 Develop 25

Tell Students In Today's Lesson They Will
learn the doubles facts.

Guided Discussion UNDERSTANDING   Whole Group

Use the shaded overhead transparency of the completed Addition Table to review the facts students have learned in the previous lessons. Then show students where the doubles facts are located on the Addition Table. Ask questions such as the following:

- **What do you notice about the doubles facts?** They make a diagonal line from the top left to the bottom right of the table.
- **Why do you think they are called *doubles*?** Each number is added to itself, or doubled.

Skill Building ENGAGING   Small Group

On a 3 × 5 index card, have students draw a person with buttons down the front of his or her clothes. On the back of the card, have students draw the back of the same person with the same number of buttons down his or her back. Each student should use a different number of buttons on his or her person (between 0 and 10 per side). Have students work in small groups, turning up the cards and deciding how many buttons there are altogether on each drawing.

Skill and Strategy Building APPLYING   Whole Group

 Doubles Game

Introduce and demonstrate the **Doubles Game** on page 50 by playing a few rounds with a student in front of the class. Students will play in pairs or small groups as they finish the student pages. Note that players can score more than 1 point per turn. For example, if a player rolls 3, 5, 7, and 7, he or she can get 1 point by saying 14 (7 + 7). If a player rolls 5, 5, 5, and 8, he or she can get 3 points (5 + 5 three times).

2 Assign Student Pages 20

Pages 49–50 APPLYING

Have students complete page 49 individually, and then play the **Doubles Game** on page 50 in pairs or small groups.

As Students Finish

 Doubles Game

 MathTools Have students use the **Addition Table** tool to find the doubles facts.

Building Blocks Have students play **Number Snapshots 8.**

LESSON 2.4 Doubles

Key Ideas

If you add a number to itself, you double the number. These facts are called the doubles.

Add.

❶ 8 + 8 = 16

❸ 4 + 4 = 8

❷ 9 + 9 = 18

❹ 6 + 6 = 12

❺
$$\begin{array}{r} 5 \\ + 5 \\ \hline 10 \end{array}$$

❻
$$\begin{array}{r} 10 \\ + 10 \\ \hline 20 \end{array}$$

❼
$$\begin{array}{r} 1 \\ + 1 \\ \hline 2 \end{array}$$

❽
$$\begin{array}{r} 0 \\ + 0 \\ \hline 0 \end{array}$$

The coats on the Button people have the same number of buttons in back as they do in front. How many buttons are on each coat? Write a number sentence to show how many.

❾

2 + 2 = 4

❿

3 + 3 = 6

📖 **Textbook** This lesson is available in the *eTextbook*.

49

Student Page

Game

Addition Practice

Doubles Game

Players: Two or three

Materials:
Number Cubes:
two 0–5 (red) and two 5–10 (blue)

HOW TO PLAY

❶ Each player rolls two red and two blue *Number Cubes.*

❷ If there are any doubles showing, the player gets 1 point for each sum he or she can correctly name.

❸ The first player to get 5 points wins.

Writing + Math **Journal**

What are the most points you could earn in one turn? Is it enough to win the game in one turn?

50   **Real Math • Chapter 2 • Lesson 4**

---

3 Reflect   10

Guided Discussion UNDERSTANDING   Whole Group

Display on the overhead projector the shaded Addition Table used in previous lessons. Remind students that they need to learn all of the 121 facts on the Addition Table and that they have already learned quite a few—the ones that have been shaded.

Show the doubles facts on the Addition Table as the diagonal line that runs from the upper left to the lower right. Ask students if they feel they know these facts well enough to be tested on them. If students feel confident, give a brief quiz on these facts. If most students show proficiency, shade the doubles facts on the Addition Table transparency. The table should now look like this:

+	0	1	2	3	4	5	6	7	8	9	10
0	0	1	2	3	4	5	6	7	8	9	10
1	1	2	3	4	5	6	7	8	9	10	11
2	2	3	4	5	6	7	8	9	10	11	12
3	3	4	5	6	7	8	9	10	11	12	13
4	4	5	6	7	8	9	10	11	12	13	14
5	5	6	7	8	9	10	11	12	13	14	15
6	6	7	8	9	10	11	12	13	14	15	16
7	7	8	9	10	11	12	13	14	15	16	17
8	8	9	10	11	12	13	14	15	16	17	18
9	9	10	11	12	13	14	15	16	17	18	19
10	10	11	12	13	14	15	16	17	18	19	20

Writing + Math **Journal** ✓

A student could win the game in one turn by rolling four 5s. Although there are only four cubes—two red and two blue—there are actually six doubles combinations: the two red 5s, the two blue 5s, the first red 5 and the first blue 5, the second red 5 and the first blue 5, the first red 5 and the second blue 5, and the second red 5 and the second blue 5.

Review **Cumulative Review:** For cumulative review of previously learned skills, see page 55–56.

Family Involvement: Assign the *Practice, Reteach,* or *Enrichment* activities depending on the needs of your students.

Concept/Question Board: Encourage students to continue to post questions, answers, and examples on the Concept/Question Board.

Math Puzzler: What doubles fact has a sum with digits that add up to 3? 6 + 6 = 12

Assess and Differentiate

 Assess Use **eAssess** to record and analyze evidence of student understanding.

A Gather Evidence

Use the Daily Class Assessment Records in **Assessment** or **eAssess** to record daily observations.

Performance Assessment
☑**Game**

Did the student **ENGAGING**
❑ pay attention to others' contributions?
❑ contribute information and ideas?
❑ improve on a strategy?
❑ reflect on and check the accuracy of his or her work?

Portfolio Assessment
☑**Journal**

Did the student **REASONING**
❑ provide a clear explanation?
❑ communicate reasons and strategies?
❑ choose appropriate strategies?
❑ argue logically?

B Summarize Findings

Analyze and summarize assessment data for each student. Determine which Assessment Follow-Up is appropriate for each student. Use the Student Assessment Record in **Assessment** or **eAssess** to update assessment records.

Assessment page T41

C Assessment Follow-Up • DIFFERENTIATE INSTRUCTION

Based on your observations, use these teaching strategies for assessment follow-up.

INTERVENTION	ENRICH	PRACTICE	RETEACH
Review student performance on **Intervention** Lesson 2.B to see if students have mastered prerequisite skills for this lesson.	**If . . .** students are proficient in the lesson concepts, **Then . . .** encourage them to work on the chapter projects or **Enrichment** Lesson 2.4.	**If . . .** students would benefit from additional practice, **Then . . .** assign **Practice** Lesson 2.4.	**If . . .** students are having difficulty memorizing the doubles facts, **Then . . .** have them model 1 + 1, 2 + 2, and so on with **Number Cubes**.

ENGLISH LEARNER
Review

Use Lesson 2.4 in **English Learner Support Guide** to review lesson concepts and vocabulary.

LESSON 2.4
Name ____ Date ____
Doubles

Doubles Bingo
Teacher Note: Lead students in completing this activity in small groups.

Materials: for each group: two 0–5 **Number Cubes**; two 5–10 **Number Cubes**; a 3 × 3 square grid for each student; nine counters per student

❶ Divide students into small groups. Distribute the counters, **Number Cubes**, and grids.

❷ Tell students they are going to play Doubles Bingo. Refer them to the grid. Have students write a double (even) number from 2 to 20 in each box. They may not repeat a number. (Only one double will be missing from each grid.)

❸ Have one student from each group go first. The first player chooses which two cubes to roll. Then the player finds the sum of numbers rolled and states the double of that sum.

❹ If the group agrees that the doubled sum is correct, the player may place a counter on that number on his or her grid. If the doubled sum is incorrect, or if it does not appear on the grid, play passes to the person on the left.

❺ The first player to cover all nine numbers wins.

14 Chapter 2 • Addition Facts   **Real Math** • Grade 2 • Enrichment Support Guide

Enrichment Lesson 2.4

LESSON 2.4
Name ____ Date ____
Doubles

Add.

❶ 5 + 5 = __10__   ❷ 8 + 8 = __16__   ❸ 10 + 10 = __20__
❹ 7 + 7 = __14__   ❺ 2 + 2 = __4__   ❻ 9 + 9 = __18__
❼ 6 + 6 = __12__   ❽ 3 + 3 = __6__   ❾ 0 + 0 = __0__
❿ 4 + 4 = __8__   ⓫ 1 + 1 = __2__   ⓬ 7 + 7 = __14__

Solve these problems.

⓭ Rodrigo had 4 crayons in his desk at school. He brought 4 more crayons from home. How many crayons does he have altogether?
__8__ crayons

⓮ Mia carried 8 jump ropes to the playground for recess. Justin also carried 8 jump ropes to the playground. How many jump ropes were there altogether?
__16__ jump ropes

⓯ Orlando won 2 first place ribbons and 2 third place ribbons during the school field day. How many ribbons did he win altogether?
__4__ ribbons

14 Chapter 2 • Addition Facts   **Real Math** • Grade 2 • Practice

Practice Lesson 2.4

OBJECTIVES

To continue reviewing the addition facts, paying special attention to the facts that are 1 more than the doubles facts

NCTM STANDARDS

Number and Operations
- Developing and using strategies for addition
- Developing fluency with basic number combinations for addition
- Understanding the effects of adding whole numbers

Representation
Creating and using representations to organize, record, and communicate mathematical ideas

Problem Solving
- Solving problems that arise in mathematics and other contexts
- Applying and adapting a variety of appropriate strategies to solve problems

MATERIALS

- *Number Cubes
- Frog Pond Game Mat
- Overhead transparency of the completed 10 + 10 Addition Table

TECHNOLOGY

- Ⓔ **Presentation** Lesson 2.5
- Ⓔ **MathTools** Addition Table
- **Building Blocks** Eggcellent: Addition Choice

TEST PREP

Cumulative Review
Mental Math reviews addition facts (Lessons 2.1–2.4).

Looking Ahead

Lesson 2.6 will require a cardboard box with slots cut in the sides to be used as a function machine.

*Manipulative Kit Item

Near Doubles

Context of the Lesson This lesson reviews the near-doubles facts. By relating the already memorized doubles facts with the facts that are 1 more, students see that the addition facts are part of an organized system, not isolated, and are thus easy to memorize.

See page 41B for Math Background for teachers for this lesson.

Planning for Learning ● DIFFERENTIATE INSTRUCTION

INTERVENTION

If . . . students lack the prerequisite skill of writing numbers in sequence,

Then . . . teach *Intervention* Lesson 2.B.

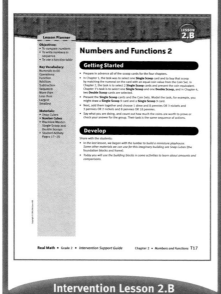

Intervention Lesson 2.B

ENGLISH LEARNER

Preview

If . . . students need language support,

Then . . . use Lesson 2.5 in *English Learner Support Guide* to preview lesson concepts and vocabulary.

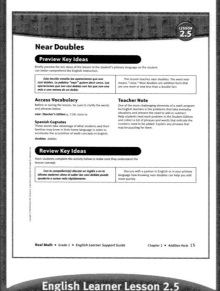

English Learner Lesson 2.5

ENRICH

If . . . students are proficient in the lesson concepts,

Then . . . emphasize game variations.

PRACTICE

If . . . students would benefit from additional practice,

Then . . . extend Guided Discussion before assigning the student pages.

RETEACH

If . . . students are having difficulty understanding near-doubles facts,

Then . . . extend Guided Discussion before assigning the student pages.

Access Vocabulary
near close to

Spanish Cognates
doubles dobles

Mental Math 5

 Review Do an addition-fact drill, concentrating on facts that have been shaded on the Addition Table. Have students use **Number Cubes** to show their answers. Give exercises such as the following:

a. 8 + 2 = 10	**b.** 7 + 2 = 9	**c.** 4 + 4 = 8
d. 8 + 8 = 16	**e.** 0 + 8 = 8	**f.** 10 + 1 = 11
g. 7 + 7 = 14	**h.** 9 + 2 = 11	**i.** 2 + 4 = 6
j. 1 + 8 = 9	**k.** 6 + 8 = 14	**l.** 8 + 6 = 14

1 Develop 20

Tell Students In Today's Lesson They Will
learn the near-doubles facts.

Guided Discussion REASONING — Whole Group

Using the shaded overhead transparency of the Addition Table from the previous lessons, initiate a brief discussion in which you point out that if students know that 6 + 6 = 12, then they also know that 6 + 7 = 13. Write these statements on the board.

Call on students to verbalize why these facts are related and to explain their thinking. For example, *If 6 + 6 = 12, then 6 + 7 must be 1 more than 12, or 13.*

Repeat for several doubles facts. Tell students that if they have memorized the doubles facts, then they can easily figure out facts that are 1 more or 1 less than a doubles fact.

Skill Practice COMPUTING — Whole Group

 To reinforce fluency with the near doubles and to evaluate student fluency, present exercises, one at a time, orally and in writing, as students show the sums with their **Number Cubes.** Write the exercises one under the other so students are continually reminded of the relationships between the facts. Give exercises such as the following:

a. 7 + 7 = 14	**b.** 7 + 8 = 15
c. 8 + 7 = 15	**d.** 6 + 6 = 12
e. 7 + 6 = 13	**f.** 6 + 7 = 13

Skill and Strategy Building ENGAGING — Whole Group

 Frog Pond Game

Demonstrate this game which practices basic addition facts. Required materials and rules of play are listed on the game mat. Students will play in pairs as they finish the student pages.

2 Assign Student Pages 25

Pages 51–52  UNDERSTANDING

Have students complete pages 51–52. If necessary, complete page 52 as a group, acting out the problems.

As Students Finish

Game Have students play the **Frog Pond Game** in pairs.

e MathTools Have students use the **Addition Table** to explore the relationships between the doubles and near-doubles facts.

Building Blocks *Eggcellent: Addition Choice*

LESSON 2.5 Near Doubles

Key Ideas

Near doubles are addition facts that are 1 more than a doubles fact. To find 6 + 7, you can think:
6 + 6 = 12, so 6 + 7 is 1 more than 12.
6 + 7 = 13

Add.

1. 6 + 7 = 13
2. 8 + 7 = 15
3. 2 + 3 = 5
4. 5 + 6 = 11
5. 7 + 8 = 15
6. 9 + 8 = 17
7. 4 + 3 = 7
8. 3 + 2 = 5

9. 6 + 5 = 11
10. 2 + 1 = 3
11. 4 + 5 = 9
12. 3 + 7 = 10
13. 7 + 3 = 10
14. 8 + 1 = 9
15. 9 + 1 = 10
16. 7 + 4 = 11

17. 4
    + 7
    ――
     11

18. 6
    + 9
    ――
     15

19. 5
    + 7
    ――
     12

20. 9
    + 6
    ――
     15

Textbook This lesson is available in the *eTextbook*.

51

LESSON 2.5 • Near Doubles

Answer these questions.

21. Dakota has 5 fish. Ryan has 1 more fish than Dakota. How many fish do they have? __11__

22. Cosmo and Chewie each had 7 dog toys. Then Cosmo lost 1 toy. Now how many toys do they have? __13__

23. Josh and Laura each had 5 hermit crabs. Then Laura got 1 more hermit crab. Now how many hermit crabs does Laura have? __6__

24. Juanita is 8 years old. She bought 8 treat sticks for her canaries. She has used 7 of them. How many treat sticks did Juanita buy? __8__

Real Math • Chapter 2 • Lesson 5
52

---

3 Reflect
10

Guided Discussion UNDERSTANDING
Whole Group

Display on the overhead projector the shaded Addition Table used in previous lessons. Review the progress the class is making toward knowing all the facts with quick recall.

Ask students if they are ready to be quizzed on the "hardest facts" (8 + 6 and 6 + 8) and the near-doubles facts. If so, do a quick-response exercise, or give a brief written quiz. If the class is mostly proficient, shade 8 + 6 and 6 + 8 and the near-doubles facts. The table should now look like this:

+	0	1	2	3	4	5	6	7	8	9	10
0	0	1	2	3	4	5	6	7	8	9	10
1	1	2	3	4	5	6	7	8	9	10	11
2	2	3	4	5	6	7	8	9	10	11	12
3	3	4	5	6	7	8	9	10	11	12	13
4	4	5	6	7	8	9	10	11	12	13	14
5	5	6	7	8	9	10	11	12	13	14	15
6	6	7	8	9	10	11	12	13	14	15	16
7	7	8	9	10	11	12	13	14	15	16	17
8	8	9	10	11	12	13	14	15	16	17	18
9	9	10	11	12	13	14	15	16	17	18	19
10	10	11	12	13	14	15	16	17	18	19	20

Help students see that by shading these facts, only 18 facts are not yet shaded. However, because of the Commutative Law, there are really only 9 facts left for students to memorize.

Cumulative Review: For cumulative review of previously learned skills, see page 55–56.

Family Involvement: Assign the *Practice, Reteach,* or *Enrichment* activities depending on the needs of your students.

Concept/Question Board: Encourage students to continue to post questions, answers, and examples on the Concept/Question Board.

Math Puzzler: Mr. Eng asked Mr. Muddle, "If I buy some bushes for my yard now, and I buy 13 more in the fall, how many will I have bought altogether?" Mr. Muddle said, "I don't think I can answer that question." Why can't he answer? He needs to know how many bushes Mr. Eng is going to buy now.

4 Assess and Differentiate

 e Assess Use *eAssess* to record and analyze evidence of student understanding.

A Gather Evidence

Use the Daily Class Assessment Records in *Assessment* or *eAssess* to record daily observations.

Informal Assessment
☑ **Guided Discussion**

Did the student **REASONING**
- ❑ provide a clear explanation?
- ❑ communicate reasons and strategies?
- ❑ choose appropriate strategies?
- ❑ argue logically?

Informal Assessment
☑ **Student Pages**

Did the student **UNDERSTANDING**
- ❑ make important observations?
- ❑ extend or generalize learning?
- ❑ provide insightful answers?
- ❑ pose insightful questions?

B Summarize Findings

Analyze and summarize assessment data for each student. Determine which Assessment Follow-Up is appropriate for each student. Use the Student Assessment Record in *Assessment* or *eAssess* to update assessment records.

Assessment page T41

C Assessment Follow-Up ● DIFFERENTIATE INSTRUCTION

Based on your observations, use these teaching strategies for assessment follow-up.

INTERVENTION	ENRICH	PRACTICE	RETEACH
Review student performance on *Intervention* Lesson 2.B to see if students have mastered prerequisite skills for this lesson.	**If . . .** students are proficient in the lesson concepts, **Then . . .** encourage them to work on the chapter projects or *Enrichment* Lesson 2.5.	**If . . .** students would benefit from additional practice, **Then . . .** assign *Practice* Lesson 2.5.	**If . . .** students are having difficulty understanding near-doubles facts, **Then . . .** assign *Reteach* Lesson 2.5.

ENGLISH LEARNER
Review

Use Lesson 2.5 in *English Learner Support Guide* to review lesson concepts and vocabulary.

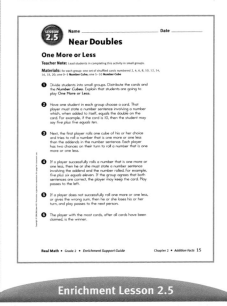

Enrichment Lesson 2.5

Practice Lesson 2.5

Reteach Lesson 2.5

Exploring Problem Solving

Objectives
- To explore the Make a Table and Act It Out strategies
- To use addition facts
- To interpret numerical results so that an answer is reasonable
- To explore ways to present solutions clearly

Materials
Play money (twenty-five $1 bills for each group)

Context of the Lesson
Reasoning and problem solving are prevalent in every **Real Math** lesson. This lesson and other special problem-solving lessons allow more time for students to share and compare their strategies. The lesson also provides additional opportunities for students to use the addition skills they have been working on in previous lessons.

1 Develop 5

Tell Students In Today's Lesson They Will
solve a problem about saving money to buy a cage for a pet.

Guided Discussion

Have students look at the illustration on top of page 53. Read this problem to students:

For her birthday, Cindy received a pet hamster in a small cage. She wants to buy a bigger cage with a wheel, a tower, and some tunnels for her new pet. She saw the cage she wants at the pet store. It costs $20. Cindy already has $3, and she gets $4 each week for allowance. She is going to save all of her allowance each week. She is not going to spend any until she has enough money to buy the cage. In how many weeks will she be able to buy the cage?

Have students look at the top of page 53, and ask the following questions:

- **How much does the cage cost?** $20
- **How much money does Cindy have?** $3
- **Is that enough to buy the cage? Why or why not?** no, because $3 is less than $20
- **How much can she save each week?** $4
- **What is the problem asking you to find?** how long it will take her to save enough money to buy the cage

Exploring Problem Solving

Name _____ Date _____

Listen to the problem.

Cindy has $3.

She saves $4 each week.

In how many weeks will she have enough money to buy the cage?

Bianca is making a table to solve the problem.

$3	first week $7			

Textbook This lesson is available in the *eTextbook*. 53

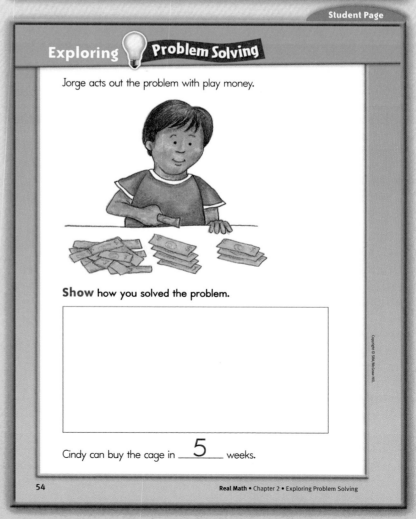

Exploring Problem Solving

Jorge acts out the problem with play money.

Show how you solved the problem.

Cindy can buy the cage in ___5___ weeks.

54 **Real Math • Chapter 2 • Exploring Problem Solving**

Using Student Pages

Analyzing Sample Solution 1: Make a Table

Have students look at the picture on page 53 of Bianca solving the problem. Ask questions about the strategy, such as the following:

- **How is Bianca trying to solve this problem?** She is using a table to keep track of how many times she has added $4.
- **Why do you think Bianca wrote the number 3 in the first box of her table?** to show how much money Cindy already has
- **Why do you think Bianca wrote the number 7 in the second box?** to show how much Cindy will have in one week, after she saves $4
- **What number do you think Bianca will write in the next box?** 11, to show how much Cindy will have in another week
- **What does Bianca need to do to keep track of how long Cindy has been saving?** use headings over the boxes to show how many weeks have gone by
- **How can Bianca use this method to find the answer to the problem?** She can continue to add $4 until the amount reaches $20. Then she can count how many weeks it took.

Analyzing Sample Solution 2: Act It Out

Tell students that Jorge is using a different strategy to try to solve the problem. Have students look at the picture of Jorge's approach on page 54. Ask questions such as the following:

- **Why do you think Jorge made a stack of three $1 bills?** to show how much money Cindy started with
- **Why do you think Jorge is making a stack of four $1 bills?** to show how much Cindy will save the first week
- **How can Jorge keep track of how many weeks go by?** He can make labels, or he can count the number of piles of $4 he has.
- **How can Jorge use his method to find the answer to the problem?** He can keep adding $4 until he has reached $20. Then he can count how many weeks it took.
- **How will you work on this problem?** Allow students to share what they like about Bianca's and Jorge's strategies and what they would do differently.

Sample Solutions Strategies

Students might use one or more of the following strategies instead of or in conjunction with the strategies presented on student pages 53 and 54.

Draw a Picture

Students may draw pictures of dollar bills to keep track of Cindy's savings.

Using Operations/Make a List

Students may recall addition facts to list Cindy's accumulating money. To find the larger sums, they may count on their fingers or use a number line, keeping track of how many times they add $4.

$3 + 4 = 7; 7 + 4 = 11; 11 + 4 = 15; 15 + 4 = 19; 19 + 4 = 23$

Skill Building

Have students work on the problem individually or in pairs. They may use Bianca's strategy, Jorge's strategy, or one of their own. Provide support as needed, remembering to suggest approaches rather than showing them the answer. Remind students to check their answers.

Extension

For students who finish early, you may present similar problems with different numbers. For example,

The cage costs $20. Cindy has $7 and saves $4 each week.
4 weeks

The cage costs $32. Cindy has $5 and saves $7 each week.
4 weeks

 **3** **Reflect** 15

 **Knowledge Age Skills**

Problem Formulation, Planning, and Strategizing Ask students to share their solutions and strategies. In discussion, bring out the following points:

- When you work on a problem, it is important to think about what the numbers mean—how they fit with what is going on in the problem. If Cindy keeps adding $4 a week, she will never get exactly $20. If she stops after 4 weeks, she will have only $19, which is not enough to buy the cage. She must save for 5 weeks to have enough to buy the cage, even though that will give her more than the cost of the cage.
- It is important to organize your work so you can keep track of the steps you take and the different parts of the problem.
- Different people might prefer to use different strategies.

4 **Assess** 15

When evaluating student work, focus not only on the correctness of the answer but also on whether the student thought rationally about the problem. Questions to consider include the following:

- Did the student understand the problem?
- Did the student understand the Sample Solutions Strategies?
- Was the student able to explain his or her strategy?

Cumulative Review

Assign Pages 55–56

Use the Cumulative Review as a review of concepts and skills that students have previously learned.

Here are different ways that you can assign these problems to your students as they work through the chapter:

- With some of the lessons in the chapter, assign a set of cumulative review problems to be completed as practice or for homework.
  Lesson 2.1—Problems 1–3
  Lesson 2.2—Problems 4–13
  Lesson 2.3—Problems 14–15
  Lesson 2.4—Problem 16
  Lesson 2.5—Problems 17–18
- At any point during the chapter, assign part or all of the cumulative review problems to be completed as practice or for homework.

Cumulative Review

Problems 1–3 review place value and money, Lesson 1.5.

Problems 4–13 review addition and the Commutative Law, Lesson 2.2.

Problems 14–15 review counting on and counting back in number sentences and word problems, Lesson 1.8.

Problem 16 reviews numbers in the 100 Table, Lesson 1.9.

Problems 17–18 review counting on and counting back and writing numbers, Lesson 1.1.

Monitoring Student Progress

If . . . students miss more than one problem in a section,

Then . . . refer to the indicated lesson for remediation suggestions.

Cumulative Review

Name _____ Date _____

Place Value and Money Lesson 1.5

How much money? Write the answers.

1. $5
2. $20
3. $10

The Commutative Law Lesson 2.2

Complete these exercises.

4. $9 + 2 = 11$ 5. $2 + 9 = 11$ 6. $1 + 4 = 5$
7. $4 + 1 = 5$ 8. $2 + 6 = 8$ 9. $6 + 2 = 8$

10. $\begin{array}{r} 8 \\ + 5 \\ \hline 13 \end{array}$ 11. $\begin{array}{r} 5 \\ + 8 \\ \hline 13 \end{array}$ 12. $\begin{array}{r} 4 \\ + 9 \\ \hline 13 \end{array}$ 13. $\begin{array}{r} 9 \\ + 4 \\ \hline 13 \end{array}$

Counting Applications Lesson 1.8

Solve these problems.

14. Katie is 3 centimeters taller than Ann. Ann is 88 centimeters tall. How tall is Katie? __91 cm__

15. Jamal had $80. He bought a present for his niece for $2. Then he earned $3. How much money does Jamal have now? __$81__

 Textbook This lesson is available in the *eTextbook*.   55

Student Page

Cumulative Review

Comparing Numbers Lesson 1.9

Fill in the blanks on this table.

16.

1	2	3	4	5	6	7	8	9	10
11	12	13	14	15	16	17	18	19	20
21	22	23	24	25	26	27	28	29	30
31	32	33	34	35	36	37	38	39	40
41	42	43	44	45	46	47	48	49	50
51	52	53	54	55	56	57	58	59	60
61	62	63	64	65	66	67	68	69	70
71	72	73	74	75	76	77	78	79	80
81	82	83	84	85	86	87	88	89	90
91	92	93	94	95	96	97	98	99	100

Counting and Writing Numbers Lesson 1.1

Count on or count back.
Fill in the missing numbers.

17.

31	30	29	28	27	26	25	24

18.

12	13	14	15	16	17	18	19

Individual Oral Assessment

Purpose of the Test

The Individual Oral Assessment is designed to measure students' growing knowledge of chapter concepts. It is administered individually to each student, and it requires oral responses from each student. The test takes about five minutes to complete. See **Assessment** for detailed instructions for administering and interpreting the test, and record students' answers on the Student Assessment Recording Sheet.

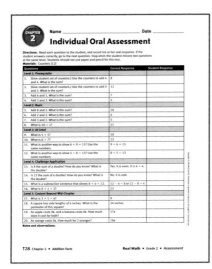

Assessment, page T28

Directions

Read each question to the student, and record his or her oral response. If the student answers correctly, go to the next question. Stop when the student misses two questions at the same level. Students should not use scrap paper.

Materials

Counters

Questions

Level 1: Prerequisite

1. Use the counters to add 4 + 4. What is the sum? 8

2. Use the counters to add 9 + 3. What is the sum? 12

3. Add 6 + 1 in your head. What is the sum? 7

4. Add 3 + 2 in your head. What is the sum? 5

Level 2: Basic

5. Add 8 + 2 in your head. What is the sum? 10

6. Add 2 + 2 in your head. What is the sum? 4

7. Add 3 + 2 in your head. What is the sum? 5

8. What is 10 + 1? 11

Level 3: At Level

9. What is 5 + 5? 10

10. What is 6 + 7? 13

11. What is another way to show 6 + 9 = 15? Use the same numbers. 9 + 6 = 15

12. What is another way to show 5 + 8 = 13? Use the same numbers. 8 + 5 = 13

Level 4: Challenge Application

13. Is 8 the sum of a double? How do you know? yes; because it is even. It is 4 + 4.

14. Is 13 the sum of a double? How do you know? no; because it is odd. It is 7 + 6.

15. What is a subtraction sentence that shows 8 + 4 = 12? 12 − 4 = 8 or 12 − 8 = 4

16. What is 9 + 1 + 3? 13

Level 5: Content Beyond Mid-Chapter

17. What is 3 + 1 + 4? 8

18. A square has side lengths of 6 inches. What is the perimeter of this square? 24

19. An apple costs 9¢, and a banana costs 8¢. How much does it cost for both? 17¢

20. An orange costs 9¢. How much for two oranges? 18¢

OBJECTIVES
- To continue reviewing the addition facts
- To reintroduce function machines from Grade 1

NCTM STANDARDS
Number and Operations
- Developing and using strategies for addition
- Developing fluency with basic number combinations for addition
- Understanding the effects of adding whole numbers

Representation
Creating and using representations to organize, record, and communicate mathematical ideas

Algebra
Understanding functions

MATERIALS
- *Number Cubes
- Overhead transparency of the completed 10 + 10 Addition Table
- A cardboard box with slots cut on opposite sides (to be used as the function machine)

TECHNOLOGY
- **e Presentation** Lesson 2.6
- **e MathTools** Function Machine
- **Building Blocks** Function Machine 1

TEST PREP
Cumulative Review
Mental Math reviews addition facts (Lessons 2.1–2.5).

Remaining Facts and Function Machines

Context of the Lesson This lesson continues review of the addition facts, paying special attention to the facts that have not yet been systematically reviewed. This lesson integrates addition-fact practice with review of functions and function machine problems. Function machine problems were used extensively in the first-grade program and will be used in different contexts throughout this and subsequent grades.

See page 41B for Math Background for teachers for this lesson.

Planning for Learning ● DIFFERENTIATE INSTRUCTION

INTERVENTION

If . . . students lack the prerequisite skill of writing numbers in sequence,

Then . . . teach **Intervention** Lesson 2.C.

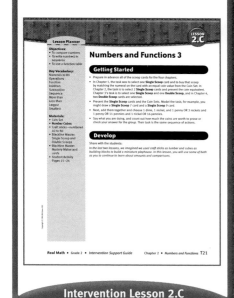

Intervention Lesson 2.C

ENGLISH LEARNER

Preview

If . . . students need language support,

Then . . . use Lesson 2.6 in **English Learner Support Guide** to preview lesson concepts and vocabulary.

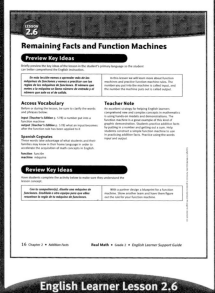

English Learner Lesson 2.6

ENRICH

If . . . students are proficient in the lesson concepts,

Then . . . emphasize exploring **eMathTools**.

PRACTICE

If . . . students would benefit from additional practice,

Then . . . extend Guided Discussion before assigning the student pages.

RETEACH

If . . . students are having difficulty understanding function machines,

Then . . . extend Skill Building before assigning the student pages.

Vocabulary
function machine *n.* a machine that supplies one output for each input, according to a rule

Access Vocabulary
input a number put into a function machine

output what an input becomes after the function rule has been applied to it

Spanish Cognates
function función

machine máquina

---

*Manipulative Kit Item

Mental Math 5

  Do an addition-fact drill. Have students use **Number Cubes** to show their answers. Give exercises such as the following:

a. 10 + 3 = 13	**b.** 10 + 0 = 10	**c.** 0 + 0 = 0
d. 8 + 2 = 10	**e.** 7 + 6 = 13	**f.** 8 + 1 = 9
g. 4 + 5 = 9	**h.** 9 + 4 = 13	**i.** 6 + 2 = 8
j. 8 + 7 = 15	**k.** 4 + 10 = 14	**l.** 4 + 4 = 8
m. 9 + 9 = 18	**n.** 3 + 9 = 12	**o.** 8 + 9 = 17

1 Develop 25

Tell Students In Today's Lesson They Will

- learn the remaining facts on the Addition Table.
- use a function machine.

Guided Discussion REASONING
Whole Group

Using the shaded overhead transparency of the Addition Table from previous lessons, discuss the students' progress reviewing and memorizing all the addition facts.

With the students' help, list the remaining facts on the board:

5 + 3 = 8	7 + 3 = 10	8 + 3 = 11
3 + 5 = 8	3 + 7 = 10	3 + 8 = 11
6 + 3 = 9	7 + 4 = 11	8 + 4 = 12
3 + 6 = 9	4 + 7 = 11	4 + 8 = 12
6 + 4 = 10	7 + 5 = 12	8 + 5 = 13
4 + 6 = 10	5 + 7 = 12	5 + 8 = 13

Allow students to offer explanations about why some of these facts might be easy to learn. Possible explanations could include the following:

- The +3 facts are easy because they are 1 more than the +2 facts, which students already know.
- The facts 6 + 4, 4 + 6, 3 + 7, and 7 + 3 are easy because they add up to 10.
- The +5 facts can be remembered by thinking about adding with fingers. For example, to add 7 + 5 a student could hold up 5 fingers on one hand and 2 on the other to show 7. Then the student could think that if 5 more fingers were added (perhaps if a friend also held up a hand), the two sets of 5 would make 10 fingers plus 2 fingers being displayed on the other hand, or 12 fingers.
- Because of the Commutative Law, after they remember one fact, it is easy to remember the related fact.

Tell students they will need to practice the remaining facts but that if they can pass a final test they will know all 121 addition facts.

Skill Building ENGAGING
Whole Group

Prepare in advance a function machine by using a cardboard box (a copy-paper box would work well). Cut holes or slots on opposite sides of the box, and decorate the bottom of the box to look like a machine (the bottom of the box will be facing the students as the box is being used). Place the box on your desk.

1. Call attention to the box on your desk, and explain that it can change numbers according to certain rules. Explain further that you can make the rules and that you can also change them.
2. Allow one student to come to the front of the room and place a slip of paper with a number written on it into the box. Suppose the student put a 5 into the box. Take the slip of paper, cross off the number the student wrote, and write a new number that is 1 more on the slip. Then pass the slip out through the opposite slot.
3. Draw a function table (similar to those on page 57) on the board, and enter 5 as the input and 6 as the output.
4. Repeat steps 2 and 3 with other students and other inputs, but keep the +1 rule constant.
5. After three or four students have participated, ask the class if they can figure out the rule (+1). Write that rule in the appropriate place on the function table.
6. Now ask the class if they can figure out what went into the machine if a 10 came out. Help students see that they can "reverse" the machine by figuring out what 1 is added to if 10 is the desired result.

Repeat the above steps with new rules several times.

2 Assign Student Pages 20

Pages 57–58 APPLYING

Have students complete pages 57–58 independently. Remind students that the tables on page 57 record the work of the function machine. The first column shows the numbers that have gone into the machine, and the second column shows the numbers that have come out.

As Students Finish

 Give students a choice of games from those previously introduced, or assign games based on individual needs.

e MathTools Have students use the **Function Machine** tool to continue to explore functions.

Building Blocks *Function Machine 1*

Name _____ Date _____

LESSON 2.6 Remaining Facts and Function Machines

Key Ideas

Each function machine has a rule. A number goes into the function machine. The number is changed according to the rule. Then a number comes out of the function machine.

| 3 | in | + 2 | out | 5 |

Find the missing numbers and the rule.

①

in	out
3	5
6	8
4	6
7	9

The rule is +2.

②
in	out
6	16
4	14
0	10
5	15

The rule is +10.

③
in	out
4	8
2	4
5	10
6	12

The rule is double the number.

④
in	out
5	12
8	15
3	10
3	10

The rule is +7.

⑤
in	out
2	8
4	10
3	9
4	10

The rule is +6.

⑥
in	out
1	10
5	14
2	11
5	14

The rule is +9.

Textbook This lesson is available in the *eTextbook*.

57

LESSON 2.6 • Remaining Facts and Function Machines

Add.

⑦ $0 + 8 = 8$

⑧ $9 + 9 = 18$

⑨ $6 + 6 = 12$

⑩ $3 + 7 = 10$

⑪ $7 + 6 = 13$

⑫ $6 + 8 = 14$

⑬ $9 + 2 = 11$

⑭ $1 + 5 = 6$

⑮ $3 + 6 = 9$

⑯ $10 + 10 = 20$

⑰ $8 + 8 = 16$

⑱ $7 + 2 = 9$

⑲ $7 + 9 = 16$

⑳ $2 + 9 = 11$

㉑ $10 + 4 = 14$

㉒ $9 + 8 = 17$

㉓
$$\begin{array}{r} 6 \\ + 9 \\ \hline 15 \end{array}$$

㉔
$$\begin{array}{r} 8 \\ + 4 \\ \hline 12 \end{array}$$

㉕
$$\begin{array}{r} 4 \\ + 8 \\ \hline 12 \end{array}$$

㉖
$$\begin{array}{r} 9 \\ + 6 \\ \hline 15 \end{array}$$

---

3 Reflect 10

Guided Discussion UNDERSTANDING
Whole Group

Display on the overhead projector the shaded Addition Table transparency used in previous lessons. Review the progress the class is making toward knowing all the facts with quick recall.

Ask students if they are ready to be quizzed on the remaining facts. If so, do a quick-response exercise, or give a brief written quiz. If the class is proficient, shade the remaining facts. The table should now be completely shaded. Commend students on accomplishing the important and difficult task of learning all the facts, but explain that they still must work on their speed of recall, something they will be focusing on in the next few lessons.

RESEARCH IN ACTION

"Number sense develops as students understand the size of numbers, develop multiple ways of thinking about and representing numbers, use numbers as referents, and develop accurate perceptions about the effects of operations on numbers."

National Council of Teachers of Mathematics. *Principles and Standards for School Mathematics.* Reston, VA: NCTM, 2000, p. 80.

 Cumulative Review: For cumulative review of previously learned skills, see page 67–68.

 Family Involvement: Assign the ***Practice, Reteach,*** or ***Enrichment*** activities depending on the needs of your students.

 Concept/Question Board: Encourage students to continue to post questions, answers, and examples on the Concept/Question Board.

 Math Puzzler: Manolita spent all afternoon writing letters. She wrote three pages to her Aunt Sheila, five pages to her grandmother, and four pages to her pen pal. How many envelopes does Manolita need to send her letters? three

Assess and Differentiate

 Assess Use **eAssess** to record and analyze evidence of student understanding.

A Gather Evidence

Use the Daily Class Assessment Records in **Assessment** or **eAssess** to record daily observations.

Informal Assessment
☑ **Mental Math**

Did the student **COMPUTING**
- ❏ respond accurately?
- ❏ respond quickly?
- ❏ respond with confidence?
- ❏ self-correct?

Informal Assessment
☑ **Concept/Question Board**

Did the student **APPLYING**
- ❏ apply learning in new situations?
- ❏ contribute concepts?
- ❏ contribute answers?
- ❏ connect mathematics to real-world situations?

B Summarize Findings

Analyze and summarize assessment data for each student. Determine which Assessment Follow-Up is appropriate for each student. Use the Student Assessment Record in **Assessment** or **eAssess** to update assessment records.

Assessment page T41

C Assessment Follow-Up • DIFFERENTIATE INSTRUCTION

Based on your observations, use these teaching strategies for assessment follow-up.

INTERVENTION	ENRICH	PRACTICE	RETEACH
Review student performance on **Intervention** Lesson 2.B to see if students have mastered prerequisite skills for this lesson.	**If . . .** students are proficient in the lesson concepts, **Then . . .** encourage them to work on the chapter projects or **Enrichment** Lesson 2.6.	**If . . .** students would benefit from additional practice, **Then . . .** assign **Practice** Lesson 2.6.	**If . . .** students are having difficulty finding the input of a function, **Then . . .** have them find the rule first, and then work backward.

ENGLISH LEARNER

Review

Use Lesson 2.6 in **English Learner Support Guide** to review lesson concepts and vocabulary.

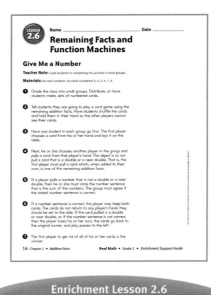

Enrichment Lesson 2.6

Practice Lesson 2.6

Lesson Planner

OBJECTIVES

- To continue reviewing the addition facts, paying special attention to speed and fluency
- To review addition exercises in which there are more than two addends

NCTM STANDARDS

Number and Operations

- Developing and using strategies for addition
- Developing fluency with basic number combinations for addition
- Understanding the effects of adding whole numbers

Communication
Communicating mathematical thinking coherently and clearly to peers, teachers, and others

MATERIALS
*Number Cubes

TECHNOLOGY
🔲 **Presentation** Lesson 2.7
🔲 **Games** Roll a 15 Game
Building Blocks Shape Parts 3

TEST PREP
Cumulative Review
Mental Math reviews addition facts (Lessons 2.1–2.6).

Using Multiple Addends

Context of the Lesson This lesson introduces addition exercises in which there are more than two addends. The **Roll a 15 Game,** introduced in this lesson, integrates addition facts for two, three, and four addends with probabilistic thinking.
See page 41B for Math Background for teachers for this lesson.

Planning for Learning ● DIFFERENTIATE INSTRUCTION

INTERVENTION

If . . . students lack the prerequisite skill of using a function table,

Then . . . teach **Intervention** Lesson 2.C.

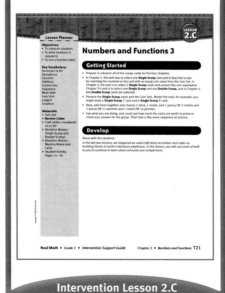

Intervention Lesson 2.C

ENGLISH LEARNER

Preview

If . . . students need language support,

Then . . . use Lesson 2.7 in **English Learner Support Guide** to preview lesson concepts and vocabulary.

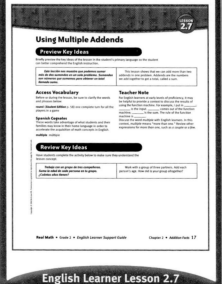

English Learner Lesson 2.7

ENRICH

If . . . students are proficient in the lesson concepts,

Then . . . emphasize game strategies.

PRACTICE

If . . . students would benefit from additional practice,

Then . . . extend game play before assigning the student pages.

RETEACH

If . . . students are having difficulty adding multiple addends,

Then . . . extend Guided Discussion before assigning the student pages.

Vocabulary
addend \ad´end\ *n.* a number to be added

Access Vocabulary
round one complete turn for all the players in a game

Spanish Cognates
multiple múltiple

Mental Math 5

  Do a fast-paced drill in which you give addition exercises and students use **Number Cubes** to show their answers. Give exercises such as the following:

a. 7 + 5 = 12 **b.** 4 + 4 = 8 **c.** 8 + 10 = 18
d. 9 + 8 = 17 **e.** 4 + 3 = 7 **f.** 7 + 7 = 14
g. 9 + 5 = 14 **h.** 8 + 4 = 12 **i.** 6 + 8 = 14
j. 3 + 5 = 8 **k.** 1 + 10 = 11 **l.** 6 + 7 = 13

1 Develop 20

Tell Students In Today's Lesson They Will
learn to add more than two numbers.

Guided Discussion UNDERSTANDING Whole Group

Write the following on the board, and establish that the sum is 11:

4 + 7 = 11

Now write this addition exercise on the board, and ask for different ways of finding the sum:

4 + 7 + 6 = 17

Allow that there are three ways that are usually used to find the sum. Write these on the board as you think aloud.

4 + 7 = 11   4 + 6 = 10   7 + 6 = 13
          or   or
11 + 6 = 17   10 + 7 = 17   13 + 4 = 17

Through discussion note that each method gave the same sum. Ask if students believe this is always true, and allow them to try different groups of three addends until they are convinced that this appears to be always true. Review that the Commutative Law states that you will arrive at the same sum regardless of the order of addition. Explain that the Commutative Law holds true whether there are two, three, or more addends.

Ask students to look back at the original exercise, 4 + 7 + 6 = 17, and the different methods for finding the sum. Ask,

■ **Is one way of finding the sum easier than the other ways?**
Possible answer: Finding two addends that sum to 10 makes the addition easier.

Finally, write a few more exercises on the board, and have students find different ways of finding the sums. Include some where two of the addends sum to 10 and some that do not. Possible exercises include the following:

- 3 + 4 + 7 = 14
- 6 + 5 + 7 = 18
- 5 + 6 + 4 = 15

If you feel that students are ready, write a few exercises with four or more addends and have students find the sums. Possible exercises include the following:

- 3 + 6 + 7 + 4 = 20
- 2 + 7 + 3 + 8 = 20
- 5 + 6 + 3 + 5 = 19
- 8 + 4 + 2 + 6 + 5 = 25

Skill Practice   COMPUTING Whole Group

 To reinforce fluency with multiple addends, present exercises one at a time, orally and in writing, as students show the sums with their **Number Cubes.** Give exercises such as the following:

a. 7 + 7 + 7 = 21 **b.** 7 + 3 + 8 = 18 **c.** 8 + 2 + 7 = 17
d. 2 + 0 + 6 = 8 **e.** 4 + 5 + 6 = 15 **f.** 2 + 7 + 4 = 13

Skill and Strategy Building ENGAGING

  Games Roll a 15 Game

Introduce and demonstrate the **Roll a 15 Game.** The game provides practice with addition facts but also allows students to develop and practice their thinking skills and probability concepts as they try to improve their chance of winning. Rules for play are on student page 60. Students will play in pairs as they finish page 59.

2 Assign Student Pages 25

Pages 59–60 ENGAGING Small Group

Have students complete page 59 individually or in small groups. Then have students play the **Roll a 15 Game** on page 60.

Monitoring Student Progress

If . . . students have difficulty adding multiple addends,

Then . . . suggest students write down subtotals as they add to keep track of their calculations.

As Students Finish

   Roll a 15 Game

 Games *Roll a 15 Game*

  Shape Parts 3

LESSON 2.7 Using Multiple Addends

Name _____   Date _____

Key Ideas

You can add more than two numbers at once.

$3 + 6 + 7 = 16$

You can find the sum in different ways.

$6 + 7 = 13$	or	$3 + 6 = 9$	or	$3 + 7 = 10$
$13 + 3 = 16$		$9 + 7 = 16$		$10 + 6 = 16$

You might find that one way is easier than another.

Add.

1. $5 + 5 + 4 = 14$
2. $10 + 4 + 4 = 18$
3. $10 + 8 + 0 = 18$
4. $5 + 5 + 5 = 15$

5. $4 + 8 + 2 = 14$
6. $1 + 0 + 8 = 9$
7. $4 + 5 + 9 = 18$
8. $8 + 2 + 7 = 17$

9.
```
  5
  5
+ 5
---
 15
```
10.
```
  7
  3
+ 8
---
 18
```
11.
```
  6
  4
  8
+ 1
---
 19
```
12.
```
  4
  6
+ 9
---
 19
```
13.
```
  9
  0
+ 5
---
 14
```
14.
```
  4
  5
+ 6
---
 15
```
15.
```
  3
  3
  3
+ 5
---
 14
```
16.
```
  2
  7
+ 4
---
 13
```

Textbook This lesson is available in the *eTextbook*.

59

Game

Addition and Strategies Practice

Roll a 15 Game

Players: Two

Materials:
Number Cubes:
two 0–5 (red) and
two 5–10 (blue)

HOW TO PLAY

1. Players take turns rolling cubes one at a time. Try to get as close to 15 as possible.
2. Players may stop after any roll. Each cube may be rolled only one time.
3. The player whose sum is closest to 15 wins the round. The number can be greater than or less than 15.
4. The winner of a round rolls first in the next round.

Sample Game

- Palo rolls a red cube. He rolls 5. Then he rolls a blue cube. He rolls 6. His sum is 11. Then he rolls the other red cube. He rolls 2. His sum is 13. Palo stops.
- Gretchen rolls a blue cube. She rolls 7. Then she rolls the other blue cube. She rolls 9. Her sum is 16. Gretchen stops.
- Gretchen wins because her sum is closer to 15.

60

Games This game is available as an *eGame*.

---

3 Reflect

10

Guided Discussion   REASONING

Whole Group

Ask what strategies, if any, students used to play the **Roll a 15 Game**. Ask questions such as the following:

- **Did you decide it was better to start with a red cube or a blue cube? Why?**
- **If you have a score of 13, should you roll another cube? If so, which cube would be better to roll?**

Cumulative Review: For cumulative review of previously learned skills, see page 67–68.

Family Involvement: Assign the *Practice, Reteach,* or *Enrichment* activities depending on the needs of your students.

Concept/Question Board: Have students attempt to answer any unanswered questions on the Concept/Question Board.

Math Puzzler: "Bowser likes to be walked exactly 20 blocks a day," said Mr. Breezy. "He was walked 7 blocks this morning, I walked him 8 blocks after lunch, and I'll be walking him another 5 blocks this afternoon." How many blocks will Bowser want to walk this evening? zero, because he will have already walked 20 blocks

4 Assess and Differentiate

 Assess Use **eAssess** to record and analyze evidence of student understanding.

A Gather Evidence

Use the Daily Class Assessment Records in **Assessment** or **eAssess** to record daily observations.

Informal Assessment
☑ **Skill Practice**

Did the student **COMPUTING**
- ❑ respond accurately?
- ❑ respond quickly?
- ❑ respond with confidence?
- ❑ self-correct?

Performance Assessment
☑ **Game**

Did the student **ENGAGING**
- ❑ pay attention to others' contributions?
- ❑ contribute information and ideas?
- ❑ improve on a strategy?
- ❑ reflect on and check the accuracy of his or her work?

B Summarize Findings

Analyze and summarize assessment data for each student. Determine which Assessment Follow-Up is appropriate for each student. Use the Student Assessment Record in **Assessment** or **eAssess** to update assessment records.

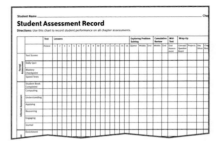

Assessment page T41

C Assessment Follow-Up ● DIFFERENTIATE INSTRUCTION

Based on your observations, use these teaching strategies for assessment follow-up.

INTERVENTION

Review student performance on **Intervention** Lesson 2.C to see if students have mastered prerequisite skills for this lesson.

ENGLISH LEARNER

Review

Use Lesson 2.7 in **English Learner Support Guide** to review lesson concepts and vocabulary.

ENRICH

If . . . students are proficient in the lesson concepts,

Then . . . encourage them to work on the chapter projects or **Enrichment** Lesson 2.7.

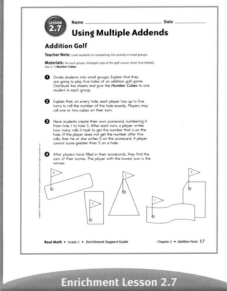

Enrichment Lesson 2.7

PRACTICE

If . . . students would benefit from additional practice,

Then . . . assign **Practice** Lesson 2.7.

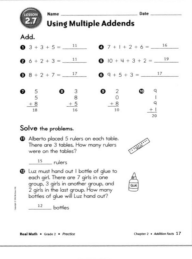

Practice Lesson 2.7

RETEACH

If . . . students are having difficulty adding together multiple addends,

Then . . . remind them that the Commutative Law states that they can add a series of numbers in any order.

Lesson Planner

OBJECTIVES

- To continue reviewing the addition facts, paying special attention to speed and fluency
- To review addition exercises in which there are more than two addends
- To introduce missing addend problems
- To introduce the concept of perimeter

NCTM STANDARDS

Number and Operations

- Developing and using strategies for addition
- Developing fluency with basic number combinations for addition
- Understanding the effects of adding whole numbers

Geometry
Recognizing and naming two-dimensional shapes

Measurement
Recognizing the attribute of length

MATERIALS
*Number Cubes

TECHNOLOGY
ⓔ **Presentation** Lesson 2.8
Building Blocks Barkley's Bones 1–20

TEST PREP

Cumulative Review ⟲Review
Mental Math reviews using multiple addends (Lesson 2.7).

Extended Response ⟹
Problem 5

Looking Ahead

Lesson 2.9 introduces the Paper Explorer. You should familiarize yourself with the Paper Explorer in advance.

Applying Addition

Context of the Lesson This is the last in a series of eight lessons that reviews the addition facts and focuses on achieving fluency. As a culminating lesson, the first addition-fact speed test is introduced. This is also the second of two lessons that focuses on adding three or more numbers. This lesson provides an application of this skill—finding the perimeter of polygons.

See page 41B for Math Background for teachers for this lesson.

Planning for Learning ● DIFFERENTIATE INSTRUCTION

INTERVENTION

If . . . students lack the prerequisite skill of using a function table,

Then . . . teach **Intervention** Lesson 2.C.

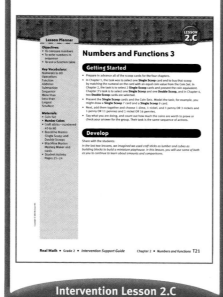

Intervention Lesson 2.C

ENGLISH LEARNER

Preview

If . . . students need language support,

Then . . . use Lesson 2.8 in **English Learner Support Guide** to preview lesson concepts and vocabulary.

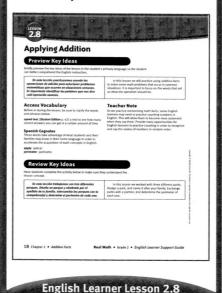

English Learner Lesson 2.8

ENRICH

If . . . students are proficient in the lesson concepts,

Then . . . emphasize chapter projects.

PRACTICE

If . . . students would benefit from additional practice,

Then . . . extend Skill Practice before assigning the student pages.

RETEACH

If . . . students are having difficulty understanding addition applications,

Then . . . extend Guided Discussion before assigning the student pages.

Vocabulary
perimeter \pə rim´ i tər\ *n.* the distance around a figure

Access Vocabulary
garden a part of the yard set aside for growing plants

Spanish Cognates
apply aplicar

perimeter perímetro

Mental Math 5

Do a drill in which you say and write on the board an addition statement with three or four addends. Students show their answers with **Number Cubes.** Use examples in which two of the addends add up to 10. Possible examples include the following:

a. $3 + 7 + 2 + 1 = 13$ **b.** $4 + 3 + 2 + 7 = 16$ **c.** $2 + 8 + 5 = 15$

d. $5 + 6 + 4 + 3 = 18$ **e.** $0 + 3 + 5 + 7 = 15$ **f.** $6 + 7 + 4 = 17$

g. $7 + 8 + 2 + 3 = 20$ **h.** $3 + 7 + 1 + 9 = 20$ **i.** $3 + 7 + 4 = 14$

1 Develop 25

Tell Students In Today's Lesson They Will

use addition to solve problems.

Guided Discussion UNDERSTANDING Whole Group

Referring to the illustration at the top of page 61, explain that Mrs. Kinney wants to put a fence around her garden to keep the rabbits from eating her vegetables. To find out how many meters of fence she needs, she needs to know the distance around the garden. Remind students that the garden has the shape of a triangle and that the distance around the triangle (or any figure) is called the perimeter. Ask the following questions:

■ **How would you find the distance around a figure?** Measure the length of each side.

■ **What would you do after you found the length of each side?** Add them together to find the distance around the entire figure.

■ **How many meters of fence does Mrs. Kinney need?** $3 + 4 + 5 = 12$

■ **Suppose you wanted to find the perimeter of the classroom? How could you find it?** Measure each side of the classroom, and then add the lengths together.

Skill Practice COMPUTING Whole Group

Draw different figures on the board, and have students find the perimeters. Then find, hide, and show the answers with their **Number Cubes.** Use the opportunity to review the names and definitions for each figure. (They were introduced in the Grade 1 program.) For example:

a. Draw a square with sides of 3 units. Label each side. 12

b. Draw a rectangle with sides of 2 and 5 units. Label each side. 14

c. Draw a triangle with sides of 4, 9, and 6 units. Label each side. 19

d. Draw a regular pentagon with sides of 4 units. Label each side. 20

e. Draw a rectangle with one side labeled 4 units and a second side labeled 5 units. Students should be able to determine the lengths of the other two sides. 18

2 Assign Student Pages 20

Pages 61–62 APPLYING

Have students complete page 61 independently.

Page 62 is the first speed test. Allow two minutes for students to complete the exercises. Before beginning, help students feel comfortable. Emphasize that there will be plenty of time to improve scores and that students will be asked to improve upon their previous scores, not compete with each other.

Monitoring Student Progress

If . . . students have difficulty adding multiple addends,	Then . . . provide individual instruction that shows these students how to group multiple addends into known addition facts.
If . . . students did not finish the test but their answers were accurate,	Then . . . assign fast-paced flash card practice.
If . . . students made more than a few errors on the speed test,	Then . . . interview them to determine if the errors stem from faulty understanding or recall of addition facts or if students were just nervous because of time pressure. If it is the former, continue doing remedial work as suggested earlier in this chapter. If it is the latter, reassure all students, and let them know that it is not necessary that they finish all twenty-five exercises on the test.

As Students Finish

Give students a choice of games from those previously introduced, or assign games based on individual needs.

Building **B**locks *Barkley's Bones 1–20*

LESSON 2.8 Applying Addition

Name _____ Date _____

Key Ideas

To find the **perimeter**, add the distances around the outside of a figure.

For example, Mrs. Kinney can add these numbers to find the perimeter of her garden, which is shaped like a triangle:

$3 + 4 + 5 = 12$

Find the perimeter.

① Square

Perimeter = 20

③ Pentagon

Perimeter = 15

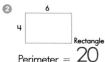
② Rectangle

Perimeter = 20

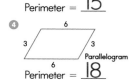
④ Parallelogram

Perimeter = 18

⑤ **Extended Response** Maple Leaf Park is shaped like a rectangle. It has a perimeter of 26 miles.

a. Could two of the sides be 13 miles and 2 miles? __no__

b. Why do you think so? If two sides are 13 and 2, the other sides __must be 13 and 2, which would make the perimeter more than 26.__

⬛ Textbook This lesson is available in the *eTextbook*.

61

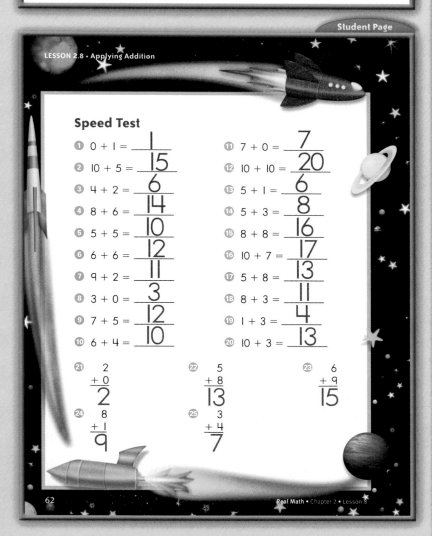

LESSON 2.8 • Applying Addition

Speed Test

① $0 + 1 =$ 1
② $10 + 5 =$ 15
③ $4 + 2 =$ 6
④ $8 + 6 =$ 14
⑤ $5 + 5 =$ 10
⑥ $6 + 6 =$ 12
⑦ $9 + 2 =$ 11
⑧ $3 + 0 =$ 3
⑨ $7 + 5 =$ 12
⑩ $6 + 4 =$ 10

⑪ $7 + 0 =$ 7
⑫ $10 + 10 =$ 20
⑬ $5 + 1 =$ 6
⑭ $5 + 3 =$ 8
⑮ $8 + 8 =$ 16
⑯ $10 + 7 =$ 17
⑰ $5 + 8 =$ 13
⑱ $8 + 3 =$ 11
⑲ $1 + 3 =$ 4
⑳ $10 + 3 =$ 13

㉑
$\begin{array}{r} 2 \\ + 0 \\ \hline 2 \end{array}$

㉒
$\begin{array}{r} 5 \\ + 8 \\ \hline 13 \end{array}$

㉓
$\begin{array}{r} 6 \\ + 9 \\ \hline 15 \end{array}$

㉔
$\begin{array}{r} 8 \\ + 1 \\ \hline 9 \end{array}$

㉕
$\begin{array}{r} 3 \\ + 4 \\ \hline 7 \end{array}$

62 **Real Math • Chapter 2 • Lesson 8**

LESSON 2.8

3 Reflect 10

Guided Discussion ✓ **REASONING** Whole Group

1. Briefly discuss the results of the first speed test, and encourage students to practice so they will improve their scores on the next test.

2. Pose the following question:

■ **Rosa's garden has the shape of a rectangle and a perimeter of 24 meters. What might the shape of the rectangle look like?**

Have students draw possible rectangles at their desks and share their drawings. Help students understand that just knowing the perimeter and that the garden is shaped like a rectangle is insufficient information to know the exact shape of the garden. For instance, two sides of the rectangle could be 1 meter long, and the other two sides could be 11 meters long, making a long and thin rectangle. Or each side could be 6 meters long, making the rectangle a square.

Conclude by asking students to think about what other information is needed to know the exact shape of the rectangle. You also need to know the length of one of the sides. It is not necessary to have students answer the question right away—it is sufficient that they think about it.

Extended Response ▶

Problem 5 Discuss students' answers. Students should recognize that opposite sides of a rectangle are the same length. Therefore, if two of the sides are 13 miles and 2 miles, then the other two sides must also be 13 miles and 2 miles.

📋 RESEARCH IN ACTION

"Children come to understand the meaning of addition in the context of word problems . . . children move from counting to more general methods to solve different classes of problems. As they do, they also develop greater fluency with each specific method."

Kilpatrick, J., J. Swafford, and B. Findell, eds. *Adding It Up: Helping Children Learn Mathematics*. Washington, D.C.: National Research Council/National Academy Press, 2001, pp. 187–190.

Review **Cumulative Review:** For cumulative review of previously learned skills, see page 67–68.

Family Involvement: Assign the *Practice, Reteach,* or *Enrichment* activities depending on the needs of your students.

Concept/Question Board: Have students attempt to answer any unanswered questions on the Concept/Question Board.

Math Puzzler: What two numbers meet both of the following rules? They are only one number apart from each other. Their sum is two digits that equal 6 when added together. *8, 7*

Assess and Differentiate

 e Assess Use **eAssess** to record and analyze evidence of student understanding.

A Gather Evidence

Use the Daily Class Assessment Records in **Assessment** or **eAssess** to record daily observations.

Formal Assessment
☑ **Speed Test**

Did the student **COMPUTING**
- ☐ complete the exercises with at least 80% accuracy?
- ☐ complete the exercises within the time limit?

Informal Assessment
☑ **Guided Discussion**

Did the student **REASONING**
- ☐ provide a clear explanation?
- ☐ communicate reasons and strategies?
- ☐ choose appropriate strategies?
- ☐ argue logically?

B Summarize Findings

Analyze and summarize assessment data for each student. Determine which Assessment Follow-Up is appropriate for each student. Use the Student Assessment Record in **Assessment** or **eAssess** to update assessment records.

Assessment page T41

C Assessment Follow-Up ● DIFFERENTIATE INSTRUCTION

Based on your observations, use these teaching strategies for assessment follow-up.

INTERVENTION	ENRICH	PRACTICE	RETEACH
Review student performance on **Intervention** Lesson 2.C to see if students have mastered prerequisite skills for this lesson.	**If . . .** students are proficient in the lesson concepts, **Then . . .** encourage them to work on the chapter projects or **Enrichment** Lesson 2.8.	**If . . .** students would benefit from additional practice, **Then . . .** assign **Practice** Lesson 2.8.	**If . . .** students are having difficulty understanding addition applications, **Then . . .** model the problems by using concrete objects.

ENGLISH LEARNER
Review

Use Lesson 2.8 in **English Learner Support Guide** to review lesson concepts and vocabulary.

Enrichment Lesson 2.8

Practice Lesson 2.8

Lesson Planner

OBJECTIVES
- To introduce the Paper Explorer as a model to add single-digit numbers
- To learn that the same sum can be expressed in different ways

NCTM STANDARDS
Number and Operations
- Developing and using strategies for addition
- Developing fluency with basic number combinations for addition
- Understanding the effects of adding whole numbers
- Using a variety of methods and tools to compute, including objects, mental computation, estimation, paper and pencil, and calculators

Representation
- Creating and using representations to organize, record, and communicate mathematical ideas
- Selecting, applying, and translating among mathematical representations to solve problems

MATERIALS
- Blank transparency to write on
- Overhead transparency of the Paper Explorer on *Practice* page 121
- *Counters

TECHNOLOGY
ⓔ **Presentation** Lesson 2.9
Building Blocks Double Compare 1–20

TEST PREP
Cumulative Review
Mental Math reviews inequalities and equalities (Lesson 1.9).

Looking Ahead
Lesson 3.1 will require pairs of slips of paper with the numbers 0 through 10 written on them for use in the Numbers on the Back Activity.

The Paper Explorer—Single-Digit Addition

Context of the Lesson In this lesson students continue to review addition facts as they use the Paper Explorer to investigate the relationships among the addition facts. Using the Paper Explorer requires some manual dexterity because counters must be moved simultaneously. Some students may have difficulty moving the counters at first and will need time for more practice. The Paper Explorer will be used again in later chapters to explore multidigit addition and subtraction.

See page 41B for Math Background for teachers for this lesson.

Planning for Learning ● DIFFERENTIATE INSTRUCTION

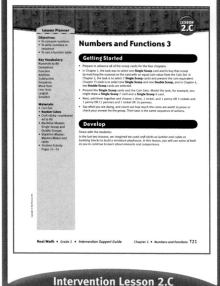

INTERVENTION
If . . . students lack the prerequisite skill of using a function table,

Then . . . teach *Intervention* Lesson 2.C.

Intervention Lesson 2.C

ENGLISH LEARNER
Preview

If . . . students need language support,

Then . . . use Lesson 2.9 in *English Learner Support Guide* to preview lesson concepts and vocabulary.

English Learner Lesson 2.9

ENRICH
If . . . students are proficient in the lesson concepts,

Then . . . emphasize chapter projects.

PRACTICE
If . . . students would benefit from additional practice,

Then . . . extend using the student pages.

RETEACH
If . . . students are having difficulty understanding the Paper Explorer,

Then . . . extend Guided Discussion before assigning the student pages.

Access Vocabulary
thumbs-up a signal given by holding out a fist with the thumb pointing up

Spanish Cognates
explorer explorador

*Manipulative Kit Item

Mental Math 5

  Write pairs of number expressions on the board, and have students show thumbs-up if the sum of the expression on the left is greater than the sum on the right, thumbs-down if the sum of the expression on the left is less than the sum on the right, and open hand if the sums are exactly the same. Give exercises such as the following:

a. 47 + 10 ◯ 47 + 11 down   **b.** 75 + 10 ◯ 10 + 75 open

c. 20 + 40 ◯ 10 + 30 up   **d.** 35 + 70 ◯ 30 + 70 up

e. 35 + 40 ◯ 35 + 60 down   **f.** 25 + 20 ◯ 24 + 20 up

1 Develop 25

Tell Students In Today's Lesson They Will
use the Paper Explorer to find sums.

Guided Discussion UNDERSTANDING   Whole Group

Draw two large circles on a blank transparency. Place 3 counters in one circle and 5 counters in the other. Ask students the following:

■ **How many counters?** 8

When students agree that there are 3 + 5 = 8 counters, write 3 + 5 = 8 on the transparency.

Next move 1 counter from the circle of 3 to the circle of 5. Ask the following:

■ **How many counters?** 8

When students agree that there are 2 + 6 = 8 counters, write that on the board under the previous statement. Have students read each statement aloud. Keep moving counters one at a time as you write the corresponding statements on the transparency, and have students read the statements aloud.

Repeat the above steps for 8 + 5, but now use the Paper Explorer as well. Place 8 counters in one circle and 5 counters in the other. At the same time, place one counter in the 8 box and one in the 5 box on the transparency of the Paper Explorer. Now move one counter from the 5 circle to the 8 circle, and then, moving both counters simultaneously, move the Paper Explorer counters one box in the opposite direction so they are in the 9 and 4 boxes. Say, *8 plus 5 is the same as 9 plus 4* as you move the counters.

Help students see that by moving one counter from one circle to the other, you have not changed the total number of counters. At the same time, moving the counters on the Paper Explorer in opposite directions did not change the total value on the Explorer.

Now move one more counter in the circles so there are 10 in one circle and 3 in the other. Also move the counters in the Explorer in opposite directions, and say, *9 plus 4 is the same as 10 plus 3* as you do so.

Using the Student Pages APPLYING   Small Group

Have students work in pairs using student page 63. Create problems orally. Students put counters in the circles and move them to get the sum. Have one student do the moving and the other student say the sums represented. Have students stop when one circle has ten counters so that the sum can be reported as 10 and a number.

2 Assign Student Pages 20

Page 64 UNDERSTANDING

Have students turn their books so the Paper Explorer on page 64 runs horizontally across the page and the problems to be worked are under the Explorer. Do the first problem together with students, having them move the counters at the same time they whisper the facts. For example, *6 plus 5 is the same as 7 plus 4. 7 plus 4 is the same as 8 plus 3. 8 plus 3 is the same as 9 plus 2. 9 plus 2 is the same as 10 plus 1. 10 plus 1 equals 11.* Then write the corresponding facts on the board as follows:

6 + 5 = 11

7 + 4 = 11

8 + 3 = 11

9 + 2 = 11

10 + 1 = 11

Have students complete the rest of the problems on their own.

Monitoring Student Progress

If . . . students are having difficulty getting the correct sums on the Paper Explorer,	**Then . . .** they are likely having difficulty moving the counters simultaneously. These students should be helped by reassuring them that they can do it and by having them go more slowly. Make sure students are whispering the facts, as they were instructed above. Because students will not be using the Paper Explorer as a regular part of the curriculum, extensive extra teaching and practice is not essential.
If . . . students enjoyed using this device and appear to be interested in why it works,	**Then . . .** challenge them to figure out how to use the Paper Explorer to subtract.

As Students Finish

Building Blocks *Double Compare 1–20*

Name _____ Date _____

LESSON
2.9
**The Paper Explorer—
Single-Digit Addition**

Key Ideas

You can express the same sum in many
different ways.

3 + 5 = 8   2 + 6 = 8   1 + 7 = 8

Move counters between the circles.
Say the addition facts represented by the
groups of counters.

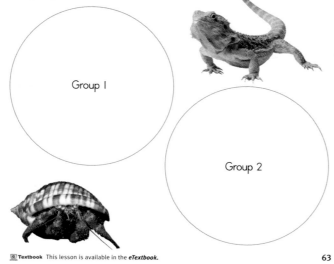

Group 1

Group 2

Copyright © SRA/McGraw-Hill.

ⓔ **Textbook** This lesson is available in the *eTextbook*.

63

Add with the Paper Explorer. Try to
match those below.

① 6 + 5 = 11
② 8 + 7 = 15
③ 7 + 6 = 13

④ 5 + 9 = 14
⑤ 9 + 9 = 18
⑥ 8 + 8 = 16

Try to get sums to

0 1 2 3 4 5 6 7 8 9

10

LESSON 2.9 • The Paper Explorer—Single-Digit Addition

Copyright © SRA/McGraw-Hill.

64   **Real Math** • Chapter 2 • Lesson 9

---

3 Reflect   10

Guided Discussion REASONING   Whole Group

Ask students if they can think of a way to use the Paper Explorer
to add three numbers. Through discussion, demonstrate how this
is done using the previously prepared Paper Explorer overhead
transparency.

To add 6 + 7 + 8, place counters on the 6, 7, and 8 boxes. Then
choose any two of the numbers (the order of addition makes no
difference) to add. For example, move and say, 8 *plus 7 is the same as*
9 plus 6. 9 plus 6 is the same as 10 plus 5. Stop now that one of those
counters is on the 10 box. Next add 6 and 5, moving the counters
and saying, *6 plus 5 is the same as 7 plus 4, which is the same as 8 plus*
3, which is the same as 9 plus 2, which is the same as 10 plus 1. Stop
now that one of those counters is on the 10 box. There are now two
counters in the 10 box and one counter in the 1 box. So the sum is
2 tens and 1, or 21.

✓ Use Mastery Checkpoint 4 found in **Assessment** to evaluate
students' mastery of addition facts. By this time students
should be able to correctly answer eighty percent of the Mastery
Checkpoint items.

Cumulative Review: For cumulative review of previously
learned skills, see page 67–68.

Family Involvement: Assign the **Practice, Reteach,** or
Enrichment activities depending on the needs of your students.

Concept/Question Board: Have students attempt to answer
any unanswered questions on the Concept/Question Board.

Math Puzzler: Ellen is carrying a 10-pound bag of potatoes
and two melons. Each melon weighs 2 pounds. How many pounds
of food is she carrying? 14

4 Assess and Differentiate

 **Assess** Use **eAssess** to record and analyze evidence of student understanding.

A Gather Evidence

Use the Daily Class Assessment Records in **Assessment** or **eAssess** to record daily observations.

Formal Assessment

☑ **Mastery Checkpoint**

Did the student
- ❏ use correct procedures?
- ❏ respond with at least 80% accuracy?

Assessment page T53

B Summarize Findings

Analyze and summarize assessment data for each student. Determine which Assessment Follow-Up is appropriate for each student. Use the Student Assessment Record in **Assessment** or **eAssess** to update assessment records.

Assessment page T41

C Assessment Follow-Up • DIFFERENTIATE INSTRUCTION

Based on your observations, use these teaching strategies for assessment follow-up.

INTERVENTION

Review student performance on **Intervention** Lesson 2.C to see if students have mastered prerequisite skills for this lesson.

ENGLISH LEARNER

Review

Use Lesson 2.9 in **English Learner Support Guide** to review lesson concepts and vocabulary.

ENRICH

If . . . students are proficient in the lesson concepts,

Then . . . encourage them to work on the chapter projects or **Enrichment** Lesson 2.9.

Enrichment Lesson 2.9

PRACTICE

If . . . students would benefit from additional practice,

Then . . . assign **Practice** Lesson 2.9.

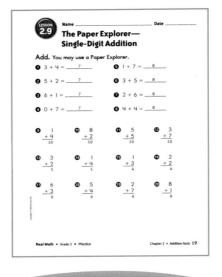

Practice Lesson 2.9

RETEACH

If . . . students are having difficulty using the Paper Explorer,

Then . . . reassure them that they do not need to use the Paper Explorer to find sums.

Exploring Problem Solving

Objectives
- To solve and present solutions to nonroutine problems
- To develop an understanding that a problem can have more than one answer
- To use addition facts

Materials
- Counters (about 25 for each group) or play money ($1, $5, and $10 bills, with at least ten $1 bills for each group)
- Scratch paper

Context of the Lesson In this lesson students continue to work with addition facts while solving and discussing nonroutine problems. The lesson also provides practice in working with money, which was introduced in Lesson 1.5.

1 Develop   5

Tell Students In Today's Lesson They Will
find a way to share the first-place prizes at a pet show.

Guided Discussion

Have students look at the illustration at the top of page 65. Read this problem to students:

Ian and his sister decided to have a pet show. They invited all the neighbors to enter their pets. They had a basket full of prizes for the winner in each category. In the dog show, the judges decided that there were two dogs that tied for first place. This meant that the two dogs would have to share first prize. How could the judges divide the prize so that the owners of each dog would get a prize basket of equal value? Look at the prizes in the second picture, and decide how you could make two baskets that have the same value.

To make sure students understand the problem, ask questions such as the following:

■ **How many prizes are in the first-place basket for the dog winner?** six
■ **Are all the prizes worth the same amount?** No, some are worth more, and some are worth less.
■ **What is the problem asking you to find?** Allow students to word this in different ways. Possible answers include how to share the prize in a fair way and how to divide the prizes into two groups so that each group is worth the same amount.
■ **Would it be fair if you just give each dog owner three of the dog prizes?** not necessarily, because one owner might get the more expensive prizes

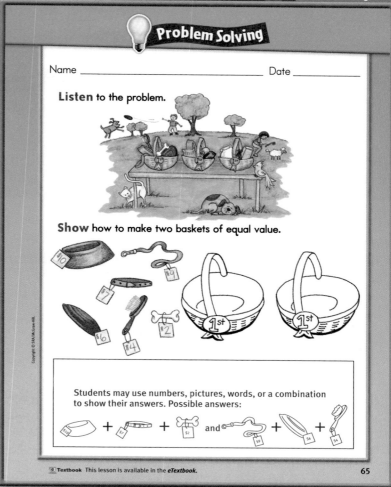

Problem Solving

Name _____ Date _____

Listen to the problem.

Show how to make two baskets of equal value.

Students may use numbers, pictures, words, or a combination to show their answers. Possible answers:

Textbook This lesson is available in the *eTextbook*.   65

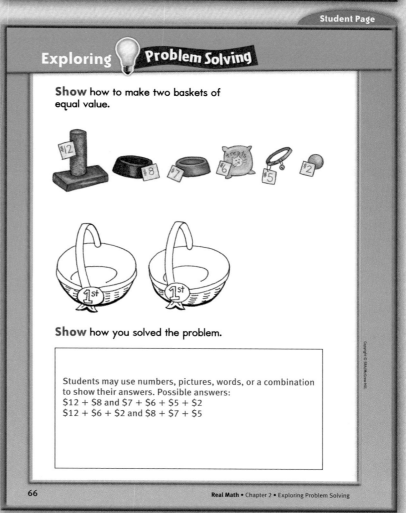

Exploring Problem Solving

Show how to make two baskets of equal value.

Show how you solved the problem.

Students may use numbers, pictures, words, or a combination to show their answers. Possible answers:
$12 + $8 and $7 + $6 + $5 + $2
$12 + $6 + $2 and $8 + $7 + $5

66   Real Math • Chapter 2 • Exploring Problem Solving

2 Exploring Problem Solving 25

Using Student Pages

Have students work with a partner on pages 65 and 66. Distribute scratch paper and bags of counters or play money. Encourage students to find more than one way to share the prizes equally. Provide help as needed.

3 Reflect 15

Effective Communication Ask students to share their answers and methods. After each group's presentation, ask students what they like about the strategy and how it was presented. On the board, record all the different solutions. In discussion, bring out the following points:

- Some problems have more than one correct answer.
- There may be different ways to show the same answer. For example, one person might write number sentences, another might list words, and someone else might draw pictures.
- Equal number doesn't necessarily mean equal value.
- Different people may use different strategies to solve a problem.

Sample Solutions Strategies

Students might use one or more of the following strategies.

Act It Out with Objects

Students might use the play money to represent the prices of the various items and combine the different amounts until they find combinations that are equal.

Guess, Check, and Adjust

Students might combine different amounts at random. If they are not equal, they will then try different combinations until they find some that are equal.

Use Number Sense

Students might recognize equal combinations by counting on or by comparing numbers to each other.

4 Assess 15

When evaluating student work, focus not only on the correctness of the answers but also on whether students thought rationally about the problem. Questions to consider include the following:

- Did the student understand the problem?
- When stuck, did the student keep trying?
- Was the student able to record an answer in a reasonably clear way?
- Was the student able to find more than one answer?
- Was the student able to explain his or her thinking?

Cumulative Review

Cumulative Review

Assign Pages 67–68

Use the Cumulative Review as a review of concepts and skills that students have previously learned.

Here are different ways that you can assign these problems to your students as they work through the chapter:

- With some of the lessons in the chapter, assign a set of cumulative review problems to be completed as practice or for homework.
  Lesson 2.6—Problems 1–4
  Lesson 2.7—Problems 5–10
  Lesson 2.8—Problems 11–20
  Lesson 2.9—Problems 21–26
- At any point during the chapter, assign part or all of the cumulative review problems to be completed as practice or for homework.

Cumulative Review

Problems 1–4 review place value and money, Lesson 1.5.

Problems 5–10 review equalities and inequalities in number statements, Lesson 1.9.

Problems 11–20 review adding and subtracting on a number line, Lesson 1.10.

Problems 21–26 review applying addition and using multiple addends, Lesson 2.8.

Monitoring Student Progress

If . . . students miss more than one problem in a section,

Then . . . refer to the indicated lesson for remediation suggestions.

Cumulative Review

Name _____ Date _____

Place Value and Money Lesson 1.5

Draw coins to make the correct amount.
Try to use the fewest number of coins possible.

1. 65¢ The drawing should include 2 quarters, 1 dime, and 1 nickel.

2. 14¢ The drawing should include 1 dime and 4 pennies.

3. 23¢ The drawing should include 2 dimes and 3 pennies.

4. 37¢ The drawing should include 1 quarter, 1 dime, and 2 pennies.

Comparing Numbers Lesson 1.9

Draw the correct sign: <, >, or =.

5. $12 + 12 < 12 + 13$

6. $19 + 5 > 19 + 4$

7. $19 + 3 < 19 + 6$

8. $17 + 6 = 19 + 4$

9. $19 + 4 < 19 + 5$

10. $79 - 3 > 79 - 4$

Textbook This lesson is available in the *eTextbook*.

67

Cumulative Review

Relating Addition and Subtraction Lesson 1.10

Use the number line to find the answers.

11. $6 - 1 = 5$
12. $7 - 3 = 4$
13. $3 - 2 = 1$
14. $4 + 2 + 2 + 1 = 9$
15. $1 + 3 = 4$

16. $8 - 1 - 1 - 1 = 5$
17. $8 - 2 = 6$
18. $4 + 2 + 1 + 1 = 8$
19. $6 - 2 = 4$
20. $7 - 1 - 2 - 1 = 3$

Applying Addition Lesson 2.8

Find the perimeter.

21. 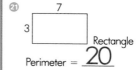 Rectangle Perimeter = 20

22. 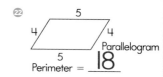 Parallelogram Perimeter = 18

Add.

23. $4 + 5 + 6 = 15$
24. $4 + 8 + 2 = 14$
25. $4 + 6 + 9 = 19$
26. $2 + 7 + 4 = 13$

68

Real Math · Chapter 2

Wrap-Up

1 Discuss

5

Concept/Question Board

Review the Concept/Question Board with students.

- Discuss students' contributions to the Concept side of the Board.
- Have students repose their questions, and lead a discussion to find satisfactory answers.

Chapter Projects APPLYING

Provide an opportunity for students who have worked on one or more of the projects outlined on page 42C to share their work with the class. Allow each student or student group five minutes to present or discuss their projects. For formal assessment, use the rubrics found in *Across the Curriculum Math Connections;* the rubric for **Illustrate a Book about Pet Care** is on page 25, and the rubric for **Communicate Needs as a Pet** is on page 31. For informal assessment, use the following rubric and questions.

	Exceeds Expectations	Meets Expectations	Minimally Meets Expectations
Applies mathematics in real-world situations:	❏	❏	❏
Demonstrates strong engagement in the activity:	❏	❏	❏

Illustrate a Book about Pet Care

- What tasks did you use to make drawings?
- How many minutes did each task take? How many minutes in total?
- How did you order the drawings in your book?
- What other items did you include in your book?
- Did using a book map help you lay out the drawings for your book? Why?
- What other tasks could you add to your book?

Communicate Needs as a Pet

- What was one thing you learned about cats or dogs?
- Which animal did your group pick? Would you change your animal? Why?
- What things did your group pick to care for a pet? Why did you pick those things?
- What actions and sounds did you pick for your pet and how to take care of it?
- How did you use the Addition Table in this activity?
- Which action and sound did you perform? Did you enjoy performing these? Why or why not?
- What are other ways that we can communicate with our pets?

2 Assign Student Pages · 25

Key Ideas Review ✓ UNDERSTANDING

Have students complete the Review questions independently or in small groups. Then discuss each question as a class.

Possible Answers

Problem ❶ Problems 1–2 review showing addition facts on the Addition Table. Students should color the doubles facts, which run diagonally from the top left to the bottom right.

Problem ❷ Students should color the +10 facts, which are located in the column on the far right and the row on the bottom.

Problem ❸ Problem 3 reviews function machines. Students may complete the function machine table with any inputs and outputs, provided that each output is the sum of the input plus 2. Possible answers are shown.

Problem ❹ Problem 4 reviews a strategy for remembering the +9 facts. Students should explain that they can know the +9 facts because they are 1 less than the corresponding +10 facts, which are easy to remember.

Problem ❺ Problem 5 reviews adding multiple addends to find perimeter. Students should add the length of each side to reach a sum of 22.

Problem ❻ Problem 6 reviews the Commutative Law. The answer is c.

Problem ❼ Problem 7 reviews use of the Paper Explorer. Students should remember that the counters always move away from one another in opposite directions. The answer is b.

Problem ❽ Problems 8–10 review using addition to solve problems. The answer is 5 + 1 = 6.

Problem ❾ The answer is 3 + 2 = 5.

Problem ❿ The answer is 4 + 4 = 8.

CHAPTER 2 Key Ideas Review

Name _____ Date _____

In this chapter you practiced addition. You learned to use the Addition Table and how to remember addition facts. You used addition to solve problems.

Follow the directions.

❶ Color the doubles facts.

❷ Color the +10 facts.

❸ Fill in this +2 function machine with inputs and outputs that follow the rule. Possible answers are shown.

+	0	1	2	3	4	5	6	7	8	9	10
0	0	1	2	3	4	5	6	7	8	9	10
1	1	2	3	4	5	6	7	8	9	10	11
2	2	3	4	5	6	7	8	9	10	11	12
3	3	4	5	6	7	8	9	10	11	12	13
4	4	5	6	7	8	9	10	11	12	13	14
5	5	6	7	8	9	10	11	12	13	14	15
6	6	7	8	9	10	11	12	13	14	15	16
7	7	8	9	10	11	12	13	14	15	16	17
8	8	9	10	11	12	13	14	15	16	17	18
9	9	10	11	12	13	14	15	16	17	18	19
10	10	11	12	13	14	15	16	17	18	19	20

in → +2 → out

1	3
2	4
5	7
10	12

❺ Add the length of all the sides: 7 + 7 + 4 + 4 = 22.

Use words or pictures to answer the following questions.
Possible answers are shown.

❹ How does knowing the sum of 10 + 4 help you know the sum of 9 + 4?
The sum of 9 + 4 is 1 less than the sum of 10 + 4.

❺ How would you find the perimeter of this rectangle?

7

4

CHAPTER 2 Key Ideas Review

Ring the letter of the correct answer.

❻ If you know 2 + 6 = 8, then you also know that 6 + 2 = 8. This is an example of _____.

a. near-doubles facts
b. doubles facts
c. the Commutative Law

❼ Ethan is adding with the Paper Explorer. He can use the Paper Explorer to show that 8 + 8 is the same as _____.

a. 9 + 9
b. 9 + 7
c. 7 + 7

Write an addition fact you can use to solve each problem.

❽ Kori had 5 hamsters. Then she got 1 more. Now how many hamsters does Kori have?

__5__ + __1__ = __6__

❾ Jasmine bought 3 fish. Jamal bought 1 less. How many fish did they buy altogether?

__3__ + __2__ = __5__

❿ Mr. Thomas needs to buy new horseshoes for his horses. He has 2 horses. Each horse needs 4 shoes. How many horseshoes does Mr. Thomas need to buy?

__4__ + __4__ = __8__

Chapter Review

Use the Chapter 2 Review to indicate areas in which each student is having difficulty or in which the class may need help. If students do well on the Chapter 2 Review, you may wish to skip directly to the Chapter Test; if not, you may want to spend a day or so helping students overcome their individual difficulties before taking the Practice Test.

Next to each set of problems is a list of the lessons in the chapter that covered those concepts. If they need help, students can refer to a specific lesson for additional instruction. You can also use this information to make additional assignments based on the previous lesson concepts.

Have students complete pages 71–72 on their own.

Monitoring Student Progress

Problems 1–3 Lesson 2.7

If . . . students have difficulty with these problems,

Then . . . first determine whether they are having problems with the multistep addition or the cost of items, and then review one or both of those concepts.

Problems 4–9 Lesson 2.3

If . . . students write an incorrect answer,

Then . . . determine whether the +9 addition or the +10 addition is the difficulty, and then review accordingly.

Problems 10–11 Lesson 2.6

If . . . students have difficulty with these problems,

Then . . . review function machines, and have students illustrate the problems with craft sticks.

Problems 12–30 Lessons 2.1–2.5

If . . . students have difficulty with these problems,

Then . . . have two or three students play the **Doubles Game** or the **Addition Table Game.**

Problems 31–32 Lesson 2.8

If . . . students have difficulty with these problems,

Then . . . review the definition of *perimeter* and the problems from the Guided Discussion.

Name _____ Date _____

Lesson 2.7 **Figure** out how much each group of items costs. Write the answers.

① 3 cat cards 18¢

② 1 cat card and 1 horse card 15¢

③ 1 cat card, 1 horse card, and 1 dog card 18¢

Lesson 2.3 **Add.**

④ 10 + 8 = 18   ⑦ 2 + 9 = 11

⑤ 9 + 8 = 17   ⑧ 5 + 10 = 15

⑥ 2 + 10 = 12   ⑨ 5 + 9 = 14

Lesson 2.6 **Find** the missing numbers and the rule.

⑩

in	out
3	11
5	13
2	10
6	14

The rule is __+8__.

⑪

in	out
3	6
7	14
2	4
5	10

The rule is _double the number_.

Textbook This lesson is available in the *eTextbook*.   71

Student Page

Lessons 2.1–2.5 **Add.**

⑫ 2 + 4 = 6   ⑬ 0 + 3 = 3   ⑭ 1 + 7 = 8

⑮ 4   ⑯ 3   ⑰ 7   ⑱ 6   ⑲ 2
  + 2   + 0   + 1   + 2   + 6
   6   3   8   8   8

⑳ 10 + 10 = 20   ㉑ 1 + 1 = 2   ㉒ 3 + 3 = 6

㉓ 8 + 7 = 15   ㉔ 6 + 5 = 11   ㉕ 8 + 9 = 17

㉖ 7   ㉗ 6   ㉘ 9   ㉙ 9   ㉚ 6
  + 7   + 6   + 9   + 10   + 5
  14   12   18   19   11

Lesson 2.8 **Find** the perimeter.

㉛
Pentagon Perimeter = 10

㉜ **Extended Response** My porch is shaped like a square. It has a perimeter of 20 feet.

a. Could two of the sides be 5 feet and 3 feet? _no_

b. Why do you think so? _____

The lengths of the sides of a square are equal. They would have to be 5 feet to have a perimeter of 20 feet.

3 Chapter Tests

40

Practice Test

Student Pages 73–76

- The Chapter 2 Practice Test on **Student Edition** pages 73–76 provides an opportunity to formally evaluate students' proficiency with concepts developed in this chapter.
- The content is similar to the Chapter 2 Review, in standardized format.

Problems 25 and 26   **Extended Response**

Students practice addition and subtraction skills in different situations. For Problem 25, encourage students to notice the patterns in the table as they fill it in. Have them look for diagonal as well as vertical and horizontal patterns. For Problem 26, students focus on function tables and the rules governing these tables. This will be a key concept to develop for algebraic thinking.

CHAPTER 2 Practice Test

Name _____ Date _____

Add.

1. $4 + 4 = 8$
3. $7 + 7 = 14$
2. $3 + 4 = 7$
4. $9 + 9 = 18$

5.
$$\begin{array}{r} 5 \\ + 6 \\ \hline 11 \end{array}$$
6.
$$\begin{array}{r} 6 \\ + 6 \\ \hline 12 \end{array}$$
7.
$$\begin{array}{r} 5 \\ + 5 \\ \hline 10 \end{array}$$
8.
$$\begin{array}{r} 9 \\ + 8 \\ \hline 17 \end{array}$$

Add. Then use the same numbers to write another addition fact.

9. $4 + 6 = 10$
$6 + 4 = 10$

10. $7 + 5 = 12$
$5 + 7 = 12$

Solve.

11. Maya cut out a square. One side of the square is 3 inches long. What is the perimeter of the square? ___12 inches___

12. Mike drew a rectangle. Two sides of the rectangle are 4 inches long. The other two sides of the rectangle are 3 inches long. What is the perimeter of the rectangle? ___14 inches___

eTextbook This lesson is available in the *eTextbook*.

73

CHAPTER 2 Practice Test

Solve.

13. Jean had 7 new pencils. Then she got 8 more new pencils. How many new pencils did she have then?
   a. 7   b. 8   (c.) 15   d. can't tell

14. Jada sees 6 birds on the fence. She sees 4 birds in the tree. How many birds does she see altogether?
   a. 2   b. 4   c. 6   (d.) 10

15. Ashley read 12 pages in her book in the morning. Then she read 10 pages in the afternoon. How many pages did Ashley read altogether?
   a. 2   b. 10   c. 12   (d.) 22

Solve. Use the pictures to find the answers.

16. How much money is it for 2 backpacks?
   (a.) $20   b. $12   c. $10   d. $4

17. How much money is it for 1 skateboard and 1 paint set?
   a. $8   b. $10   c. $12   (d.) $14

18. How much money is it for 1 skateboard, 1 backpack, and 1 paint set?
   a. $12   b. $16   c. $18   (d.) $24

74   **Real Math** • Chapter 2

Name _____ Date _____

How much money?

⑲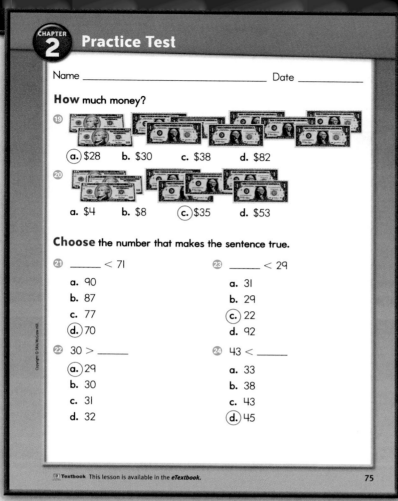

   (a.) $28   b. $30   c. $38   d. $82

⑳

   a. $4   b. $8   (c.) $35   d. $53

Choose the number that makes the sentence true.

㉑ _____ < 71

   a. 90
   b. 87
   c. 77
   (d.) 70

㉒ 30 > _____

   (a.) 29
   b. 30
   c. 31
   d. 32

㉓ _____ < 29

   a. 31
   b. 29
   (c.) 22
   d. 92

㉔ 43 < _____

   a. 33
   b. 38
   c. 43
   (d.) 45

Textbook This lesson is available in the eTextbook.

75

Student Page

Solve.

㉕ Extended Response Write the missing numbers in the Addition Table.

+	0	1	2	3	4	5	6	7	8	9	10
0	0	1	2	3	4	5	6	7	8	9	10
1	1	2	3	4	5	6	7	8	9	10	11
2	2	3	4	5	6	7	8	9	10	11	12
3	3	4	5	6	7	8	9	10	11	12	13

What is one pattern in the table? __Possible answers: Each number across and down is 1 more than the number before it; sums for doubles are in a diagonal line; matching sums are in a diagonal line.__

㉖ Extended Response **Create** two different function tables. Write the rule for each table.

in ◯ out

in ◯ out

Students should identify a different rule for each table, specify the input values for each table, and correctly follow each rule to complete each output value.

The rule is _____.   The rule is _____.

76   **Real Math • Chapter 2**

Chapter Test ✓ COMPUTING

For further evaluation instead of or in addition to this test, you may wish to have students take the Chapter 2 Test provided in **Assessment.**

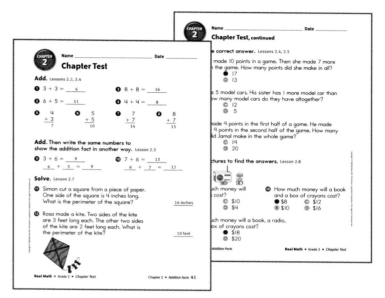

Assessment, pages 41–42

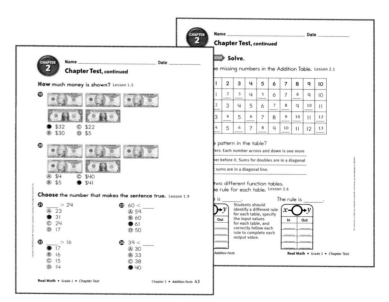

Assessment, pages 43–44

4 Assess and Differentiate

 Assess Use *eAssess* to record and analyze evidence of student understanding.

A Gather Evidence

Use the Daily Class Assessment Records in **Assessment** or *eAssess* to record Informal and Formal Assessments.

Informal Assessment

☑ **Key Ideas Review** 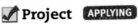 UNDERSTANDING

Did the student
- ❑ make important observations?
- ❑ extend or generalize learning?
- ❑ provide insightful answers?
- ❑ pose insightful questions?

Informal Assessment

☑ **Project** APPLYING

Did the student
- ❑ meet the project objectives?
- ❑ communicate clearly?
- ❑ complete the project accurately?
- ❑ connect mathematics to real-world situations?

Formal Assessment

☑ **Chapter Test**  COMPUTING

Score the test, and record the results.

B Summarize Findings

Analyze and summarize assessment data for each student. Determine which Chapter Follow-Up is appropriate for each student. Use the Student Assessment Record in **Assessment** or *eAssess* to update assessment records.

C Chapter Follow-Up • DIFFERENTIATE INSTRUCTION

Based on your observations, use these teaching strategies for chapter follow-up.

ENRICH	PRACTICE	RETEACH	INTERVENTION
If . . . students demonstrate a **secure understanding** of chapter concepts,	**If . . .** students demonstrate **competent understanding** of chapter concepts,	**If . . .** students demonstrate **emerging understanding** of chapter concepts,	**If . . .** students demonstrate **minimal understanding** of chapter concepts,
Then . . . move on to the next chapter.	**Then . . .** move on to the next chapter.	**Then . . .** move on to the next chapter, but continue to provide cumulative review.	**Then . . .** intensive intervention is still needed before they start the next chapter.

Plenty of Time

Context of the Thinking Story Trixie runs errands at Mr. Breezy's training school for dogs. Trixie tries to hurry, but she and Mr. Breezy have very different ideas about time.

Lesson Planner

OBJECTIVES
To develop logical thinking while integrating reading skills with mathematics

NCTM STANDARDS

Number and Operations
- Adding whole numbers
- Counting with understanding

Measurement
- Recognizing the attributes of time
- Using repetition of a single unit to measure something larger than the unit

READING STANDARDS
- Listening for details
- Drawing conclusions
- Evaluating information
- Making inferences

Using the Thinking Story

The Thinking Story may be used at any time throughout the chapter. Read the Thinking Story "Plenty of Time" to your class. As you read the story, give students time to think about each question, but not so much that they forget the point being made.

Plenty of Time

Trixie runs errands at Mr. Breezy's training school for dogs. Mr. Breezy is always in a hurry. He thinks that Trixie should be in a hurry too. Trixie tries to hurry, but she and Mr. Breezy have very different ideas about time.

One morning Mr. Breezy called Trixie into his office. "Here's what I'd like you to do, Trixie. First I'd like you to walk each dog around the block three times. Each dog likes to walk alone. So you need to walk all ten dogs, one at a time. Then would you please go to the drugstore and buy me a newspaper?"

"Sure," said Trixie. "I'll be back in about an hour."

"About an hour!" said Mr. Breezy. "That should be enough time to walk ten turtles. If it takes ten minutes to walk a dog, 15 minutes ought to be plenty of time to do everything."

Did Mr. Breezy give Trixie enough time to do the errands? no

How can you tell? It takes 10 minutes for each dog, and there are 10 dogs. That will take at least 100 minutes, or one hour and 40 minutes.

Trixie ran each dog around the block, ran to buy a newspaper, and then ran back to the school. She was out of breath when she got back. She had been running for more than an hour and a half.

How much time did Mr. Breezy think the errands would take? fifteen minutes

Why did it take Trixie so much longer? because she walked each dog individually

"Did you get lost?" Mr. Breezy asked Trixie when she got back.

"No," said Trixie, huffing and puffing. "I think you forgot—there are ten dogs, so I had to run around the block 30 times and then get a newspaper."

"You must be tired," said Mr. Breezy. "I'll make this next errand much easier. First walk to the grocery store. That should take ten minutes, even if you walk slowly. Then buy a large box of dog biscuits. That will take another ten minutes. So the whole trip should take you only twenty minutes."

What did Mr. Breezy forget to count? **walking back from the grocery store**

How long should the trip really take? **thirty minutes**

When Trixie returned from the grocery store, Mr. Breezy said, "You'll be happy to hear about the next job I have for you. It has only one part to it. You need to get a dog magazine at the newsstand on the corner."

"About how long will that take?" asked Trixie.

"An hour," he answered.

Is Mr. Breezy right? **No; it won't take that long.**

How long should it take? **five or ten minutes**

Trixie bought the magazine and returned in five minutes. "You were really quick this time," said Mr. Breezy. "It's getting near lunchtime. Luckily there are only five more things that need to be done."

Trixie groaned to herself. She knew that meant she was going to miss lunch.

"Now the first thing," said Mr. Breezy, "is that Bowser is acting like a very sad dog these days, and I'd like you to take him over to the park and let him run around for 15 minutes."

Trixie wrote *15 minutes* on a sheet of paper so she would remember.

"And while Bowser is running around, I'd like you to keep saying 'nice doggie' and things like that to him to make him feel better."

"That's another 15 minutes," Trixie thought sadly, writing it down.

Will that really take 15 more minutes? no

Why not? It's done at the same time Bowser is running around.

"I also want you to notice carefully what the weather is like," Mr. Breezy said, "because I'm trying to decide whether to play golf this afternoon."

"Five more minutes," Trixie thought, writing it down.

"And I want you to breathe deeply and run around a little yourself," Mr. Breezy added. "You're looking a bit run-down, and I think it will do you good."

Trixie wrote *ten minutes* on the sheet of paper.

"And finally I want you to keep an eye on Bowser all the time and see that he doesn't get into any trouble."

"How long will that take?" Trixie asked.

"About 15 minutes," Mr. Breezy said.

Trixie looked at the numbers she had written down: 15, 15, 5, 10, and 15.

About how much will these numbers add up to? Can anyone figure it out exactly? **60 minutes**

"Sixty minutes," Trixie said unhappily. "A whole hour!"

Should all these things take an hour to do? **no**

Why not? **They can be done at the same time.**

Trixie took Bowser to the park and let him run around. She had to run quite a bit to stay close enough to keep an eye on Bowser and so that Bowser could hear her saying *nice doggie* and things like

that. At the end of 15 minutes, Trixie was breathing hard from running around so much, but she felt good because it was such a bright, sunny day. "Now what's the next thing I have to do?" she asked herself, trying to remember all the things Mr. Breezy had told her.

What chores does Trixie have left to do? **none**

How much time has she spent? **15 minutes**

Why did the chores take so little time? **She did all of them at the same time.**

Trixie realized that she had already done all the things Mr. Breezy had asked her to do and that it had taken only 15 minutes instead of an hour. "Sometimes I'm so fast I surprise myself," she said happily.

The End

Guided Discussion

As students answer the questions in the story, ask them to communicate how they chose their answers. Allow students to debate the answers if necessary.

Using Student Pages 77–78

Have students follow the instructions and complete the **Student Edition** activities. Read the instructions aloud if students are having difficulty.

Name _____ Date _____

Thinking Story

Plenty of Time

Untangle the leashes. Trace the path of each leash to the correct dog.

Textbook This lesson is available in the *eTextbook*.

77

Student Page

Look at the list of errands. How long will the errands take altogether?

To Do List

Walk dog— 10 minutes

Buy dog food— 15 minutes

Brush dog— 5 minutes

Give dog a bath— 20 minutes

Total time _____ 50 minutes

78

Real Math • Chapter 2

Lesson Study

Reflect on each of the lessons you taught in this chapter. Rate each one on the following scale, and then consider ways to maintain or improve positive teaching experiences in the future.

Lessons	Very Effective	Effective	Less Effective	What Worked	Ways to Improve
2.1 Basic Addition Facts and Table					
2.2 The Commutative Law					
2.3 +10 and +9 Addition Facts					
2.4 Doubles					
2.5 Near Doubles					
2.6 Remaining Facts and Function Machines					
2.7 Using Multiple Addends					
2.8 Applying Addition					
2.9 The Paper Explorer—Single-Digit Addition					

Subtraction Facts

Teaching for Understanding

This chapter focuses on developing automatic and quick recall of subtraction facts. The objective is to relate the subtraction facts to the addition facts students previously memorized. By emphasizing the inverse operations and by teaching several new techniques for remembering subtraction facts, students will gain mastery. Students will also study the effects of subtracting whole numbers in real-world applications. Students will use representations to develop and use strategies of whole-number subtraction computations.

Prerequisite Skills and Concepts

- Addition Facts ● Counting Back on a Number Line ● Recognizing Addition and Subtraction Situations

Subtraction Facts Skills Trace

Before Grade 2	Grade 2	After Grade 2
Grades K–1 Informally and formally introduced subtraction to 100	**Chapter 2** reviewed addition facts and properties of addition. **This chapter** develops fluency with computational strategies for subtraction.	Review and mastery of the meaning of subtraction and basic facts Formal introduction of larger numbers and more complex patterns

Problem Solving

Problem solving is in every lesson. This chapter includes the following:

CHAPTER INTRODUCTION Students will create paper bridges and then compare numbers to see how much stronger one bridge is than another. (pp. 79I–80C)

EXPLORING PROBLEM SOLVING Lessons provide a specific focus on problem-solving strategies. (pp. 87–88, 88A and 99–100, 100A)

THINKING STORY In "Ferdie Knows the Rules" students expand on the characters' discussions of rules that work and rules that do not work. (pp. 111A–111E, 111–112)

Games

Develop reasoning skills, and provide extensive practice.

- **Space Game** (Lesson 3.2)
- **Roll 20 to 5 Game** (Lessons 3.3, 3.4, 3.6, 3.7)

Math Background

Subtraction Facts

About Subtraction

- Addition and subtraction are inverse operations; that is, they have the opposite effect or "undo" each other. Thus if $7 + 3 = 10$, then $10 - 7 = 3$ and $10 - 3 = 7$. Studying inverse operations helps students see the relationship between addition and subtraction.

- Subtraction exercises can be thought of as "adding up to" or "taking away from." For example, to find $8 - 3$, students can think "3 plus what makes 8?" or "What is 3 less than 8?"

- In **Real Math** subtraction facts are not taught systematically in the same way as addition facts are because most subtraction facts are best recalled by knowing addition facts. Facts that involve subtracting 0, 5, 9, and 10 and differences of 10 are generally quick to find, and these facts are taught explicitly.

Speed Tests

- Speed tests on addition and subtraction facts should be administered periodically throughout the year. These exercises are important because many students get correct answers to addition and subtraction problems by learning to count quickly. They appear to have the facts memorized, but in fact never succeed in doing so.

- By decreasing the time students have to respond to computation exercises, we encourage memorization and discourage fast counting.

- Be sure to emphasize that students should aim to improve their performance by increasing the number of correct answers in the given amount of time. They should not be competing with each other.

Types of Subtraction Problems

Three types of subtraction problems are illustrated by the following examples, all of which can be described by the statement $7 - 4 = \underline{\quad}$:

1. <u>Take away.</u> Sari had 7 erasers. She lost 4 of them. Now how many does she have? Here we start with a set of 7 objects and take away a subset of 4 objects.

2. <u>How many more?</u> Sari has 4 erasers, and she wants to have 7. How many more does she need? Here we start with a set of 4 objects and want to know how many more objects must be added to the set.

3. <u>Compare.</u> Sari has 7 erasers, and Shayna has 4 erasers. How many more erasers does Sari have? Here we are comparing a set of 7 objects with a set of 4 objects.

Subtraction Fact Helpers

These strategies can help with some of the subtraction facts. For other subtraction facts, think of the corresponding addition fact.

To subtract:	Think of:
0	No change
5	Take away 5 fingers.
9	Add 10 then subtract 1.
10	Subtract 1 from tens digit.
Differences of 10	For numbers 0–19, if the ones digits are the same, the difference is 10.

What Research Says

About Strategy Development for Addition and Subtraction

How Children Develop Strategies for Addition and Subtraction

Composing and decomposing are combining and separating operations that allow children to build concepts of parts and wholes. Most prekindergartners can see that two items and one item make three items. Later, children learn to separate a group into parts in various ways and then to count to produce all the number partners of a given number. Eventually children think of a number and know the different addition facts that make that number.

The ability to add and subtract fluently develops over the course of several years. Over time, a child gains counting strategies and greater understanding of part/whole relationships. Children come to recognize that larger numbers can be decomposed, or broken into smaller parts, and they develop greater flexibility in their use of strategies for finding sums and differences.

As children first develop counting strategies and greater understanding of part/whole relationships, they recognize that numbers can be composed of or decomposed into smaller collections or units in a variety of ways. The young child acquires an awareness of part/whole relationships with numbers in the process of developing counting, subitizing, and comparison abilities in working with collections of objects.

Learning Trajectories for Composing Numbers

Key steps from the learning trajectory for composing numbers for children in Grades 1 and 2 are described below. For the complete trajectory, see Appendix B.

Stage	Description
Composer to 7	A sign of development is when a child knows number combinations to totals of 7. A child at this level quickly names parts of any whole or the whole when given parts and can double numbers to 10. For example, when shown 6 and 4 are secretly hidden, then shown the 2 remaining, the child quickly says 4 are hidden.
Composer with Tens and Ones	At the next level the child understands two-digit numbers as tens and ones, can count with dimes and pennies, and can perform two-digit addition with regrouping. For example, a child at this level can explain, "17 plus 36 is like 17 plus 3, which equals 20, plus 33, which equals 53."

Clements, Douglas and J. Sarama, eds. *Engaging Young Children in Mathematics: Standards for Early Childhood Mathematics Education.* Mahwah, New Jersey: Lawrence Erlbaum Associates, Publishers, 2004.

Research-Based Teaching Techniques

It is very important for teachers to provide children with opportunities to recognize the meaning of mathematical symbols, mathematical operations, and the patterns or relationships represented in the child's work with numbers. For example, the number sense that a child acquires should be based upon an understanding that inverse operations such as addition and subtraction undo the operations of the other. Instructionally, teachers must encourage their students to think beyond simply finding the answer and to actually have them think about the numerical relationships that are being represented or modeled by the symbols, words, or materials being used in the lesson.

Kilpatrick, J., J. Swafford, and B. Findell, eds. *Adding It Up: Helping Children Learn Mathematics.* Washington, D.C.: National Research Council/National Academy Press, 2001, pp. 270–271.

"As children work with numbers, they gradually develop flexibility in thinking about numbers, which is a hallmark of number sense. … Number sense develops as students understand the size of numbers, develop multiple ways of thinking about and representing numbers, use numbers as referents, and develop accurate perceptions about the effects of operations on numbers."

National Council of Teachers of Mathematics. *Principles and Standards for School Mathematics.* Reston, VA: NCTM, p. 80.

RESEARCH IN ACTION

Counting—Chapter 3 continues to reinforce the development of effective and efficient procedures for counting, combining, and separating collections of objects.

Composing and Decomposing Collections—Throughout Chapter 3 students explore and develop additional strategies, concepts, and procedures for adding and subtracting collections.

Equalities and Inequalities—Chapter 3 focuses on ways that the child can represent equalities and inequalities for use in problem-solving contexts.

Vocabulary

addend (Lesson 3.1) a number that is to be added to another

difference (Lesson 3.4) the remainder left after subtracting one quantity from another. $7 - 5 = 2$; 2 is the **difference** of 7 minus 5.

English Learner

Cognates

For English learners, a quick way to acquire new English vocabulary is to build on what is known in the primary language.

English	Spanish
explain	explica
subtraction	sustracción
functions	funciones
difference	diferencia
distance	distancia
dollar	dólar
calculations	calculaciones

Access Vocabulary

English learners may understand words in different contexts or not understand idioms. Review chapter vocabulary for this concern. For example:

undo	reverse the action
a tie	when both competitors end with the same score
input	numbers that go into the function machine
solve the following	find the answer
decrease	get smaller in number; have fewer
price	how much something costs
souvenirs	items you purchase to remember a trip or event

Chapter Planner

Lessons	Objectives	NCTM Standards	State Standards
3.1 Missing Addends and Subtraction pages 81A–82A 45–60 minutes	To review the inverse relation between addition and subtraction and to show the relation between missing addends and subtraction	Number and Operations, Communication	
3.2 Subtraction Facts and the Addition Table pages 83A–84A 45–60 minutes	To continue reviewing the inverse relation between addition and subtraction focusing on using the Addition Table to find differences	Number and Operations, Problem Solving	
3.3 Addition and Subtraction Functions pages 85A–86A 45–60 minutes	To practice addition and subtraction using the function machine	Number and Operations, Algebra	
3.4 Subtraction Involving 10 and 9 pages 91A–92A 45–60 minutes	To learn subtraction facts that involve 10 and 9	Number and Operations, Representation	
3.5 Subtraction Facts pages 93A–94A 45–60 minutes	To continue reviewing subtraction focusing on quick recall of those facts	Number and Operations, Representation	
3.6 Applications of Addition and Subtraction pages 95A–96A 45–60 minutes	To continue reviewing addition and subtraction focusing on problem-solving applications	Number and Operations, Problem Solving	
3.7 Chain Calculations pages 97A–98A 45–60 minutes	To introduce chain calculations focusing on adding and subtracting three or more numbers	Number and Operations, Problem Solving	

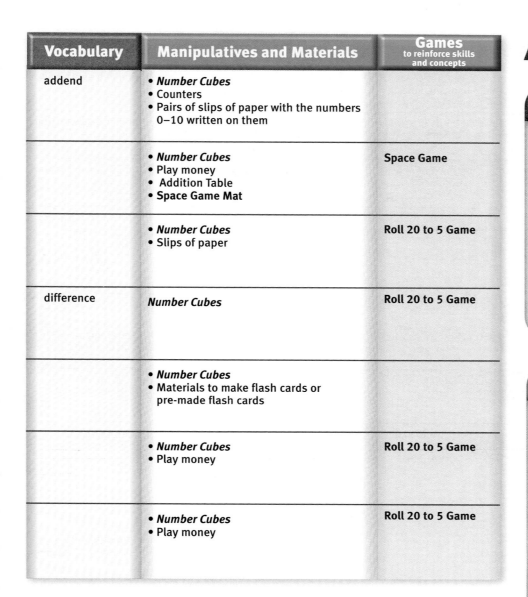

Vocabulary	Manipulatives and Materials	Games to reinforce skills and concepts
addend	• *Number Cubes* • Counters • Pairs of slips of paper with the numbers 0–10 written on them	
	• *Number Cubes* • Play money • Addition Table • **Space Game Mat**	**Space Game**
	• *Number Cubes* • Slips of paper	**Roll 20 to 5 Game**
difference	*Number Cubes*	**Roll 20 to 5 Game**
	• *Number Cubes* • Materials to make flash cards or pre-made flash cards	
	• *Number Cubes* • Play money	**Roll 20 to 5 Game**
	• *Number Cubes* • Play money	**Roll 20 to 5 Game**

Additional Resources

Differentiated Instruction

Intervention Support Guide Provides instruction for the following prerequisite skills:

- Lesson 3.A Addition and Subtraction–1
- Lesson 3.B Addition and Subtraction–2
- Lesson 3.C Addition and Subtraction–3

Enrichment Support Guide Extends lesson concepts

Practice Reinforces lesson skills and concepts

Reteach Support Guide Provides alternate instruction for lesson concepts

English Learner Support Guide Previews and reviews lesson concepts and vocabulary for English learners

Technology

The following electronic resources are available:

🅴 **Planner** Lessons 3.1–3.7

🅴 **Presentation** Lessons 3.1–3.7

🅴 **Textbook** Lessons 3.1–3.7

🅴 **Assess** Lessons 3.1–3.7

🅴 **MathTools** *Sets Former* Lessons 3.1, 3.2, 3.4
　　　　　　Addition Table Lessons 3.2, 3.5
　　　　　　Function Machine Lesson 3.3
　　　　　　Coins and Money Lessons 3.6, 3.7
　　　　　　Number Line Lesson 3.2

🅴 **Games** *Roll 20 to 5 Game* Lessons 3.3, 3.4, 3.6, 3.7

Building Blocks *Pizza Pizzazz 5* Lesson 3.1
　　　　　Barkley's Bones 1–20 Lesson 3.2
　　　　　Function Machine 1 Lesson 3.3
　　　　　Word Problems with Tools 3 Lesson 3.6

Assessment
Informal Assessment rubrics at the end of each lesson provide daily evaluation of student math proficiency.

Chapter Planner, continued

Problem Solving	When to Use	Objectives	NCTM Standards	Skills Covered
Chapter Introduction (pp. 79I–80C) 15–30 minutes	Use before beginning Chapter 3.	To introduce chapter concepts in a problem-solving setting	Problem Solving, Communication	Basic addition and subtraction facts
Exploring Problem Solving (pp. 87–88, 88A) 30–45 minutes	Use anytime during the chapter.	To explore methods of solving nonroutine problems	Problem Solving, Communication	Basic addition and subtraction facts
Exploring Problem Solving (pp. 99–100, 100A) 45–60 minutes	Use anytime during the chapter.	To explore methods of solving nonroutine problems	Problem Solving, Communication	Basic addition and subtraction facts
Thinking Story—Ferdie Knows the Rules (pp. 111A–111E, 111–112) 20–30 minutes	Use anytime during the chapter.	To develop logical reasoning while integrating reading skills with mathematics	Number and Operations, Problem Solving	Basic addition and subtraction rules

Review				
Cumulative Review (p. 89–90) 15–30 minutes	Use anytime after Lesson 3.3.	To review concepts and skills taught earlier in the year	Number and Operations	Subtraction strategies, Subtraction facts
Cumulative Review (p. 101–102) 15–30 minutes	Use anytime after Lesson 3.7.	To review concepts and skills taught earlier in the year	Number and Operations	Subtraction strategies, Applications of subtraction
Chapter 3 Review (pp. 105A, 105–106) 30–45 minutes	Use after Lesson 3.7.	To review concepts and skills taught in the chapter	Number and Operations	Subtraction strategies, Applications of subtraction

Assessment				
Informal Assessment Rubrics (pp. 82A–98A) 5 minutes per student	Use at the end of each lesson.	To provide daily evaluation of math proficiency	Number and Operations, Communication	Computing, Understanding, Reasoning, Applying, Engaging
Pretest (*Assessment* pp. 46–47) 15–30 minutes	Use prior to Chapter 3.	To provide assessment of prerequisite and chapter topics	Number and Operations, Problem Solving	Computing, Understanding, Reasoning, Applying, Engaging
Individual Oral Assessment (p. 90A) 5 minutes per student	Begin use after Lesson 3.3.	To provide alternate means of assessing students' progress	Number and Operations	Addition and subtraction facts
Mastery Checkpoint (*Assessment* p. T55) 5 minutes per student	Use after Lesson 3.6.	To provide assessment of mastery of key skills	Number and Operations	Subtraction facts
Chapter 3 Practice Test (pp. 107–108, 109–110) 30–45 minutes	Use after or in place of the Chapter 3 Review.	To provide assessment of the chapter concepts	Data Analysis and Probability, Number and Operations	Subtraction facts
Chapter 3 Test (*Assessment* pp. 52–55) 30–45 minutes	Use after or in place of the Chapter 3 Review.	To provide assessment of the chapter concepts	Data Analysis and Probability, Number and Operations	Subtraction facts

Technology Resources and Support

Visit SRAonline.com for online versions of the **Real Math** eSuite.

Technology for Teachers

e Presentation	Lessons 3.1–3.7 Use the *ePresentation* to interactively present chapter content.
e Planner	Use the Chapter and Lesson Planners to outline activities and time frames for Chapter 3.
e Assess	Students can take the following assessments in *eAssess:* • Chapter Pretest • Mastery Checkpoint **Lesson 3.6** • Speed Test **Lesson 3.5** • Chapter Test Teachers can record results and print reports for all assessments in this chapter.
e MathTools	**Sets Former** Lessons 3.1, 3.2, 3.4 **Addition Table** Lessons 3.2, 3.5 **Function Machine** Lesson 3.3 **Coins and Money** Lessons 3.6, 3.7 **Number Line** Lesson 3.2

Technology for Students

e Textbook	An electronic, interactive version of the **Student Edition** is available for all lessons in Chapter 3.
e MathTools	**Sets Former** Lessons 3.1, 3.2, 3.4 **Addition Table** Lessons 3.2, 3.5 **Function Machine** Lesson 3.3 **Coins and Money** Lessons 3.6, 3.7 **Number Line** Lesson 3.2
e Games	**Roll 20 to 5 Game** Lessons 3.3, 3.4, 3.6, 3.7
TECH KNOWLEDGE	*TechKnowledge* Level 2 provides lessons that specifically teach the Unit 10 Internet and Unit 6 Presentation applications that students can use while working on this chapter's projects.
Building Blocks	**Pizza Pizzazz 5** Lesson 3.1 **Barkley's Bones 1–20** Lesson 3.2 **Function Machine 1** Lesson 3.3 **Word Problems with Tools 3** Lesson 3.6

CHAPTER 3 Introduction

Subtraction Facts

 Introduce Chapter 3 10

Chapter Objectives

Explain to students that in this chapter they will build on what they already know about subtraction. They will

- subtract numbers.
- apply addition and subtraction to real-world situations.
- perform chain calculations.

Pretest **COMPUTING**

Administer the Pretest on **Assessment** pages 46 and 47.

The Pretest covers the following prerequisite skills and topics from this chapter:

- Numerical and visual estimating (Problems 1–4)
- Comparing amounts (Problems 5–8)
- Addition and subtraction to 20 (Problems 9–15)
- Missing Addends (Problems 16–18)
- Function tables (Problems 19–20)

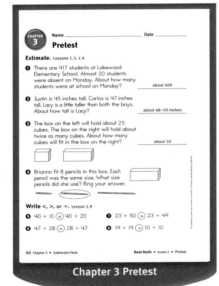

Chapter 3 Pretest

Access Prior Knowledge **UNDERSTANDING**

Have students talk about things they have made by folding paper. If any students have heard the term *origami,* have them tell the class what it means. Introduce origami by reading to the class a related story, such as *The Paper Crane* by Molly Bang.

You might want to teach students an origami project such as those found in one of the following books:

Absolute Beginner's Origami by Nick Robinson
Origami 1-2-3 by David Petty
Origami in the Classroom by Chiyo Araki

2 Exploring Problem Solving 15

Tell Students In Today's Lesson They Will

- make and test paper bridges.
- compare numbers to see how much stronger one bridge is than the other.

Materials

- Sheets of paper for folding
- Safety scissors (or other similar objects for use as weights)

Guided Discussion **UNDERSTANDING**

Have students look at the photograph on page 79. Explain that origami is a process of folding paper into shapes that represent other things. It originated in Japan. Ask questions such as the following:

- **What do these origami sculptures look like?** Possible answers: birds, flowers
- **How do you think they were made?** by folding paper; by following directions
- **What might people do with these paper figures?** use them for decoration; give them to other people; play with them

Strategy Building **REASONING**

Have students look at the first illustration on page 80. Ask questions such as the following:

- **How are the two sheets of paper alike?** Both have folds; the folds go the same way; the folds go with the long side of the paper.
- **How are the two sheets different?** One has more folds than the other; one has three folds, the other has nine folds.
- **Which paper do you think is stronger?** Allow students to speculate and offer reasons.
- **How could you find out?** Allow students to offer suggestions. The illustration on page 80 will give them one idea.

Have students look at the second illustration on page 80. Explain that the students in the illustration are experimenting with paper folding to see how to build the strongest bridge they can build. To help students understand the activity, ask questions such as the following:

- **What do you think these students are doing?** seeing how strong the paper bridges are; seeing how many scissors a sheet of paper can hold
- **What are they using to test how strong the bridges are?** scissors
- **How will that tell them which bridge is stronger?** The bridge that supports more pairs of scissors before it collapses is stronger.

CHAPTER 3 **Subtraction Facts**

In This Chapter You Will Learn
- basic subtraction facts.
- applications of addition and subtraction.
- chain calculations.

79

Problem Solving

Name _____ Date _____

Which is stronger?

Measure to find out. Record your results in the table.

Paper Bridge	Amount It Held

The paper for the stronger bridge held _____ more scissors than the paper for the weaker bridge. Results may vary, but in all cases the one with many folds held more than the one with a few folds.

Show how you solved it.

80   Real Math • Chapter 3

Using Student Pages APPLYING

Give each group two or three sheets of plain paper. Demonstrate each step of the activity illustrated on page 80. Have students work in their groups to do the activity themselves by following the steps below. Give help as needed.

- Fold one paper so it has exactly three creases and the other paper so it has nine creases.
- Make a paper bridge by supporting each end of one of the folded sheets. Students can use thick books such as dictionaries, school boxes, or other classroom objects to support the sheets.
- Carefully place a pair of safety scissors across the paper bridge. Slowly, one by one, keep adding more pairs of scissors until the bridge collapses.
- Record the number of scissors in the table on page 80.
- Test the other sheet of paper in the same way.

Extensions APPLYING

Have students compare sheets with other numbers of creases.

Have students compare sheets with creases that are parallel to the long side of the paper with sheets with creases that are parallel to the short side of the paper.

Concept/Question Board APPLYING

Questions
Have students think of and write three questions they have about subtraction and how it can be used. Then have them select one question to post on the Question side of the Board.

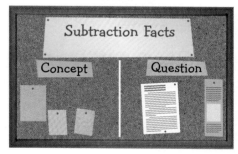

Concepts
As students work through the chapter, have them collect examples of how subtraction is used in everyday situations. For each example, have them write a problem that relates to the item(s). Have them display their examples on the Concept side of the Board. Suggest the following:

- gardening
- telling time

Answers
Throughout the chapter, have students post answers to the questions and solutions to the problems on the Board.

3 Reflect

20

Knowledge Age Skills

Effective Communication Have each group present their results, including how many more items one bridge held than the other. Record all the results on the board. Ask questions such as the following:

■ **Can we tell which paper is stronger?** Yes; in all cases the one with many folds held more than the one with just a few folds.
■ **Can we predict how many more scissors the stronger paper will hold?** Because test results will not be exactly the same, students might disagree about this.

In discussion, bring out the following points:

● Even though everyone did the same test, some of the results were different. That does not mean that some results are wrong or that the test is not useful.
● You can draw conclusions even when results of tests or measurements are not all the same.
● Knowing how much more one thing is than another can be a useful way to compare them.
● There are many ways to find out how much more one number is than another.

Sample Solutions Strategies

To find the difference between two numbers, students might use one or more of the following strategies.

Make a Physical Graph/Make a Model

Students might line up scissors in two rows, one to show how many the weaker bridge supported and the other to show how many the stronger bridge supported. Then they might eliminate the matching ones and count how many are left. Or they might simply count the excess in the longer row.

Draw a Picture

Students might draw a picture to show the number of scissors supported by the stronger bridge. Then they might cross out the number the weaker bridge supported and count what is left.

Use Operation Sense

Students might ask themselves: *How many do I need to add to the small number to make it the same as the big number?*

Home Connection

At this time, you may want to send home the letter on pages 10–13 of *Home Connection.* This letter describes what students will be learning and what activities they can do at home to support their work in school.

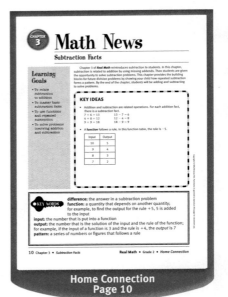

Home Connection
Page 10

Assess and Differentiate

 Assess Use *eAssess* to record and analyze evidence of student understanding.

A Gather Evidence

Use the Daily Class Assessment Records in *Assessment* or *eAssess* to record Informal and Formal Assessments.

Informal Assessment
☑ **Access Prior Knowledge**
Did the student  **UNDERSTANDING**
- ❑ make important observations?
- ❑ extend or generalize learning?
- ❑ provide insightful answers?
- ❑ pose insightful questions?

Informal Assessment
☑ **Concept/Question Board**
Did the student **APPLYING**
- ❑ apply learning in new situations?
- ❑ contribute concepts?
- ❑ contribute answers?
- ❑ connect mathematics to real-world situations?

Formal Assessment
☑ **Pretest** 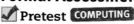 **COMPUTING**
Review student answers in each problem set.
- ❑ Numerical and visual estimating (Problems 1–4)
- ❑ Comparing amounts (Problems 5–8)
- ❑ Addition and subtraction to 20 (Problems 9–15)
- ❑ Missing Addends (Problems 16–18)
- ❑ Function tables (Problems 19–20)

B Summarize Findings

Analyze and summarize assessment data for each student. Determine which Assessment Follow-Up is appropriate for each student. Use the Student Assessment Record in *Assessment* or *eAssess* to update assessment records.

C Assessment Follow-Up • DIFFERENTIATE INSTRUCTION

Based on your observations of each student, use these teaching strategies for a general approach to the chapter. Look for specific Differentiate Instruction and Monitoring Student Progress strategies in each lesson that relate specifically to the lesson content.

ENRICH	PRACTICE	RETEACH	INTERVENTION	ENGLISH LEARNER
If . . . students demonstrate a **secure understanding** of chapter concepts, **Then . . .** move quickly through the chapter or use *Enrichment* Lessons 3.1–3.7 as assessment follow-up to extend and apply understanding.	**If . . .** students grasp chapter concepts with **competent understanding**, **Then . . .** use *Practice* Lessons 3.1–3.7 as lesson follow-up to develop fluency.	**If . . .** students have prerequisite understanding but demonstrate **emerging understanding** of chapter concepts, **Then . . .** use *Reteach* Lesson 3.5 to reteach lesson concepts.	**If . . .** students are not competent with prerequisite skills, **Then . . .** use *Intervention* Lessons 3.A–3.C before each lesson to develop fluency with prerequisite skills.	Use *English Learner Support Guide* Lessons 3.1–3.7 for strategies to preteach lesson vocabulary and concepts.

Math Across the Curriculum

Preview the chapter projects with students. Assign projects or have students choose from the projects to extend and enrich concepts in this chapter.

Create an Origami Flower 2–3 weeks

MATH OBJECTIVE
To reinforce studies of addition and subtraction by calculating the total amount of folds

FINE ARTS OBJECTIVE
To reinforce studies of the element of form by creating an origami flower

TECHNOLOGY OBJECTIVE
To use a scanner and printer to create origami paper

Have students use mathematics to create an origami flower. To broaden the fine arts concept, have students incorporate elements of form you are currently studying.

As part of the project, students should consider the following issues:

- how to design origami paper
- how to follow directions to create an origami form
- the relationship between addition and subtraction
- how to use a scanner and a printer

For specific step-by-step instructions for this project, see **Across the Curriculum Math Connections** pages 32–35.

Creative Work with Ideas Students create origami paper with floral motifs.

Problem Formulation, Planning, and Strategizing Students follow steps to create origami flowers.

Present the History of Origami 2–3 weeks

MATH OBJECTIVE
To reinforce studies of subtraction by calculating time between historic dates

LANGUAGE ARTS OBJECTIVE
To reinforce studies of details by including details in a presentation about origami

TECHNOLOGY OBJECTIVE
To use a presentation program to present the history of origami

Have students use technology to

- research the history of origami and take a quiz on origami history.
- create a slide show about the history of origami.

For this project, students use the Internet to investigate the following information:

- the history of origami
- examples of origami
- an interview with an origami expert

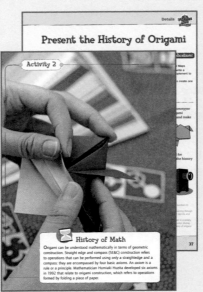

For specific step-by-step instructions for this project, see **Across the Curriculum Math Connections** pages 36–41.

High-Level Responsibility Students become "experts" on the history of origami.

Effective Communication Students communicate clearly and convincingly in writing, slide shows, and presentations.

TechKnowledge Level 2 provides lessons that specifically teach the Unit 10 Internet and Unit 6 Presentation applications that students can use in this project.

Lesson Planner

OBJECTIVES
- To show the relation between missing addends and subtraction
- To review the inverse relation between addition and subtraction
- To show how knowledge of addition facts can aid in the recall of subtraction facts

NCTM STANDARDS

Number and Operations
- Understanding the effects of adding and subtracting whole numbers
- Developing and using strategies for whole-number computations
- Developing fluency with basic number combinations for addition and subtraction

Communication
Organizing and consolidating mathematical thinking through communication

MATERIALS
- *Number Cubes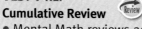
- *Counters
- Pairs of slips of paper with the numbers 0 through 10 written on them

TECHNOLOGY
- ⓔ **Presentation** Lesson 3.1
- ⓔ **MathTools** Sets Former
- **Building Blocks** Pizza Pizzazz 5

TEST PREP

Cumulative Review
- Mental Math reviews addition facts (Lessons 2.1–2.6).
- Problems 1–24 review addition facts (Lessons 2.1–2.6).

Extended Response
Problem 25

Looking Ahead
You will need the function machine you made for Lesson 2.6 in Lesson 3.3.

Missing Addends and Subtraction

Context of the Lesson This is the first lesson that covers subtraction. In this lesson students begin to develop an understanding of subtraction by solving missing-addend problems. If your students have already mastered subtraction, you may be able to skip this chapter or move through it rapidly.

See page 79B for Math Background for teachers for this lesson.

Planning for Learning ● DIFFERENTIATE INSTRUCTION

INTERVENTION

If . . . students lack the prerequisite skill of addition facts,

Then . . . teach **Intervention** Lesson 3.A.

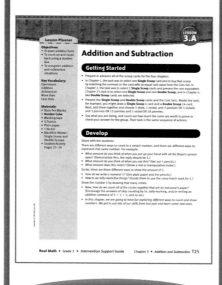

Intervention Lesson 3.A

ENGLISH LEARNER

Preview

If . . . students need language support,

Then . . . use Lesson 3.1 in **English Learner Support Guide** to preview lesson concepts and vocabulary.

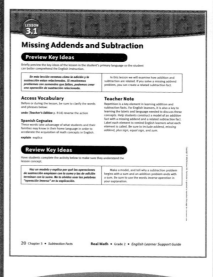

English Learner Lesson 3.1

ENRICH

If . . . students are proficient in the lesson concepts,

Then . . . emphasize Guided Discussion in Reflect.

PRACTICE

If . . . students would benefit from additional practice,

Then . . . extend Skill Practice before assigning the student pages.

RETEACH

If . . . students are having difficulty understanding subtraction,

Then . . . extend Guided Discussion before assigning the student pages.

Vocabulary
addend \ad´end\ *n.* a number that is to be added to another

Access Vocabulary
undo reverse the action

Spanish Cognates
explain explica

*Manipulative Kit Item

Mental Math 5

  Ask a series of basic addition problems, and have students find, hide, and show answers with **Number Cubes.** Possible examples include the following:

a. 4 + 2 = 6   **b.** 2 + 4 = 6   **c.** 3 + 8 = 11
d. 5 + 7 = 12   **e.** 7 + 5 = 12   **f.** 9 + 10 = 19

1 Develop 20

Tell Students In Today's Lesson They Will
learn about missing addends and their relationship to subtraction.

Whole Group

Guided Discussion MathTools REASONING

Inverse Relationships
Discuss the relationship between addition and subtraction. Use counters or **eMathTools: Sets Former** to demonstrate.

Write a problem on the board for students: 7 − 3 = 4, 4 + 3 = 7

- Students should see that problems involving addition generally bring together two sets of things to make a bigger set. Subtraction generally takes a smaller set of things from a larger set, leaving another small set.
- Subtraction can be thought of as undoing addition, and addition can also be thought of as undoing subtraction. So if you know that 4 + 3 = 7, you also know that 7 − 3 = 4.

Missing Addends
Present word problems as you write the corresponding expressions on the board. Use counters or **eMathTools: Sets Former** to demonstrate.

- **There were 8 people in a room. Then 6 more came into the room. How many were there altogether? 8 + 6 = 14**

Next try a problem that involves a missing addend. For example:

- There were some people in a room. Then 6 more came into the room, and there were 14. How many were in the room to start? ___ + 6 = 14   14 − 6 = 8

Now do a similar problem with the same numbers but this time with a missing second term. For example:

- There were 8 people in a room. Some more came in. Then there were 14 in the room. How many came in? 8 + ___ = 14; 14 − 8 = 6

Skill Building  UNDERSTANDING

Whole Group

Numbers on the Back Activity
- You will need pairs of slips of paper, each with numbers written on them—two slips with 0, two slips with 1, two slips with 2, and so on through 10.
1. Call two students to the front of the room, have them stand with their backs to the class, and attach a number to each student's back.

2. Allow each student to see the number on the other student's back.
3. Tell students that they are to determine the number on their own back but that first they will need a clue from the class.
4. Tell the class to give the sum of the two numbers as the clue. Each student is to determine the number on his or her back.
5. Repeat with other students, adjusting the difficulty level each time to the ability of students.

- As students engage in this activity, they are solving missing-term problems. For example, if students have the numbers 6 and 8 on their backs, then one student is solving the missing-addend problem 6 + ___ = 14, and the other student is solving the missing-addend problem 8 + ___ = 14.

Monitoring Student Progress

If . . . a student has difficulty determining the number on his or her back in front of the class,

Then . . . help the student by thinking aloud as you write the problem on the board. For example: *We know that Mark has a 5 on his back, and we know that the sum of both numbers is 7. So 5 + ___ = 7. Could you have a 3 on your back? No, because 5 + 3 is 8. So you must have a number smaller than 3 on your back. What could it be? You must have a 2 on your back because 5 + 2 = 7.*

Skill Practice COMPUTING

Whole Group

Solving for Missing Addends
 Students will need two **Number Cubes** each (0–5 and 5–10). Have them show you solutions to more pairs of equations similar to those in the Guided Discussion. Write the expressions on the board above each other. For example:

a. 8 + _8_ = 16 , 16 − 8 = _8_   **b.** _7_ + 7 = 14, 14 − 7 = _7_
c. 10 + _7_ = 17, 17 − 10 = _7_   **d.** _6_ + 9 = 15, 15 − 9 = _6_

2 Assign Student Pages 20

Pages 81–82
Have students complete pages 81 and 82 independently.

Monitoring Student Progress

If . . . students are having difficulty with inverse operations,

Then . . . have students use concrete objects to practice adding and subtracting.

As Students Finish

Building Blocks Have students use **Pizza Pizzazz 5** to practice solving missing-addend problems.

 MathTools Have students create missing-addend problems with **Sets Former.**

Name _____ Date _____

LESSON 3.1 Missing Addends and Subtraction

Key Ideas

Anna needs 8 dollars. She already has 5 dollars.
How many more dollars does she need?

$$5 + \underline{3} = 8$$

$$8 - 5 = \underline{3}$$

Solve for each missing term.

1. $3 + \underline{5} = 8$
2. $8 - 3 = \underline{5}$
3. $7 + \underline{7} = 14$
4. $14 - 7 = \underline{7}$
5. $\underline{3} + 5 = 8$
6. $8 - 5 = \underline{3}$

7. $4 + \underline{10} = 14$
8. $14 - 4 = \underline{10}$
9. $9 + \underline{6} = 15$
10. $15 - 6 = \underline{9}$
11. $\underline{4} + 10 = 14$
12. $14 - 4 = \underline{10}$

Textbook This lesson is available in the *eTextbook*.

81

LESSON 3.1 · Missing Addends and Subtraction

Solve.

13. $8 + \underline{7} = 15$
14. $15 - 7 = \underline{8}$
15. $8 + \underline{8} = 16$
16. $16 - 8 = \underline{8}$
17. $4 + \underline{7} = 11$
18. $11 - 4 = \underline{7}$

19. $\underline{9} + 9 = 18$
20. $18 - 9 = \underline{9}$
21. $\underline{3} + 8 = 11$
22. $11 - 3 = \underline{8}$
23. $10 + \underline{5} = 15$
24. $15 - 5 = \underline{10}$

25. **Extended Response** There are 5 swings on the playground. Twelve students want to swing. How many more swings would the playground need for everyone to swing at once? Danny solved the problem this way:
$5 + 7 = 12$.
Melinda solved the problem this way:
$12 - 5 = 7$.
Who is correct?
How would you solve it?

Both of them are correct.
_____

82   **Real Math • Chapter 3 • Lesson 1**

---

3 Reflect 10

Guided Discussion REASONING
Whole Group

Do the Numbers on the Back Activity, asking the class to give the *difference* of the numbers as a clue this time. Have two student volunteers come to the front of the room, and pin numbers on their backs. Ask the volunteers with numbers on their backs the following questions:

■ **What number is on your back? Can you be sure? What other information do you need?** Help students see that to know what number is on their backs, they must know the difference and who has the greater number.

For example, if the number on one student's back is 5 and the number on the other student's back is 8, knowing only the difference will not allow them to determine the number. The student who sees the 5 could correctly think that he or she has a 2 or an 8. The student who sees 8 could correctly think he or she has a 5 or an 11. Only if they also know whose number is greater can they determine what is on their backs.

Finally write the problem each of the students solved as you verbalize it. For example:

● Max knew that Beth had a 5 on her back. He also knew that his number was greater and that the difference was 3. So he thought, $8 - 3 = 5$.

Beth knew that Max had an 8 on his back. She did not know what was on her back, but she knew the difference was 3 and that she had the smaller number. So she thought, $8 - 5 = 3$.

From this discussion, point out that although $5 + 3 = 3 + 5$, the same is not true for subtraction; $8 - 5$ is not equal to $5 - 8$.

Extended Response

Problem 25 Discuss students' answers. Students should have realized that both answers are correct and the problem can be solved either way.

 Cumulative Review: For cumulative review of previously learned skills, see page 89–90.

 Family Involvement: Assign the *Practice, Reteach,* or *Enrichment* activities depending on the needs of your students. Have students create missing-addend problems with a family member.

 Concept/Question Board: Have students look for additional examples that use subtraction and post them on the Concept/Question Board.

 Math Puzzler: Ari bought a $5 book and a $3 comic. He paid with a $10 bill. How much change should he get back? $2

4 Assess and Differentiate

 **Assess** Use *eAssess* to record and analyze evidence of student understanding.

A Gather Evidence

Use the Daily Class Assessment Records in *Assessment* or *eAssess* to record daily observations.

Informal Assessment
☑ **Skill Practice**

Did the student `COMPUTING`
- ❑ respond accurately?
- ❑ respond quickly?
- ❑ respond with confidence?
- ❑ self-correct?

Portfolio Assessment
☑ **Extended Response**

Did the student `REASONING`
- ❑ provide a clear explanation?
- ❑ communicate reasons and strategies?
- ❑ choose appropriate strategies?
- ❑ argue logically?

B Summarize Findings

Analyze and summarize assessment data for each student. Determine which Assessment Follow-Up is appropriate for each student. Use the Student Assessment Record in *Assessment* or *eAssess* to update assessment records.

Student Assessment Record

Assessment page T41

C Assessment Follow-Up • DIFFERENTIATE INSTRUCTION

Based on your observations, use these teaching strategies for assessment follow-up.

INTERVENTION

Review student performance on *Intervention* Lesson 3.A to see if students have mastered prerequisite skills for this lesson.

ENGLISH LEARNER

Review

Use Lesson 3.1 in *English Learner Support Guide* to review lesson concepts and vocabulary.

ENRICH

If . . . students are proficient in the lesson concepts,

Then . . . encourage them to work on the chapter projects or *Enrichment* Lesson 3.1.

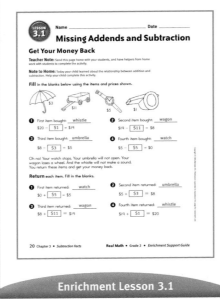

Enrichment Lesson 3.1

PRACTICE

If . . . students would benefit from additional practice,

Then . . . assign *Practice* Lesson 3.1.

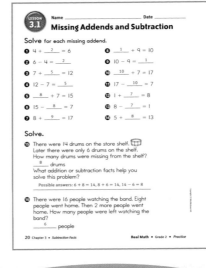

Practice Lesson 3.1

RETEACH

If . . . students are struggling with missing addends,

Then . . . have them use a double-pan balance and determine where weights should be placed to make both sides even.

Lesson Planner

OBJECTIVES
- To review the inverse relation between addition and subtraction
- To review the use of the Addition Table in finding differences

NCTM STANDARDS
Number and Operations
- Understanding various meanings of addition and subtraction
- Understanding the relation between addition and subtraction

Problem Solving
- Building new mathematical knowledge
- Solving problems that arise in mathematics
- Monitoring and reflecting on the process of problem solving

MATERIALS
- *Number Cubes (0–5 and 5–10)
- *Play Money
- Addition Table
- Counters
- Number Line
- Space Game Mat

TECHNOLOGY
- **e Presentation** Lesson 3.2
- **e MathTools** Sets Former; Addition Table; Number Line
- **Building Blocks** Barkley's Bones 1–20

TEST PREP
Cumulative Review
- Mental Math reviews addition facts (Lessons 2.1–2.6).
- Problems 1–12 review addition and subtraction facts (Lessons 2.1–2.6).

Extended Response ➡
Problem 13

Writing + Math
Journal

*Manipulative Kit Item

Subtraction Facts and the Addition Table

Context of the Lesson This lesson teaches students how subtraction facts can be inferred from the Addition Table. Students used the Addition Table in Chapter 2.

See page 79B for Math Background for teachers for this lesson.

Planning for Learning ● DIFFERENTIATE INSTRUCTION

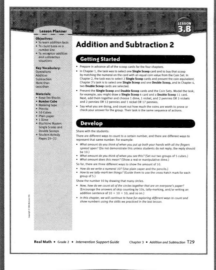

INTERVENTION
If . . . students lack the prerequisite skill of counting back on a number line,

Then . . . teach *Intervention* Lesson 3.B.

Intervention Lesson 3.B

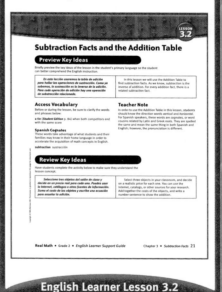

ENGLISH LEARNER
Preview

If . . . students need language support,

Then . . . use Lesson 3.2 in *English Learner Support Guide* to preview lesson concepts and vocabulary.

English Learner Lesson 3.2

ENRICH
If . . . students are proficient in the lesson concepts,

Then . . . emphasize exploring *eMathTools*.

PRACTICE
If . . . students would benefit from additional practice,

Then . . . extend Strategy Building before assigning the student pages.

RETEACH
If . . . students are having difficulty understanding subtraction,

Then . . . extend Guided Discussion before assigning the student pages.

Access Vocabulary
a tie when both competitors end with the same score

Spanish Cognates
subtraction sustracción

Mental Math 5

Give basic addition-fact practice. Students find, hide, and show answers with **Number Cubes**. Possible examples include the following:

a. $5 + 2 = 7$ **b.** $2 + 5 = 7$ **c.** $7 - 2 = 5$
d. $7 - 5 = 2$ **e.** $7 + 6 = 13$ **f.** $9 + 3 = 12$

1 Develop 20

Tell Students In Today's Lesson They Will
find differences.

Whole Group

Guided Discussion **MathTools**

Finding the Difference
Discuss different ways of finding the answer to subtraction exercises.

■ **What is $14 - 6$?** Encourage students to discuss what the answer is and how they can figure out the answer if they don't know it from memory.

Discuss and model, using counters or **eMathTools: Sets Former,** three possible ways of finding the difference; for example:

1. Because I know that $6 + 8 = 14$, then $14 - 6$ must be 8.
2. Count out 14 objects. Remove 6 of the objects, and count the number of objects left.
3. Count back 6 from 14 using a number line or **eMathTools: Number Line.**

Whole Group

Strategy Building **MathTools**

Subtraction and the Addition Table
Use **eMathTools: Addition Table** to demonstrate how to find the difference between two numbers. For example, to find the answer for $17 - 9$, follow this procedure:

● Go to the 9 column, and run your finger down that column until you come to the number 17.
● While keeping a finger on 17, move another finger along the same row toward the left side of the table.

The number of that row (in this case, 8) is the answer to the problem. (You can arrive at the same answer by finding 17 in the 9 row and then following that column to the top, where the answer, 8, appears.)

Repeat this activity several times with other addition and subtraction facts, checking for student understanding.

Skill and Strategy Building APPLYING Whole Group

 Game

Introduce the **Space Game** by playing a round with a student at the front of the class. Instructions can be found on the game mat.

2 Assign Student Pages 20

Pages 83–84   COMPUTING

Have students complete pages 83 and 84 independently. Students may wish to use play money for questions 13–15.

Monitoring Student Progress

If . . . students have difficulty with the word problems at the bottom of page 84,	**Then . . .** work individually or in small groups with them as you and they act out the problems. Doing so will ensure that they understand the physical situation in the problem.

As Students Finish

 Game   Have students play the **Space Game.**

Building Blocks   Have students use **Barkley's Bones 1–20** to practice solving missing-addend problems.

 MathTools   Have students practice subtraction with **Sets Former.**

RESEARCH IN ACTION

"Examining the relationships between addition and subtraction and seeing subtraction as involving a known and an unknown addend are examples of adaptive reasoning. By providing experiences for young students to develop adaptive reasoning in addition and subtraction situations, teachers are also anticipating algebra as students begin to appreciate the inverse relationships between the two operations."

Kilpatrick, J., J. Swafford, and B. Findell, eds. *Adding It Up: Helping Children Learn Mathematics.* Washington, D.C.: National Research Council/National Academy Press, 2001, p. 191.

Student Page

Name _____ Date _____

LESSON 3.2 Subtraction Facts and the Addition Table

Key Ideas

The Addition Table can be used to find subtraction facts.

For every addition fact there is a subtraction fact.

For example:

$2 + 5 = 7$ and $7 - 5 = 2$

Where can you find the subtraction fact $8 - 3 = 5$ on the Addition Table?

You may use the Addition Table to find the answer for each subtraction problem.

❶ $17 - 8 = \underline{9}$

❷ $13 - 6 = \underline{7}$

❸ $6 - 4 = \underline{2}$

❹ $9 - 5 = \underline{4}$

❺ $15 - 5 = \underline{10}$

❻ $11 - 2 = \underline{9}$

❼ $9 - 3 = \underline{6}$

❽ $16 - 7 = \underline{9}$

+	0	1	2	3	4	5	6	7	8	9	10
0	0	1	2	3	4	5	6	7	8	9	10
1	1	2	3	4	5	6	7	8	9	10	11
2	2	3	4	5	6	7	8	9	10	11	12
3	3	4	5	6	7	8	9	10	11	12	13
4	4	5	6	7	8	9	10	11	12	13	14
5	5	6	7	8	9	10	11	12	13	14	15
6	6	7	8	9	10	11	12	13	14	15	16
7	7	8	9	10	11	12	13	14	15	16	17
8	8	9	10	11	12	13	14	15	16	17	18
9	9	10	11	12	13	14	15	16	17	18	19
10	10	11	12	13	14	15	16	17	18	19	20

Textbook This lesson is available in the *eTextbook*.

83

Student Page

LESSON 3.2 · Subtraction Facts and the Addition Table

Find the missing numbers.

❾ $8 + \underline{9} = 17$ ⓫ $8 + \underline{3} = 11$

❿ $11 - 3 = \underline{8}$ ⓬ $11 - 8 = \underline{3}$

⓭ **Extended Response** If you have $15, can you buy both the chalk and the paint set? Explain your answer.

Yes, because the chalk costs $3 and the paint set costs $7; $3 + 7 = 10$. I have $15, which is more than $10, so I can buy both.

⓮ The paint set and scissors cost $15 together. If you have $21, how much money will you have left? $\underline{\$6}$

⓯ Two packs of clay cost $12. How much does one pack of clay cost? $\underline{\$6}$

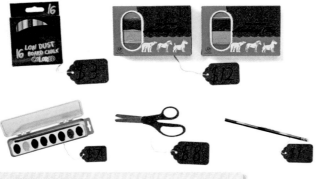

Writing + Math Journal

How would you find the answer to $13 - 4$ using the Addition Table?

 Reflect 10

Guided Discussion [REASONING]

Whole Group

Begin by reviewing the exercises on the student pages. Then direct students to find the difference for several subtraction facts using the addition fact table.

Discuss the need for students to become fluent with the subtraction facts. Ask students for suggestions about how they can work together to accomplish this. Point out that this might not be nearly as difficult as committing the addition facts to memory, because if they know the addition facts, the related subtraction facts are easier to remember.

Extended Response

Problem 13 Discuss students' answers. Students should have realized that because the chalk costs $3 and the paint set costs $7, $3 + 7 = 10$. Fifteen dollars is more than $10, so they can buy both.

Writing + Math **Journal**

Discuss student answers. Students should describe the same procedure used in Strategy Building. If other methods are mentioned, discuss and try them as a class.

 Cumulative Review: For cumulative review of previously learned skills, see page 89–90.

 Family Involvement: Assign the *Practice, Reteach,* or *Enrichment* activities depending on the needs of your students. Have students use the Addition Table to solve subtraction exercises with a family member.

Concept/Question Board: Have students look for additional examples that use subtraction and post them on the Concept/Question Board.

 Math Puzzler: Yesterday there were 15 muffins on a plate. Today there are 7. How many muffins were eaten? 8

Assess and Differentiate

 Assess Use *eAssess* to record and analyze evidence of student understanding.

A Gather Evidence

Use the Daily Class Assessment Records in *Assessment* or *eAssess* to record daily observations.

Informal Assessment

☑ **Student Pages**

Did the student [COMPUTING]
- ❏ respond accurately?
- ❏ respond quickly?
- ❏ respond with confidence?
- ❏ self-correct?

Portfolio Assessment

☑ **Extended Response**

Did the student [REASONING]
- ❏ provide a clear explanation?
- ❏ communicate reasons and strategies?
- ❏ choose appropriate strategies?
- ❏ argue logically?

B Summarize Findings

Analyze and summarize assessment data for each student. Determine which Assessment Follow-Up is appropriate for each student. Use the Student Assessment Record in *Assessment* or *eAssess* to update assessment records.

Assessment page T41

C Assessment Follow-Up ● DIFFERENTIATE INSTRUCTION

Based on your observations, use these teaching strategies for assessment follow-up.

INTERVENTION	ENRICH	PRACTICE	RETEACH
Review student performance on *Intervention* Lesson 3.B to see if students have mastered prerequisite skills for this lesson.	**If . . .** students are proficient in the lesson concepts, **Then . . .** encourage them to work on the chapter projects or *Enrichment* Lesson 3.2.	**If . . .** students would benefit from additional practice, **Then . . .** assign *Practice* Lesson 3.2.	**If . . .** students are having difficulty tracing columns and rows on the Addition Table, **Then . . .** have students work in pairs and use straightedges to keep track of columns and rows.

ENGLISH LEARNER

Review

Use Lesson 3.2 in *English Learner Support Guide* to review lesson concepts and vocabulary.

Enrichment Lesson 3.2

Practice Lesson 3.2

Lesson Planner

OBJECTIVES
- To review the addition and subtraction facts in a new context—that of the function machine
- To provide students with experience using simple functions

NCTM STANDARDS
Number and Operations
- Understanding various meanings of addition and subtraction
- Understanding the relation between addition and subtraction

Algebra
- Modeling situations that involve addition and subtraction of whole numbers
- Illustrating general principles and properties of operations

MATERIALS
- *Number Cubes (0–5 and 5–10)
- Slips of paper

TECHNOLOGY
- e Presentation Lesson 3.3
- e Games Roll 20 to 5
- e MathTools Function Machine
- Building Blocks Function Machine 1

TEST PREP
Cumulative Review
- Mental Math reviews addition and subtraction facts (Lessons 2.1–2.9, 3.1–3.2).
- Guided Discussion reviews applying functions (Lesson 2.6).
- Problems 1–9 review addition and subtraction facts (Lessons 2.1–2.9, 3.1–3.2).

Looking Ahead
In Lesson 3.5 students will need materials to make flash cards, or have pre-made flash cards available for each student.

*Manipulative Kit Item

Addition and Subtraction Functions

Context of the Lesson Students used functions throughout the first-grade program, so many students will be familiar with the topic. Functions were also covered in Chapter 2. This is the third of seven lessons leading to memorization of the subtraction facts.

See page 79B for Math Background for teachers for this lesson.

Planning for Learning • DIFFERENTIATE INSTRUCTION

INTERVENTION

If . . . students lack the prerequisite skill of recognizing addition and subtraction situations,

Then . . . teach *Intervention* Lesson 3.C.

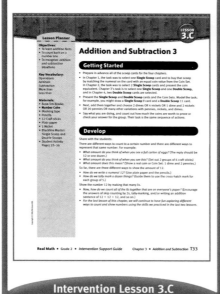

Intervention Lesson 3.C

ENGLISH LEARNER

Preview

If . . . students need language support,

Then . . . use Lesson 3.3 in *English Learner Support Guide* to preview lesson concepts and vocabulary.

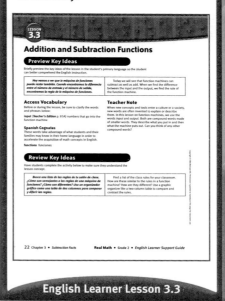

English Learner Lesson 3.3

ENRICH

If . . . students are proficient in the lesson concepts,

Then . . . emphasize additional game time.

PRACTICE

If . . . students would benefit from additional practice,

Then . . . extend Skill Building before assigning the student pages.

RETEACH

If . . . students are having difficulty understanding subtraction functions,

Then . . . extend Guided Discussion before assigning the student pages.

Access Vocabulary
input numbers that go into the function machine

Spanish Cognates
functions funciones

Mental Math 5

  Give basic addition- and subtraction-fact practice. Students find, hide, and show answers with their **Number Cubes.** Possible examples include the following:

a. 6 + 6 = 12   **b.** 8 + 6 = 14
c. 12 − 3 = 9   **d.** 11 − 2 = 9
e. 3 + 9 = 12   **f.** 8 + 8 = 16
g. 10 + 10 = 20   **h.** 15 − 3 = 12

1 Develop 20

Tell Students In Today's Lesson They Will

use a function table to practice subtraction and solving for missing addends.

Guided Discussion   Whole Group

Using a Function Machine

Students may remember this activity from the first-grade program or from Chapter 2.

Call attention to the function machine that you made, and explain that it can change numbers according to certain rules. Explain that you can make the rules and that you can also change them.

- Allow one student to come to the front of the room and place a slip of paper with a number written on it into a box. Suppose the student put a 5 into the box. Cross off the number the student put into the box, write a new number on the slip that is 4 less, and show the class. (You will be demonstrating the −4 rule first.)

Skill Building  MathTools UNDERSTANDING Whole Group

Next draw a function table (similar to those on the student book pages) on the board or overhead projector, or use **eMathTools: Function Machine,** and enter 5 as input and 1 as output. Explain that a function table can help keep track of the inputs and outputs of a function machine.

- Repeat the activity with other students and other inputs, keeping the "−4 rule" constant while you fill in the function table.

After several students have participated, ask the following:

■ **What is the rule?** −4

Write that rule in the appropriate place on the function table.

■ **Can you figure out what went into the machine if a 10 came out?** 14

Help students see that they can reverse the −4 machine by doing +4 to get 14. Thus, −4 and +4 undo each other.

Solve this problem, and do a few more examples. Then repeat this activity with new rules several times.

- Refer to the function machine on student page 85, and do the first two or three problems with the class, making sure they understand the format by identifying the output values and the input values and finding the rules. If necessary, help students see that finding input values is much the same as solving missing-addend problems.

Skill and Strategy Building Whole Group

 Roll 20 to 5 Game

Demonstrate and then play the **Roll 20 to 5 Game,** which provides students with practice subtracting 10 or less from numbers through 20. This game also encourages students to think about probability and problem solving.

2 Assign Student Pages 20

Pages 85–86 COMPUTING

Have students complete the rest of page 85 and page 86 independently.

Monitoring Student Progress

| **If . . .** you notice that students are calculating each fact within a fact family separately on the student pages, indicating that they may not see the relationships between the facts in the family, | **Then . . .** work individually or in small groups with students, pointing out that if you know, for example, that 6 + 4 = 10, then you also know that 4 + 6 = 10. If necessary, lay out a group of 4 objects and a group of 6 objects and establish that there are 10 objects altogether. Then rearrange the objects so that you add 2 objects to the group of 4 and take away 2 objects from the group of 6. Establish that there are still 10 objects. Next take away one of the groups, pointing out that if you take away the group of 4, you are left with 6 objects, so 10 − 4 = 6; if you take away the group of 6 objects, you are left with 4, so 10 − 6 = 4. Repeat as necessary. |

As Students Finish

 Have students play the **Roll 20 to 5 Game.**

e Games *Roll 20 to 5 Game*

Building Blocks Have students practice using function machines by using **Function Machine 1.**

e MathTools Have students practice using function machines by using **Function Machine.**

Name _____ Date _____

LESSON 3.3 Addition and Subtraction Functions

Key Ideas
Function machines can subtract as well as add.

5 in → −4 → out 1

Fill in the missing numbers.

❶ in +5 out

3	8
5	10
2	7

❷ in +6 out

2	8
4	10
3	9

❸ in −3 out

10	7
8	5
4	1

❹ in −7 out

8	1
9	2
10	3
11	4

❺ in +3 out

5	8
10	13
9	12
1	4

❻ in −4 out

10	6
6	2
6	2
5	1

❼ in ◯ out

8	0
18	10
19	11
9	1

The rule is __−8__.

❽ in ◯ out

6	12
4	10
3	9
4	10

The rule is __+6__.

❾ in ◯ out

30	29
18	17
35	34
23	22

The rule is __−1__.

Textbook This lesson is available in the *eTextbook*.

85

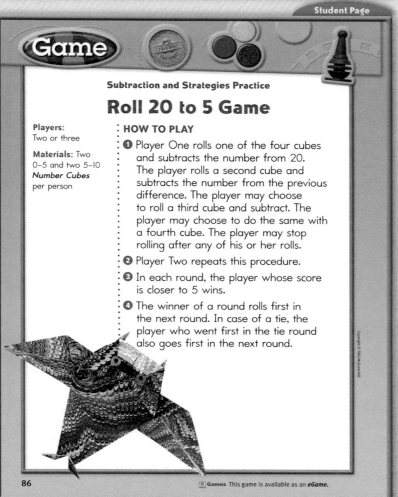

Game

Subtraction and Strategies Practice

Roll 20 to 5 Game

Players:
Two or three

Materials: Two 0–5 and two 5–10 *Number Cubes* per person

HOW TO PLAY

❶ Player One rolls one of the four cubes and subtracts the number from 20. The player rolls a second cube and subtracts the number from the previous difference. The player may choose to roll a third cube and subtract. The player may choose to do the same with a fourth cube. The player may stop rolling after any of his or her rolls.

❷ Player Two repeats this procedure.

❸ In each round, the player whose score is closer to 5 wins.

❹ The winner of a round rolls first in the next round. In case of a tie, the player who went first in the tie round also goes first in the next round.

86
Games This game is available as an *eGame*.

 LESSON 3.3

3 Reflect
10

Guided Discussion [REASONING]
Whole Group

Use one of the completed function tables to show students how it might represent a word problem. For example, the first table on page 1, which uses a +5 "rule" or function, might represent the following story:

The students in Jeremy's class had the opportunity to earn $5 by doing lawn work.

■ **Before starting, Jeremy had $3. How much does he have now?** $8
■ **Megan had $4. How much does she have now?** $9
■ **Melissa had $7. How much does she have now?** $12

Relate one or two more functions to word problems if there is time and students show interest.

 Cumulative Review: For cumulative review of previously learned skills, see page 89–90.

 Family Involvement: Assign the *Practice, Reteach,* or *Enrichment* activities depending on the needs of your students. Have students play the **Roll 20 to 5 Game** with a family member.

 Concept/Question Board: Encourage students to continue to post questions, answers, and examples on the Concept/Question Board.

 Math Puzzler: Write the following number patterns on the board or overhead projector, and have students describe and complete them.
a. 21, 24, 27, 30, ____, ____ +3; 33, 36
b. 47, 57, 67, 77, ____, ____ +10; 87, 97

4 Assess and Differentiate

e Assess Use *eAssess* to record and analyze evidence of student understanding.

A Gather Evidence

Use the Daily Class Assessment Records in *Assessment* or *eAssess* to record daily observations.

Informal Assessment
☑ Skill Building

Did the student **UNDERSTANDING**
- ❏ make important observations?
- ❏ extend or generalize learning?
- ❏ provide insightful answers?
- ❏ pose insightful questions?

Informal Assessment
☑ Student Pages

Did the student **COMPUTING**
- ❏ respond accurately?
- ❏ respond quickly?
- ❏ respond with confidence?
- ❏ self-correct?

B Summarize Findings

Analyze and summarize assessment data for each student. Determine which Assessment Follow-Up is appropriate for each student. Use the Student Assessment Record in *Assessment* or *eAssess* to update assessment records.

Assessment page T41

C Assessment Follow-Up ● DIFFERENTIATE INSTRUCTION

Based on your observations, use these teaching strategies for assessment follow-up.

INTERVENTION

Review student performance on *Intervention* Lesson 3.C to see if students have mastered prerequisite skills for this lesson.

ENGLISH LEARNER

Review

Use Lesson 3.3 in *English Learner Support Guide* to review lesson concepts and vocabulary.

ENRICH

If . . . students are proficient in the lesson concepts,

Then . . . encourage them to work on the chapter projects or *Enrichment* Lesson 3.3.

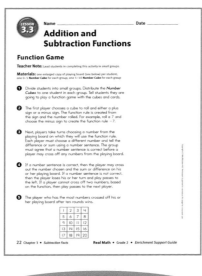

Enrichment Lesson 3.3

PRACTICE

If . . . students would benefit from additional practice,

Then . . . assign *Practice* Lesson 3.3.

Practice Lesson 3.3

RETEACH

If . . . students are having difficulty with function tables,

Then . . . have them perform the same function rule to a series of numbers while using concrete objects.

CHAPTER 3

Exploring Problem Solving

Objectives

- To explore the Make a Table and Draw a Picture strategies
- To use subtraction facts
- To interpret numerical results so an answer is reasonable
- To explore ways to present solutions clearly

Materials

Counters

Context of the Lesson Reasoning and problem solving are prevalent in every *Real Math* lesson. This lesson and other special problem-solving lessons allow more time for students to share and compare their strategies. The lesson also provides additional opportunities for students to use the subtraction skills they have been working on in previous lessons.

 Develop   5

Tell Students In Today's Lesson They Will

solve a problem about how long a stack of origami paper will last.

Guided Discussion

Have students look at the illustration at the top of page 87. Read this problem to the students.

Mr. Wilson is in charge of the Origami Club, which meets after school on Monday, Wednesday, and Friday. There are five students in the club. Monday's meeting is about to begin, and Mr. Wilson has twenty-eight sheets of origami paper. He uses five sheets for each meeting, one for each student. Mr. Wilson will need to order more paper. He wants to know when he will need the new paper.

Have the students look at page 87. Ask the following questions:

- **In the problem, what day is it?** Monday
- **Will the Origami Club meet tomorrow?** No; the next meeting will be on Wednesday.
- **How many sheets of origami paper does Mr. Wilson have now, before today's meeting?** twenty-eight
- **How many sheets does the club use at each meeting?** five
- **What is the problem asking you to find?** when the club will need more paper
- **Does anyone have an idea about how to solve the problem?** Allow students to offer strategies.
- **Does this problem remind anyone of another problem we solved?** Allow students to suggest problems and explain why this reminds them of the other problem. Later you can compare this problem to the one on page 53.

Exploring Problem Solving

Name _____ Date _____

Listen to the problem.

The Origami Club has 28 sheets of paper.
They use 5 sheets at each meeting.
On what day will they need more paper?

Elena is making a table to help solve the problem.

Day	Mon.	Wed.	Fri.
Number of sheets left	28	23	

Textbook This lesson is available in the *eTextbook*.   87

Exploring Problem Solving

Nori is drawing a picture to solve the problem.

Show how you solved the problem.

The club will need more paper on ___Friday___ of next week.

88   Real Math · Chapter 3 · Exploring Problem Solving

Using Student Pages

Analyzing Sample Solution 1: Make a Table

Have students look at the picture on page 87 of Elena solving the problem. Ask questions about the strategy, such as the following:

■ **How is Elena approaching this problem?** She is using a table to keep track of how many sheets are left after each meeting.

■ **Why do you think Elena wrote the number 28 in the first box of her table?** to show how many sheets of paper the club starts with

■ **Does 28 tell you how many sheets there are before the meeting or after the meeting on Monday?** before the meeting

■ **Why do you think Elena wrote the number 23 in the second box?** to show how many sheets of paper the club will have to start the meeting on Wednesday

■ **How will Elena know what number to write in the box for Friday?** She can take away 5 from 23.

■ **What day will Elena write after Friday?** Monday; That will be the next day that the club meets.

■ **How can Elena use her strategy to find the answer to the problem?** She can continue to subtract 5 until there are fewer than 5 left. Then she can see on her table what day that will be.

Analyzing Sample Solution 2: Draw a Picture

Tell students that Nori is using a different strategy to try to solve the problem. Have students look at the picture on page 88 of Nori's approach. Ask questions such as the following:

■ **Why do you think Nori drew 28 squares?** to show the 28 origami sheets the club started with

■ **Why do you think Nori put an X through 5 of the colored squares?** to show how many sheets were used at Monday's meeting

■ **How is Nori keeping track of how many meetings go by?** by circling each group of five as he crosses them out and then counting the groups

■ **How can Nori keep track of the days?** He can write Monday next to the first group, Wednesday next to the second group, and so on.

■ **How will you work on this problem?** Allow students to share what they like about Elena's strategy and Nori's strategy and what they would do differently.

Skill Building

Have students work on the problem individually or in pairs. They may use Elena's strategy, Nori's strategy, or one of their own. Provide support as needed, remembering to suggest approaches rather than show students the answer. Remind students to check their answers.

Sample Solutions Strategies

Students might use one or more of the following strategies instead of or in conjunction with the strategies presented on student pages 87 and 88.

Act It Out

Students might use counters to act out the problem by starting with 28 counters and subtracting 5 at a time until they can no longer take away a whole group of 5.

Using Operations/Make a List

Students might recall subtraction facts and use other methods to list the diminishing number of origami sheets. To subtract from the larger numbers, they might count back on their fingers or use a number line, keeping track of how many times they subtract 5.

$28 - 5 = 23$; $23 - 5 = 18$; $18 - 5 = 13$; $13 - 5 = 8$; $8 - 5 = 3$

Draw a Picture (Number Line)

Students might draw a number line and then count back 5 steps at a time, keeping track of how many times they have subtracted 5.

Extension

For students who finish early, you might present similar problems with different numbers, for example:

The club starts with 34 sheets and uses 8 sheets each time. on Wednesday of next week

The club starts with 21 sheets and uses 4 sheets each time. on Friday of next week

 **Reflect** 10

 **Knowledge Age Skills**

Problem Formulation, Planning, and Strategizing Ask students to share their solutions and their strategies. In discussion, bring out the following points:

● When you work on a problem, it is important to think about what the numbers mean—how they fit with what is going on in the problem. If the Origami Club uses 5 sheets of paper each day, they will not end a meeting with exactly 0 papers. After 5 meetings, they will still have 3 sheets of paper, but that will not be enough for the sixth meeting, which will be on Friday of next week.

● It is important to organize your work so you can keep track of the steps you take and the different parts of the problem.

● Different people might prefer to use different strategies.

● The problem in this lesson is similar to the problem on page 53 because both involve repeating the same change. The main difference is that in this problem the total decreases each time by a certain amount, whereas in the other the total increases each time by a certain amount.

 Assess 15

When evaluating student work, focus not only on the correctness of the answer but also on whether the student thought rationally about the problem. Questions to consider include the following:

● Did the student understand the problem?
● Did the student understand the Sample Solutions Strategies?
● Was the student able to explain his or her strategy?

Cumulative Review

Assign Pages 89–90

Use the Cumulative Review as a review of concepts and skills that students have previously learned.

Here are different ways that you can assign these problems to your students as they work through the chapter:

- With some of the lessons in the chapter, assign a set of cumulative review problems to be completed as practice or for homework.
  Lesson 3.1—Problems 1–7
  Lesson 3.2—Problems 8–15
  Lesson 3.3—Problems 16–18
- At any point during the chapter, assign part or all of the cumulative review problems to be completed as practice or for homework.

Cumulative Review

Problems 1–7 review dates and days of the week using a calendar, Lesson 1.6.

Problems 8–15 review missing addends and subtraction, Lesson 3.1.

Problems 16–18 review addition and subtraction function machines, Lesson 3.3.

Monitoring Student Progress

If . . . students miss more than one problem in a section,

Then . . . refer to the indicated lesson for remediation suggestions.

Cumulative Review

Name _____ Date _____

The Calendar Lesson 1.6

Fill in the missing numbers. Then use the calendar to answer the questions.

1. Write the dates on the calendar. January has 31 days.

			January			
SUN	MON	TUE	WED	THU	FRI	SAT
1	2	3	4	5	6	7
8	9	10	11	12	13	14
15	16	17	18	19	20	21
22	23	24	25	26	27	28
29	30	31				

Write the answer.

2. What day of the week is January 2? __Monday__
3. What day of the week is January 14? __Saturday__
4. What is the fifth day of this month? __Thursday__
5. Wednesday, January 4, is the __fourth__ day of the month.
6. On January 9 Josh found out that he would have a test on January 13. How many nights does Josh have to prepare? __four nights__
7. Antwan joined a reading competition that lasts for two weeks. It started Monday, January 2nd. During the competition, Antwan was told they would have 3 extra days. What date will the competition end? __January 18th__

Textbook This lesson is available in the eTextbook.   89

Student Page

Cumulative Review

Missing Addends and Subtraction Lesson 3.1
Solve.

8. $9 + \underline{8} = 17$
9. $16 - \underline{3} = 13$
10. $9 + \underline{6} = 15$
11. $13 - \underline{8} = 5$
12. $8 + \underline{3} = 11$
13. $12 - \underline{6} = 6$

14. **Extended Response** Explain how to solve the following problem:
    $\underline{\quad} + 5 = 12$. __7; Students may have counted back from 12 to 5, counted on from 5 to 12, or known the addition fact and filled in the missing number.__

15. There were 16 leaves on the plant. Four were knocked off by the cat. Two more fell off when the dog ran into the plant. The rest stayed on the plant. How many leaves are on the plant? __10__

Addition and Subtraction Functions Lesson 3.3
Fill in the blanks.

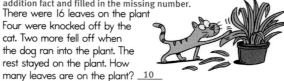

16. in → (+11) → out		17. in → (+4) → out		18. in → (−3) → out	
2	13	1	5	14	11
4	15	5	9	17	14
3	14	9	13	4	1
5	16	8	12	11	8

90   **Real Math • Chapter 3**

Individual Oral Assessment

Purpose of the Test

The Individual Oral Assessment is designed to measure students' growing knowledge of chapter concepts. It is administered individually to each student, and it requires oral responses from each student. The test takes about five minutes to complete. See **Assessment** for detailed instructions for administering and interpreting the test, and record students' answers on the Student Assessment Recording Sheet.

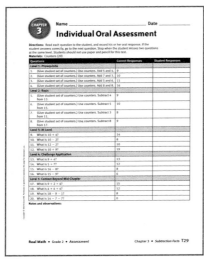

Assessment page T29

Directions

Read each question to the student, and record his or her oral response. If the student answers correctly, go to the next question. Stop when the student misses two questions at the same level. Students should not use scrap paper.

Materials

20 counters

Questions

Level 1: Prerequisite
1. Use counters. Add 5 and 4. 9
2. Use counters. Add 7 and 3. 10
3. Use counters. Add 5 and 6. 11
4. Use counters. Add 8 and 8. 16

Level 2: Basic
5. Use counters. Subtract 4 from 13. 9
6. Use counters. Subtract 5 from 15. 10
7. Use counters. Subtract 3 from 11. 8
8. Use counters. Subtract 8 from 17. 9

Level 3: At Level
9. What is 10 + 4? 14
10. What is 10 − 2? 8
11. What is 12 − 2? 10
12. What is 10 + 9? 19

Level 4: Challenge Application
13. What is 9 + 4? 13
14. What is 5 + 7? 12
15. What is 16 − 8? 8
16. What is 15 − 9? 6

Level 5: Content Beyond Mid-Chapter
17. What is 9 + 2 + 4? 15
18. What is 4 + 4 + 4? 12
19. What is 18 − 9 − 1? 8
20. What is 14 − 7 − 7? 0

Lesson Planner

OBJECTIVES
To focus attention on subtraction exercises involving 10 and 9

NCTM STANDARDS

Number and Operations
- Using a variety of methods and tools to compute
- Developing and using strategies for whole-number computations
- Understanding the effects of adding and subtracting whole numbers

Representation
- Creating and using representations to communicate mathematical ideas
- Selecting, applying, and translating among mathematical representations to solve problems

MATERIALS
- *Number Cubes (0–5 and 5–10)

TECHNOLOGY
- 🅔 **Presentation** Lesson 3.4
- 🅔 **MathTools** Sets Former
- 🅔 **Games** Roll 20 to 5

TEST PREP

Cumulative Review
- Mental Math reviews addition and subtraction facts (Lessons 2.1–2.9, 3.1–3.3).

Extended Response
Problem 20

Writing + Math
Journal

Subtraction Involving 10 and 9

Context of the Lesson In this lesson students subtract 10 and 9. Students learned how to subtract 10 and 9 in Grade 1.
See page 79B for Math Background for teachers for this lesson.

Planning for Learning • DIFFERENTIATE INSTRUCTION

INTERVENTION	ENGLISH LEARNER	ENRICH
If . . . students lack the prerequisite skill of addition facts,	Preview	**If . . .** students are proficient in the lesson concepts,
Then . . . teach *Intervention* Lesson 3.A.	**If . . .** students need language support,	**Then . . .** emphasize additional game time.
	Then . . . use Lesson 3.4 in *English Learner Support Guide* to preview lesson concepts and vocabulary.	

PRACTICE

If . . . students would benefit from additional practice,

Then . . . extend Skill Practice before assigning the student pages.

RETEACH

If . . . students are having difficulty understanding subtraction,

Then . . . extend Guided Discussion before assigning the student pages.

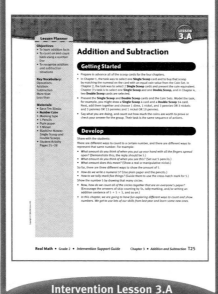

Intervention Lesson 3.A

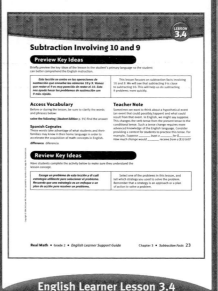

English Learner Lesson 3.4

Vocabulary
difference \dif´rəns\ *n.* the remainder left after subtracting one quantity from another

$7 - 5 = 2$; 2 is the **difference** of 7 minus 5.

Access Vocabulary
solve the following find the answer

Spanish Cognates
difference diferencia

---

*Manipulative Kit Item

Mental Math　5

  Give basic addition- and subtraction-fact practice. Students find, hide, and show answers with their **Number Cubes.** Possible examples include the following:

a. $10 + 3 = 13$ **b.** $8 + 3 = 11$
c. $14 - 1 = 13$ **d.** $8 + 0 = 8$
e. $8 - 0 = 8$ **f.** $9 - 4 = 5$
g. $12 - 9 = 3$ **h.** $5 + 7 = 12$

1 Develop　20

Tell Students In Today's Lesson They Will
subtract 9 and 10 from a number.

Guided Discussion UNDERSTANDING　Whole Group

Subtracting 10
Model the subtraction problem $17 - 10$ by having two students hold up fingers in front of the class. One student holds up all 10 fingers; the other holds up 7. Ask the following:

■ **How many fingers are there altogether?** 17 **Take away the 10.**
■ **How many are left?** 7

Start over by having two students hold up fingers for 17. Take away the 7, and ask the following:

■ **How many are left?** 10

Subtracting 9
Start over, and say you intend to take away only 9 this time (so the person who started with 10 fingers up still has 1 finger up). Ask the following:

■ **How many are left?** $7 + 1$, or 8

Start over with 17, and take away 8 . . . all the fingers of the person with 7 up and 1 more finger. Ask the following:

■ **How many are left?** $10 - 1$, or 9 Repeat this activity a few times with different numbers.

Finally have one person hold up all 10 fingers and model this problem:

Put down 4 fingers.

■ **How many are up?** 6

Put up all 10 fingers. Put down seven fingers.

■ **How many are up?** 3

Skill Practice COMPUTING　Whole Group

 Write exercises such as the following on the board, and have students show their answers with **Number Cubes.**

a. $17 - 10 = 7$ **b.** $19 - 10 = 9$ **c.** $12 - 10 = 2$

Accept answers such as the following: Another name for seventeen is ten and seven, so if we take away ten we are left with seven.

Next write two related number sentences on the board, such as the following:

$16 - 10 = 6$ and $16 - 9 = 7$

Discuss why, if you know the answer to the first sentence, the answer to the second sentence is 1 more. Accept answers similar to this: If I have 16 marbles and I give away 10, I will have 6 left, but if I give away only 9 marbles, I will have 1 more than 6, or 7, left.

Give several other examples, and then ask the following:

■ **Can you think of a rule for subtracting nine?** Accept rules such as the following: If you subtract nine from a number, the answer is always one more than if you had subtracted ten.

2 Assign Student Pages　20

Pages 91–92 COMPUTING
Have students complete pages 91 and 92 independently.

> #### Monitoring Student Progress
>
> **If . . .** students have difficulty seeing the relation between the +10 and the +9 addition facts,
>
> **Then . . .** get two containers. As students watch, put 7 marbles or other objects in one of the containers and 10 in the other. Establish that there are $10 + 7$, or 17, marbles altogether. Now take 1 marble out of the container with 10. Now there are $9 + 7$ marbles. Ask the following:
>
> ■ **Is 9 and 7 one less than 10 and 7?** yes
>
> Repeat with other examples if necessary.

As Students Finish

 Allow students enough time to play the **Roll 20 to 5 Game.**

e Games *Roll 20 to 5 Game*

e MathTools Have students practice subtracting 10 and 9 using **Sets Former.**

LESSON 3.4 Subtraction Involving 10 and 9

Key Ideas

17 − 10 = 7

17 − 9 = 8

If 18 − 10 = 8, what is the answer or **difference** for 18 − 9? ___ 9

Solve the following subtraction problems.

① 16 − 6 = __10__

② 12 − 2 = __10__

③ 16 − 10 = __6__

④ 12 − 10 = __2__

⑤ 19 − 9 = __10__

⑥ 13 − 10 = __3__

⑦ 15 − 9 = __6__

⑧ 15 − 6 = __9__

⑨ 17 − 8 = __9__

⑩ 14 − 9 = __5__

⑪ 12 − 3 = __9__

⑫ 9 − 3 = __6__

⑬ 10 − 2 = 8

⑭ 10 − 9 = 1

⑮ 10 − 4 = 6

⑯ 11 − 9 = 2

Textbook This lesson is available in the *eTextbook*.

LESSON 3.4 · Subtraction Involving 10 and 9

Answer the following questions.

$7 $6 $2

Kaya has $10.

⑰ Suppose Kaya buys the ball. How much change will she get? $__3__

⑱ How much change if she buys the car? $__4__

⑲ How much change if she buys the origami paper? $__8__

⑳ Extended Response Does Kaya have enough money to buy the ball and the car? __no__ Explain your answer. __Kaya has $10. The ball is $7, and the car is $6; 7 + 6 = 13; $13 is more than $10.__

Writing + Math Journal

What are the addition expressions that would go with

17 − 10 = 7?

17 − 9 = 8?

Game Play the **Roll 20 to 5 Game.**

---

3 Reflect 10

Guided Discussion REASONING

Whole Group

Review the problems on student pages 91 and 92. Discuss the problem situations and strategies used by students.

Have a brief discussion with the class on the importance of becoming fluent with all 121 subtraction facts, but assure them that just as they have become fluent with the addition facts, they will be able to do the same for subtraction. Point out that they probably know most of the facts already—the −0, −1, −2, −10, and −9 facts—and that if they really know these, there are only 36 more facts to memorize.

Extended Response ✓

Problem 20 Discuss students' answers. Students should have realized that Kaya does not have enough money to buy the ball and car because the ball and car cost a total of $13, which is more than $10.

Writing + Math Journal

Discuss student answers. Because addition is the inverse of subtraction, they should have answered 7 + 10 = 17, 10 + 7 = 17, 8 + 9 = 17, and 9 + 8 = 17.

Cumulative Review: For cumulative review of previously learned skills, see page 101–102.

Family Involvement: Assign the *Practice, Reteach,* or *Enrichment* activities depending on the needs of your students. Have students practice subtracting 10 and 9 with family members.

Concept/Question Board: Encourage students to continue to post questions, answers, and examples on the Concept/Question Board.

Math Puzzler: How many different three-digit numbers can you make from the digits 1, 2, and 3? What are they? six different numbers; 123, 132, 213, 231, 321, 312

4 Assess and Differentiate

 Assess Use *eAssess* to record and analyze evidence of student understanding.

A Gather Evidence

Use the Daily Class Assessment Records in *Assessment* or *eAssess* to record daily observations.

Informal Assessment
☑ **Mental Math**

Did the student COMPUTING
- ❏ respond accurately?
- ❏ respond quickly?
- ❏ respond with confidence?
- ❏ self-correct?

Informal Assessment
☑ **Guided Discussion**

Did the student UNDERSTANDING
- ❏ make important observations?
- ❏ extend or generalize learning?
- ❏ provide insightful answers?
- ❏ pose insightful questions?

B Summarize Findings

Analyze and summarize assessment data for each student. Determine which Assessment Follow-Up is appropriate for each student. Use the Student Assessment Record in *Assessment* or *eAssess* to update assessment records.

Assessment page T41

C Assessment Follow-Up ● DIFFERENTIATE INSTRUCTION

Based on your observations, use these teaching strategies for assessment follow-up.

INTERVENTION
Review student performance on *Intervention* Lesson 3.A to see if students have mastered prerequisite skills for this lesson.

ENGLISH LEARNER
Review

Use Lesson 3.4 in *English Learner Support Guide* to review lesson concepts and vocabulary.

ENRICH
If . . . students are proficient in the lesson concepts,

Then . . . encourage them to work on the chapter projects or *Enrichment* Lesson 3.4.

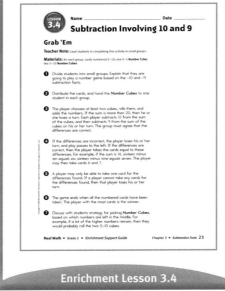

Enrichment Lesson 3.4

PRACTICE
If . . . students would benefit from additional practice,

Then . . . assign *Practice* Lesson 3.4.

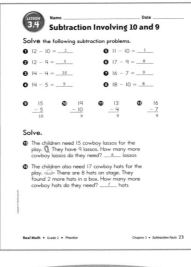

Practice Lesson 3.4

RETEACH
If . . . students are having difficulty understanding subtraction with 10 and 9,

Then . . . have them solve groups of exercises that subtract 10 and then groups of exercises that subtract 9. Have them compare the answers.

Lesson Planner

OBJECTIVES
- To provide practice with addition and subtraction facts
- To focus on quick recall of the subtraction facts

NCTM STANDARDS
Number and Operations
- Using a variety of methods and tools to compute
- Developing and using strategies for whole-number computations
- Understanding the effects of adding and subtracting whole numbers

Representation
- Creating and using representations to communicate mathematical ideas
- Selecting, applying, and translating among mathematical representations to solve problems

MATERIALS
- *Number Cubes (0–5 and 5–10)
- Materials to make flash cards or pre-made flash cards

TECHNOLOGY
- **e Presentation** Lesson 3.5
- **e MathTools** Addition Table

TEST PREP
Cumulative Review
- Mental Math reviews subtraction facts (Lessons 2.1–3.4).
- Problems 1–10 review subtraction facts (Lessons 3.1–3.4).

Subtraction Facts

Context of the Lesson This lesson introduces additional strategies to help students remember subtraction facts. This lesson also includes the first subtraction speed test. Speed tests should be given often so students can assess their improvement and what they have left to learn.
See page 79B for Math Background for teachers for this lesson.

Planning for Learning ● DIFFERENTIATE INSTRUCTION

INTERVENTION
If . . . students lack the prerequisite skill of counting back on a number line,

Then . . . teach *Intervention* Lesson 3.B.

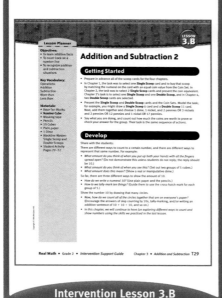

Intervention Lesson 3.B

ENGLISH LEARNER
Preview
If . . . students need language support,

Then . . . use Lesson 3.5 in *English Learner Support Guide* to preview lesson concepts and vocabulary.

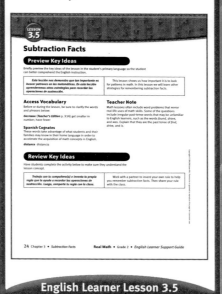

English Learner Lesson 3.5

ENRICH
If . . . students are proficient in the lesson concepts,

Then . . . emphasize additional game time.

PRACTICE
If . . . students would benefit from additional practice,

Then . . . extend Skill Practice before assigning the student pages.

RETEACH
If . . . students are having difficulty understanding subtraction,

Then . . . extend Guided Discussion before assigning the student pages.

Access Vocabulary
decrease get smaller in number; have fewer

Spanish Cognates
distance distancia

*Manipulative Kit Item

Mental Math 5

  Give a fast-paced drill on the subtraction facts involving 10 and 9. Students find, hide, and show answers with **Number Cubes.** Possible examples include the following:

a. 17 − 10 = 7   **b.** 17 − 9 = 8
c. 17 − 7 = 10   **d.** 14 − 4 = 10
e. 14 − 5 = 9   **f.** 12 − 10 = 2
g. 12 − 9 = 3   **h.** 12 − 8 = 4

1 Develop 20

Tell Students In Today's Lesson They Will
learn about remaining facts and take a speed test.

Small Group

Guided Discussion MathTools ENGAGING

Discuss strategies to remember other subtraction facts with students.

Subtracting 5
Students can imagine taking away five fingers to remember the −5 facts.

Doubles Facts
Students can remember subtraction doubles facts by thinking of the doubles addition facts. There are only two numbers to remember—the difference and the number being subtracted from.

Corresponding Addition Facts
Students can remember any subtraction fact by using the corresponding addition fact.

Skill Building
Provide or have students make flash cards with subtraction facts. Have them work in pairs to review the facts using the flash cards. Encourage students to answer quickly. If they know a fact, they can remove that card from the set. Display the Addition Table on the overhead projector or use **eMathTools: Addition Table** as a reference to the facts while students are working. This activity is not a competitive exercise. It should be used only to help students learn what facts they need to work on.

Skill Practice COMPUTING

Whole Group

 Engage students in basic subtraction-fact practice by using the strategies covered in Guided Discussion. Have students use **Number Cubes** to show their answers. Possible examples include the following:

a. 12 − 5 = 7   **b.** 12 − 6 = 6   **c.** 12 − 4 = 8
d. 8 − 4 = 4   **e.** 7 − 5 = 2   **f.** 6 − 5 = 1

2 Assign Student Pages 10

Pages 93–94 UNDERSTANDING

Have students complete pages 93 and 94 independently.

Page 94 is the first subtraction speed test. Before beginning, help students feel comfortable. Emphasize that there will be plenty of time to improve scores and that students will be asked to improve on their previous scores, not to compete with each other.

Monitoring Student Progress

| **If . . .** students have difficulty solving for basic subtraction facts, | **Then . . .** have students work in pairs using flash cards to practice. |

As Students Finish

Game Allow students enough time to play a game of their choice, or assign a game based on their needs.

Have students practice subtraction facts with a partner using their flash cards.

RESEARCH IN ACTION

"An understanding of addition and subtraction . . . is fundamental to success with school mathematics. For example, the former is essential for understanding more advanced and related topics such as multiplication."

Baroody, Arthur J. "The Developmental Bases for Early Childhood Number and Operations Standards" in Clements, Douglas and J. Sarama, eds. *Engaging Young Children in Mathematics: Standards for Early Childhood Mathematics Education.* Mahwah, New Jersey: Lawrence Erlbaum Associates, Publishers, 2004, p. 210.

Student Page

LESSON 3.5 Subtraction Facts

Name _____ Date _____

Key Ideas

Subtraction is taking away a number of items.

$$12 - 5 = 7$$

Subtract.

1. $16 - 8 = 8$
2. $17 - 10 = 7$
3. $14 - 5 = 9$
4. $15 - 5 = 10$
5. $13 - 8 = 5$

6. $14 - 7 = 7$
7. $10 - 5 = 5$
8. $11 - 8 = 3$
9. $18 - 9 = 9$
10. $9 - 5 = 4$

Textbook This lesson is available in the *eTextbook*.   93

Student Page

LESSON 3.5 · Subtraction Facts

Speed Test

1. $8 - 8 = 0$
2. $9 - 7 = 2$
3. $4 - 2 = 2$
4. $6 - 5 = 1$
5. $8 - 4 = 4$
6. $12 - 9 = 3$
7. $6 - 1 = 5$
8. $12 - 8 = 4$
9. $17 - 5 = 12$
10. $16 - 6 = 10$

11. $14 - 7 = 7$
12. $4 - 1 = 3$
13. $11 - 7 = 4$
14. $19 - 6 = 13$
15. $13 - 9 = 4$
16. $9 - 4 = 5$
17. $12 - 3 = 9$
18. $7 - 6 = 1$
19. $4 - 4 = 0$
20. $16 - 10 = 6$

21. $\begin{array}{r} 17 \\ -5 \\ \hline 12 \end{array}$
22. $\begin{array}{r} 13 \\ -8 \\ \hline 5 \end{array}$
23. $\begin{array}{r} 14 \\ -6 \\ \hline 8 \end{array}$

24. $\begin{array}{r} 8 \\ -1 \\ \hline 7 \end{array}$
25. $\begin{array}{r} 17 \\ -8 \\ \hline 9 \end{array}$

94   **Real Math • Chapter 3 · Lesson 5**

---

3 Reflect   5

Guided Discussion **REASONING**   Whole Group

Call students' attention to page 93. Allow them to describe how they completed the exercises and what shortcuts they used. For example, exercises 3, 4, 7, and 10 all subtract 5. Exercises 1, 6, 7, and 9 are all doubles facts.

Cumulative Review: For cumulative review of previously learned skills, see page 101–102.

Family Involvement: Assign the *Practice, Reteach,* or *Enrichment* activities depending on the needs of your students. Have students practice subtraction flash cards with family members.

Concept/Question Board: Encourage students to continue to post questions, answers, and examples on the Concept/Question Board.

Math Puzzler: Mr. Ito's cat weighs 11 pounds. The cat used to weigh 9 pounds. How much weight did the cat gain? 2 pounds

Chapter 3 · Lesson 5   **93–94**

Assess and Differentiate

 Assess Use *eAssess* to record and analyze evidence of student understanding.

A Gather Evidence

Use the Daily Class Assessment Records in *Assessment* or *eAssess* to record daily observations.

Informal Assessment

☑ **Skill Practice**

Did the student **COMPUTING**
- ❑ respond accurately?
- ❑ respond quickly?
- ❑ respond with confidence?
- ❑ self-correct?

Informal Assessment

☑ **Guided Discussion**

Did the student **REASONING**
- ❑ provide a clear explanation?
- ❑ communicate reasons and strategies?
- ❑ choose appropriate strategies?
- ❑ argue logically?

B Summarize Findings

Analyze and summarize assessment data for each student. Determine which Assessment Follow-Up is appropriate for each student. Use the Student Assessment Record in *Assessment* or *eAssess* to update assessment records.

Assessment page T41

C Assessment Follow-Up ● DIFFERENTIATE INSTRUCTION

Based on your observations, use these teaching strategies for assessment follow-up.

INTERVENTION

Review student performance on *Intervention* Lesson 3.B to see if students have mastered prerequisite skills for this lesson.

ENGLISH LEARNER

Review

Use Lesson 3.5 in *English Learner Support Guide* to review lesson concepts and vocabulary.

ENRICH

If . . . students are proficient in the lesson concepts,

Then . . . encourage them to work on the chapter projects or *Enrichment* Lesson 3.5.

Enrichment Lesson 3.5

PRACTICE

If . . . students would benefit from additional practice,

Then . . . assign *Practice* Lesson 3.5.

Practice Lesson 3.5

RETEACH

If . . . students are having difficulty understanding basic subtraction facts,

Then . . . reteach the concept using *Reteach* Lesson 3.5.

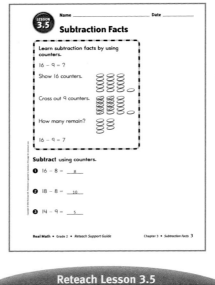

Reteach Lesson 3.5

Lesson Planner

OBJECTIVES
To solve problems using addition and subtraction

NCTM STANDARDS
Number and Operations
- Developing fluency with basic number combinations for addition and subtraction
- Using a variety of methods to compute
- Understanding the effects of adding and subtracting whole numbers

Problem Solving
- Applying and adapting a variety of appropriate strategies to solve problems
- Monitoring and reflecting on the process of mathematical problem solving

MATERIALS
- *Number Cubes (0–5 and 5–10)
- *Play money

TECHNOLOGY
- e **Presentation** Lesson 3.6
- e **Games** Roll 20 to 5 Game
- e **MathTools** Coins and Money
- **Building Blocks** Word Problems with Tools 3

TEST PREP
Cumulative Review
- Mental Math reviews addition and subtraction facts (Lessons 2.1–3.5).
- Problems 1–6 review applications of addition (Lessons 2.1–2.6).

Extended Response
Problems 2–5

Multistep
Problem 6

Applications of Addition and Subtraction

Context of the Lesson The previous lessons developed fluency with subtraction facts. In this lesson we provide applications in which students can use the subtraction and addition facts.

See page 71B for Math Background for teachers for this lesson.

Planning for Learning ● DIFFERENTIATE INSTRUCTION

INTERVENTION
If . . . students lack the prerequisite skill of recognizing addition and subtraction situations,

Then . . . teach *Intervention* Lesson 3.C.

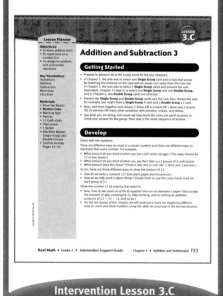

Intervention Lesson 3.C

ENGLISH LEARNER
Preview

If . . . students need language support,

Then . . . use Lesson 3.6 in *English Learner Support Guide* to preview lesson concepts and vocabulary.

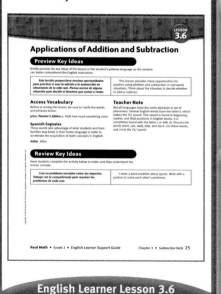

English Learner Lesson 3.6

ENRICH
If . . . students are proficient in the lesson concepts,

Then . . . emphasize Guided Discussion in Reflect.

PRACTICE
If . . . students would benefit from additional practice,

Then . . . extend Skill Practice before assigning the student pages.

RETEACH
If . . . students are having difficulty understanding applications of addition and subtraction,

Then . . . extend Guided Discussion before assigning the student pages.

Access Vocabulary	**Spanish Cognates**
price how much something costs	**dollar** dólar

---

*Manipulative Kit Item

Mental Math 5

 Give students practice solving basic addition and subtraction facts such as the following:

a. $3 + 4 = 7$ **b.** $7 - 4 = 3$ **c.** $5 + 5 = 10$ **d.** $10 - 5 = 5$
e. $9 + 2 = 11$ **f.** $11 - 2 = 9$ **g.** $5 + 3 = 8$ **h.** $8 - 5 = 3$

1 Develop 20

Tell Students In Today's Lesson They Will

solve word problems.

Whole Group

Guided Discussion MathTools UNDERSTANDING

Word Problems

Give some written and verbal word problems.

Have students first identify what the problem is.

- **What are we trying to find out?**
- **What information is there already?** Help students identify the information already given in the problem and what the problem situation is.
- **What can I do to solve this problem?**

Solve the problem together, and ask the following:

- **Does the answer make sense?** If the answer makes sense, then the problem is solved. If the answer does not make sense, then try to solve the problem again.

If students are having difficulty, act out the problems with play money, *eMathTools: Coins and Money,* or other appropriate materials.

Here are some examples of problems:

a. Vincent has a $10 bill to buy a birthday present for his cousin. The toy store has a football that costs $6 and a toy airplane that costs $3. Does Vincent have enough money to buy both?

- **What are we trying to find out?** Can Vincent buy the football and the toy airplane?
- **What information do we already have?** We know that Vincent has $10, the football costs $6, and the toy airplane costs $3.
- **What can we do to find the answer?** We need to add the cost of the toys and compare the sum to $10. Because $9 is less than $10, he has enough money to buy both.
- **Does the answer make sense?** yes

Continue with the same procedure for the next sample problem.

b. There are seven days in a week. How many days are there in two weeks?

- **What are we trying to find out?** how many days are in two weeks
- **What information do we already have?** There are seven days in one week.
- **What can we do to find the answer?** We can add two weeks' worth of days, or $7 + 7 = 14$.
- **Does the answer make sense?** yes

If necessary, count the number of days on a class calendar for two weeks.

Skill Practice APPLYING

Whole Group

Have students open their books to page 95 and work Problem 1 together, emphasizing the steps of problem solving. Ask students the following:

- **What are we trying to find out?** how long it will take Mark to walk to the library and back
- **What information do we already have?** Mark can walk from his house to the library in six minutes.
- **What can we do to find the answer?** We can add: $6 + 6 = 12$. It will take Mark twelve minutes to walk to the library and back to his house.
- **Does the answer make sense?** yes

Look at the last question for Problem 1: *About how many minutes will it take him to walk to school?*

- **What are we trying to find out?** how many minutes it will take Mark to walk to school
- **What information do we have?** We have no information about how far away the school is or how long it will take him to walk there.
- **How can we answer this question?** We will have to say, "We cannot tell unless we get more information."

2 Assign Student Pages 20

Pages 95–96 APPLYING

Have students complete the rest of pages 95 and 96 independently, allowing them to act out the problems using play money if needed. Read the word problems to students who have trouble with reading. Bring the class together to discuss their solutions.

Monitoring Student Progress

| If . . . students have difficulty answering the third question in Problem 2, | Then . . . be sure they understand that Sara *had* $15, but now *has* only $9. |

As Students Finish

 Allow students enough time to play the **Roll 20 to 5 Game.**

Games *Roll 20 to 5 Game*

Building Blocks Have students use **Word Problems with Tools 3** to practice problem-solving strategies.

Applications of Addition and Subtraction

LESSON 3.6 Applications of Addition and Subtraction

Key Ideas

Addition and subtraction are used to solve problems.

When solving problems, it is important to understand the situation.

Solve.

1 Mark can walk from his house to the library in 6 minutes. About how many minutes will it take him to walk back? __about 6 minutes__
About how many minutes will it take him to walk to the library and back? __about 12 minutes__ About how many minutes will it take him to walk to school? __cannot tell__

2 **Extended Response** Sara had $15. She bought a book and now has $9. How much did the book cost? __$6__ Could she have a $5 bill? Explain. __yes, a $5 bill and four $1 bills__
Could she have a $10 bill? Explain. __no, $10 is more than $9__

3 **Extended Response** Zane can do a page of addition and subtraction facts in about 10 minutes. His sister can do the same page in about 5 minutes. If they work together, about how many minutes will it take them? Explain. __cannot tell__
You need to know if they work faster or slower when they work together.

Textbook This lesson is available in the *eTextbook*.

95

LESSON 3.6 · Applications of Addition and Subtraction

4 **Extended Response** Max has $3. He wants to buy a ball for $10. He can earn $2 an hour mowing lawns. How many hours must he mow lawns to have $10? Explain. __4 hours—or 3½ hours__

5 **Extended Response** How many bananas can you buy if you have $4 and bananas cost 50¢ each? Explain. __8__

6 The score was Sluggers 9 and Bearcats 3 at the end of the eighth inning. If the Sluggers score 1 more run, how many runs must the Bearcats score to win the game? __8__

4 In 3 hours he will have earned $6 (2 + 2 + 2 = 6) giving him $9. So if he works one more hour, he'll have (9 + 2 = 11) $11. But if he works only one more half hour, he'll have earned one more dollar (9 + 1 = 10) and will have $10 exactly.

5 Two bananas will cost $1, 4 bananas/$2, 6 bananas/$3, and 8 bananas/$4 (2 + 2 + 2 + 2 = 8); or because bananas cost 50¢, or half of a dollar, there are 8 half dollars in $4.

Game Play the **Roll 20 to 5 Game.**

Real Math • Chapter 3 • Lesson 6

---

3 Reflect

10

Guided Discussion **REASONING**

Whole Group

Have students refer to Problem 2 on page 95.

■ **Could Sara have given the cashier a $15 bill?** no; There is no $15 bill in the United States.
■ **What bills did Sara probably have to begin with?** She probably had a $10 bill and a $5 bill, but other answers are possible.
■ **If she had a $10 bill and a $5 bill, what would she have given the cashier?** the $10 bill
■ **How much change would she get?** $1

Extended Response

Problems 2–5 Discuss students' answers. Refer to the Guided Discussion in Reflect to address the answers to Problem 2.

☑ Use Mastery Checkpoint 5 found in *Assessment* to evaluate student mastery of subtraction facts. By this time, students should be able to answer eighty percent of the Mastery Checkpoint items.

 Cumulative Review: For cumulative review of previously learned skills, see page 101–102.

 Family Involvement: Assign the *Practice, Reteach,* or *Enrichment* activities depending on the needs of your students. Have students create word problems with a family member.

 Concept/Question Board: Have students attempt to answer any unanswered questions on the Concept/Question Board.

 Math Puzzler: James started out with 12 pencils. He gave away 3 to a friend. He bought 4 more after school. How many pencils does he have now? 13

4 Assess and Differentiate

e Assess Use **eAssess** to record and analyze evidence of student understanding.

A Gather Evidence

Use the Daily Class Assessment Records in **Assessment** or **eAssess** to record daily observations.

Formal Assessment

☑ **Mastery Checkpoint**

Did the student
☐ use correct procedures?
☐ respond with at least 80% accuracy?

5 Mastery Checkpoint 5
Subtraction Facts
The student demonstrates mastery by correctly answering thirty-two of the forty problems.
Check your math skills.

❶ 14 − 3 = __11__   ⓫ 12 − 4 = __8__
❷ 9 − 7 = __2__   ⓬ 10 − 9 = __1__
❸ 11 − 2 = __9__   ⓭ 15 − 5 = __10__
❹ 15 − 7 = __8__   ⓮ 14 − 7 = __7__
❺ 12 − 8 = __4__   ⓯ 13 − 6 = __7__
❻ 17 − 9 = __8__   ⓰ 17 − 8 = __9__
❼ 20 − 10 = __10__   ⓱ 11 − 0 = __11__

Assessment page T55

B Summarize Findings

Analyze and summarize assessment data for each student. Determine which Assessment Follow-Up is appropriate for each student. Use the Student Assessment Record in **Assessment** or **eAssess** to update assessment records.

Student Name
Student Assessment Record
Directions: Use this chart to record student performance on all chapter assessments.

Assessment page T41

C Assessment Follow-Up ● DIFFERENTIATE INSTRUCTION

Based on your observations, use these teaching strategies for assessment follow-up.

INTERVENTION	ENRICH	PRACTICE	RETEACH
Review student performance on **Intervention** Lesson 3.C to see if students have mastered prerequisite skills for this lesson.	**If . . .** students are proficient in the lesson concepts, **Then . . .** encourage them to work on the chapter projects or **Enrichment** Lesson 3.6.	**If . . .** students would benefit from additional practice, **Then . . .** assign **Practice** Lesson 3.6.	**If . . .** students struggle with addition and subtraction applications, **Then . . .** have them read the word problem and think through the situation while using manipulatives if needed.

ENGLISH LEARNER

Review

Use Lesson 3.6 in **English Learner Support Guide** to review lesson concepts and vocabulary.

LESSON 3.6
Applications of Addition and Subtraction

Animal Problems

Teacher Note: Send this page home with your students, and have helpers from home work with students to complete the activity.

Note to Home: Today your child learned to solve problems using addition and subtraction. Help your child complete this activity.

Ring how many of each kind of animal will be taken to another farm. Write number problems for each. For each type of animal, tell how many there are altogether, how many will go to another farm, and how many will stay behind. Finally, tell how many of all the animals have stayed behind and how many have gone to other farms.
Check that students' equations agree with the number of animals circled.

Totals

Real Math • Grade 2 • Enrichment Support Guide   **Chapter 3 • Subtraction Facts 25**

Enrichment Lesson 3.6

LESSON 3.6
Applications of Addition and Subtraction

Solve these problems.

❶ At one bus stop, 7 children got on the bus. At the next bus stop, 4 children got on the bus. How many children got on the bus at these two stops?
__11__ children
Explain. __7 + 4 = 11__

❷ Elizabeth has $12. The price of a fishbowl is $8. The price of a goldfish is $3. Does Elizabeth have enough money to buy the bowl and a goldfish?
__yes__ Explain.
$8 + $3 = $11, $11 < $12

❸ Marcus saw 14 caterpillars in a tree. Marcella saw 6 fewer caterpillars than Marcus. How many caterpillars did Marcella see?
__8__ caterpillars
Explain. __14 − 6 = 8__

Lin saw more caterpillars than Marcella, but fewer than Marcus. How many caterpillars did she see? _____ caterpillars
Answers will vary. Possible answers: 9, 10, 11, 12, or 13

Real Math • Grade 2 • Practice   **Chapter 3 • Subtraction Facts 25**

Practice Lesson 3.6

Lesson Planner

OBJECTIVES
To introduce and practice chain calculations with the addition and subtraction of three or more numbers

NCTM STANDARDS
Number and Operations
- Developing and using strategies for whole-number combinations
- Developing fluency with basic number combinations
- Understanding meanings of addition and subtraction

Problem Solving
- Applying and adapting a variety of strategies to solve problems
- Monitoring and reflecting on the process of mathematical problem solving

MATERIALS
- *Number Cubes (0–5 and 5–10)
- *Play money

TECHNOLOGY
- e **Presentation** Lesson 3.7
- e **Games** Roll 20 to 5 Game
- e **MathTools** Coins and Money

TEST PREP
Cumulative Review
Mental Math reviews addition and subtraction facts (Lessons 2.1–3.6).

Extended Response
Problem 20

Looking Ahead
Lesson 4.1 will require large sheets of paper at least the length of students' bodies.

Chain Calculations

Context of the Lesson The previous lesson and this lesson focus on applications of addition and subtraction facts.

See page 71B for Math Background for teachers for this lesson.

Planning for Learning • DIFFERENTIATE INSTRUCTION

INTERVENTION
If . . . students lack the prerequisite skill of recognizing addition and subtraction situations,

Then . . . teach *Intervention* Lesson 3.A.

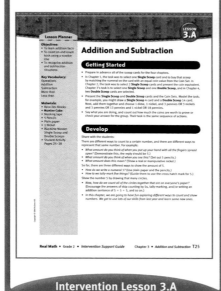

Intervention Lesson 3.A

ENGLISH LEARNER
Preview

If . . . students need language support,

Then . . . use Lesson 3.7 in *English Learner Support Guide* to preview lesson concepts and vocabulary.

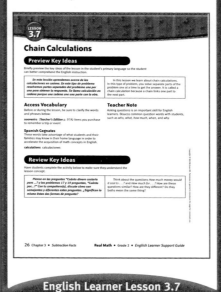

English Learner Lesson 3.7

ENRICH
If . . . students are proficient in the lesson concepts,

Then . . . emphasize Guided Discussion in Reflect.

PRACTICE
If . . . students would benefit from additional practice,

Then . . . extend Skill Practice before assigning the student pages.

RETEACH
If . . . students are having difficulty understanding addition and subtraction situations,

Then . . . extend Guided Discussion before assigning the student pages.

Access Vocabulary
souvenirs items you purchase to remember a trip or event

Spanish Cognates
calculations calculaciones

Mental Math 5

  Review   Give a fast-paced addition- and subtraction-fact drill such as the following:

a. $10 + 4 = 14$

b. $6 + 7 = 13$

c. $10 - 5 = 5$

d. $6 + 9 = 15$

e. $5 - 5 = 0$

f. $7 + 3 = 10$

g. $6 - 4 = 2$

h. $4 + 9 = 13$

1 Develop 20

Tell Students In Today's Lesson They Will

practice chain calculations with addition and subtraction.

Guided Discussion UNDERSTANDING Whole Group

Addition and Subtraction Involving Several Numbers

Write a sentence like this on the board: $4 + 6 + 7 = $ _____

■ **What is the answer?** 17

■ **How did you find the answer?** Possible answer: by adding 4 and 6, which makes 10, and then by adding 7, which makes 17

If someone suggests a different order, explain that any order will work with addition problems, but with subtraction we must always be very careful.

Do another problem, being careful not to get a *partial sum,* or subtotal, larger than 10. For example: $5 + 4 + 9 = \underline{18}$

Explain that sometimes we write addition problems involving three or more numbers vertically, with the plus sign at the bottom only. Show and solve an example such as the following:

$$\begin{array}{r} 3 \\ 2 \\ + 4 \\ \hline 9 \end{array}$$

Next try a problem involving subtraction. For example:
$14 - 8 + 2 = \underline{8}$

Here students must start by subtracting 8 from 14 and then adding 2. A problem such as this will always be written horizontally and start at the left, working to the right.

Give one or two more problems involving subtraction such as the following:

$6 + 8 - 7 = \underline{7}$ $15 - 6 - 8 = \underline{1}$

Skill Practice ✓ COMPUTING Whole Group

 Give an oral drill in adding or subtracting several numbers, going slowly at first and gradually increasing the speed. Make sure that partial sums, or subtotals, are no greater than ten because students are not yet proficient at handling such sums. They should have no difficulty with an oral drill in which there are four or more numbers because they will be carrying in their heads only one number at a time; however, a very long sequence will be frustrating to students who get lost near the beginning. Students will show answers with **Number Cubes.** Possible examples include the following:

a. $3 + 5 + 7 = \underline{15}$

b. $10 - 5 - 5 + 4 = \underline{4}$

c. $8 + 2 + 9 = \underline{19}$

d. $8 + 0 - 6 + 5 = \underline{7}$

e. $10 - 5 + 7 = \underline{12}$

f. $7 + 3 + 8 - 2 = \underline{16}$

g. $18 - 9 + 5 = \underline{14}$

h. $10 + 8 - 7 = \underline{11}$

i. $5 + 8 - 7 + 6 = \underline{12}$

j. $16 - 9 + 7 - 4 = \underline{10}$

Monitoring Student Progress

| **If . . .** students have difficulty doing chain calculations during the response exercise, | **Then . . .** give written practice with similar chain calculations as they verbalize what they are thinking. Then take away the written exercises and give slow oral practice. Gradually speed up the oral practice, keeping pace with students' abilities. These procedures will take time over a period of days. |

2 Assign Student Pages 20

Pages 97–98 ✓   MathTools UNDERSTANDING

Have students complete pages 97 and 98 independently.

Make sure students work these exercises from left to right. Allow students to use play money or **eMathTools: Coins and Money** for page 98, if they wish.

As Students Finish

 Game Allow students enough time to play the **Roll 20 to 5 Game.**

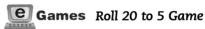 **e Games** *Roll 20 to 5 Game*

Name _____ Date _____

LESSON 3.7 **Chain Calculations**

Key Ideas

When adding more than two numbers, it is helpful to work the problem in parts.

5 + 3 + 7 = ?

First add 5 + 3.

$$\begin{array}{r} 8 \\ + 7 \\ \hline 15 \end{array}$$

Then add 7 to that answer.

Work these problems. Watch the signs.

1. 11 − 4 + 4 = **11**
2. 5 + 5 + 5 = **15**
3. 10 − 8 + 7 = **9**
4. 16 − 0 − 8 = **8**
5. 4 + 8 − 2 = **10**
6. 4 + 5 + 9 = **18**

7.
$$\begin{array}{r} 8 \\ 2 \\ + 7 \\ \hline 17 \end{array}$$

8.
$$\begin{array}{r} 5 \\ 5 \\ + 5 \\ \hline 15 \end{array}$$

9.
$$\begin{array}{r} 7 \\ 3 \\ + 8 \\ \hline 18 \end{array}$$

10.
$$\begin{array}{r} 6 \\ 5 \\ + 8 \\ \hline 19 \end{array}$$

11.
$$\begin{array}{r} 6 \\ 6 \\ + 9 \\ \hline 21 \end{array}$$

12.
$$\begin{array}{r} 9 \\ 0 \\ + 5 \\ \hline 14 \end{array}$$

13.
$$\begin{array}{r} 4 \\ 5 \\ + 6 \\ \hline 15 \end{array}$$

14.
$$\begin{array}{r} 3 \\ 3 \\ + 3 \\ \hline 9 \end{array}$$

15.
$$\begin{array}{r} 4 \\ 2 \\ 7 \\ + 4 \\ \hline 13 \end{array}$$

Textbook This lesson is available in the *eTextbook*.

97

LESSON 3.7 · Chain Calculations

Aaron went to a baseball game.
The following items were for sale at the game.

16. How much money would it cost to buy 3 baseballs? **$9**

17. How much for 2 T-shirts and 1 baseball? **$19**

18. How much would it cost to buy 4 baseball caps? **$16**

19. How much for 2 baseballs and 1 baseball cap? **$10**

20. **Extended Response** Jason has $15. Can he buy 2 baseballs and 2 baseball caps? **yes** Explain how you found your answer. **Add all the items together, and then subtract the sum from $15.**

Game Play the **Roll 20 to 5 Game.**

98

---

3 Reflect

10

Guided Discussion **REASONING**

Whole Group

Have students select a problem on page 97 and try to solve it in a different order. Does the answer make sense? Discuss student results. Have them experiment by combining addition and subtraction exercises and completing the operations in different orders. The class should determine that when using addition only, the order makes no difference. However, when subtracting, it does make a difference which order the operations are performed. Have students illustrate this by using manipulatives and creating chain calculations.

Extended Response

Problem 20 Discuss students' answers. Students should have realized that we add together all the items and then subtract the sum from $15.

Cumulative Review: For cumulative review of previously learned skills, see page 101–102.

Family Involvement: Assign the **Practice, Reteach,** or **Enrichment** activities depending on the needs of your students. Have students practice subtraction flash cards with a family member.

Concept/Question Board: Have students attempt to answer any unanswered questions on the Concept/Question Board.

Math Puzzler: Carl, Hector, and Tara are standing in a line. How many different ways can they line up? six ways: Carl, Hector, Tara; Carl, Tara, Hector; Tara, Hector, Carl; Tara, Carl, Hector; Hector, Carl, Tara; Hector, Tara, Carl

4 Assess and Differentiate

 Assess Use *eAssess* to record and analyze evidence of student understanding.

A Gather Evidence

Use the Daily Class Assessment Records in *Assessment* or *eAssess* to record daily observations.

Informal Assessment
✔ **Skill Practice**

Did the student **COMPUTING**
❏ respond accurately?
❏ respond quickly?
❏ respond with confidence?
❏ self-correct?

Informal Assessment
✔ **Student Pages**

Did the student **UNDERSTANDING**
❏ make important observations?
❏ extend or generalize learning?
❏ provide insightful answers?
❏ pose insightful questions?

B Summarize Findings

Analyze and summarize assessment data for each student. Determine which Assessment Follow-Up is appropriate for each student. Use the Student Assessment Record in *Assessment* or *eAssess* to update assessment records.

Assessment page T41

C Assessment Follow-Up ● DIFFERENTIATE INSTRUCTION

Based on your observations, use these teaching strategies for assessment follow-up.

INTERVENTION

Review student performance on *Intervention* Lesson 3.A to see if students have mastered prerequisite skills for this lesson.

ENGLISH LEARNER

Review

Use Lesson 3.7 in *English Learner Support Guide* to review lesson concepts and vocabulary.

ENRICH

If . . . students are proficient in the lesson concepts,

Then . . . encourage them to work on the chapter projects or *Enrichment* Lesson 3.7.

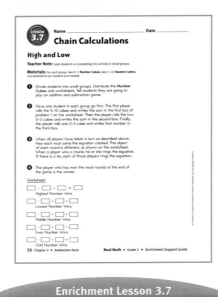

Enrichment Lesson 3.7

PRACTICE

If . . . students would benefit from additional practice,

Then . . . assign *Practice* Lesson 3.7.

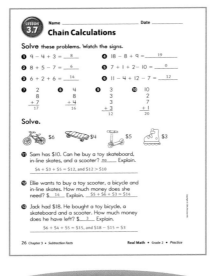

Practice Lesson 3.7

RETEACH

If . . . students are having difficulty with chain calculations,

Then . . . have them break it into simpler parts to solve.

Exploring Problem Solving

Objectives

- To explore working backward and other strategies for solving nonroutine problems
- To explain solutions
- To explore a situation in which addition and subtraction partially undo each other
- To use addition and subtraction facts

Materials

Counters (about 20 for each pair of students)

Context of the Lesson In this lesson students explore a real-world situation that highlights the relationship between addition and subtraction. The lesson provides practice in solving and sharing solutions to nonroutine problems.

1 Develop 5

Tell Students In Today's Lesson They Will

use addition and subtraction to solve problems about origami.

Guided Discussion

Have students look at the illustration on page 99. Give students a chance to talk about what they think the pictures show. At this time, allow any speculation that matches the illustrations. Ask questions such as the following:

- **What do you see in the first picture?** a boy with a collection of origami birds
- **What do you think is happening in the second picture?** The boy is giving away some of his origami birds.
- **What do you think is happening in the third picture?** Someone is giving the boy some origami birds.
- **What do you think is happening in the fourth picture?** Someone is giving the boy more origami birds.
- **What do you think is happening in the fifth picture?** The boy is giving away some of his origami birds.
- **What do you think is happening in the sixth picture?** The boy has a lot of origami birds.

Read this problem to the students as they follow along on the student page.

Joey belonged to Mr. Wilson's Origami Club. When the club was over at the end of the school year, the students decided to share the shapes they had made. Joey gave Mark six of his cranes to use to make a mobile. Denise knew that Joey loved origami birds, so she gave him five of her blue jays. Mr. Wilson gave each member of the club some of his own origami.

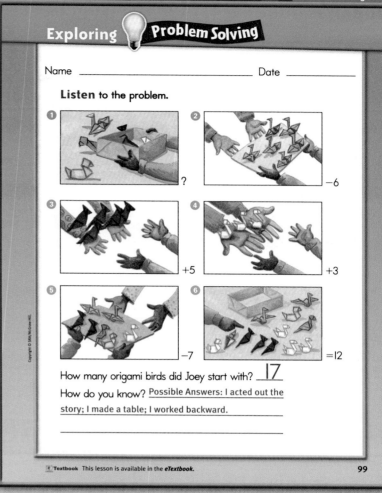

Exploring Problem Solving

Student Page

Name _____ Date _____

Listen to the problem.

1 2 —6

3 +5 4 +3

5 —7 6 =12

How many origami birds did Joey start with? __17__

How do you know? Possible Answers: I acted out the story; I made a table; I worked backward. _____

_____

Textbook This lesson is available in the *eTextbook*. 99

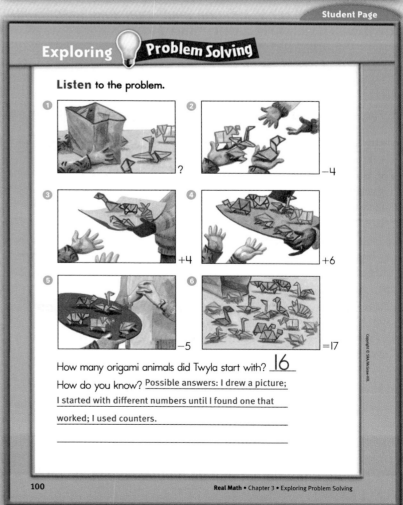

Exploring Problem Solving

Student Page

Listen to the problem.

1 2 —4

3 +4 4 +6

5 —5 6 =17

How many origami animals did Twyla start with? __16__

How do you know? Possible answers: I drew a picture; I started with different numbers until I found one that worked; I used counters. _____

_____

100 Real Math • Chapter 3 • Exploring Problem Solving

He gave Joey three swans. When Joey went to visit his grandmother, he offered her some of his origami birds. She picked out seven of her favorites to keep. When Joey went home, he counted all of his paper birds. He had twelve. His mom asked him how many origami birds were in his collection when the club ended and before the sharing began. Can you figure that out?

To make sure students understand the problem, ask questions such as the following:

- **What is the problem asking you to find?** how many origami birds Joey had at the beginning of the story
- **Can you tell by looking at the picture?** no; because some of them might be in the box, on the part of the table that we cannot see, or somewhere else
- **What useful information does the story tell you?** He gave six cranes away, he received five blue jays and three swans, he gave away seven birds, and he has twelve birds at the end.
- **Does anyone have an idea how to solve this problem?** Students might suggest methods such as drawing pictures; acting out the story with counters; or using guess, check, and revise.

Using Student Pages

Have students work in pairs or small groups on page 99. Students who finish early can begin work on page 100, which illustrates a problem similar to the one on page 99.

If students have no idea how to begin, you might help them get started by asking the following questions and demonstrating with counters if needed.

- **How many origami birds does Joey have at the end of the story?** twelve
- **What did Joey do just before the end of the story?** He gave seven birds to his grandmother.
- **If he has 12 now, how many did he have before he gave 7 to his grandmother?** 19
- **How do you know?** Possible answer: If he got back the 7 from his grandmother, he would have 19.

Circulate as students work, and give help as needed. If students are having difficulty but not getting frustrated, allow them to struggle with the problem for a while before offering suggestions such as the following:

- **Would it help you to look at the pictures as you work on this problem?**
- **How could you use counters to help you keep track of the origami birds?**

Sample Solutions Strategies

Students might use one or more of the following strategies.

Guess, Check, and Revise

Students might go through the events of the story with different starting numbers until they find a number that shows how Joey ends up with twelve origami birds.

Act It Out with Objects

Students might use counters to go through the steps of the story either forward or backward.

Draw a Picture

Students might keep track of the origami pieces with pictures.

Make a Table

Students might create a table to keep track of the number of origami pieces in each step of the story.

Use Operation Sense

Students might realize that Joey gives away 13 and receives 8, so he ends up with 5 fewer than when he started. Then they can add 5 to 12 to get the answer.

Effective Communication Have each group present its answers and methods. After each presentation, ask students what they like about the strategy and how it was presented. Also ask students how they know their answer is correct.

In discussion, bring out the following points:

- Sometimes we can start at the end of a story and work backward step by step to solve a problem.
- When you work backward to solve a problem, you can check the answer by working forward.

When evaluating student work, focus on whether students thought rationally about the problem. Questions to consider include the following:

- Did the student understand the problem?
- Did the student continue to work on trying to solve the problem even though he or she might have encountered difficulty?
- Did the student ask for help immediately, or did he or she try different strategies?
- Was the student able to keep track of what happened in the story?

Cumulative Review

Assign Pages 101–102

Use the Cumulative Review as a review of concepts and skills that students have previously learned.

Here are different ways that you can assign these problems to your students as they work through the chapter:

- With some of the lessons in the chapter, assign a set of cumulative review problems to be completed as practice or for homework.
  Lesson 3.4—Problems 1–2
  Lesson 3.5—Problems 3–12
  Lesson 3.6—Problem 13
  Lesson 3.7—Problems 14–17
- At any point during the chapter, assign part or all of the cumulative review problems to be completed as practice or for homework.

Cumulative Review

Problems 1–2 review fractional parts, Grade 1 Lesson 10.7.

Problems 3–12 review basic addition facts, Lesson 2.1.

Problem 13 reviews making estimates based on visual cues, Lesson 1.4.

Problems 14–17 review chain calculations, Lesson 3.7.

Monitoring Student Progress

If . . . students miss more than one problem in a section,

Then . . . refer to the indicated lesson for remediation suggestions.

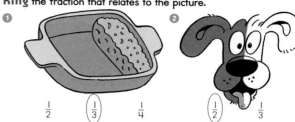

Cumulative Review

Name _____ Date _____

Fractional Parts Grade 1 Lesson 10.7

Ring the fraction that relates to the picture.

1. $\frac{1}{2}$ $\boxed{\frac{1}{3}}$ $\frac{1}{4}$

2. $\boxed{\frac{1}{2}}$ $\frac{1}{3}$ $\frac{1}{4}$

Basic Addition Facts and Table Lesson 2.1

Complete the following addition exercises.

3. $5 + 3 = \underline{8}$ 4. $5 + 2 = \underline{7}$ 5. $5 + 6 = \underline{11}$

6. $2 + 6 = \underline{8}$ 7. $0 + 1 = \underline{1}$ 8. $7 + 6 = \underline{13}$

9. $6 + 2 = \underline{8}$ 10. $1 + 0 = \underline{1}$ 11. $6 + 7 = \underline{13}$

12. Sierra is 6 years old. She had a list of 10 chores. She finished 8 of them. How many chores does she have left? __2__

Textbook This lesson is available in the *eTextbook*.

101

Cumulative Review

Making Estimates Lesson 1.4

Estimate and write the number.

13. About how many magnets will fit from the bottom to the top of the refrigerator door? (The refrigerator door is on the bottom.) Use the drawings on the refrigerator to help you. __about 20–25__

Explain. _____
Because 3 magnets are as tall as half of a page, then 6 magnets would be the same height as a full page ($3 + 3 = 6$). The refrigerator door is four pages tall. You have to add 6 magnets 4 times to get to the top of the refrigerator door. ($6 + 6 + 6 + 6 = 24$)

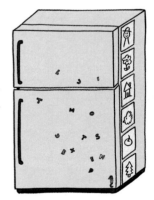

Chain Calculations Lesson 3.7

Solve.

14. $3 + 7 + 8 = \underline{18}$

15. $5 + 5 + 5 = \underline{15}$

16. $9 + 1 + 3 = \underline{13}$

17. $3 + 6 + 8 = \underline{17}$

102   **Real Math** • Chapter 3

Wrap-Up

1 Discuss 5

Concept/Question Board

Review the Concept/Question Board with students.

- Discuss students' contributions to the Concept side of the Board.
- Have students repose their questions, and lead a discussion to find satisfactory answers.

Chapter Projects APPLYING

Provide an opportunity for students who have worked on one or more of the projects outlined on page 80C to share their work with the class. Allow each student or student group five minutes to present or discuss their projects. For formal assessment, use the rubrics found in **Across the Curriculum Math Connections;** the rubric for **Create an Origami Flower** is on page 35, and the rubric for **Present the History of Origami** is on page 41. For informal assessment, use the following rubric and questions.

	Exceeds Expectations	Meets Expectations	Minimally Meets Expectations
Applies mathematics in real-world situations:	❏	❏	❏
Demonstrates strong engagement in the activity:	❏	❏	❏

Create an Origami Flower

- What was the total amount of folds?
- How did you calculate the number of folds required to make the flower?
- What design did you create for your origami paper?
- Did you find it difficult to create your origami flower? Why or why not? What was the hardest part?
- If you could make another form or paper design, what would you make? Why?

Present the History of Origami

- What is origami?
- How did you calculate the number of years between dates?
- What details did you include in your presentation?
- What else could you have added to your slide show?
- Is a slide show the best way to present the history of origami? Why or why not?
- What other ways could you present this information?
- What is the most interesting detail you learned about the history of origami?

2 Assign Student Pages 25

Key Ideas Review ☑ UNDERSTANDING

Have students complete the Review questions independently or in small groups. Then discuss each question as a class.

Possible Answers

Problem ❶ Problem 1 reviews the meaning of subtraction. Students' drawings should show that there were 10 objects and then 5 were taken away (perhaps by crossing them out).

Problem ❷ Problem 2 reviews subtraction vocabulary. The difference is 6.

Problem ❸ Problems 3–5 review using subtraction to solve problems. The answer is b.

Problem ❹ The answer is d.

Problem ❺ The answer is a.

Problem ❻ Problem 6 reviews adding multiple addends. Students should remember to add the first two addends, and then add the third addend to the sum of the first two.

Problem ❼ Problem 7 reviews function machines. Students should realize this is a −4 machine. Students should complete the function table with the answers shown.

Problem ❽ Problem 8 reviews the Commutative Law. Students should realize that the Commutative Law does not apply to subtraction.

Problem ❾ Problem 9 reviews missing-addend problems. The answer is 7.

Problem ❿ Problem 10 reviews the relationship between addition facts and subtraction facts. The answer is 17 − 9 = 8.

CHAPTER 3 Key Ideas Review

Name _____ Date _____

In this chapter you learned about subtraction. You learned about how subtraction is related to addition. You learned to find answers to problems by using information you already know.

❶ Draw a picture to represent 10 − 5.

⊗ ⊗ ⊗ ⊗ ⊗
○ ○ ○ ○ ○

❷ Ring the *difference*: 8 − 2 = ⑥

Ring the letter of the correct answer.

❸ Sami had $12. She bought a book, and then she had $7. Which number sentence can you use to find out how much the book cost?

   a. 12 + 7   **ⓑ** 12 − 7   **c.** 7 − 12

❹ Connor made 4 origami cranes and 3 flowers. Then he gave away 2 flowers and 2 cranes. Which number sentence can you use to find out how many cranes Connor has?

   a. 4 + 3   **b.** 2 + 2   **c.** 4 − 3   **ⓓ** 4 − 2

❺ Knowing 14 − 6 = 8 also helps you know the answer to which of the following?

   ⓐ 14 − 8   **b.** 8 − 6   **c.** 6 − 14

📖 **Textbook** This lesson is available in the *eTextbook*.   103

CHAPTER 3 Key Ideas Review

❻ Solve 4 + 6 + 7. Show your steps.
   <u>4 + 6 = 10, and 10 + 7 = 17</u>

❼ Complete the function table to show the answers to this problem.

  Four students each bought a ticket to a movie. A movie ticket costs $4. Maria started with $10. Kyle started with $7. Suzy started with $6. Matt started with $4. How much did each student have after buying a ticket?

in ─(−4)→ out

in	out
10	6
7	3
6	2
4	0

❽ If 5 + 3 is the same as 3 + 5, then is 5 − 3 the same as 3 − 5? Explain using words or pictures.
   <u>No, because you can take away 3 objects from 5,</u>
   <u>but you cannot take away 5 objects from 3.</u>

❾ Maya's class is doing the Numbers on the Back Activity. The sum is 11. What number is on Maya's back? <u>7</u>

❿ What subtraction fact does the table show?
   <u>17 − 9 = 8</u>

+	0	1	2	3	4	5	6	7	8	9	10
0	0	1	2	3	4	5	6	7	8	9	10
1	1	2	3	4	5	6	7	8	9	10	11
2	2	3	4	5	6	7	8	9	10	11	12
3	3	4	5	6	7	8	9	10	11	12	
4	4	5	6	7	8	9	10	11			
5	5	6	7	8	9	10	11				
6	6	7	8	9	10						
7	7	8	9								
8	8										

Math • Chapter 3

Chapter 3 • Subtraction Facts   **103–104**

Chapter Review

Use the Chapter 3 Review to indicate areas in which each student is having difficulty or in which the class may need help. If students do well on the Chapter 3 Review, you may wish to skip directly to the Chapter Test; if not, you may want to spend a day or so helping students overcome their individual difficulties before taking the Practice Test.

Next to each set of problems is a list of the lessons in the chapter that covered those concepts. If they need help, students can refer to a specific lesson for additional instruction. You can also use this information to make additional assignments based on the previous lesson concepts.

Have students complete pages 105–106 on their own.

Monitoring Student Progress

Problems 1–6 Lessons 3.2, 3.4–3.5

If . . . students miss more than two of these problems,

Then . . . have them play the **Roll 20 to 5 Game.**

Problems 7–10 Lesson 3.7

If . . . students have difficulty with these problems,

Then . . . have them rewrite each problem as two different mathematical statements.

Problems 11–12 Lesson 3.6

If . . . students write an incorrect answer,

Then . . . have them use play money to help them answer the problems.

Problems 13–22 Lessons 3.3, 3.1

If . . . students have difficulty with these problems,

Then . . . have them use counters to illustrate each problem.

Name _____ Date _____

Lessons 3.2, 3.4, 3.5 **Find** the difference.

① 7
− 3
4

② 4
− 2
2

③ 9
− 4
5

④ 13
− 6
7

⑤ 19 − 4 = **15** ⑥ 17 − 10 = **7**

Lesson 3.7 **Work** these problems from left to right.

⑦ 13 − 3 + 2 = **12** ⑧ 18 − 2 − 2 = **14**

⑨ 2 + 2 + 2 = **6** ⑩ 10 + 4 + 3 = **17**

Lesson 3.6 ⑪ **Extended Response** Christy has $12 in bills in her purse. Could she have a $5 bill? __yes__

Explain. <u>She could have one $5 bill and seven $1 bills, or she could have two $5 bills and two $1 bills.</u>

50 cents each

⑫ **Extended Response** How many origami figures can you buy if you have $3 and origami figures cost 50¢ each? __6__

Explain. <u>Two figures will cost $1, 4 figures will cost $2, and 6 figures will cost $3 (2 + 2 + 2 = 6).</u>

Textbook This lesson is available in the *eTextbook*.

Lesson 3.3 **Fill** in the missing numbers. Look at the rule.

⑬ Rule +7

in +7 → out	
4	11
1	8
6	13
3	10

⑭ Rule −2

in −2 → out	
9	7
6	4
5	3
13	11

Find the rule.

⑮

in → out	
7	2
8	3
19	14
18	13

The rule is **−5**.

⑯

in → out	
41	39
40	38
26	24
15	13

The rule is **−2**.

Lesson 3.1 **Solve** for each missing addend.

⑰ 5 + **1** = 6 ⑱ 13 − **7** = 6

⑲ 4 + **6** = 10 ⑳ 12 − **6** = 6

㉑ **8** + 4 = 12 ㉒ 13 − **9** = 4

3

3 Chapter Tests 40

Practice Test

Student Pages 107–110

- The Chapter 3 Practice Test on **Student Edition** pages 107–110 provides an opportunity to formally evaluate students' proficiency with concepts developed in this chapter.
- The content is similar to the Chapter 3 Review, in standardized format.

Problems ㉑ and ㉒   Extended Response

Students practice their problem-solving, reasoning, addition, and subtraction skills. For Problem 21, remind students to decide if each statement represents an addition or subtraction operation. Encourage them to draw illustrations to help with the problem solving. For Problem 22, students focus primarily on addition with multiple addends. Remind students of different strategies they can use to add more than two addends.

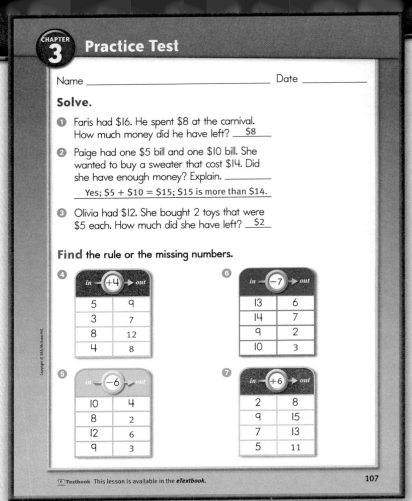

CHAPTER 3 Practice Test

Name _____ Date _____

Solve.

1. Faris had $16. He spent $8 at the carnival. How much money did he have left? __$8__

2. Paige had one $5 bill and one $10 bill. She wanted to buy a sweater that cost $14. Did she have enough money? Explain. _____
   Yes; $5 + $10 = $15; $15 is more than $14.

3. Olivia had $12. She bought 2 toys that were $5 each. How much did she have left? __$2__

Find the rule or the missing numbers.

4. in → +4 → out

5	9
3	7
8	12
4	8

6. in → −7 → out

13	6
14	7
9	2
10	3

5. in → −6 → out

10	4
8	2
12	6
9	3

7. in → +6 → out

2	8
9	15
7	13
5	11

eTextbook This lesson is available in the *eTextbook*.   107

Student Page

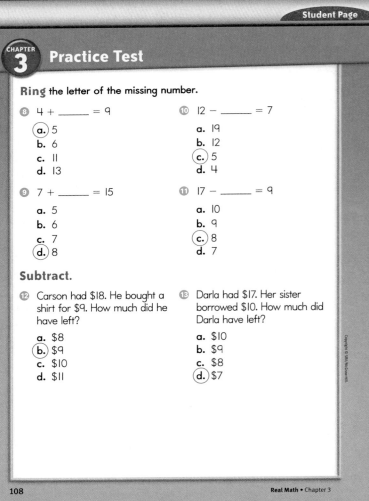

CHAPTER 3 Practice Test

Ring the letter of the missing number.

8. 4 + _____ = 9
   - **(a.) 5**
   - b. 6
   - c. 11
   - d. 13

10. 12 − _____ = 7
   - a. 19
   - b. 12
   - **(c.) 5**
   - d. 4

9. 7 + _____ = 15
   - a. 5
   - b. 6
   - c. 7
   - **(d.) 8**

11. 17 − _____ = 9
   - a. 10
   - b. 9
   - **(c.) 8**
   - d. 7

Subtract.

12. Carson had $18. He bought a shirt for $9. How much did he have left?
   - a. $8
   - **(b.) $9**
   - c. $10
   - d. $11

13. Darla had $17. Her sister borrowed $10. How much did Darla have left?
   - a. $10
   - b. $9
   - c. $8
   - **(d.) $7**

108   **Real Math • Chapter 3**

Name _____ Date _____

⑭ Denzel spent $7 on a pizza and $2 on a drink. How much change did he get back from a $10 bill?

(a.) $1   b. $3   c. $8   d. $9

Add or subtract from left to right.

⑮ 3 + 3 + 5 = _____

(a.) 11   b. 10   c. 8   d. 6

⑯ 5 + 1 + 7 = _____

a. 14   (b.) 13   c. 12   d. 11

⑰ 16 − 9 − 3 = _____

a. 13   b. 7   c. 5   (d.) 4

Use doubles to solve.

⑱ Antonio made 5 base hits in the first baseball game. He made twice as many base hits in the second game. How many base hits did he have in the second game?

a. 7   (b.) 10   c. 12   d. 15

⑲ Dannah has 6 model cars. Jan has twice as many cars as Dannah. How many model cars does Jan have?

a. 6   b. 10   (c.) 12   d. 14

⑳ Blake worked 8 hours on Monday and 8 hours on Tuesday. How many hours did he work on these 2 days?

(a.) 16   b. 17   c. 18   d. 19

ⓔTextbook This lesson is available in the *eTextbook*.

CHAPTER 3 Practice Test

Extended Response Solve.

㉑ Tia, Dan, and Jacob each had $7. Tia owed Jacob $2. Dan owed Tia $4. Jacob owed Dan $1. Everyone paid what they owed. How much money does each person have now? Explain how you found the amounts.

Tia has $9, Dan has $4, and Jacob has $8.

Tia = 7 + 4 − 2; Dan = 7 + 1 − 4; Jacob = 7 + 2 − 1

Students could also use manipulatives to solve.

㉒ Liliana rode her bicycle from home to school. After school, she rode to a bookstore and to the park. Then she rode home. Use the table to find the total number of miles that Liliana rode her bicycle. Explain how you found the total.

Places	Miles
Home to School	1
Home to Bookstore	4
Home to Park	5
School to Bookstore	3
Park to Bookstore	2

1 + 3 + 2 + 5 = 11 miles

Find by adding the total distances she rode.

Chapter Test ✓ COMPUTING

For further evaluation instead of or in addition to this test, you may wish to have students take the Chapter 3 Test provided in *Assessment*.

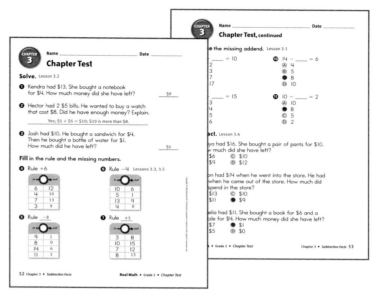

Assessment, pages 52–53

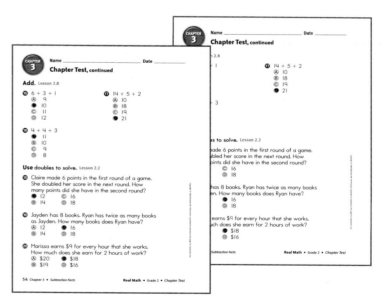

Assessment, pages 54–55

Assess and Differentiate

 **Assess** Use *eAssess* to record and analyze evidence of student understanding.

 ## Gather Evidence

Use the Daily Class Assessment Records in **Assessment** or *eAssess* to record Informal and Formal Assessments.

Informal Assessment

☑ **Key Ideas Review** `UNDERSTANDING`

Did the student
- ❑ make important observations?
- ❑ extend or generalize learning?
- ❑ provide insightful answers?
- ❑ pose insightful questions?

Informal Assessment

☑ **Project** `APPLYING`

Did the student
- ❑ meet the project objectives?
- ❑ communicate clearly?
- ❑ complete the project accurately?
- ❑ connect mathematics to real-world situations?

Formal Assessment

☑ **Chapter Test** `COMPUTING`

Score the test, and record the results.

 ## Summarize Findings

Analyze and summarize assessment data for each student. Determine which Chapter Follow-Up is appropriate for each student. Use the Student Assessment Record in **Assessment** or *eAssess* to update assessment records.

Chapter Follow-Up ● DIFFERENTIATE INSTRUCTION

Based on your observations, use these teaching strategies for chapter follow-up.

ENRICH	PRACTICE	RETEACH	INTERVENTION
If . . . students demonstrate a **secure understanding** of chapter concepts,	**If . . .** students demonstrate **competent understanding** of chapter concepts,	**If . . .** students demonstrate **emerging understanding** of chapter concepts,	**If . . .** students demonstrate **minimal understanding** of chapter concepts,
Then . . . move on to the next chapter.	**Then . . .** move on to the next chapter.	**Then . . .** move on to the next chapter, but continue to provide cumulative review.	**Then . . .** intensive intervention is still needed before they start the next chapter.

Ferdie Knows the Rules

Context of the Thinking Story Ferdie and Portia discuss rules and discover that some rules don't always work.

Using the Thinking Story

The Thinking Story may be used at any time throughout the chapter. Read the Thinking Story "Ferdie Knows the Rules" to your class. As you read the story, give students time to think about each question, but not so much that they forget the point being made.

Ferdie Knows the Rules

In school Ferdie learned many rules. For instance, he learned the rule that when you add 0 to a number the number stays the same. He learned the rule that when you are writing a sentence you should always start it with a capital letter. Ferdie decided that rules were a good thing, and he began using rules all the time. He even started telling Portia rules that she should follow.

Do you know any other good rules? Are rules always a good thing? **Encourage students to identify what they consider to be "good" and "bad" rules.**

One day Portia was going to take a book over to Marcus's house. As she started out the front door of the apartment building, Ferdie stopped her, saying, "That's not the way to get to Marcus's house. There's a rule for that. The rule is, 'The quickest way to get from one place to another is in a straight line.'"

Is that always a good rule? Can you think of any times when it wouldn't be? **not always; not when something you want to get to is on the other side of a wall, for example**

"Marcus's house is in back of our building," Ferdie said. "So the quickest way to get there is to go straight out the back door, straight across our backyard, straight across Marcus's backyard, and right up to his back door. That's what the rule tells you to do, and the rule is always right."

"I think I'd better go out the front door and along the sidewalk," said Portia. She knew that it had rained a lot during the night.

Why does Portia want to use the sidewalk? to avoid the wet or muddy yard

Both backyards were full of mud, and a small stream had formed between Marcus's house and the apartment building where Ferdie and Portia lived.

"Have you been outside today?" Portia asked.

"I don't have to go outside," argued Ferdie. "The sidewalk is not a straight line, and my rule is the best rule."

"Maybe sometimes," said Portia, "but I don't think your rule will work this time."

"Never mind," snapped Ferdie. "I'll prove it to you. We'll have a race. I'll go my way, and you go yours. We'll see who gets there first."

Is Ferdie's rule best this time? no

What do you think will happen? Possibilities include that Ferdie will get stuck in the mud.

"Get ready, get set, go!" said Ferdie, as he headed out the back door. Portia went out the front door and ran along the sidewalk. Ferdie dragged through the mud and water, muttering to himself, "I have to take the shortest way, and this must be it."

By the time Ferdie reached Marcus's house, Portia was already inside talking to Marcus and his father. "I can't let you in the house like that, Ferdie," said Mrs. Breezy. "You're all muddy."

"That's all right," said Ferdie.

"I'll wait out here."

As Portia came out, Ferdie called to her. "Come on, Portia. Let's walk home along the sidewalk."

As they were walking home, Ferdie said, "Maybe my rule about the straight line works only when it's not muddy. But I know another rule that works all the time. The rule is, 'When you get more, you always add.'"

Can you think of any times when the rule wouldn't work? Encourage students to think of times when they "got more" to see whether Ferdie's rule holds true.

Portia thought about Ferdie's rule for a long time. Finally she said, "I think that's a pretty good rule, Ferdie, but I wonder if it works for my classroom. There used to be five empty desks in my room. Then two more children came into the class. How many empty desks do you think there are now?"

How many empty desks are there now? three

Is Ferdie's rule always right? no

"But there are only three empty desks now," Portia said. "There used to be five empty desks, but the new children took two of them, so now there are only three."

"That's not fair!" Ferdie said. "You didn't tell me that they took two of them. When you take away, then you subtract. That's another rule. If you told me the right way, I would have used the right rule and I would have gotten the right answer."

Portia was beginning to have fun with her brother's rules. "Is that another rule that works all the time," she asked, "that when you take away you subtract?"

"All the time," Ferdie said, although he was beginning to look a bit worried.

"Then try it on this," Portia said. "There used to be three origami shapes missing from my collection. Then someone I know took away two origami shapes. How many origami shapes are missing now? I suppose you'll tell me just one!"

Why does Portia think Ferdie will say that only one origami shape is missing? **She knows that he will subtract, and 3 − 2 = 1.**

"Don't worry," said Ferdie. "You'll get all five origami shapes back, even if it doesn't fit with the rule."

How did Ferdie know there were five origami shapes missing? **He probably had them, because he said that Portia would get them back.**

The End

Guided Discussion

As students answer the questions in the story, ask them to communicate how they chose their answers. Allow students to debate the answers if necessary.

Using Student Pages 111–112

Have students follow the instructions and complete the **Student Edition** activities. Read the instructions aloud if students are having difficulty.

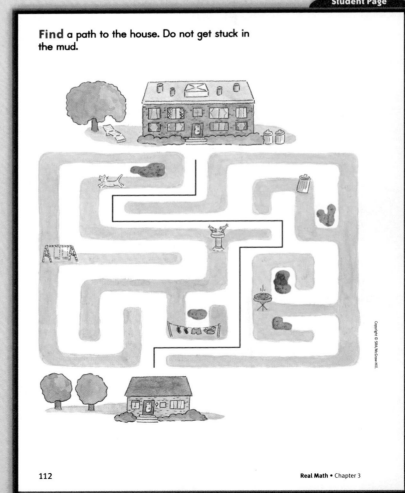

Lesson Study

Reflect on each of the lessons you taught in this chapter. Rate each one on the following scale, and then consider ways to maintain or improve positive teaching experiences in the future.

Lessons	Very Effective	Effective	Less Effective	What Worked	Ways to Improve
3.1 Missing Addends and Subtraction					
3.2 Subtraction Facts and the Addition Table					
3.3 Addition and Subtraction Functions					
3.4 Subtraction Involving 10 and 9					
3.5 Subtraction Facts					
3.6 Applications of Addition and Subtraction					
3.7 Chain Calculations					

Lessons

Uses of Measurement, Graphing, and Probability

Teaching for Understanding

In this chapter students are introduced to uses of measurement, graphing, and probability. Students will measure length in nonstandard and standard units. Students will use various methods of data collection and organization and will analyze the results of probability experiments.

Prerequisite Skills and Concepts

- Measuring Length
- Naming Points on a Number Line
- Reading a Table

Measurement, Graphing, and Probability Skills Trace

Before Grade 2	Grade 2	After Grade 2
Grades K–1 Measured length in nonstandard and standard units Introduced to combining data collection, data organization, and graphs with a study of probability	**This chapter** reviews estimating and measuring length. This chapter also reviews data collection and organization integrated with a study of probability. **Chapter 10** deals with measurement of temperature, weight, capacity, and time.	Formal introduction to more standard units of measure Formal introduction to more complex graphs Review and mastery of data organization and probability

Problem Solving

Problem solving is in every lesson. This chapter includes the following:

CHAPTER INTRODUCTION Students use measurement to design a stuffed animal and a hat for someone else's stuffed animal (pp. 113I–114C).

EXPLORING PROBLEM SOLVING In the first lesson students use knowledge of measurement to solve a problem about toys (pp. 125–126, 126A). In the second lesson students make a graph with information about another toy store order (pp. 145–146, 146A).

THINKING STORY In "Take a Chance," students help characters find a fair way to determine which students will get to take a tour of a toy factory (pp. 157A–157E, 157–158).

Games

Develop reasoning skills, and provide extensive practice.

Find the Distance Game Mat (Lesson 4.2)

Math Background
Measurement, Graphing, and Probability

Measuring Length

- Measuring a given length in a given unit means finding the number of units that when lined up end to end cover the same distance as the given length.

- To simplify the task of lining up units end to end, we use rulers with markings showing the length of each unit.

- Ideally, rulers should start at 0 and end with a whole number of units (for example, be exactly 12 inches long so the 12-inch mark coincides with the end of the ruler). This would allow multiple rulers to be placed end to end to measure lengths longer than the length of the ruler. For example, a distance that is 43 inches long could be measured by placing four rulers in a row, and noting that the distance ends at the 7-inch mark of the fourth ruler.

- However, because physical objects tend to wear out, most rulers are made so the zero mark and the last mark are set a small distance from the ends of the ruler. To use rulers like these to measure length, students should carefully line up the zero mark (not the left edge of the ruler) with the beginning of the length. To use such a ruler to measure lengths longer than the ruler, students can mark off the location of the last unit marking along the length being measured, then move the ruler so the zero mark aligns with this mark and repeat as necessary. If rulers do not start precisely at 0, they should not be lined up end to end when measuring.

Estimating and Measuring

- Measuring alone can often be a passive activity in which students use a ruler or other measuring tool without actively thinking about the quantities being measured.

- Throughout **Real Math** whenever students make measurements, they are first asked to make an estimate of what the measurement will be. By having students first estimate and then measure to check, we are allowing them to think, an activity that is more likely to help them understand the measures and quantities.

- Frequent activities involve a series of measurements in which students estimate and measure one object, then estimate another object's measure in the same units, measure to check, and repeat. Students should be able to refine their estimates based on feedback from prior estimates.

Range and Mode

- The *mode* is the most frequently occurring number in a data set. For example, in the set of numbers "2, 5, 3, 4, 5, 2, 5, 7, 5," the mode is 5.

- A set may have more than one mode. However, if a set has more than two modes, then the modes typically do not provide useful information.

- The *range* of a set of numbers can be expressed in two different ways. The range can be given as the difference between the greatest and least numbers. For example, if the test scores in a class are 84, 87, 78, 92, 86, 95, 98, 86, and 90, we can say that the range is 20 because the highest score is 98, the lowest score is 78, and $98 - 78 = 20$.

- The range can also be expressed using the greatest and least values. We can say that the range of scores is 78 to 98.

The Metric System

- Most of the world uses the metric system. The only countries that are not on this system are the United States, Myanmar, and Liberia. Even in the United States the metric system is used routinely for scientific applications, although customary units are used more frequently for road signs, retail pricing, and so on.

- The metric and the customary systems of measurement are introduced and developed in **Real Math.** We do not ask students to convert from one system to another; we encourage them to think in terms of each system independently. Each system is taught separately so students will not think of one as "growing out of" the other or in some way being dependent on the other.

What Research Says

About Measurement

How Children Develop and Use Measurement Skills and Concepts

"Measurement is one of the main real-world applications of mathematics . . . counting is a type of measurement—it measures how many items in a collection. Measurement of continuous quantities involves assigning a number to attributes such as length, area, and weight. Together, number and measurement are components of quantitative reasoning. In this vein, measurement helps connect the two realms of number and geometry, each providing conceptual support to the other."

Clements, Douglas and J. Sarama, eds. *Engaging Young Children in Mathematics: Standards for Early Childhood Mathematics Education.* Mahwah, New Jersey: Lawrence Erlbaum Associates, Publishers, 2004, pp. 43–50.

Learning Trajectories for Measurement

Children typically follow an observable developmental progression in learning to measure with recognizable stages or levels. This developmental path can be described as part of a learning trajectory. Key steps in the learning trajectory for measurement from the 2nd grade range are described below. For the complete trajectory, see Appendix B.

Stage	Description
Serial Orderer to 6+	At this stage, a child can order lengths, marked in 1 to 6 units. For example, given towers of cubes, a child at this stage puts in order, 1 to 6.
Indirect Length Comparer	A sign of further development is when a child can compare the length of two objects by representing them with a third object. For example, a child might compare length of two objects with a piece of string.
	Additional evidence of this stage is that when asked to measure, the child may assign a length by guessing or moving along a length while counting (without equal length units). The child may also move a finger along a line segment, saying 10, 20, 30, 31, 32.
End-to-End Length Measurer	At the next stage the child can lay units end-to-end, although he or she may not see the need for equal-length units. For example, a child might lay 9 inch cubes in a line beside a book to measure how long it is.

Clements, Douglas and J. Sarama, eds. *Engaging Young Children in Mathematics: Standards for Early Childhood Mathematics Education.* Mahwah, New Jersey: Lawrence Erlbaum Associates, Publishers, 2004.

Research-Based Teaching Techniques

Research has shown that the development of measurement ability and understandings in children is a complex developmental process. The child must develop a recognition that attributes such as length, height, weight and capacity can be measured both formally and informally. They must gain experience in using nonstandard and standard units for measuring and then learn various strategies for using those units to accurately assign values to the attributes being measured.

Students gradually acquire knowledge and language associated with standard systems and units of measure. They gain an appreciation of the benefits of using one system or unit over another and become more skillful in using tools of measurement to accurately determine numbers of units when measuring.

Measurement provides children a means to describe, classify and categorize objects in the world around them. It adds richness to their developing sense of space and time.

Teaching that builds on students' intuitive understandings and informal measurement experiences helps them to understand the attributes to be measured as well as what it means to measure. A foundation in measurement concepts that enables students to use measurement systems, tools, and techniques should be established through direct experiences with comparing objects, counting units, and making connections between spatial concepts and number.

National Council of Teachers of Mathematics. *Principles and Standards for School Mathematics.* Reston, VA: NCTM, 2000.

 **RESEARCH IN ACTION**

Measurement Chapter 4 reinforces the development of effective and accurate procedures for estimating and measuring attributes using metric and standard units of measure.

Units of measure In Chapter 4 students develop an awareness of the units of measure used for both the metric and standard measurement systems.

Representation of Data In Chapter 4 students will collect and record the data they gather through making measurements. Students will then read and interpret the data displayed on charts, tables, or graphs to make observations and predictions.

Vocabulary

data (Lesson 4.7) information from which conclusions can be drawn

length (Lesson 4.2) how long something is

measure (Lesson 4.1) to find the dimensions, weight, extent, quantity, or capacity of

mode (Lesson 4.8) the number that appears most often in a set of data

pictograph (Lesson 4.9) a graph that uses pictures to represent data

ruler (Lesson 4.3) a straight-edged strip of wood, plastic, metal, or other material marked off into measuring units

tally marks (Lesson 4.6) marks used in recording a number of acts or objects, usually consisting of vertical lines

English Learner

Cognates

For English learners, a quick way to acquire new English vocabulary is to build on what is known in the primary language.

English	Spanish
units	unidades
centimeters	centímetros
meter	metro
object	objeto
yards	yardas
prediction	predicción
diagram	diagrama
mode	modo
range	rango
pictograph	pictografía
graphs	gráficas
horizontal	horizontal
information	información
results	resultados

Access Vocabulary

English learners might understand words in different contexts and might not understand idioms. Review chapter vocabulary for this concern. For example:

outline	a shape created when we trace around the outside of something
opposite	In a rectangle, the opposite sides are across from one another.
fill in the blanks	write the answers in the empty spaces
foot	In this context a foot is a unit of measure, not a part of a person's body.
width	how wide something is
vowels	English letters such as *a, e, i, o,* and *u* that are part of every syllable of words
similarities	ways things are alike
pod	the part of certain plants that carries the seeds
drive	an organized group effort for some specific purpose
bar	a long, straight line on a graph
vertical	upright
average high temperature	Each day has a high and a low temperature. The average high temperature compares all the high temperatures for all the days in the month and finds the one that most usually occurred.
recorded	wrote down or kept track of
keep track of	make a record of; write down

Chapter Planner

Lessons	Objectives	NCTM Standards	State Standards
4.1 **Measuring Using Nonstandard Units** pages 115A–116A 45–60 minutes	To measure length using nonstandard units such as paper clips or shoes	Measurement, Number and Operations	
4.2 **Measuring Length—Centimeters** pages 117A–118A 45–60 minutes	To introduce centimeters as a standard unit of measure while reviewing the concept of perimeter	Measurement, Number and Operations	
4.3 **Measurement—Meters and Centimeters** pages 119A–120A 45–60 minutes	To introduce the meter as a standard unit of measure and to demonstrate the relationship between centimeters and meters	Measurement, Connections	
4.4 **Measuring Length—Inches** pages 121A–122A 45–60 minutes	To introduce inches and feet as customary units of length measurement while providing practice in estimating and measuring	Measurement, Connections	
4.5 **Measurement—Yards, Feet, and Inches** pages 123A–124A 45–60 minutes	To introduce the yard as a customary unit of measure and to provide practice converting among inches, feet, and yards	Measurement, Connections	
4.6 **Collecting and Recording Data** pages 129A–130A 45–60 minutes	To provide practice in recording information using tally marks	Data Analysis and Probability, Communication	
4.7 **Venn Diagrams** pages 131A–132A 45–60 minutes	To have students collect and record data about themselves and then compare the data using Venn diagrams	Data Analysis and Probability, Communication	
4.8 **Range and Mode** pages 133A–134A 45–60 minutes	To introduce determining the range and mode while emphasizing the importance of sample size	Data Analysis and Probability, Communication	
4.9 **Pictographs** pages 135A–136A 45–60 minutes	To read a pictograph and to solve problems with the use of information obtained from a pictograph	Representation, Communication	
4.10 **Vertical Bar Graphs** pages 137A–138A 45–60 minutes	To make, read, and interpret a vertical bar graph while studying probability	Data Analysis and Probability, Communication	
4.11 **Horizontal Bar Graphs** pages 139A–140A 45–60 minutes	To make, read, and interpret a horizontal bar graph	Data Analysis and Probability, Communication	
4.12 **Graphs on a Grid** pages 141A–142A 45–60 minutes	To read and interpret a line graph and to compare the use of different types of graphs for presenting data	Data Analysis and Probability, Communication	
4.13 **Using Probability** pages 143A–144A 45–60 minutes	To predict results of a probability experiment and to collect, record, and analyze the data	Data Analysis and Probability, Communication	

Vocabulary	Manipulatives and Materials	Games to reinforce skills and concepts
measure	• *Number Cubes* • Large sheets of paper (the length of a student's body) • Paper clips	
length	• *Number Cubes* • Centimeter rulers • **Find the Distance Game Mat**	**Find the Distance Game**
ruler	• *Number Cubes* • Metersticks and centimeter rulers • **Find the Distance Game Mat**	**Find the Distance Game**
	• *Number Cubes* • 12-inch rulers	
	• *Number Cubes* • 12-inch rulers • Tape measures or yardsticks	
tally marks	• *Number Cubes* • 1 reading book per student	
data	• *Number Cubes* • Overhead attribute blocks	
mode	• *Number Cubes* • A large package of sweet peas with the pods intact	
pictograph	• *Number Cubes* • A graph with a column for each month of the year • Identical stickers	
	• *Number Cubes* • An opaque can or other container • Marbles or colored counters	
	• *Number Cubes* • Average high temperature data for your city	
	Number Cubes	
	Number Cubes	

Additional Resources

Differentiated Instruction

Intervention Support Guide Provides instruction for the following prerequisite skills:

- Lesson 4.A Tables and Measurement–1
- Lesson 4.B Tables and Measurement–2
- Lesson 4.C Tables and Measurement–3

Enrichment Support Guide Extends lesson concepts

Practice Reinforces lesson skills and concepts

Reteach Support Guide Provides alternate instruction for lesson concepts

English Learner Support Guide Previews and reviews lesson concepts and vocabulary for English learners

Technology

The following electronic resources are available:

ⓔ **Planner** Lessons 4.1–4.13

ⓔ **Presentation** Lessons 4.1–4.13

ⓔ **Textbook** Lessons 4.1–4.13

ⓔ **Assess** Lessons 4.1–4.13

ⓔ **MathTools** *Metric/Customary Conversion* Lessons 4.4, 4.5
Venn Diagram Lesson 4.7
Spreadsheet Lessons 4.8, 4.11, 4.13
Graphing Tool Lessons 4.10, 4.11, 4.12
Probability Lesson 4.10

Building Blocks *Workin' on the Railroad* Lesson 4.1
Reptile Ruler Lessons 4.2, 4.3

Assessment
Informal Assessment rubrics at the end of each lesson provide daily evaluation of student math proficiency.

Chapter Planner, continued

Problem Solving	When to Use	Objectives	NCTM Standards	Skills Covered
Chapter Introduction (pp. 113I–114C) 15–30 minutes	Use after the Chapter 4 Pretest.	To introduce chapter concepts in a problem-solving setting	Problem Solving, Communication	Measurement
Exploring Problem Solving (pp. 125–126, 126A) 30–45 minutes	Use anytime during the chapter.	To explore methods of solving nonroutine problems	Problem Solving, Communication	Measurement
Exploring Problem Solving (pp. 145–146, 146A) 45–60 minutes	Use anytime during the chapter.	To explore methods of solving nonroutine problems	Problem Solving, Communication	Graphing
Thinking Story—Take a Chance (pp. 157A–157E, 157–158) 20–30 minutes	Use anytime during the chapter.	To develop logical reasoning while integrating reading skills with mathematics	Number and Operations, Problem Solving	Probability

Review	When to Use	Objectives	NCTM Standards	Skills Covered
Cumulative Review (p. 127–128) 15–30 minutes	Use anytime after Lesson 4.5.	To review concepts and skills taught earlier in the year	Number and Operations	Measurement, Addition, Subtraction
Cumulative Review (p. 147–148) 15–30 minutes	Use anytime after Lesson 4.13.	To review concepts and skills taught earlier in the year	Number and Operations	Measurement, Addition, Subtraction
Chapter 4 Review (pp. 151A, 151–152) 30–45 minutes	Use after Lesson 4.13.	To review concepts and skills taught in the chapter	Number and Operations	Measurement, Graphing, Probability

Assessment	When to Use	Objectives	NCTM Standards	Skills Covered
Informal Assessment Rubrics (pp. 116A–144A) 5 minutes per student	Use at the end of each lesson.	To provide daily evaluation of math proficiency	Number and Operations, Communication	Computing, Understanding, Reasoning, Applying, Engaging
Pretest (*Assessment* pp. 57–58) 15–30 minutes	Use prior to Chapter 4.	To provide assessment of prerequisite and chapter topics	Number and Operations, Problem Solving	Computing, Understanding, Reasoning, Applying, Engaging
Individual Oral Assessment (p. 128A) 5 minutes per student	Use after Lesson 4.5.	To provide alternate means of assessing students' progress	Number and Operations	Measurement
Mastery Checkpoint (*Assessment* p. T57) 5 minutes per student	Use after Lesson 4.5.	To provide assessment of mastery of key skills	Number and Operations	Measurement
Chapter 4 Practice Test (pp. 153–154, 155–156) 30–45 minutes	Use after or in place of the Chapter 4 Review.	To provide assessment or additional practice of the chapter concepts	Number and Operations, Problem Solving	Measurement, Graphing, Probability
Chapter 4 Test (*Assessment* pp. 66–69) 30–45 minutes	Use after or in place of the Chapter 4 Review.	To provide assessment of the chapter concepts	Number and Operations, Problem Solving	Measurement, Graphing, Probability

Technology Resources and Support

Visit SRAonline.com for online versions of the **Real Math** eSuite.

Technology for Teachers

e Presentation	Lessons 4.1–4.13 Use the **ePresentation** to present chapter content interactively.
e Planner	Use the Chapter and Lesson Planners to outline activities and time frames for Chapter 4.
e Assess	Students can take the following assessments in **eAssess:** • Chapter Pretest • Mastery Checkpoint **Lesson 4.5** • Chapter Test Teachers can record results and print reports for all assessments in this chapter.
e MathTools	**Metric/Customary Conversion** Lessons 4.4, 4.5 **Venn Diagram** Lesson 4.7 **Spreadsheet** Lessons 4.8, 4.11, 4.13 **Graphing Tool** Lessons 4.10, 4.11, 4.12 **Probability** Lesson 4.10

Technology for Students

e Textbook	An electronic, interactive version of the **Student Edition** is available for all lessons in Chapter 4.
e MathTools	**Metric/Customary Conversion** Lessons 4.4, 4.5 **Venn Diagram** Lesson 4.7 **Spreadsheet** Lessons 4.8, 4.11, 4.13 **Graphing Tool** Lessons 4.10, 4.11, 4.12 **Probability** Lesson 4.10
TECH KNOWLEDGE	**TechKnowledge** Level 2 provides lessons that specifically teach the Unit 10 Internet and Unit 8 Database applications that students can use while working on this chapter's projects.
Building Blocks	**Workin' on the Railroad** Lesson 4.1 **Reptile Ruler** Lessons 4.2, 4.3

Uses of Measurement, Graphing, and Probability

1 Introduce Chapter 4 — 10

Chapter Objectives

Explain to students that in this chapter they will build on what they already know about measurement, graphing, and probability. Explain that in this chapter they will

- measure using standard and nonstandard units.
- collect data and display data on graphs.
- predict results using concepts of probability.

Pretest COMPUTING

Administer the Pretest on **Assessment** pages 57 and 58.

The Pretest covers the following skills and topics from the chapter:

- Calendar (Problems 1–4)
- Function tables (Problems 5 and 6)
- Adding and subtracting more than two numbers (Problems 7–10)
- Measurement and perimeter (Problems 11 and 12)
- Bar graphs (Problems 13–15)

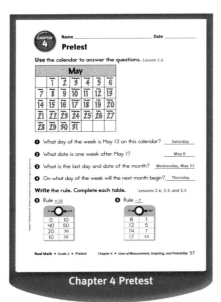

Chapter 4 Pretest

Access Prior Knowledge UNDERSTANDING

Ask students if they have ever gone on a shopping trip to buy clothes. How did they decide how big to get their clothes? How did they know if what they were buying would fit?

2 Exploring Problem Solving — 15

Tell Students In Today's Lesson They Will

- design a stuffed animal.
- make a hat to fit someone else's stuffed animal.

Materials

- Extra paper for each student for making a paper hat
- Scissors
- 2 toy telephones

Preparation: Before class begins, on a sheet of paper make a simple sketch of a teddy bear (or other stuffed animal) with a triangular hat. Do not show this to students.

Strategy Building REASONING

Tell students that today you and they are going to pretend to be in the toy business. You, the teacher, are a toy maker; you have a stuffed-animal factory. They, the students, are hatmakers. You have designed a teddy bear that you will make in your factory. Because they are hatmakers, you want each student to make a hat for the bear. You want the hat to be in the shape of a triangle.

Distribute paper, pencils, and scissors. Ask each student to draw and cut out a triangular hat for your bear. (If students ask to see the bear, explain that your factories are in different cities, and you can talk to them only over the telephone.)

When students have made their hats, show them the picture you drew of the bear with its hat. Compare the hats they made to the hat you drew. Students will have created many different sizes of hats, but probably none will be exactly like the one you wanted.

Explain that you realize you made a mistake in your order. You did not give them enough information for them to make the exact size and shape hat that you wanted.

Ask and discuss questions such as the following:

- **What did I tell you I wanted?** a triangular hat for a stuffed bear
- **How many of you were able to make a hat just like I had in mind?** probably none
- **What kind of information would you have needed to know to make the hat I had in mind?** how tall and how wide the hat should be
- **What could I tell you that will help you know how tall and how wide to make the hat?** Help students suggest ways to refer to common objects such as paper clips, cubes, and crayons to help describe how high and how wide to make the hat.

CHAPTER 4 Uses of Measurement, Graphing, and Probability

In This Chapter You Will Learn
- how to measure using standard and nonstandard units.
- how to collect data and display data on graphs.
- about probability.

113

Problem Solving

Name _____ Date _____

Draw your stuffed animal and a hat for it.

Order Form	
How high?	How wide?

114 **Real Math** • Chapter 4

Using Student Pages APPLYING

Students are going to pretend to be toy makers. They will draw a stuffed animal with a triangular hat and then telephone a hatmaker to order the hat. They will not be able to show a picture of the hat or indicate with their hands anything about the hat.

Have students look at page 114.

- Ask students to use the drawing space on the page to draw a toy animal with a triangle hat on it.
- Tell students they will need to fill out an order form for ordering the hats for their animals. Discuss how to describe the hat so that the hatmakers will be able to make one that fits properly. Have each student use the first line on the order form to write his or her order. Provide help as needed.

Organize students into groups of three or four. Have each group choose a different student for each of three roles:

- Choose one student's toy animal.
- Choose another student to be the person who phones in the order for the hat.
- Choose another student who will write the hat order from another group.

Seat the groups in a circle, for example,

Group 5 Group 1 Group 2 Group 3 Group 4

One transaction at a time, have the groups phone in their orders as follows:

1. Group 1 orders a hat from Group 2. The order giver in Group 1 "telephones" Group 2 and reads the hat order. The order taker in Group 2 writes the order in the unused line on the order form on the student page. The other groups can listen.
2. In a similar manner, Group 2 orders a hat from Group 3.
3. Continue until all groups have ordered a hat.

As needed, remind students that they can use words and numbers to describe the hat, but they cannot use pictures or gestures.

Have the groups work for a few minutes to draw and cut out the hat that has been ordered from them.

Concept/Question Board APPLYING

Questions

Have students think of and write three questions they have about measurement, graphing, and probability and how they can be used. Then have them select one question to post on the Question side of the Board.

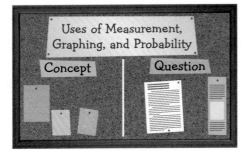

Concepts

As students work through the chapter, have them collect examples of how measurement, graphing, and probability are used in everyday situations. For each example, have them write a problem that relates to the item(s). Have them display their examples on the Concept side of the Board. Suggest the following:

- shoe sizes
- golf

Answers

Throughout the chapter, have students post answers to the questions and solutions to the problems on the Board.

3 Reflect 15

 Knowledge Age Skills

Effective Communication Have groups present the hats they made and explain how they used the information given to them to make the hat. Hold up each hat next to the picture of the stuffed animal for which it was made. Ask questions such as the following:

- ■ **Did you get what you wanted?**
- ■ **How well did it fit your toy animal?**
- ■ **Why did or didn't the hat fit well?**
- ■ **What would you do differently if you were going to order another hat?**
- ■ **What would you do differently if you were going to make another hat for someone?**

In discussion, bring out the following points:

- Because they mean different things to different people, words such as *big*, *skinny*, *short*, and *tall* may not be as useful as other ways to describe the size of something.
- If you want something to be a certain size, you can use words and numbers to help describe the size.

Home Connection

 At this time, you may want to send home the letter on pages 14–17 of **Home Connection.** This letter describes what students will be learning and what activities they can do at home to support their work in school.

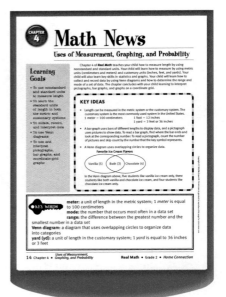

Assess and Differentiate

 Assess   Use *eAssess* to record and analyze evidence of student understanding.

A   Gather Evidence

Use the Daily Class Assessment Records in **Assessment** or **eAssess** to record Informal and Formal Assessments.

Informal Assessment
☑ **Access Prior Knowledge**
Did the student   **UNDERSTANDING**
- ❏ make important observations?
- ❏ extend or generalize learning?
- ❏ provide insightful answers?
- ❏ pose insightful questions?

Informal Assessment
☑ **Concept/Question Board**
Did the student   **APPLYING**
- ❏ apply learning in new situations?
- ❏ contribute concepts?
- ❏ contribute answers?
- ❏ connect mathematics to real-world situations?

Formal Assessment
☑ **Pretest**   **COMPUTING**
Review student answers in each problem set.
- ❏ Calendar (Problems 1–4)
- ❏ Function tables (Problems 5–6)
- ❏ Adding and subtracting more than two numbers (Problems 7–10)
- ❏ Measurement and Perimeter (Problems 11–12)
- ❏ Bar graphs (Problems 13–15)

B   Summarize Findings

Analyze and summarize assessment data for each student. Determine which Assessment Follow-Up is appropriate for each student. Use the Student Assessment Record in **Assessment** or **eAssess** to update assessment records.

C   Assessment Follow-Up ● DIFFERENTIATE INSTRUCTION

Based on your observations of each student, use these teaching strategies for a general approach to the chapter. Look for specific Differentiate Instruction and Monitoring Student Progress strategies in each lesson that relate specifically to the lesson content.

ENRICH	PRACTICE	RETEACH	INTERVENTION	ENGLISH LEARNER
If . . . students demonstrate a **secure understanding** of chapter concepts, **Then . . .** move quickly through the chapter or use *Enrichment* Lessons 4.1–4.13 as assessment follow-up to extend and apply understanding.	**If . . .** students grasp chapter concepts with **competent understanding**, **Then . . .** use *Practice* Lessons 4.1–4.13 as lesson follow-up to develop fluency.	**If . . .** students have prerequisite understanding but demonstrate **emerging understanding** of chapter concepts, **Then . . .** use *Reteach* Lessons 4.6 and 4.11 to reteach lesson concepts.	**If . . .** students are not competent with prerequisite skills, **Then . . .** use *Intervention* Lessons 4.A–4.C before each lesson to develop fluency with prerequisite skills.	Use *English Learner Support Guide* Lessons 4.1–4.13 for strategies to preteach lesson vocabulary and concepts.

Math Across the Curriculum

Preview the chapter projects with students. Assign projects or have students choose from the projects to extend and enrich concepts in this chapter.

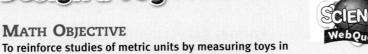

Design a Toy 1–3 weeks

SCIENCE WebQuest

MATH OBJECTIVE
To reinforce studies of metric units by measuring toys in centimeters

SCIENCE OBJECTIVE
To reinforce studies of motion by designing and creating a moving toy

TECHNOLOGY OBJECTIVE
To enter information into a class database

Have students use technology to research how to make different kinds of toys.

For this project, students use the Internet to investigate the following information:

- metric units of length
- how simple machines make toys move
- how to make different kinds of toys

For specific step-by-step instructions for this project, see **Across the Curriculum Math Connections** pages 42–47.

Problem Formulation, Planning, and Strategizing Students plan the construction of moving toys and strategize to improve the designs of their toys.

Creative Work with Ideas Students incorporate scientific principles of motion to design and create functional toys.

TECH KNOWLEDGE *TechKnowledge* Level 2 provides lessons that specifically teach the Unit 10 Internet and Unit 8 Database applications that students can use in this project.

Write about the History of Toys 2–3 weeks

SOCIAL STUDIES

MATH OBJECTIVE
To reinforce studies of collecting and recording data by organizing data in a table

SOCIAL STUDIES OBJECTIVE
To reinforce studies of American culture by studying the history of toys

TECHNOLOGY OBJECTIVE
To use a word processing program to create a text document

Have students use mathematics to relate significant events in the history of toys. To broaden the social studies concept, have them study toys important to cultures you are currently studying.

As part of the project, students should consider the following issues:

- which toys have made an impact on American culture
- why some toys have remained part of American culture

For specific step-by-step instructions for this project, see **Across the Curriculum Math Connections** pages 48–51.

Creative Work with Ideas Students create time lines to represent significant inventions in toy history.

Problem Formulation, Planning, and Strategizing Students narrow down events to select the most important.

OBJECTIVES
To measure using nonstandard units

NCTM STANDARDS
Measurement
- Recognizing the attributes of length
- Comparing and ordering objects according to length
- Understanding how to measure using standard and nonstandard units

Number and Operations
- Counting with understanding
- Using a variety of methods and tools to compute

MATERIALS
- *Number Cubes
- Large sheets of paper (the length of a student's body, 1 per student)
- Paper clips

TECHNOLOGY
ⓔ **Presentation** Lesson 4.1
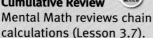 Workin' on the Railroad

TEST PREP
Cumulative Review (Review)
Mental Math reviews chain calculations (Lesson 3.7).

Writing + Math
Journal

Measuring Using Nonstandard Units

Context of the Lesson This is the first of five lessons on measuring length. In this lesson students measure length in nonstandard units. In the next lesson students will discover the need for standard units of measure, and centimeters will be introduced. Measurement of length in nonstandard, metric, and customary units was covered in Grade 1.

See page 113B for Math Background for teachers for this lesson.

Planning for Learning ● DIFFERENTIATE INSTRUCTION

INTERVENTION

If . . . students lack the prerequisite skill of measuring length,

Then . . . teach **Intervention** Lesson 4.A.

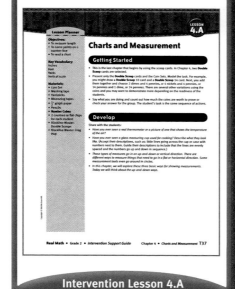

Intervention Lesson 4.A

ENGLISH LEARNER

Preview

If . . . students need language support,

Then . . . use Lesson 4.1 in **English Learner Support Guide** to preview lesson concepts and vocabulary.

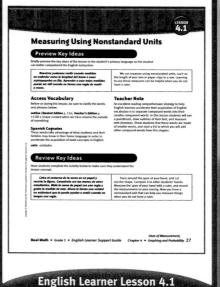

English Learner Lesson 4.1

ENRICH

If . . . students are proficient in the lesson concepts,

Then . . . emphasize **Building Blocks.**

PRACTICE

If . . . students would benefit from additional practice,

Then . . . extend Skill Building before assigning the student pages.

RETEACH

If . . . students are having difficulty understanding measuring length,

Then . . . extend Guided Discussion before assigning the student pages.

Vocabulary
measure \mezh´ ər\ v. to find the dimensions, weight, extent, quantity, or capacity of

Access Vocabulary
outline a shape created when we trace around the outside of something

Spanish Cognates
units unidades

*Manipulative Kit Item

Teaching Lesson 4.1

Mental Math 5

 Continue to develop fluency and quick recall of the basic addition and subtraction facts by doing chain calculations, such as the following:

a. $6 + 4 + 0 = 10$ **b.** $8 + 0 + 2 = 10$
c. $9 + 5 + 5 = 19$ **d.** $10 - 1 - 1 - 8 = 0$
e. $5 + 4 + 3 = 12$ **f.** $3 + 4 + 5 = 12$
g. $4 + 4 + 4 - 4 = 8$ **h.** $3 + 3 - 3 + 4 = 7$

1 Develop 20

Tell Students In Today's Lesson They Will
measure length using objects found in the classroom.

Guided Discussion REASONING Whole Group

1. Have one student lie on his or her back on the floor with legs straight. Ask:

■ **What things in the classroom could we use to measure the length of this student?** Record students' ideas, discussing the practicality of suggested units.

After a number of units have been suggested, choose a relatively long one and a relatively short one, and have students speculate on which we would need more of and why.

Demonstrate using the selected units to measure the student, explaining measurement techniques such as measuring from one end to the other and laying units end to end.

When the two groups of units (long and short) have been laid beside the student, have students count with you while you say each number. Ask:

■ **Were there more short units or more long units?** short units
■ **Why do you think this is so?** The shorter the unit is, the more you need. The longer the unit is, the fewer you need.

2. Measure the length of one or two classroom objects, using nonstandard units of measure. You might, for example, measure a pencil in paper-clip units or **Number Cube** units. Then record the results on the board.

Skill Building ENGAGING Small Group

Have students work in small groups to trace and cut out outlines of their own bodies from the large sheets of paper. (Students may want to color and decorate their bodies later as part of an art-related activity—this is optional.) Because one aim of this activity is to discover a real-world proportional relationship, accuracy is important. Have each student measure the length of his or her body in shoe units by starting at one end of his or her outline and counting while walking heel-to-toe. They should record this measurement on page 116. When students have finished, ask questions such as the following:

■ **How many shoe units is the length of your body?** This will vary depending on the length of the student's feet and body.
■ **If another student came into this room and measured his or her body length with his or her feet, how many shoe units do you think it would be?** The length of this student probably would be similar to your length.
■ **What would happen if your teacher measured the length of his or her body?** The length of our teacher probably would be much longer than a student's length.

2 Assign Student Pages 20

Pages 115–116 UNDERSTANDING

Have students work independently on pages 115–116.

As Students Finish

Game Allow students to play a game of their choice, or assign games based on needed skill practice.

Building Blocks *Workin' on the Railroad*

Name _____ Date _____

LESSON 4.1 Measuring Using Nonstandard Units

Key Ideas

We can measure using objects found in the classroom.

Use paper clips to measure. Measurements will depend on the length of the unit being used.

① _____

② _____

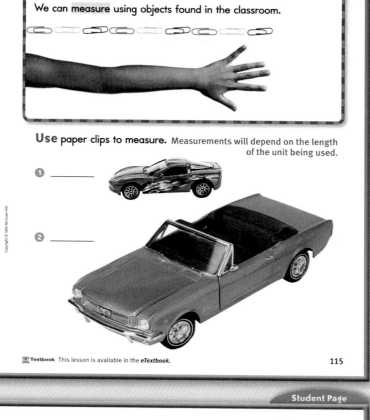

📖 **Textbook** This lesson is available in the *eTextbook*.

115

LESSON 4.1 • Measuring Using Nonstandard Units

❸ **Draw** an outline of your shoe.

❹ My body is _____ shoe units long.

The length of the student's body will depend on the length of his or her shoe.

Writing + Math ▶ **Journal**

How would you estimate the height of the classroom in shoe units without using a ladder?

116

Real Math • Chapter 4 • Lesson 1

---

③ Reflect
10

Guided Discussion **REASONING**
Whole Group

Remind students of the lengths of their bodies in shoe units. Using this information, have students estimate the lengths in shoe units of other objects or distances in the classroom. Then have students measure to check their estimates.

Estimates should get better with practice as students use feedback from previous measures to make new related estimates.

Writing + Math ▶ **Journal**

Students' strategies for estimating the height of the classroom in shoe units without using a ladder may involve using what they know about the length of their own bodies in shoe units. For example, a student may estimate that the height of the classroom is about three times the length of the student's body. If the student found that his or her body is 8 shoe units long, then the height of the ceiling would be about 24 shoe units.

 Cumulative Review: For cumulative review of previously learned skills, see page 127–128.

 Family Involvement: Assign the *Practice, Reteach,* or *Enrichment* activities depending on the needs of your students.

 Concept/Question Board: Have students look for additional examples using measurement and post them on the Concept/Question Board.

 Math Puzzler: Draw the following figure on the board. Have students copy the figure and then tell how many rectangles there are.
9 including the squares, which are also rectangles

4 Assess and Differentiate

 Assess Use *eAssess* to record and analyze evidence of student understanding.

A Gather Evidence

Use the Daily Class Assessment Records in *Assessment* or *eAssess* to record daily observations.

Informal Assessment
☑ **Mental Math**

Did the student **COMPUTING**
- ❏ respond accurately?
- ❏ respond quickly?
- ❏ respond with confidence?
- ❏ self-correct?

Informal Assessment
☑ **Guided Discussion**

Did the student **REASONING**
- ❏ provide a clear explanation?
- ❏ communicate reasons and strategies?
- ❏ choose appropriate strategies?
- ❏ argue logically?

B Summarize Findings

Analyze and summarize assessment data for each student. Determine which Assessment Follow-Up is appropriate for each student. Use the Student Assessment Record in *Assessment* or *eAssess* to update assessment records.

Assessment page T41

C Assessment Follow-Up ● DIFFERENTIATE INSTRUCTION

Based on your observations, use these teaching strategies for assessment follow-up.

INTERVENTION
Review student performance on *Intervention* Lesson 4.A to see if students have mastered prerequisite skills for this lesson.

ENGLISH LEARNER
Review

Use Lesson 4.1 in *English Learner Support Guide* to review lesson concepts and vocabulary.

ENRICH
If . . . students are proficient in the lesson concepts,

Then . . . encourage them to work on the chapter projects or *Enrichment* Lesson 4.1.

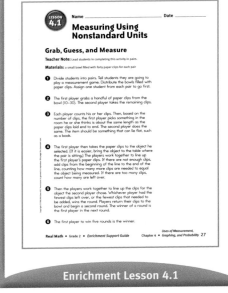

Enrichment Lesson 4.1

PRACTICE
If . . . students would benefit from additional practice,

Then . . . assign *Practice* Lesson 4.1.

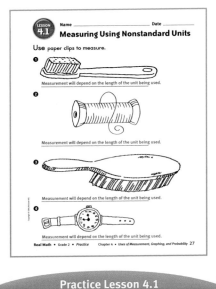

Practice Lesson 4.1

RETEACH
If . . . students are having difficulty measuring in nonstandard units,

Then . . . have them think of a variety of objects that could be used to measure.

OBJECTIVES
- To review length measurement and introduce the centimeter as a standard unit of measure
- To review the concept of perimeter

NCTM STANDARDS

Measurement
- Recognizing the attributes of length
- Comparing and ordering objects according to length
- Understanding how to measure using standard and nonstandard units

Number and Operations
- Counting with understanding
- Using a variety of methods and tools to compute

MATERIALS
- *Number Cubes
- Centimeter rulers
- Find the Distance Game Mat

TECHNOLOGY
e Presentation Lesson 4.2
Building Blocks Reptile Ruler

TEST PREP

Cumulative Review
- Mental Math reviews chain calculations (Lesson 3.7).
- Problems 4–6 review perimeter (Lesson 2.8).

Measuring Length— Centimeters

Context of the Lesson This is the second of five lessons on measuring length. This lesson and the following lesson focus on measuring in metric units. Students may be familiar with measuring in centimeters, as it was covered in Grade 1.

See page 113B for Math Background for teachers for this lesson.

Planning for Learning ● DIFFERENTIATE INSTRUCTION

INTERVENTION

If . . . students lack the prerequisite skill of measuring length,

Then . . . teach *Intervention* Lesson 4.A.

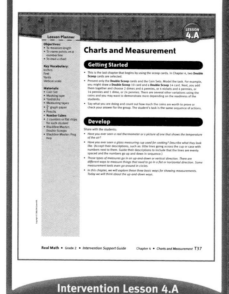

Intervention Lesson 4.A

ENGLISH LEARNER

Preview

If . . . students need language support,

Then . . . use Lesson 4.2 in *English Learner Support Guide* to preview lesson concepts and vocabulary.

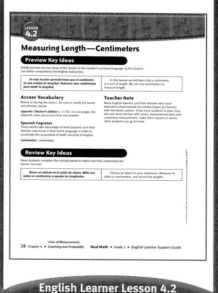

English Learner Lesson 4.2

ENRICH

If . . . students are proficient in the lesson concepts,

Then . . . emphasize *Building Blocks*.

PRACTICE

If . . . students would benefit from additional practice,

Then . . . extend Skill Practice before assigning the student pages.

RETEACH

If . . . students are having difficulty understanding measuring length,

Then . . . extend the Guided Discussion before assigning the student pages.

Vocabulary
length \lengkth\ *n.* how long something is

Access Vocabulary
opposite In a rectangle, the *opposite* sides are across from one another.

Spanish Cognates
centimeters centímetros

*Manipulative Kit Item

Mental Math 5

Continue to develop fluency and quick recall of the basic addition and subtraction facts by doing chain calculations, such as the following:

a. 3 + 5 + 7 = 15
b. 10 − 5 − 5 + 4 = 4
c. 8 + 2 + 9 = 19
d. 8 + 0 − 6 + 5 = 7
e. 10 − 5 + 7 = 12
f. 7 + 3 + 8 − 2 = 16
g. 18 − 9 + 5 = 14
h. 10 + 8 − 7 = 11

1 Develop 20

Tell Students In Today's Lesson They Will

measure using centimeter rulers.

Guided Discussion REASONING Whole Group

Measure the length of a classroom object using a nonstandard unit of measure, such as paper-clip units or **Number Cube** units. Record the results on the board.

Remind students that in the previous lesson they measured the lengths of their bodies in a nonstandard unit: shoe units. Establish the need for standard units by asking questions such as the following:

■ **What if you wanted to share this information with a relative who lived far away? Would he or she be able to understand?** The relative would not be able to understand the exact length of the student in shoe units because the relative's shoe size is probably not exactly the same as the student's shoe size.

■ **What if you reported the measurement in paper-clip units?** The relative would still need to know if the paper clips used were small or large.

Discuss and explain that the lengths of standard units are agreed on by large numbers of people and that because these lengths do not vary, they are useful for communicating measures.

Skill Building ENGAGING Whole Group

Distribute the centimeter rulers or metersticks, explaining that the centimeter is a standard unit of length. Then remeasure in centimeters the object you measured in the Guided Discussion. Show students how to do this. Note that if the ruler scale starts exactly at the end of the ruler, students can line up the end of the ruler with one end of the object. However, many rulers have a scale that starts a slight distance from the end of the ruler. In this case students must place the point where the scale starts, not the end of the ruler, at the end of the object. Be sure to check which type of rulers students are using, and adjust your instruction accordingly.

Repeat for one or two other objects. Then allow students to select and measure two or more objects on their own. As they do so, circulate around the room, giving individual help as needed.

Skill Practice COMPUTING Whole Group

 Introduce a new type of response exercise in which students practice estimating the lengths of objects in centimeters. Use a technique similar to the following:

● Present an object to the class.
● Have students estimate its length in centimeters. Students will then use **Number Cubes** to find, hide, and show their estimates on command.
● Measure the object in front of the class to check.
● Repeat the activity several times using different objects.

Monitoring Student Progress

If . . . students make estimates that are contrary to reason (for example, a student who estimates the length of an object as being shorter than another object that is, in fact, shorter),

Then . . . those students will need more practice making estimates and measuring to check.

Skill and Strategy Building APPLYING Whole Group

Game **Find the Distance Game**

Demonstrate the **Find the Distance Game.** Rules for how to play and required materials can be found on the game mat. Students will play in pairs or small groups as they finish pages 117 and 118.

2 Assign Student Pages 20

Pages 117–118 UNDERSTANDING

Before beginning these pages, tell students that *cm* is the abbreviation used to stand for centimeters. Have students complete pages 117 and 118 independently.

As Students Finish

Game Have students play the **Find the Distance Game** in pairs.

 Reptile Ruler

Name _____ Date _____

Key Ideas

The centimeter is a unit of length.

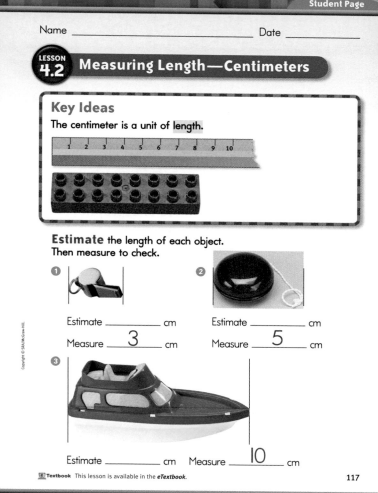

Estimate the length of each object.
Then measure to check.

1

Estimate _____ cm

Measure _____ **3** _____ cm

2

Estimate _____ cm

Measure _____ **5** _____ cm

3

Estimate _____ cm   Measure _____ **10** _____ cm

📖 **Textbook** This lesson is available in the *eTextbook*.

117

LESSON 4.2 • Measuring Length—Centimeters

Review **Measure** the sides. Then add them to find the perimeter.

4 Rectangle

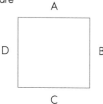

Side	Centimeters
A	5
B	2
C	5
D	2
Perimeter	14

5 Square

Side	Centimeters
A	4
B	4
C	4
D	4
Perimeter	16

6 Triangle

Side	Centimeters
A	3
B	4
C	5
Perimeter	12

Game Play the **Find the Distance Game.**

118   **Real Math** • Chapter 4 • Lesson 2

---

3 ## Reflect   10 ⏱

Guided Discussion [UNDERSTANDING]   Whole Group

Call students' attention to student page 118 and ask the following questions:

- **What is the fewest number of measurements you must make to find the perimeter of a rectangle?** 2 **Why?** because the opposite sides are equal in length
- **What is the fewest number of measurements you must make to find the perimeter of a square?** 1 **Why?** because all the sides are the same length. For example, if the length of one side is 4 centimeters, the perimeter in centimeters is 4 + 4 + 4 + 4 = 16 centimeters.
- **What is the fewest number of measurements you must make to find the perimeter of the triangle on page 118?** 3 **Why?** All of the sides are a different length.

📋 RESEARCH IN ACTION

"Measurement is one of the main real-world applications of mathematics . . . counting is a type of measurement—it measures how many items in a collection. Measurement of continuous quantities involves assigning a number to attributes such as length, area, and weight. Together, number and measurement are components of quantitative reasoning. In this vein, measurement helps connect the two realms of number and geometry, each providing conceptual support to the other."

Clements, Douglas and J. Sarama, eds. *Engaging Young Children in Mathematics: Standards for Early Childhood Mathematics Education.* Mahwah, New Jersey: Lawrence Erlbaum Associates, Publishers, 2004, pp. 43–50.

Review **Cumulative Review:** For cumulative review of previously learned skills, see page 127–128.

🎒 **Family Involvement:** Assign the *Practice, Reteach,* or *Enrichment* activities depending on the needs of your students.

Concept/Question Board: Have students look for additional examples using measurement and post them on the Concept/Question Board.

🧩 **Math Puzzler:** Which is greater—4 tens and 5 or 5 tens and 4? How can you tell? The combination of 5 tens and 4 is greater because there are more tens or because 54 is greater than 45.

Assess and Differentiate

 Assess Use *eAssess* to record and analyze evidence of student understanding.

A Gather Evidence

Use the Daily Class Assessment Records in *Assessment* or *eAssess* to record daily observations.

Informal Assessment
☑ **Guided Discussion**

Did the student **REASONING**
- ❏ provide a clear explanation?
- ❏ communicate reasons and strategies?
- ❏ choose appropriate strategies?
- ❏ argue logically?

Informal Assessment
☑ **Skill Practice**

Did the student **COMPUTING**
- ❏ respond accurately?
- ❏ respond quickly?
- ❏ respond with confidence?
- ❏ self-correct?

B Summarize Findings

Analyze and summarize assessment data for each student. Determine which Assessment Follow-Up is appropriate for each student. Use the Student Assessment Record in *Assessment* or *eAssess* to update assessment records.

Assessment page T41

C Assessment Follow-Up • DIFFERENTIATE INSTRUCTION

Based on your observations, use these teaching strategies for assessment follow-up.

INTERVENTION	ENRICH	PRACTICE	RETEACH
Review student performance on *Intervention* Lesson 4.A to see if students have mastered prerequisite skills for this lesson.	**If . . .** students are proficient in the lesson concepts, **Then . . .** encourage them to work on the chapter projects or *Enrichment* Lesson 4.2.	**If . . .** students would benefit from additional practice, **Then . . .** assign *Practice* Lesson 4.2.	**If . . .** students are having difficulty measuring in centimeters, **Then . . .** have them work in groups to measure objects and to check the measures of the other students.

ENGLISH LEARNER
Review

Use Lesson 4.2 in *English Learner Support Guide* to review lesson concepts and vocabulary.

Enrichment Lesson 4.2

Practice Lesson 4.2

Objectives

- To introduce the meter as a standard unit of measure
- To demonstrate the relationship between centimeters and meters
- To provide experience estimating and measuring length using metric units
- To extend the number range students work with to the hundreds

NCTM Standards

Measurement
- Recognizing the attributes of length
- Using tools to measure
- Developing common referents for measures to make comparisons and estimates

Connections
- Recognizing and using connections among mathematical ideas
- Understanding how mathematical ideas interconnect and build on one another

Materials

- *Number Cubes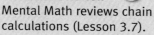
- *Metersticks and centimeter rulers
- Find the Distance Game Mat

Technology

Ⓔ **Presentation** Lesson 4.3
Building Blocks Reptile Ruler

Test Prep

Cumulative Review
Mental Math reviews chain calculations (Lesson 3.7).

Measurement—Meters and Centimeters

Context of the Lesson This is the third of five lessons on measuring length and the second of two lessons on measuring in metric units. This lesson also provides an informal introduction to numbers of more than one hundred. The next two lessons will focus on customary units of measure: inches, feet, and yards.

See page 113B for Math Background for teachers for this lesson.

Planning for Learning ● DIFFERENTIATE INSTRUCTION

INTERVENTION

If . . . students lack the prerequisite skill of measuring length,

Then . . . teach **Intervention** Lesson 4.A.

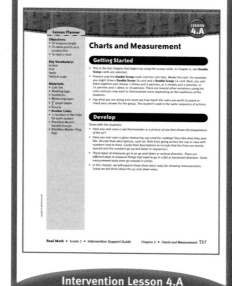

Intervention Lesson 4.A

ENGLISH LEARNER

Preview

If . . . students need language support,

Then . . . use Lesson 4.3 in **English Learner Support Guide** to preview lesson concepts and vocabulary.

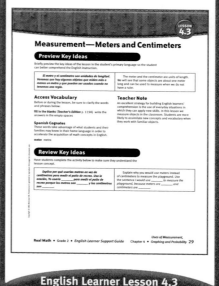

English Learner Lesson 4.3

ENRICH

If . . . students are proficient in the lesson concepts,

Then . . . emphasize **Building Blocks.**

PRACTICE

If . . . students would benefit from additional practice,

Then . . . extend Skill Practice before assigning the student pages.

RETEACH

If . . . students are having difficulty understanding measuring length,

Then . . . extend the Skill Building before assigning the student pages.

Vocabulary
ruler \rü´lər\ *n.* a straight-edged strip of wood, plastic, metal, or other material marked off into measuring units

Access Vocabulary
fill in the blanks write the answers in the empty spaces

Spanish Cognates
meter metro

Mental Math 5

  Continue to develop fluency and quick recall of the basic addition and subtraction facts by doing chain calculations such as the following:

a. $10 + 5 - 6 = 9$ **b.** $10 + 5 - 7 = 8$

c. $14 - 7 - 7 = 0$ **d.** $16 - 8 - 8 = 0$

e. $3 + 4 + 5 = 12$ **f.** $4 + 5 + 6 = 15$

g. $15 - 6 - 5 - 4 = 0$ **h.** $8 + 8 - 8 = 8$

1 Develop 20

Tell Students In Today's Lesson They Will

measure in meters and centimeters.

Skill Building ENGAGING
Whole Group

Have several metersticks available for students to study. Show the class that the stick is the length of 1 meter and that 100 centimeters is the same length as 1 meter. Allow students to look at the meterstick, observing the centimeters marked.

Direct students to estimate the length of an object in the room that is about 1 meter (for instance, the width of the classroom door).

When students decide on an object, have them measure it and report their results.

Repeat this activity several times.

Show students that the measurement of an object that is longer than 1 meter may be given orally and in writing in both meters and centimeters or just in centimeters, for example, 1 meter and 23 centimeters, or 123 centimeters.

Direct students to estimate and measure the lengths of objects that are about 2 meters, 3 meters, and 4 meters long. Have them report the measures; for example, 243 centimeters, 562 centimeters, 3 meters and 22 centimeters, and so on.

Skill Practice COMPUTING
Whole Group

 Begin an estimating measure response exercise in which you choose an object, students estimate its length in centimeters and show their estimates with **Number Cubes,** and then you measure to check. Then choose a related object, and have students show estimates and measure to check again. Related objects might be the heights of two or three students. For example, choose a first student, have students estimate his or her height, and measure to check. Then choose a second, shorter student, and have him or her stand next to the first student. The estimates for the height of the second student should be slightly less than the measured height of the first student. Repeat as time permits.

Monitoring Student Progress

If . . . students' estimates are contrary to reason (for example, a student who estimates a greater height for the shorter student),

Then . . . those students will need individual instruction on the use of rulers, followed by practice.

2 Assign Student Pages 20

Pages 119–120 UNDERSTANDING
Small Group

You might want to do page 119 as a class. Then organize students into small groups to complete page 120. Before beginning, remind students that *cm* stands for *centimeter,* and explain that *m* stands for *meter.*

As Students Finish

Game Have students play the **Find the Distance Game** in pairs.

Building Blocks Reptile Ruler

RESEARCH IN ACTION

"Accurate measuring procedures such as placing manipulative units without leaving spaces between them can be developed through many experiences. Similarly, with rulers, teachers can help children develop concepts and procedures such as accurate alignment, starting at zero, and focusing on the points rather than only the numbers on the ruler. Counting points rather than line segments is more likely in ruler activities and partitioning tasks. That is, accepting earlier use of rulers is *not* the same as believing that such use implies mastery either of the tool or of measurement concepts. Rather, it is an additional way to present experiences and problems that will help children develop understanding."

Clements, Douglas and J. Sarama, eds. *Engaging Young Children in Mathematics: Standards for Early Childhood Mathematics Education.* Mahwah, New Jersey: Lawrence Erlbaum Associates, Publishers, 2004, p. 52.

LESSON 4.3 Measurement—Meters and Centimeters

Key Ideas

The meter and the centimeter are units of length.
There are 100 centimeters in 1 meter.

These are some objects that are about
1 meter long.

Do the Measuring Activity.

List three objects in the classroom that are
about 1 meter long. Measure and write their lengths
in centimeters.

Object	Centimeters
❶ _____	_____
❷ _____	_____
❸ _____	_____

Copyright © SRA/McGraw-Hill.

📖 Textbook This lesson is available in the *eTextbook*.

119

Student Page

LESSON 4.3 • Measurement—Meters and Centimeters

List three objects that are about 2 meters long
or 2 meters high.

Measure and write their lengths in centimeters.

Object	Centimeters
❹ _____	_____
❺ _____	_____
❻ _____	_____

1 meter = 100 centimeters

Use this information to fill in the blanks.

❼ 2 m = **200** cm   ⓬ 3 m = **300** cm

❽ 4 m = **400** cm   ⓭ 6 m = **600** cm

❾ 7 m = **700** cm   ⓮ **4** m = 400 cm

❿ 10 m = **1,000** cm   ⓯ **8** m = 800 cm

⓫ **5** m = 500 cm   ⓰ **1** m = 100 cm

Copyright © SRA/McGraw-Hill.

120   **Real Math • Chapter 4 • Lesson 3**

Measurement—Meters and Centimeters **LESSON 4.3**

③ Reflect

10

Guided Discussion [REASONING]

Whole Group

Have students estimate the length of the perimeter of the school grounds. Ask:

■ **Would you estimate in centimeters or meters?** Help students understand that the choice of unit (centimeter or meter) is a matter of convenience and that in this case it makes sense to estimate in meters.

Direct students to estimate how far it is from school to some other building or place on the other side of town. Ask:

■ **Are centimeters a convenient unit?** no
■ **Are meters a convenient unit?** Meters are more convenient than centimeters.

Explain that there are units of measure that are greater than a meter. Great distances are often measured in kilometers. One kilometer is equal to 1,000 meters. It is not necessary to go into further detail about kilometers at this time.

 Cumulative Review: For cumulative review of previously learned skills, see page 127–128.

 Family Involvement: Assign the ***Practice, Reteach,*** or ***Enrichment*** activities depending on the needs of your students.

 Concept/Question Board: Have students look for additional examples using measurement and post them on the Concept/Question Board.

 Math Puzzler: Henry bought two pens that cost 50 cents each. Aiko bought one pen for 80 cents. Who spent more money? How much more? Henry spent 20 cents more.

4 Assess and Differentiate

 Assess Use *eAssess* to record and analyze evidence of student understanding.

A Gather Evidence

Use the Daily Class Assessment Records in *Assessment* or *eAssess* to record daily observations.

Informal Assessment
☑ **Mental Math**

Did the student **COMPUTING**
❏ respond accurately?
❏ respond quickly?
❏ respond with confidence?
❏ self-correct?

Informal Assessment
☑ **Student Pages**

Did the student **UNDERSTANDING**
❏ make important observations?
❏ extend or generalize learning?
❏ provide insightful answers?
❏ pose insightful questions?

B Summarize Findings

Analyze and summarize assessment data for each student. Determine which Assessment Follow-Up is appropriate for each student. Use the Student Assessment Record in *Assessment* or *eAssess* to update assessment records.

Assessment page T41

C Assessment Follow-Up ● DIFFERENTIATE INSTRUCTION

Based on your observations, use these teaching strategies for assessment follow-up.

INTERVENTION	**ENRICH**
Review student performance on *Intervention* Lesson 4.A to see if students have mastered prerequisite skills for this lesson.	**If . . .** students are proficient in the lesson concepts, **Then . . .** encourage them to work on the chapter projects or *Enrichment* Lesson 4.3.

ENGLISH LEARNER

Review

Use Lesson 4.3 in *English Learner Support Guide* to review lesson concepts and vocabulary.

PRACTICE	**RETEACH**
If . . . students would benefit from additional practice, **Then . . .** assign *Practice* Lesson 4.3.	**If . . .** students are having difficulty understanding the length of a meter, **Then . . .** have students examine metersticks as you review that 1 meter is equal to 100 centimeters.

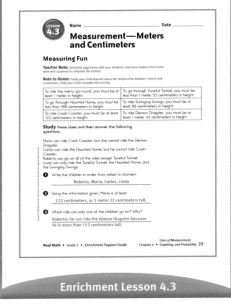

Enrichment Lesson 4.3

Practice Lesson 4.3

Lesson Planner

OBJECTIVES
- To introduce the inch as a customary unit of length measurement
- To provide practice in estimating and measuring length in inches
- To make students aware of the two systems of measurement: customary and metric

NCTM STANDARDS

Measurement
- Recognizing the attributes of length
- Using tools to measure
- Developing common referents for measurements to make comparisons and estimates

Connections
- Recognizing and using connections among mathematical ideas
- Understanding how mathematical ideas interconnect and build on one another

MATERIALS
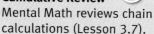
- *Number Cubes
- *12-inch rulers

TECHNOLOGY
- **ⓔ Presentation** Lesson 4.4
- **ⓔ MathTools** Metric and Customary Conversion Tool

TEST PREP

Cumulative Review
Mental Math reviews chain calculations (Lesson 3.7).

Extended Response
Problem 10

Measuring Length—Inches

Context of the Lesson This is the fourth of five lessons on measuring length. The previous lessons focused on metric measures. This lesson and the next lesson focus on customary units.

See page 113B for Math Background for teachers for this lesson.

Planning for Learning ● DIFFERENTIATE INSTRUCTION

INTERVENTION

If . . . students lack the prerequisite skill of measuring length,

Then . . . teach **Intervention** Lesson 4.A.

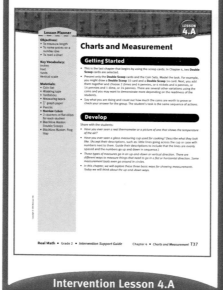

Intervention Lesson 4.A

ENGLISH LEARNER

Preview

If . . . students need language support,

Then . . . use Lesson 4.4 in **English Learner Support Guide** to preview lesson concepts and vocabulary.

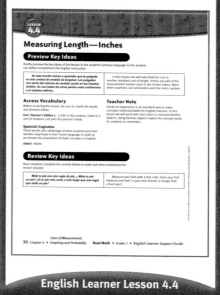

English Learner Lesson 4.4

ENRICH

If . . . students are proficient in the lesson concepts,

Then . . . emphasize exploring **eMathTools**.

PRACTICE

If . . . students would benefit from additional practice,

Then . . . extend Skill Practice before assigning the student pages.

RETEACH

If . . . students are having difficulty understanding measuring length,

Then . . . extend the Guided Discussion before assigning the student pages.

Access Vocabulary
foot In this context a *foot* is a unit of measure, not a part of a person's body.

Spanish Cognates
object objeto

Mental Math 5

Continue to develop fluency and quick recall of the basic addition and subtraction facts by doing chain calculations such as the following:

a. $8 + 8 - 4 = 12$
b. $10 - 8 + 7 = 9$
c. $5 + 4 + 3 + 2 + 1 = 15$
d. $4 + 8 - 2 = 10$
e. $6 + 5 + 4 + 3 + 2 = 20$
f. $5 + 5 + 5 = 15$
g. $11 - 4 + 4 = 11$
h. $16 - 0 - 8 = 8$

1 Develop 20

Tell Students In Today's Lesson They Will
measure with inch rulers.

Guided Discussion REASONING Whole Group

Start by distributing the inch rulers with which students are likely to be familiar from the first-grade program. Allow students to explore and to measure with them.

Discuss the following concepts:
- These are inch rulers, and they are used to measure length in inches.
- There are 12 inches in 1 foot.
- There are two systems of measurement in general use in the United States, and it is important that they be familiar with both systems.
- The metric system—the system used in the two previous lessons—is widely used in other countries and by many people in the United States.

Using Student Pages   APPLYING Whole Group

1. Introduce student page 121 as a group activity. Have students estimate in inches the length of each item pictured. Then measure the item to check the length in inches. It is important to always measure the length that has just been estimated before making the next estimation.

2. Continue on to student page 122, allowing students to work on the first three problems in small groups or with a partner while they measure classroom objects about 1 foot in length.

As students begin page 122, they will notice that the objects they measure are not an exact number of inches. Ask students:

■ **How can you record your measures?** Explain that they should measure to the nearest inch, that is, record the number of inches to which the measurement is closer. When the question arises, bring the class together, and give one or two demonstrations of how to do this. Note: At this time it is not important to report fractional inches.

Skill Practice COMPUTING Whole Group

 As in the previous lessons, do an estimating measure activity in which students estimate (and show their estimates with **Number Cubes**), and then measure the length of various related objects in inches.

After a while, present longer objects, and have students estimate the lengths and respond by showing the estimate to the nearest foot.

2 Assign Student Pages 20

Page 122 UNDERSTANDING

Have students complete the rest of page 122 independently.

As Students Finish

 Allow students enough time to play a game of their choice, or assign games based on needed skill practice.

e MathTools *Metric and Customary Conversion Tool* Have students use this tool to explore converting between inches and feet (however, do not have students convert between metric and customary units at this time).

Student Page

Name _____ **Date** _____

LESSON 4.4 **Measuring Length—Inches**

Key Ideas

The inch is a unit of length.

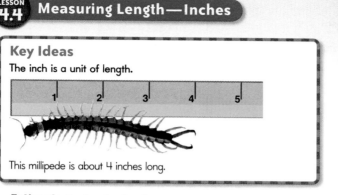

1 2 3 4 5

This millipede is about 4 inches long.

Estimate the length of each object. Then measure to check.

① Estimate _____ inches
Measure __2__ inches

② Estimate _____ inches
Measure __3__ inches

③ Estimate _____ inches
Measure __4__ inches

Textbook This lesson is available in the *eTextbook*.

121

Student Page

LESSON 4.4 • Measuring Length—Inches

1 foot = 12 inches

List some objects in your classroom that are about 1 foot long. Measure to the nearest inch.

Object	Nearest Inch
④ _____	_____
⑤ _____	_____
⑥ _____	_____

List some objects in your classroom that are about 2 feet long. Measure to the nearest inch.

Object	Nearest Inch
⑦ _____	_____
⑧ _____	_____
⑨ _____	_____

⑩ **Extended Response** Explain how you measured an object 2 feet long using an inch ruler. _____
See Reflect in *Teacher's Edition*.

122

Real Math • Chapter 4 • Lesson 4

---

3 Reflect

10

Guided Discussion REASONING

Whole Group

Select a student to come to the front of the room.

Have other students measure his or her height. Ask students:

■ **Suppose the child is 52 inches tall. How should the height be reported—about 4 feet, between 4 and 5 feet, about 52 inches, or about 4 feet 4 inches?** Allow students to discuss. Conclude the discussion by pointing out that the two most common ways of reporting this are *52 inches* and *4 feet 4 inches*. The other choices are, however, not wrong.

Extended Response

Problem 10 Discuss students' answers. Students should realize that they can use strategies such as counting on by ones, using known facts to add two sets of numbers, or aligning two rulers.

 Cumulative Review: For cumulative review of previously learned skills, see page 127–128.

 Family Involvement: Assign the *Practice, Reteach,* or *Enrichment* activities depending on the needs of your students.

 Concept/Question Board: Encourage students to continue to post questions, answers, and examples on the Concept/Question Board.

 Math Puzzler: Maia is 140 centimeters tall. Is she taller or shorter than a meter and by how much? She is 40 cm taller.

4 Assess and Differentiate

 e Assess Use **eAssess** to record and analyze evidence of student understanding.

A Gather Evidence

Use the Daily Class Assessment Records in **Assessment** or **eAssess** to record daily observations.

Informal Assessment
✓ **Using Student Pages**

Did the student **APPLYING**
- ☐ apply learning in new situations?
- ☐ contribute concepts?
- ☐ contribute answers?
- ☐ connect mathematics to real-world situations?

Informal Assessment
✓ **Concept/Question Board**

Did the student **APPLYING**
- ☐ apply learning in new situations?
- ☐ contribute concepts?
- ☐ contribute answers?
- ☐ connect mathematics to real-world situations?

B Summarize Findings

Analyze and summarize assessment data for each student. Determine which Assessment Follow-Up is appropriate for each student. Use the Student Assessment Record in **Assessment** or **eAssess** to update assessment records.

Assessment page T41

C Assessment Follow-Up • DIFFERENTIATE INSTRUCTION

Based on your observations, use these teaching strategies for assessment follow-up.

INTERVENTION

Review student performance on **Intervention** Lesson 4.A to see if students have mastered prerequisite skills for this lesson.

ENGLISH LEARNER

Review

Use Lesson 4.4 in **English Learner Support Guide** to review lesson concepts and vocabulary.

ENRICH

If . . . students are proficient in the lesson concepts,

Then . . . encourage them to work on the chapter projects or **Enrichment** Lesson 4.4.

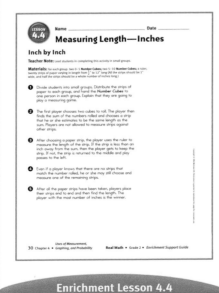

Enrichment Lesson 4.4

PRACTICE

If . . . students would benefit from additional practice,

Then . . . assign **Practice** Lesson 4.4.

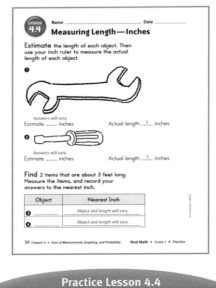

Practice Lesson 4.4

RETEACH

If . . . students are having difficulty measuring in inches and feet,

Then . . . have them work in groups to measure objects and to check the measures of the other students.

OBJECTIVES
- To introduce the yard as a customary unit of measure
- To provide practice estimating and measuring in inches, feet, and yards
- To show students how to convert between these units

NCTM STANDARDS
Measurement
- Recognizing the attributes of length
- Using tools to measure
- Developing common referents for measures to make comparisons and estimates

Connections
- Recognizing and using connections among mathematical ideas
- Understanding how mathematical ideas interconnect and build on one another

MATERIALS
- *Number Cubes
- *12-inch rulers
- *Tape measures or yardsticks

TECHNOLOGY
- **e Presentation** Lesson 4.5
- **e MathTools** Metric and Customary Conversion Tool

TEST PREP
Cumulative Review
Mental Math reviews chain calculations (Lesson 3.7).

Extended Response
Problem 14

Measurement—Yards, Feet, and Inches

Context of the Lesson This is the last of five lessons on measuring length. More measurement lessons are included in Chapter 10. Although most students cannot yet do the efficient, conventional arithmetic for converting inches to feet to yards, we provide opportunities in this lesson for students to construct their own inefficient methods for doing so.

See page 113B for Math Background for teachers for this lesson.

Planning for Learning • DIFFERENTIATE INSTRUCTION

INTERVENTION
If . . . students lack the prerequisite skill of measuring length,

Then . . . teach *Intervention* Lesson 4.A.

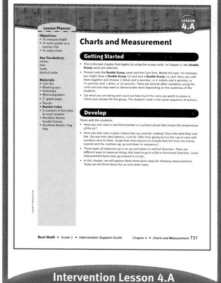

Intervention Lesson 4.A

ENGLISH LEARNER
Preview

If . . . students need language support,

Then . . . use Lesson 4.5 in *English Learner Support Guide* to preview lesson concepts and vocabulary.

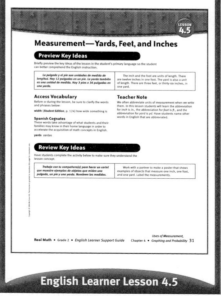

English Learner Lesson 4.5

ENRICH
If . . . students are proficient in the lesson concepts,

Then . . . emphasize exploring *eMathTools*.

PRACTICE
If . . . students would benefit from additional practice,

Then . . . extend Skill Practice before assigning the student pages.

RETEACH
If . . . students are having difficulty understanding measuring length,

Then . . . extend the Guided Discussion before assigning the student pages.

Access Vocabulary
width how wide something is

Spanish Cognates
yards yardas

---

*Manipulative Kit Item

Mental Math 5

 Continue to develop fluency and quick recall of the basic addition and subtraction facts by doing chain calculations such as the following:

a. 2 + 7 + 4 = 13
b. 6 + 6 + 9 = 21
c. 3 + 3 + 3 = 9
d. 6 + 5 + 8 = 19
e. 4 + 5 + 6 = 15
f. 7 + 3 + 8 = 18
g. 9 + 0 + 5 = 14
h. 5 + 5 + 5 = 15

1 Develop 20

Tell Students In Today's Lesson They Will
measure with inch rulers and yardsticks.

Guided Discussion REASONING Whole Group

Start by distributing 12-inch rulers and yardsticks or tape measures. Discuss the fact that there are 12 inches in 1 foot. Introduce the yardstick as a tool for measuring length by the yard. Allow students to compare the two measuring tools. Discuss similarities and differences between the two rulers.

Demonstrate measuring two or three classroom objects that are about 1 yard in length.

Ask students:

■ **How many feet are in 1 yard?** Discuss strategies such as aligning three 12-inch rulers to see that they are the same length as 1 yard.

■ **How many inches are in 1 yard?** This will be a difficult problem for many students, as they have not yet learned how to add three two-digit numbers. But through discussion, allow students to explain their strategies for solving this problem.

Some possible strategies are as follows:

1. Count the number of inches.
2. Think 10 + 2 + 10 + 2 + 10 + 2 = 30 + 6 = 36.
3. Think 12 + 12 = 10 + 2 + 10 + 2 = 24; 24 + 10 = 34; 34 + 2 = 36.

Other strategies are likely to be suggested by students.

Skill Practice COMPUTING Whole Group

As in the previous lessons, begin an estimating/measuring activity in which students estimate, report their estimates using **Number Cubes,** and then measure the length of various related objects in inches.

After a while, present longer objects, and have students estimate the lengths and respond by showing the estimate to the nearest foot.

2 Assign Student Pages 20

Student Pages 123–124 UNDERSTANDING

Have students complete page 123 independently. Continue onto page 124, allowing students to work in small, cooperative groups. When finished, have groups share and compare their measurements.

As Students Finish

Game Allow students enough time to play a game of their choice, or assign games based on needed skill practice.

MathTools *Metric and Customary Conversion Tool* Have students use this tool to explore converting among inches, feet, and yards (however, do not have students convert between metric and customary units at this time).

RESEARCH IN ACTION

"Measurement involves critical skills including techniques for comparing and measuring, either by iterating copies of a unit or using tools such as rulers. Children's development of these skills is a slow process . . . Recent research suggests that children benefit from using objects and rulers to measure at any age. Not only do children prefer using rulers, but they can use them meaningfully and in combination with manipulable units to develop understanding of length measurement. Even if they do not understand rulers fully or use them accurately, they can use rulers *along with* manipulable units such as centimeter cubes and arbitrary units to develop their measurement skills."

Clements, Douglas and J. Sarama, eds. *Engaging Young Children in Mathematics: Standards for Early Childhood Mathematics Education.* Mahwah, New Jersey: Lawrence Erlbaum Associates, Publishers, 2004, p. 51.

LESSON 4.5   Measurement—Yards, Feet, and Inches

Name _____   Date _____

Key Ideas

The inch and the foot are units of length. There are 12 inches in 1 foot.

The yard is also a unit of length. There are 3 feet or 36 inches in 1 yard.

We often use these abbreviations:

yard   yd
foot   ft
inch   in.

Fill in the blanks. Use a ruler if you need to.

1. 1 foot = __12__ inches
2. 2 feet = __24__ inches
3. 1 yard = __3__ feet = __36__ inches
4. 2 yards = __6__ feet = __72__ inches

Copyright © SRA/McGraw-Hill.

▣Textbook This lesson is available in the *eTextbook*.   123

LESSON 4.5 • Measurement—Yards, Feet, and Inches

Work with a partner to measure.
List some objects in your classroom that are about 1 yard long. Measure them. How many inches long are they?

	Object	Nearest Inch
5	_____	_____
6	_____	_____
7	_____	_____
8	_____	_____

Fill in the blanks. Use a ruler if you need to.

9. __1__ foot = 12 inches
10. __3__ feet = 36 inches
11. __2__ feet = 24 inches
12. __5__ feet = 60 inches

13. Work with a partner to measure the width of your classroom door. Record the width in inches. Answer will depend on the width of your door.

14. **Extended Response** How many feet are 48 inches? Explain how you found the answer. _____
See Reflect in *Teacher's Edition*.

Copyright © SRA/McGraw-Hill.

---

3 Reflect   10

Guided Discussion   REASONING   Whole Group

Begin by allowing groups to share and compare their measurements from Problems 5–8 on page 124.

Spend a few minutes allowing students to tell how they figured out the conversion problems on page 124, Exercises 9–12. *Note: These are difficult problems for students, so provide plenty of help and encouragement.*

Some suggestions: For Exercise 12: A yardstick is 3 feet and has 36 inches, so we need to add 2 more feet to the 36 inches. Two feet is 24 inches. So we need to add: 36 + 24.

We can rewrite the problem: 30 + 6 + 20 + 4 = 30 + 20 + 6 + 4 = 30 + 20 + 10 = 60. So there are 60 inches in 5 feet.

Extended Response

Problem 14 Discuss students' answers. Students should realize they can add 12 + 12 + 12 + 12, recognizing it would take four 12-inch rulers.

Use Mastery Checkpoint 6 found in **Assessment** to evaluate student mastery of measuring length. By this time, students should be able to correctly answer eighty percent of the Mastery Checkpoint items.

Cumulative Review: For cumulative review of previously learned skills, see page 127–128.

Family Involvement: Assign the **Practice, Reteach,** or **Enrichment** activities depending on the needs of your students.

Concept/Question Board: Encourage students to continue to post questions, answers, and examples on the Concept/Question Board.

Math Puzzler: You need to cover a table that is 24 inches wide and 52 inches long with colored paper. You have a piece of paper 36 inches wide and 96 inches long. What will you do to cover the tabletop exactly? Possible answer: Cut the 36-inch side down by 12 inches, and cut the 96-inch side down by 44 inches.

Assess and Differentiate

 Assess Use *eAssess* to record and analyze evidence of student understanding.

A Gather Evidence

Use the Daily Class Assessment Records in *Assessment* or *eAssess* to record daily observations.

Formal Assessment

☑ **Mastery Checkpoint**

Did the student
- ❏ use correct procedures?
- ❏ respond with at least 80% accuracy?

Mastery Checkpoint 6
Measuring Length
The student demonstrates mastery by accurately measuring the length of eight objects.
How long?

Object	Estimate Length	Measure Length	Difference

Assessment page T57

B Summarize Findings

Analyze and summarize assessment data for each student. Determine which Assessment Follow-Up is appropriate for each student. Use the Student Assessment Record in *Assessment* or *eAssess* to update assessment records.

Assessment page T41

C Assessment Follow-Up ● DIFFERENTIATE INSTRUCTION

Based on your observations, use these teaching strategies for assessment follow-up.

INTERVENTION

Review student performance on *Intervention* Lesson 4.A to see if students have mastered prerequisite skills for this lesson.

ENGLISH LEARNER

Review

Use Lesson 4.5 in *English Learner Support Guide* to review lesson concepts and vocabulary.

ENRICH

If . . . students are proficient in the lesson concepts,

Then . . . encourage them to work on the chapter projects or *Enrichment* Lesson 4.5.

Enrichment Lesson 4.5

PRACTICE

If . . . students would benefit from additional practice,

Then . . . assign *Practice* Lesson 4.5.

LESSON 4.5 Measurement—Yards, Feet, and Inches

Find 4 items that are about 2 yards long. Measure them. How many inches long are they?

Object	Nearest Inch
❶	Object and length will vary.
❷	Object and length will vary.
❸	Object and length will vary.
❹	Object and length will vary.

How many? You may use a ruler if needed.

❺ __3__ feet = 36 inches ❻ __7__ feet = 84 inches
❼ __6__ feet = 72 inches ❽ __8__ feet = 96 inches
❾ __4__ feet = 48 inches ❿ __5__ feet = 60 inches

Solve.

⓫ Mrs. Green wants to buy a couch. The length of the couch needs to be about 2 yards. Would a couch measuring 6 feet fit?

__yes__ Explain.

6 feet = 2 yards

Real Math • Grade 2 • *Practice* Chapter 4 • *Uses of Measurement, Graphing, and Probability* 31

Practice Lesson 4.5

RETEACH

If . . . students are having difficulty measuring in inches, feet, and yards,

Then . . . have them first identify which measure is best for each object. For instance, a shoe would be best measured in inches, while the length of a sports field would be best measured in yards.

Exploring Problem Solving

Objectives
- To explore the Use Simple Numbers, Make a Table, and Make a Model strategies
- To provide practice solving problems involving standard and nonstandard units
- To provide practice presenting solutions to nonroutine problems

Materials
- String
- Objects to use as nonstandard units such as paper clips, erasers, and cubes
- Centimeter rulers, inch rulers

Context of the Lesson This lesson and other special problem-solving lessons allow more time for students to share and compare strategies. While continuing the toy factory theme, this lesson also provides additional opportunity for students to use and compare standard and nonstandard measurements.

1 Develop 5

Tell Students In Today's Lesson They Will
figure out which stuffed penguin goes with which order form.

2 Exploring Problem Solving 25

Using Student Pages

Have students look at the picture on page 125. Present this problem:

The Perfect Puffy Penguin Company makes stuffed penguins of any size you want. You just fill out the form to tell the company how tall to make the penguin and how far apart the wing tips should be. Four second-grade children—Kendra, Joey, Jason, and Olivia—each sent in an order for a penguin. They used different objects to describe the size they wanted. Somehow the company figured out what size to make each penguin, and all the animals were ready to pack in boxes. But before the penguins were packed, someone opened a window, and the wind blew the order forms off the table. Now the packers have to decide which penguin goes to which child. How can they do that?

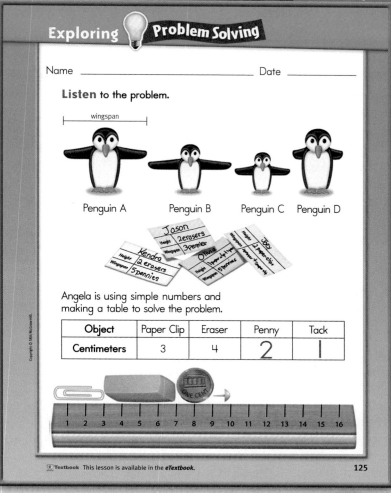

Exploring Problem Solving

Name _____ Date _____

Listen to the problem.

Penguin A   Penguin B   Penguin C   Penguin D

Angela is using simple numbers and making a table to solve the problem.

Object	Paper Clip	Eraser	Penny	Tack
Centimeters	3	4	2	1

Textbook This lesson is available in the *eTextbook*.   125

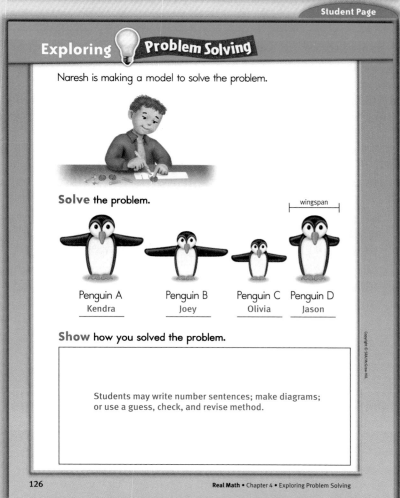

Exploring Problem Solving

Naresh is making a model to solve the problem.

Solve the problem.

| Penguin A | Penguin B | Penguin C | Penguin D |
| Kendra | Joey | Olivia | Jason |

Show how you solved the problem.

Students may write number sentences; make diagrams; or use a guess, check, and revise method.

126   **Real Math • Chapter 4 • Exploring Problem Solving**

Chapter 4 • Exploring Problem Solving **125–126**

To be sure students understand the problem, ask questions such as the following:

- **How many penguins did the company make?** 4

- **What does *wingspan* mean?** how far it would be from one wing tip to the other if the wings were spread out

- **Are all the penguins alike?** No, they are different heights and have different wingspans.

- **What is the problem asking you to do?** Figure out which penguin goes to each child.

- **Did all four children use the same measurement unit to describe the size of the penguin they wanted?** No, they used different objects.

- **What did Joey use to measure?** erasers and paper clips

- **How might using a string help you measure the wingspan?** The string can turn or curve so it can measure along things that are crooked or curved. Then it can be straightened to find out how long the crooked or curved distance is.

Tell students they are going to have a chance to solve the problem, but first they will look at how two other students are trying to solve it.

Have students look at page 125. Ask questions about Angela's strategy, such as the following:

- **Why has Angela written the number 3 under the paper clip and the number 4 under the eraser?** to show that each paper clip is 3 centimeters long and that each eraser is 4 centimeters long

- **What will Angela write in the penny column?** 2, because a penny is 2 centimeters across

- **Why do you think Angela is changing all the measurements to centimeters?** to make it easier to compare

- **What do you think Angela will do after she completes her table?** use her centimeter ruler to measure the penguins

- **How will this help her solve the problem?** She will be able to match the sizes of the penguins to the measurements on the order forms. For example, if the order says 3 pennies, she will know that means 6 centimeters because $2 + 2 + 2 = 6$.

Tell students that Naresh is using a different strategy to try to solve the problem. Have students look at the picture on page 126 of Naresh's approach. Ask questions such as the following:

- **When Naresh is finished marking this strip of paper, what could he use it for?** measuring how many pennies' long something is

- **What kind of measuring instrument is Naresh making?** He is making a ruler with the penny as the unit.

- **What do you think he will do with his penny ruler?** measure the penguins

- **Will this help him with all the measurements?** no, just the measurements that used pennies

- **What can he do to measure the other penguins?** He can make three other rulers using erasers, paper clips, and thumbtacks as units.

Have students work on the problem in pairs or small groups. Tell them when they are sure which child has ordered a particular penguin, they should write that child's name under that penguin. They may use Angela's strategy, Naresh's strategy, or one of their own. Provide support as needed, remembering to offer suggestions rather than answers.

3 Reflect 10

Effective Communication Ask students to share their solutions and their strategies. In discussion bring out the following points:

- Standard units of measurement help people understand one another.
- Some nonstandard units work better than others. The company could have had a lot of difficulty if their paper clips and erasers were longer or shorter than the ones the children used. The penny, on the other hand, comes in only one size, so it was easy for the company to know exactly what measurements using pennies meant.
- Different strategies can be used to solve the same problem.
- Different people might prefer different strategies.

Sample Solutions Strategies

Use a Physical Model

Students might act out the problem by using the actual objects mentioned on the order forms or with objects of equivalent lengths.

Use Logical Reasoning

Students might use visual information to compare measurements without actually doing the measurements. For example, seeing that an eraser is a little longer than a paper clip, they might realize that the wingspan of Joey's penguin must be a little more than its height. They could also reason that the two penguins that are the same height belong to Kendra and Jason because each of those children ordered a penguin 2 erasers tall.

4 Assess 15

When evaluating student work, remember to focus not only on the correctness of the answer but also on whether the student thought rationally about the problem. Questions to consider include the following:

- Did the student understand the problem?
- Did the student understand the Sample Solutions Strategies?
- Did the student use a reasonable method for solving the problem?
- Was the student able to explain his or her strategy?

Cumulative Review

Assign Pages 127–128

Use the Cumulative Review as a review of concepts and skills that students have previously learned.

Here are different ways that you can assign these problems to your students as they work through the chapter:

- With some of the lessons in the chapter, assign a set of cumulative review problems to be completed as practice or for homework.
  Lesson 4.1—Problems 1–3
  Lesson 4.2—Problems 4–8
  Lesson 4.3—Problems 9–10
  Lesson 4.4—Problems 11–22
  Lesson 4.5—Problems 23–24
- At any point during the chapter, assign part or all of the cumulative review problems to be completed as practice or for homework.

Cumulative Review

Problems 1–3 review counting on a number line, Lesson 1.7.

Problems 4–8 review measuring length in centimeters, Lesson 4.2.

Problems 9–10 review place value and money, Lesson 1.5.

Problems 11–22 review missing addends and subtraction, Lesson 3.1.

Problems 23–24 review perimeter and multiple addends, Lesson 2.8.

Monitoring Student Progress

If . . . students miss more than one problem in a section,

Then . . . refer to the indicated lesson for remediation suggestions.

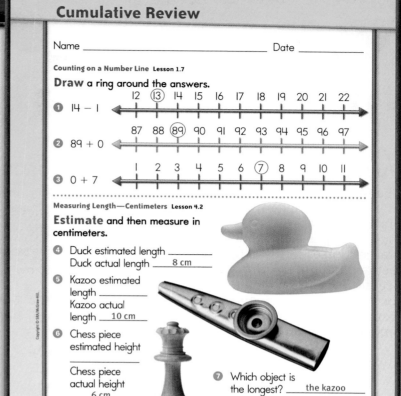

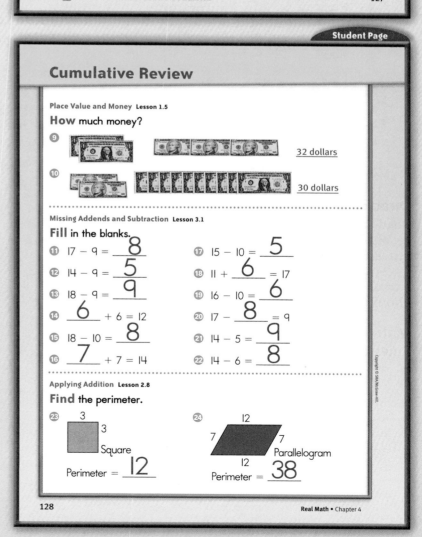

Individual Oral Assessment

Purpose of the Test

The Individual Oral Assessment is designed to measure students' growing knowledge of chapter concepts. It is administered individually to each student, and it requires oral responses from each student. The test takes about five minutes to complete. See **Assessment** for detailed instructions for administering and interpreting the test, and record students' answers on the Student Assessment Recording Sheet.

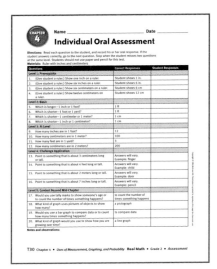

Assessment page T30

Directions

Read each question to the student, and record his or her oral response. If the student answers correctly, go to the next question. Stop when the student misses two questions at the same level. Students should not use scrap paper.

Materials

Ruler with inches and centimeters

Questions

Level 1: Prerequisite

1. Show 1 inch on a ruler.
2. Show 6 inches on a ruler.
3. Show 6 centimeters on a ruler.
4. Show 12 centimeters on a ruler.

Level 2: Basic

5. Which is longer, 1 inch or 1 foot? 1 ft
6. Which is shorter, 1 foot or 1 yard? 1 ft
7. Which is shorter, 1 centimeter or 1 meter? 1 cm
8. Which is shorter, 1 inch or 1 centimeter? 1 cm

Level 3: At Level

9. How many inches are in 1 foot? 12
10. How many centimeters are in 1 meter? 100
11. How many feet are in 1 yard? 3
12. How many centimeters are in 2 meters? 200

Level 4: Challenge Application

13. Point to something that is about 3 centimeters long or tall. Possible answer: finger
14. Point to something that is about 4 feet long or tall. Possible answer: child
15. Point to something that is about 2 meters long or tall. Possible answer: door
16. Point to something that is about 7 inches long or tall. Possible answer: pencil

Level 5: Content Beyond Mid-Chapter

17. Would you use tally marks to show someone's age or to count the number of times something happens? to count the number of times something happens
18. What kind of graph uses pictures of objects to show how many? a pictograph
19. Would you use a bar graph to compare data or to count how many times something happens? to compare data
20. What kind of graph would you use to show how you are growing over time? a line graph

Lesson Planner

OBJECTIVES
- To record information using tally marks
- To informally raise the question of what is a fair sample

NCTM STANDARDS

Data Analysis and Probability
- Posing questions and gathering data about themselves and their surroundings
- Representing data using concrete objects, pictures, and graphs
- Describing parts of the data and the set of data as a whole to determine what the data show

Communication
- Organizing and consolidating their mathematical thinking through communications
- Communicating their mathematical thinking coherently and clearly to peers and teachers

MATERIALS
- 1 reading book per student

TECHNOLOGY
e Presentation Lesson 4.6

TEST PREP
Cumulative Review
Mental Math reviews chain calculations (Lesson 3.7).

Extended Response
Problem 4

Collecting and Recording Data

Context of the Lesson This is the first of eight lessons on data collection, organization, and analysis. In this lesson students will gather data by using tally marks. Students used tally marks in the first-grade program and will use them again when doing probability experiments at the end of this chapter.

See page 113B for Math Background for teachers for this lesson.

Planning for Learning ● DIFFERENTIATE INSTRUCTION

INTERVENTION

If . . . students lack the prerequisite skill of reading a table,

Then . . . teach **Intervention** Lesson 4.B.

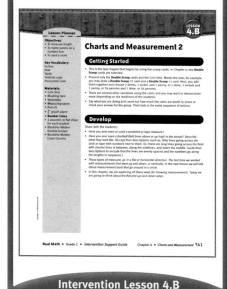

Intervention Lesson 4.B

ENGLISH LEARNER

Preview

If . . . students need language support,

Then . . . use Lesson 4.6 in **English Learner Support Guide** to preview lesson concepts and vocabulary.

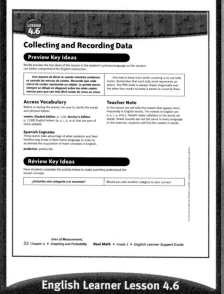

English Learner Lesson 4.6

ENRICH

If . . . students are proficient in the lesson concepts,

Then . . . emphasize chapter projects.

PRACTICE

If . . . students would benefit from additional practice,

Then . . . extend Guided Discussion before assigning the student pages.

RETEACH

If . . . students are having difficulty understanding data collection,

Then . . . extend the Guided Discussion before assigning the student pages.

Vocabulary
tally marks *n.* marks used in recording a number of acts or objects, usually consisting of vertical lines

Access Vocabulary
vowels English letters (such as *a, e, i, o,* and *u*) that are part of every syllable

Spanish Cognates
prediction predicción

*Manipulative Kit Item

Mental Math 5

 Write exercises such as the following on the board and say them aloud. Students show thumbs-up if the answer is greater than 100, thumbs-down if less than 100, and an open hand if exactly 100. Remind students that for these types of exercises, they should always work from left to right. Possible examples include the following.

a. 20 + 20 + 50 down

b. 20 + 20 + 50 + 20 up

c. 20 − 20 + 50 + 55 up

d. 13 + 13 + 32 + 70 up

e. 110 − 27 − 3 down

f. 25 + 25 + 25 + 25 open hand

1 Develop 20

Tell Students In Today's Lesson They Will

gather and record data.

Guided Discussion UNDERSTANDING
Whole Group

Review the use of tally marks. Point out that tally marks are useful for keeping track of the number of times certain things happen.

Then explain that in order to make it easier to keep track of the number of marks, most people write four vertical tally marks and then make the fifth mark across the original four:

Make a table on the board, recording information from an informal survey of your students, such as favorite colors. Use tally marks to record how many prefer each color.

Using Student Pages ENGAGING
Small Group

Vowel Frequency Activity

Have students open their books to page 129. Ask:

■ **Which of the vowels do you think appears most often in written English?** Have students record their predictions in the appropriate spot on page 129.

■ **How do you think we can find out?**

After a brief discussion, have students, working in pairs, select a standard page of text in their readers that they will use as their sample from which to determine the letter frequencies. Have students record the location of their sample in the appropriate spot on page 129. Then have one student carefully call out the vowels from the text sample as the second student uses tally marks to record the frequency in the table on page 129. After about 10 minutes, stop the activity, and have students total their results and write the totals in the table.

Briefly discuss the results.

■ **Did all groups have similar results? Might they get similar results if they chose a passage from a different book?** Leave the answers to these questions open, and perhaps they can be the subject of continuing investigations.

Finally tell students that studies have shown that the most common vowel in the English language is E, and the least common is U. The order of frequency is E, A, I, O, U.

2 Assign Student Pages 20

Page 130 UNDERSTANDING

Have students complete page 130 independently. Before beginning, make sure students understand the kind of survey shown.

As Students Finish

 Allow students enough time to play a game of their choice, or assign games based on needed skill practice.

 RESEARCH IN ACTION

"Data analysis contains one big idea: classifying, organizing, representing, and using information to ask and answer questions. The developmental continuum for data analysis includes growth in classifying and counting to sort objects and quantify their groups. . . . Children eventually become capable of simultaneously classifying and counting, for example, counting the number of colors in a group of objects."

Clements, Douglas and J. Sarama, eds. *Engaging Young Children in Mathematics: Standards for Early Childhood Mathematics Education.* Mahwah, New Jersey: Lawrence Erlbaum Associates, Publishers, 2004, p. 56.

Name _____ Date _____

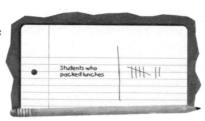

LESSON 4.6 Collecting and Recording Data

Key Ideas

Tally marks are used to record a number of objects or events.

Students who packed lunches   ꟷꟷꟷ ||

Which of the letters A, E, I, O, U do you think appears most often in writing?

My prediction _____

My sample for example, page 25 of my reader

Letter	Tallies	Totals
A		
E		
I		
O		
U		

The table is a record of how many times each vowel occurred in the sample.

📖 **Textbook** This lesson is available in the *eTextbook*.

129

LESSON 4.6 · Collecting and Recording Data

Sara made a survey of the 65 seniors at Stuyvesant High School. She asked each senior which sports he or she played. Here are her results.

Sport	How Many
Baseball	ꟷꟷꟷ ꟷꟷꟷ ꟷꟷꟷ ꟷꟷꟷ ꟷꟷꟷ
Volleyball	ꟷꟷꟷ ꟷꟷꟷ ꟷꟷꟷ ||
Basketball	ꟷꟷꟷ ꟷꟷꟷ |||
Soccer	ꟷꟷꟷ ꟷꟷꟷ ꟷꟷꟷ |||
Tennis	ꟷꟷꟷ ||
Other Sports	||||

Use the table to answer these questions.

❶ How many students play baseball? 25

❷ How many students play soccer? 18

❸ How many students do not play any sport? cannot tell

❹ **Extended Response** If there are only 65 seniors, how can these numbers be accurate?

It is possible that some students play more than one sport.

130   **Real Math • Chapter 4 • Lesson 6**

---

3 Reflect   10 🕐

Guided Discussion   **REASONING**   Whole Group

Discuss the results of the Vowel Frequency Activity students completed on page 129. Ask questions such as the following:

■ **What did you learn by doing the Vowel Frequency Activity?**
■ **What are some similar investigations you could make?** Possible answers: determining the frequencies of all letters; determining the frequencies of letters in other languages; comparing the frequencies of letters in children's books and in general books

Extended Response

Problem 4 There are only 65 seniors, but the table shows 84 tally marks. Students should realize that it is possible that some students play more than one sport.

Curriculum Connection: Students may be interested in learning about how letter frequencies can be used to solve codes.

Cumulative Review: For cumulative review of previously learned skills, see page 147–148.

Family Involvement: Assign the *Practice, Reteach,* or *Enrichment* activities depending on the needs of your students.

Concept/Question Board: Have students look for additional examples using data collection and post them on the Concept/Question Board.

Math Puzzler: Write the following coded message on the board and challenge students to break the code: 25,15,21 1,18,5   22,5,18,25   19,13,1,18,20. Offer the clue 1 = A, 2 = B. You are very smart.

Assess and Differentiate

e **Assess** Use *eAssess* to record and analyze evidence of student understanding.

A Gather Evidence

Use the Daily Class Assessment Records in *Assessment* or *eAssess* to record daily observations.

Informal Assessment
☑ **Mental Math**

Did the student **COMPUTING**
- ☐ respond accurately?
- ☐ respond quickly?
- ☐ respond with confidence?
- ☐ self-correct?

Informal Assessment
☑ **Student Pages**

Did the student **UNDERSTANDING**
- ☐ make important observations?
- ☐ extend or generalize learning?
- ☐ provide insightful answers?
- ☐ pose insightful questions?

B Summarize Findings

Analyze and summarize assessment data for each student. Determine which Assessment Follow-Up is appropriate for each student. Use the Student Assessment Record in *Assessment* or *eAssess* to update assessment records.

Assessment page T41

C Assessment Follow-Up • DIFFERENTIATE INSTRUCTION

Based on your observations, use these teaching strategies for assessment follow-up.

INTERVENTION	ENRICH	PRACTICE	RETEACH
Review student performance on *Intervention* Lesson 4.B to see if students have mastered prerequisite skills for this lesson.	**If . . .** students are proficient in the lesson concepts, **Then . . .** encourage them to work on the chapter projects or *Enrichment* Lesson 4.6.	**If . . .** students would benefit from additional practice, **Then . . .** assign *Practice* Lesson 4.6.	**If . . .** students are having difficulty understanding data collection, **Then . . .** reteach the concept using *Reteach* Lesson 4.6.

ENGLISH LEARNER
Review

Use Lesson 4.6 in *English Learner Support Guide* to review lesson concepts and vocabulary.

Enrichment Lesson 4.6

Practice Lesson 4.6

Reteach Lesson 4.6

Lesson Planner

OBJECTIVES
- To have students collect data about themselves
- To record data and compare the data using Venn diagrams

NCTM STANDARDS
Data Analysis and Probability
- Posing questions and gathering data about themselves and their surroundings
- Representing data using concrete objects, pictures, and graphs
- Describing parts of the data and the set of data as a whole to determine what the data show

Communication
- Organizing and consolidating mathematical thinking through communications
- Communicating mathematical thinking coherently and clearly to peers and teachers

MATERIALS
- blank overhead transparency
- *Overhead attribute blocks

TECHNOLOGY
- (e) **Presentation** Lesson 4.7
- (e) **MathTools** Venn Diagram

TEST PREP
Cumulative Review (Review)
Mental Math reviews addition and subtraction (Lesson 3.6).

Looking Ahead
Lesson 4.8 will require a large package of sweet peas with the pods intact. You will need about 25 pods per student.

Venn Diagrams

Context of the Lesson This is the second of eight lessons on data collection, organization, and analysis. In this lesson students will gather, record, and compare data on Venn diagrams.

See page 113B for Math Background for teachers for this lesson.

Planning for Learning ● DIFFERENTIATE INSTRUCTION

INTERVENTION

If . . . students lack the prerequisite skill of reading a table,

Then . . . teach Intervention Lesson 4.B.

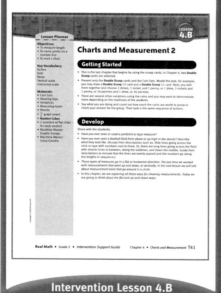

Intervention Lesson 4.B

ENGLISH LEARNER

Preview

If . . . students need language support,

Then . . . use Lesson 4.7 in *English Learner Support Guide* to preview lesson concepts and vocabulary.

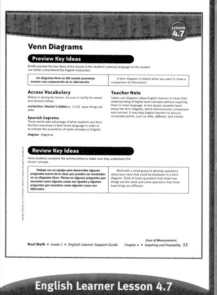

English Learner Lesson 4.7

ENRICH

If . . . students are proficient in the lesson concepts,

Then . . . emphasize exploring *eMathTools*.

PRACTICE

If . . . students would benefit from additional practice,

Then . . . extend Skill Practice before assigning the student pages.

RETEACH

If . . . students are having difficulty understanding Venn diagrams,

Then . . . extend Guided Discussion before assigning the student pages.

Vocabulary
data \dā´tə\ *n.* information from which conclusions can be drawn

Access Vocabulary
similarities ways things are alike

Spanish Cognates
diagram diagrama

*Manipulative Kit Item

Mental Math 5

  Write problems such as the following on the board, and say them aloud. Students show thumbs-up if the answer is greater than 20, thumbs-down if less than 20, and an open hand if exactly 20. Possible examples include the following:

a. 10 + 5 down **b.** 20 + 20 up
c. 2 + 50 up **d.** 13 + 13 up
e. 10 − 3 down **f.** 10 + 10 open hand

1 Develop  20

Tell Students In Today's Lesson They Will
gather and record data on a Venn diagram.

Whole Group

Guided Discussion MathTools UNDERSTANDING

Draw two large separate circles on a blank overhead transparency. Label one circle *Red Shapes* and the other circle *Shapes with 4 Sides*. Display the transparency on the overhead projector, and then, one at a time, display overhead attribute blocks that fall into only one of these two categories. Have students tell you how each attribute block should be classified. Then place the block in the appropriate circle after students agree on where it belongs. Possible examples include:

■ **red triangle** Red Shapes
■ **yellow rectangle** Shapes with 4 Sides
■ **blue square** Shapes with 4 Sides

Then, without warning, introduce a red square and have students discuss how it should be categorized. Students will probably have a difficult time deciding and will agree that it could be placed into either category. Explain that there is another way to organize data that will solve this problem. Draw on another overhead transparency, or create with **eMathTools: *Venn Diagram,*** a Venn diagram such as the following:

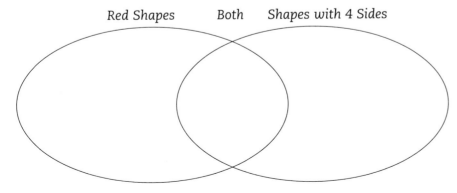

Continue to present overhead attribute blocks and place them in the appropriate part of the Venn diagram as students indicate.

Skill Practice COMPUTING
Whole Group

1. Create a new Venn diagram with labeled sections (such as *Small Shapes, Both,* and *Yellow Shapes*) and have students indicate where attribute blocks should be placed.
2. Create a new Venn diagram with unlabeled sections, and have students attempt to figure out the rules you are using to classify the attribute blocks.

Using Student Pages ENGAGING
Small Group

Demonstrate an activity in which students will collect and organize data about themselves. Have two students come to the front of the room. Label each circle of the Venn diagram with a student's name (for instance, *Tyra* and *Kyle*). Then ask questions about the students' interests or lifestyles, and write the appropriate information in each circle. Possible examples include:

■ **How do you get to school?** Tyra: walk; Kyle: bus
■ **What is your favorite class?** Tyra: gym; Kyle: music
■ **What kind of pet would you like to have?** Both: dog
■ **How old are you?** Both: 8

Once the class understands the activity, have the students break into pairs and complete the diagrams by answering questions about themselves and their partner on page 131.

2 Assign Student Pages 20

Page 132 UNDERSTANDING
Have students complete page 132 independently.

As Students Finish
 Allow students enough time to play a game of their choice, or assign games based on needed skill practice.

 MathTools *Venn Diagram*

Name _____ Date _____

LESSON 4.7 Venn Diagrams

Key Ideas

A Venn diagram is a tool for gathering and comparing data.

❶ Complete the Venn diagram with your interests, your partner's interests, and interests you share.

About Me   About _____

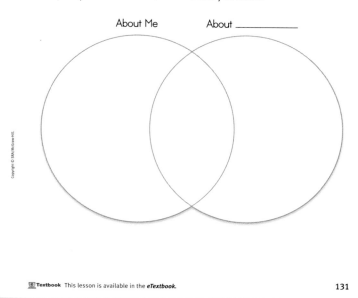

📱 **Textbook** This lesson is available in the *eTextbook*.

131

LESSON 4.7 • Venn Diagrams

❷ Draw lines to show where each figure should go in the Venn diagram.

Triangles   Both   Yellow Figures

❸ Rewrite each word in the correct section 🔤 of the Venn diagram.

Begins with a Vowel   Both   Ends in *T*

ear, ask, idea   eat, art   cat, west, set

| cat | eat | ear | art | west | ask | set | idea |

132   **Real Math** • Chapter 4 • Lesson 7

---

③ Reflect

10

Guided Discussion [REASONING]

Whole Group

Ask student pairs to share their Venn diagrams on page 131, and discuss the results. Ask questions such as the following:

■ **How does the Venn diagram show ways you and your partner are alike?** Similar interests are written in the middle section where the circles overlap.

■ **How does the Venn diagram show ways you and your partner are different?** Interests that are unique to each student are placed within that student's circle.

Curriculum Connection: Students may want to further explore different ways a list of words (such as a spelling list) can be organized.

Cumulative Review: For cumulative review of previously learned skills, see page 147–148.

Family Involvement: Assign the *Practice, Reteach,* or *Enrichment* activities depending on the needs of your students.

Concept/Question Board: Have students look for additional examples using data collection and post them on the Concept/Question Board.

Math Puzzler: Ed bought a box of 24 peaches on Monday. He ate 3 peaches on that day. He ate 3 more every day thereafter. On what day did he finish his peaches? the following Monday

Assess and Differentiate

 Assess Use *eAssess* to record and analyze evidence of student understanding.

A Gather Evidence

Use the Daily Class Assessment Records in **Assessment** or *eAssess* to record daily observations.

Informal Assessment
☑ **Skill Practice**

Did the student `COMPUTING`
- ❑ respond accurately?
- ❑ respond quickly?
- ❑ respond with confidence?
- ❑ self-correct?

Informal Assessment
☑ **Student Pages**

Did the student `UNDERSTANDING`
- ❑ make important observations?
- ❑ extend or generalize learning?
- ❑ provide insightful answers?
- ❑ pose insightful questions?

B Summarize Findings

Analyze and summarize assessment data for each student. Determine which Assessment Follow-Up is appropriate for each student. Use the Student Assessment Record in **Assessment** or *eAssess* to update assessment records.

Assessment page T41

C Assessment Follow-Up ● DIFFERENTIATE INSTRUCTION

Based on your observations, use these teaching strategies for assessment follow-up.

INTERVENTION
Review student performance on *Intervention* Lesson 4.B to see if students have mastered prerequisite skills for this lesson.

ENGLISH LEARNER
Review

Use Lesson 4.7 in *English Learner Support Guide* to review lesson concepts and vocabulary. |

ENRICH

If . . . students are proficient in the lesson concepts,

Then . . . encourage them to work on the chapter projects or *Enrichment* Lesson 4.7.

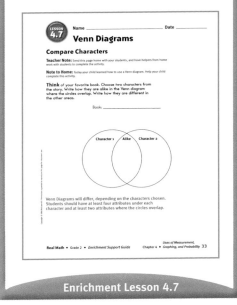

Enrichment Lesson 4.7

PRACTICE

If . . . students would benefit from additional practice,

Then . . . assign *Practice* Lesson 4.7.

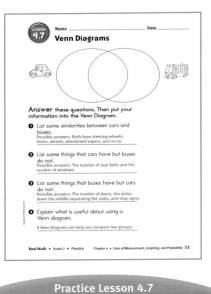

Practice Lesson 4.7

RETEACH

If . . . students are having difficulty understanding Venn diagrams,

Then . . . have them use string to form circles and move the string to overlap as data overlaps.

OBJECTIVES

To extend the students' familiarity with data to include determining the range and mode

NCTM STANDARDS

Data Analysis and Probability
- Posing questions and gathering data about themselves and their surroundings
- Representing data using concrete objects, pictures, and graphs
- Describing parts of the data and the set of data as a whole to determine what the data show

Communication
- Organizing and consolidating mathematical thinking through communications
- Communicating mathematical thinking coherently and clearly to peers and teachers

MATERIALS

- *Number Cubes
- A large package of sweet peas with the pods intact
  Note: You may substitute green beans or similar legumes if sweet peas are not available. You will need about 25 pods for each student in your class.

TECHNOLOGY

- ⓔ **Presentation** Lesson 4.8
- ⓔ **MathTools** Spreadsheet

TEST PREP

Cumulative Review
Mental Math reviews chain calculations (Lesson 3.7).

Extended Response
Problem 5

Looking Ahead

Lesson 4.9 requires a graph to be prepared on poster board in advance. See page 135B for details.

Range and Mode

Context of the Lesson This is the third of eight lessons on data collection, organization, and analysis. In this lesson students are introduced to the importance of sample size and learn that the mode and the range are useful for reporting meaningful data for a large number of objects.

See page 113B for Math Background for teachers for this lesson.

Planning for Learning • DIFFERENTIATE INSTRUCTION

INTERVENTION

If . . . students lack the prerequisite skill of reading a table,

Then . . . teach **Intervention** Lesson 4.B.

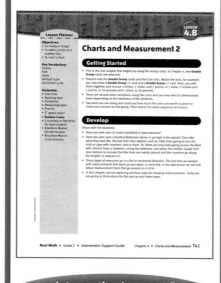

Intervention Lesson 4.B

ENGLISH LEARNER

Preview

If . . . students need language support,

Then . . . use Lesson 4.8 in **English Learner Support Guide** to preview lesson concepts and vocabulary.

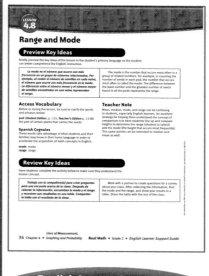

English Learner Lesson 4.8

ENRICH

If . . . students are proficient in the lesson concepts,

Then . . . emphasize exploring **eMathTools.**

PRACTICE

If . . . students would benefit from additional practice,

Then . . . extend Guided Discussion before assigning the student pages.

RETEACH

If . . . students are having difficulty understanding range and mode,

Then . . . extend Strategy Building before assigning the student pages.

Vocabulary
mode \mōd\ *n.* the number that appears most often in a set of data

Access Vocabulary
pod the part of certain plants that carries the seeds

Spanish Cognates
mode moda

range rango

Mental Math

5

Write problems such as the following on the board, and say them aloud. Students show answers with **Number Cubes.** Possible examples include the following:

a. 2 + 2 + 5 = 9

b. 5 + 5 + 5 + 6 = 21

c. 2 − 2 + 5 + 5 = 10

d. 3 + 3 + 3 + 7 = 16

e. 10 − 2 − 3 = 5

f. 5 + 5 + 5 + 5 = 20

1 Develop

30

Tell Students In Today's Lesson They Will

gather data and identify range and mode.

Strategy Building   ENGAGING

Small Group

Distribute the sweet peas (about 25 pods per student), and allow students to examine them. Many students, especially those who live in large cities, may not know that peas grow in pods. Explain that the pods contain seeds and that the peas we eat are really seeds. Ask students to tell how many seeds are in the pods they are examining. Based on the students' responses, acknowledge that the number varies.

Call attention to the table on student page 133. Then, with students working in pairs, have them count the number of seeds in each of their pods and record their results with tally marks in the first column. Note that as students do the pea counting, they will likely encounter peas that are not fully formed and will question whether or not such peas should be counted. As this happens, bring the class together and help the students decide that only fully or nearly fully formed peas should be counted. You might want to have samples of peas that are not to be counted in the front of the room so students can refer to them.

When finished, students should count the tallies and record the appropriate number in the last column. Ask:

■ **How many seeds are in a pod?**

■ **Is there a single number that comes up more often than the others?** Answers are likely to vary because of the small sample sizes.

Have each pair record the number that appears most often in their group as their mode. There may be more than one mode for a set of data. If two or more numbers tie for most often, students should list all such numbers as modes. Explain that the mode is the number that appears most often in a set of data. Next have students tell the least and greatest number of seeds they found in one pod, and help them record these data as their ranges. Note that in this lesson the term *range* refers to the low and high limits of the data set; however, in mathematics the term is also used to refer to the difference between the low and high limits.

Guided Discussion REASONING

Whole Group

Reproduce the table on student page 134 on the board. Working with the class, have each pair of students report the number of times they found a pod with 0 seeds. Collect the information, add the numbers, and record the total on the table. Have students do the same on their student pages. Repeat for 1 seed, 2 seeds, and so on. A good way to record the data from the individual groups is to write, for example, 4, 3, 0, 3, 2, 1 . . . in the middle column and then add the numbers to get the class total.

When all the data are recorded, have students record the mode and range for the class data. Lead a discussion about the results.

■ **When describing the number of seeds in a pod, which data are likely to be more reliable—the individual group data or the class data?** class data, because the sample has more peas

■ **If somebody showed you a closed pod, could you accurately predict the number of seeds in the pod without feeling the pod?** no

■ **If you had another batch of the same kind of peas, could you make a reasonable estimate of the value of the mode for the number of seeds in a pod?** yes, although students may still be uncertain from this limited experience

■ **Could you make a reasonable estimate of the values of the range?** Possibly, but here there is more uncertainty, as a single odd pod could give a very high or a very low value.

From these questions, help students see that although it might not be possible to predict the number of seeds in a single pod, it is possible to make a reasonable estimate of the mode for a large number of pods.

2 Assign Student Pages

10

Page 134 UNDERSTANDING

Have students answer the Extended Response question at the bottom of page 134.

As Students Finish

Allow students enough time to play a game of their choice, or assign games based on needed skill practice.

MathTools *Spreadsheet* Have students explore using this tool to re-create the tables from pages 133 and 134.

LESSON 4.8 **Range and Mode**

Key Ideas

Mode is the number that appears most often in a set of data. For example, in counting the number of seeds in pods, the number that appears most often is the mode.

The least and greatest number of seeds found in a group of pods is the **range**.

How many peas are in a pod?
Examples of how to record data are shown.

Number of Seeds	How many?	
	Tallies	Number
0	|||	3
1	||||	5
2	and so on	
3		
4		
5		
6		
7		
8		
9		
10		

① My mode is _____ .   ② My range is _____ to _____ .

ⓠ Textbook This lesson is available in the *eTextbook*.   **133**

LESSON 4.8 • Range and Mode

How many peas are in a pod? Examples of how to record data are shown.

Number of Seeds	Individual Reports	Class Totals
0	3, 4, 0, 1, 1, 0, 2, 1	12
1	4, 2, 3, 0, 2, 1, 1, 0	13
2	and so on	
3		
4		
5		
6		
7		
8		
9		
10		

③ The class mode is _____ .

④ The class range is _____ to _____ .

⑤ **Extended Response** If you examined another batch of the same kind of peas, what do you think the mode would be? _____ Why? _____ *See Reflect in Teacher's Edition.*

3 Reflect   10

Guided Discussion ☑ **REASONING**   Whole Group

Roll a 0–5 and a 5–10 cube several times, each time saying and recording the sum of the numbers rolled. Then have students predict whether some sums might appear more often than others. Briefly discuss. Ask students,

- **What is the range of sums that is likely to come up?** 5–15
- **What sum is likely to come up most often?** 10; Students will be unsure of this but may be allowed to do the experiment now to find out.

This probability experiment will be investigated further in Lesson 4.13.

Extended Response ▸

Problem 5 Students should predict that the mode of another batch of peas will likely be the same as the class mode from this batch. Students should realize that the more pods they examine, the more times the same number of peas will occur.

 Cumulative Review: For cumulative review of previously learned skills, see page 147–148.

 Family Involvement: Assign the **Practice, Reteach,** or **Enrichment** activities depending on the needs of your students.

 Concept/Question Board: Have students look for additional examples using data collection and post them on the Concept/Question Board.

 Math Puzzler: Fifteen people saw a movie. Three more people liked it than did not like it. How many people did not like it? 6

Assess and Differentiate

 Assess Use *eAssess* to record and analyze evidence of student understanding.

A Gather Evidence

Use the Daily Class Assessment Records in *Assessment* or *eAssess* to record daily observations.

Informal Assessment
☑ **Strategy Building**

Did the student [ENGAGING]

- ❑ make important observations?
- ❑ extend or generalize learning?
- ❑ provide insightful answers?
- ❑ pose insightful questions?

Informal Assessment
☑ **Guided Discussion**

Did the student [REASONING]

- ❑ provide a clear explanation?
- ❑ communicate reasons and strategies?
- ❑ choose appropriate strategies?
- ❑ argue logically?

B Summarize Findings

Analyze and summarize assessment data for each student. Determine which Assessment Follow-Up is appropriate for each student. Use the Student Assessment Record in *Assessment* or *eAssess* to update assessment records.

Assessment page T41

C Assessment Follow-Up ● DIFFERENTIATE INSTRUCTION

Based on your observations, use these teaching strategies for assessment follow-up.

INTERVENTION	ENRICH	PRACTICE	RETEACH
Review student performance on *Intervention* Lesson 4.B to see if students have mastered prerequisite skills for this lesson.	**If . . .** students are proficient in the lesson concepts, **Then . . .** encourage them to work on the chapter projects or *Enrichment* Lesson 4.8.	**If . . .** students would benefit from additional practice, **Then . . .** assign *Practice* Lesson 4.8.	**If . . .** students confuse the range and the mode, **Then . . .** review that the range involves finding the lowest and highest numbers while the mode involves finding the number that appears most often.

ENGLISH LEARNER

Review

Use Lesson 4.8 in *English Learner Support Guide* to review lesson concepts and vocabulary.

Enrichment Lesson 4.8

Practice Lesson 4.8

Lesson Planner

OBJECTIVES
- To show students how to read a pictograph
- To give students the opportunity to solve a problem with many solutions based on proportional reasoning, an understanding of maps, and the use of information obtained from a pictograph

NCTM STANDARDS

Representation
- Creating and using representations to organize, record, and communicate mathematical ideas
- Selecting, applying, and translating among mathematical representations to solve problems

Communication
- Organizing and consolidating mathematical thinking through communication
- Analyzing and evaluating the mathematical thinking and strategies of others

MATERIALS
- *Number Cubes
- A graph with a column for each month of the year, prepared on a large sheet of paper or poster board
- Identical stickers (such as stars or smiley faces), 1 per student

TECHNOLOGY
ⓔ Presentation Lesson 4.9

TEST PREP

Cumulative Review
Mental Math reviews addition and subtraction facts (Chapters 2 and 3).

Extended Response ➡
Problem 8

Pictographs

Context of the Lesson This is the fourth of eight lessons on data collection, organization, and analysis. This lesson introduces pictographs, which are a special kind of graph that uses pictures to represent qualitative and quantitative information. Although information depicted in a pictograph can almost always be shown using a regular bar graph (introduced in the next lesson) or pie chart, the pictograph tends to be easier for many people to interpret.

See page 113B for Math Background for teachers for this lesson.

Planning for Learning ● DIFFERENTIATE INSTRUCTION

INTERVENTION

If . . . students lack the prerequisite skill of reading a table,

Then . . . teach **Intervention** Lesson 4.B.

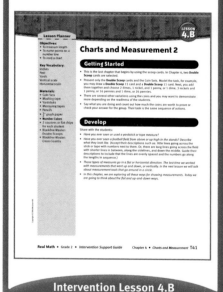

Intervention Lesson 4.B

ENGLISH LEARNER

Preview

If . . . students need language support,

Then . . . use Lesson 4.9 in **English Learner Support Guide** to preview lesson concepts and vocabulary.

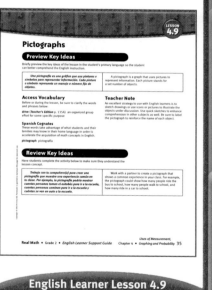

English Learner Lesson 4.9

ENRICH

If . . . students are proficient in the lesson concepts,

Then . . . emphasize chapter projects.

PRACTICE

If . . . students would benefit from additional practice,

Then . . . extend Skill Building before assigning the student pages.

RETEACH

If . . . students are having difficulty understanding pictographs,

Then . . . extend Using Student Pages.

Vocabulary
pictograph \pik´tə graf´\ *n.* a graph that uses pictures to represent data

Access Vocabulary
drive an organized group effort for some specific purpose

Spanish Cognates
pictograph pictografía

Mental Math 5

  Give basic addition and subtraction facts orally, adjusting the speed to a comfortable level. Use facts such as the following:

a. $4 + 5 = 9$ **b.** $10 + 5 = 15$ **c.** $14 - 7 = 7$

d. $16 - 8 = 8$ **e.** $7 + 5 = 12$ **f.** $4 + 6 = 10$

1 Develop 20

Tell Students In Today's Lesson They Will

create and read pictographs.

Skill Building ✓ ENGAGING Whole Group

Prepare in advance, on a large sheet of paper or poster board, a graph with a column for each month of the year. Display the graph at the front of the room. Have students come up, one at a time, and place a sticker in the column of their birthday month.

When finished, explain to the class that they have just created a *pictograph,* a graph that uses pictures to represent data. In this pictograph, each sticker represents one student. Draw conclusions from the graph by asking questions such as the following:

■ **Which month has the fewest birthdays? Which month has the most birthdays? How can you tell?**
■ **How many students have birthdays in November?**
■ **How many more students have birthdays in February than in July?**
■ **Do any two months have the same number of birthdays? How can you tell?**

Using Student Pages UNDERSTANDING Whole Group

Have students look at the pictograph on student page 135. Explain that a school had a food drive to collect canned goods. The class that collected the most canned goods would win a skating party, so the students decided to use a pictograph to keep track of the donations. Ask questions such as the following:

■ **What does each picture on this pictograph stand for?** 10 canned goods
■ **How many canned goods did Ms. Allen's class collect?** 40

Encourage students to explain how they arrived at each answer. Be sure students understand that because each photo stands for 10 canned goods, they should count by tens for each photo. Repeat the discussion and explanation for the pictograph on page 136.

2 Assign Student Pages 20

Pages 135–136 APPLYING

Have students complete pages 135 and 136 independently. Consider allowing students to work in small groups on Problem 8.

As Students Finish

 Give students a choice of games from among those previously introduced, or assign games based on needed skill practice. The **Roll a 15 Game** (introduced in Lesson 2.7) will be useful for many students because of the opportunities it provides for developing strategies based on probabilities.

RESEARCH IN ACTION

"After gathering data to answer questions, children's initial representations often do not use categories. Their interest in data is on the particulars. . . . Thus, children should use physical objects to make graphs, then picture graphs, then line plots, and finally bar graphs that include grid lines to facilitate reading frequencies. By second grade, most children should be able to organize and display data through both simple numerical summaries such as counts, tables, and tallies, and graphical displays, including picture graphs, line plots, and bar graphs. They can compare parts of the data, make statements about the data as a whole, and generally determine whether the graphs answer the questions posed initially."

Clements, Douglas and Sarama, J. eds. *Engaging Young Children in Mathematics: Standards for Early Childhood Mathematics Education.* Mahwah, New Jersey: Lawrence Erlbaum Associates, Publishers, 2004, p. 56.

LESSON
4.9 **Pictographs**

Name _____ Date _____

Key Ideas

A **pictograph** is a graph that uses pictures to represent information.

Look at the pictograph below.

Each picture of a can stands for a group of 10 canned goods.

Ms. Allen's Class					
Ms. Beck's Class					
Mr. Carl's Class					

Use the pictograph to answer these questions.

1. Which class collected the greatest number of canned goods? __Mr. Carl's__ How many? __50__

2. How many canned goods did Ms. Allen's class collect? __40__

3. How many more canned goods were collected by Mr. Carl's class than by Ms. Beck's class? __20__

4. How many canned goods were collected by Ms. Allen's class and Ms. Beck's class altogether? __70__

📖 **Textbook** This lesson is available in the *eTextbook.*

135

Student Page

LESSON 4.9 • Pictographs

Look at the pictograph below. What does each picture represent?

Each ___can___ stands for 10 gallons of gas used on a trip between two towns.

Albright to Trent						
Albright to Wayne						
Trent to Newtown						
Newtown to Wayne						

Use the pictograph to answer these questions.

5. A trip between which two towns uses the least amount of gas? __Albright and Wayne__

6. How many gallons are used on a trip from Trent to Newtown? __50__

7. A trip between which two towns uses the most gas? __Albright and Trent__

8. **Extended Response** Draw a map that shows where Albright, Trent, Wayne, and Newtown might be. Compare your map with others. Explain how you made your map.

__The maps will vary depending on students'__

__interpretations.__

136 **Real Math • Chapter 4 • Lesson 9**

---

3 Reflect

Guided Discussion ✓ **REASONING**   Whole Group

Call attention to the last problem on page 136, and allow students to show the maps they have drawn.

Then draw a map that does not fit the data (such as a map with all cities in a straight line), and have students critique it.

Extended Response

Problem 8 Maps will vary depending on students' interpretations. Based on the information given in the pictograph, it is likely that Albright and Wayne have the shortest distance between them, Albright and Trent have the longest distance between them, and Trent and Wayne are each the same distance from Newtown.

🡢 **Cumulative Review:** For cumulative review of previously learned skills, see page 147–148.

🎒 **Family Involvement:** Assign the *Practice, Reteach,* or *Enrichment* activities depending on the needs of your students.

Concept/Question Board: Encourage students to continue to post questions, answers, and examples on the Concept/Question Board.

Math Puzzler: Write the following problem on the board or overhead projector: Del has 12 model cars. His sister Maria has 9. Del gives Maria 4 of his cars. How many more cars does Maria now have than Del? 5 more

Assess and Differentiate

e Assess Use **eAssess** to record and analyze evidence of student understanding.

A Gather Evidence

Use the Daily Class Assessment Records in **Assessment** or **eAssess** to record daily observations.

Informal Assessment
☑ **Skill Building**

Did the student **ENGAGING**
- ❑ make important observations?
- ❑ extend or generalize learning?
- ❑ provide insightful answers?
- ❑ pose insightful questions?

Informal Assessment
☑ **Guided Discussion**

Did the student **REASONING**
- ❑ provide a clear explanation?
- ❑ communicate reasons and strategies?
- ❑ choose appropriate strategies?
- ❑ argue logically?

B Summarize Findings

Analyze and summarize assessment data for each student. Determine which Assessment Follow-Up is appropriate for each student. Use the Student Assessment Record in **Assessment** or **eAssess** to update assessment records.

Assessment page T41

C Assessment Follow-Up ● DIFFERENTIATE INSTRUCTION

Based on your observations, use these teaching strategies for assessment follow-up.

INTERVENTION

Review student performance on **Intervention** Lesson 4.B to see if students have mastered prerequisite skills for this lesson.

ENGLISH LEARNER

Review

Use Lesson 4.9 in **English Learner Support Guide** to review lesson concepts and vocabulary.

ENRICH

If . . . students are proficient in the lesson concepts,

Then . . . encourage them to work on the chapter projects or **Enrichment** Lesson 4.9.

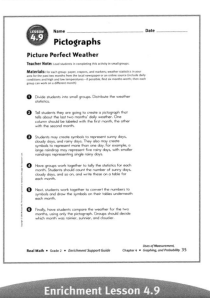

Enrichment Lesson 4.9

PRACTICE

If . . . students would benefit from additional practice,

Then . . . assign **Practice** Lesson 4.9.

Practice Lesson 4.9

RETEACH

If . . . students are having difficulty reading pictographs,

Then . . . have students work in small groups to create their own pictographs. Have students first collect data using tally marks and then show the same data with pictures.

Lesson Planner

OBJECTIVES
- To teach students how to make, read, and interpret a vertical bar graph
- To conduct a probability experiment in which students determine the relative number of colored counters in a can based on how many counters of each color are randomly drawn from the can

NCTM STANDARDS

Data Analysis and Probability
- Posing questions and gathering data about themselves and their surroundings
- Representing data using concrete objects, pictures, and graphs
- Describing parts of the data and the set of data as a whole to determine what the data show

Communication
- Organizing and consolidating mathematical thinking through communications
- Communicating mathematical thinking coherently and clearly to peers and teachers

MATERIALS
- *Number Cubes
- 1 opaque can or other container
- Marbles or colored counters

TECHNOLOGY
- e Presentation Lesson 4.10
- e MathTools Graphing Tool and Probability

TEST PREP
Cumulative Review
Mental Math reviews chain calculations of addition and subtraction (Lesson 3.7).

Looking Ahead
In Lesson 4.11 students will graph the average high temperatures for your city. You should obtain this temperature data in advance or provide resources for students to find this information.

Vertical Bar Graphs

Context of the Lesson This is the fifth of eight lessons on data collection, organization, and analysis. This lesson introduces vertical bar graphs. Horizontal bar graphs will be covered in the next lesson. This lesson also incorporates a probability experiment.

See page 113B for Math Background for teachers for this lesson.

Planning for Learning ● DIFFERENTIATE INSTRUCTION

INTERVENTION

If . . . students lack the prerequisite skill of naming points on a number line,

Then . . . teach *Intervention* Lesson 4.C.

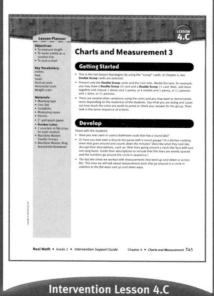

Intervention Lesson 4.C

ENGLISH LEARNER

Preview

If . . . students need language support,

Then . . . use Lesson 4.10 in *English Learner Support Guide* to preview lesson concepts and vocabulary.

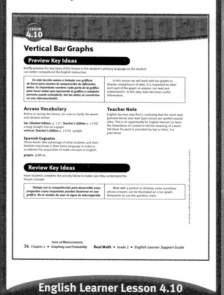

English Learner Lesson 4.10

ENRICH

If . . . students are proficient in the lesson concepts,

Then . . . emphasize exploring *eMathTools*.

PRACTICE

If . . . students would benefit from additional practice,

Then . . . extend Skill Building before assigning the student pages.

RETEACH

If . . . students are having difficulty reading a bar graph,

Then . . . extend Using Student Pages.

Access Vocabulary
bar a long straight line on a graph
vertical upright

Spanish Cognates
graphs gráficas

Mental Math 5

Give basic addition and subtraction chain calculations, such as the following:

a. $9 + 4 - 3 = 10$ **b.** $12 + 5 - 2 = 15$ **c.** $14 - 7 - 2 = 5$
d. $10 - 5 + 6 = 11$ **e.** $2 + 3 + 4 = 9$ **f.** $4 + 5 + 6 = 15$

1 Develop 20

Tell Students In Today's Lesson They Will
gather data and record the information on a vertical graph.

Skill Building   MathTools ENGAGING   Whole Group

Draw the outline of a four-column bar graph on the board or create one with **eMathTools: Graphing Tool.** Label each column a color: red, blue, yellow, green. Have spaces for about 15 rows of data.

Without the students watching, place 6 red, 3 green, 1 yellow, and 0 blue marbles or similar objects into a can.

Now draw a marble from the can, and show it to students.

Have a student come to the board and place an x in the appropriate column.

Replace the marble, shake the can, and repeat.

The graph might look like this after a few drawings.

15				
14				
13				
12				
11				
10				
9				
8				
7				
6				
5				
4				
3	x			
2	x			
1	x		x	x
	Red	Blue	Yellow	Green

Keep repeating this activity.

As the bar graph begins to take shape, discuss the results.
- **Which color do you think will get to the top of the graph first?** Accept various predictions.

Continue drawing marbles, recording the colors and replacing the marbles. When one of the colors reaches the top of the graph, tell students that there were 10 marbles in the can.
- **How many marbles do you think were red, blue, yellow, and green? Why do you think that?** Help students see that there were likely more red marbles than other colors and few, if any, blue marbles. Then reveal the actual numbers.

Using Student Pages REASONING   Whole Group

Refer to the graph on student page 137. Discuss what this bar graph represents and how to read it. Explain that the names of five people are listed along the bottom and that the bars above those names show how many books each person has read.

Ask students:
- **What do you think the numbers on the side of the graph stand for?** number of books
- **How many books has Daniel read, and how many books has Ladonna read?** 3; 10 Encourage students to explain how they arrived at their answers.

2 Assign Student Pages 20

Pages 137–138   UNDERSTANDING   Small Group

Have students complete pages 137 and 138 working in small groups. Make sure students understand the graphs on page 138. Even though there are no numbers shown on those graphs, students can determine the answers by knowing there are 18 marbles and by comparing the proportions of the bars.

As Students Finish

 Allow students to play a game of their choice, or assign games based on needed skill practice.

 MathTools **Probability** Have students use this tool to simulate color probability experiments similar to the one done in this lesson.

Name _____ Date _____

LESSON
4.10 **Vertical Bar Graphs**

Key Ideas

Bar graphs use shaded areas or bars to represent information. Look at the bar graph below.

What does each bar stand for? the number of books read

Jenni, Ryan, Ladonna, Daniel, and Adam made a bar graph showing how many books they read in one month.

Use the bar graph to answer these questions.

❶ Who has read the most books? __Ladonna__
How many? __10__

❷ Who has read the fewest books? __Daniel__
How many? __3__

❸ How many books has Jenni read? __6__

❹ How many books has Adam read? __6__

❺ How many more books did Ladonna read than Adam? __4__

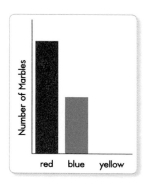

Jenni Ryan Ladonna Daniel Adam

📱 **Textbook** This lesson is available in the *eTextbook*. 137

LESSON 4.10 · Vertical Bar Graphs

These graphs show the results of probability experiments like the one you did in class. For each experiment 18 marbles were in the can.

❻ About how many marbles of each color were in the can?

__12__ red

__6__ blue

__0__ yellow

Possible answers are shown.
Accept all reasonable answers.

Number of Marbles

red blue yellow

❼ About how many marbles of each color were in the can?

__6__ red

__6__ blue

__6__ yellow

Possible answers are shown.
Accept all reasonable answers.

Number of Marbles

red blue yellow

---

3 Reflect 10

Guided Discussion REASONING

Whole Group

Ask and discuss questions referring to the graph of the color probability activity done in this lesson.

■ **Which color would get to the top first if there were 4 marbles of each color in the can?** You cannot tell because each is equally likely.

■ **Which color would get to the top first if there were 8 marbles of each color in the can?** You still cannot tell.

■ **Suppose the can had 5 red marbles, 4 blue marbles, and 0 yellow and green marbles. Which color would get to the top first?** possibly red **Can you be sure?** no **Why?** Although red is most probable, luck is also important.

■ **Suppose you doubled the number of marbles of each color in the original can (so that you had 12 red, 6 green, 2 yellow, and 0 blue). Would you expect the shape of the graph to change?** Not really; the chances of picking a marble of each color are still the same.

Cumulative Review: For cumulative review of previously learned skills, see page 147–148.

Family Involvement: Assign the *Practice, Reteach,* or *Enrichment* activities depending on the needs of your students.

Concept/Question Board: Encourage students to continue to post questions, answers, and examples on the Concept/Question Board.

Math Puzzler: Write the following patterns on the board or overhead projector and have students fill in the blanks:
a. 51, 50, 49, 41, 40, 39, 31, 30, 29, __21__, __20__, __19__
b. 12, 13, 24, 25, 36, 37, __48__, __49__

4 Assess and Differentiate

 Assess Use *eAssess* to record and analyze evidence of student understanding.

A Gather Evidence

Use the Daily Class Assessment Records in *Assessment* or *eAssess* to record daily observations.

Informal Assessment
☑ **Mental Math**

Did the student COMPUTING
❏ respond accurately?
❏ respond quickly?
❏ respond with confidence?
❏ self-correct?

Informal Assessment
☑ **Student Pages**

Did the student UNDERSTANDING
❏ make important observations?
❏ extend or generalize learning?
❏ provide insightful answers?
❏ pose insightful questions?

B Summarize Findings

Analyze and summarize assessment data for each student. Determine which Assessment Follow-Up is appropriate for each student. Use the Student Assessment Record in *Assessment* or *eAssess* to update assessment records.

Assessment page T41

C Assessment Follow-Up ● DIFFERENTIATE INSTRUCTION

Based on your observations, use these teaching strategies for assessment follow-up.

INTERVENTION	ENRICH	PRACTICE	RETEACH
Review student performance on *Intervention* Lesson 4.C to see if students have mastered prerequisite skills for this lesson.	**If . . .** students are proficient in the lesson concepts,	**If . . .** students would benefit from additional practice,	**If . . .** students are having difficulty reading a vertical bar graph,
	Then . . . encourage them to work on the chapter projects or *Enrichment* Lesson 4.10.	**Then . . .** assign *Practice* Lesson 4.10.	**Then . . .** have students think aloud about what each bar represents and use a straightedge to align the bar with the numbers on the axis.

ENGLISH LEARNER

Review

Use Lesson 4.10 in *English Learner Support Guide* to review lesson concepts and vocabulary.

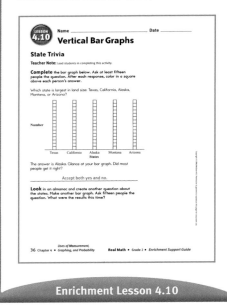

Enrichment Lesson 4.10

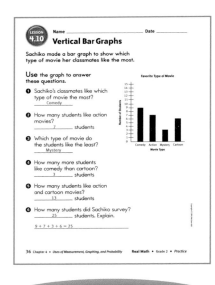

Practice Lesson 4.10

OBJECTIVES
To make and interpret horizontal bar graphs

NCTM STANDARDS
Data Analysis and Probability
- Representing data using concrete objects, pictures, and graphs
- Describing parts of the data and the set of data as a whole to determine what the data show

Communication
- Organizing and consolidating mathematical thinking through communications
- Communicating mathematical thinking coherently and clearly to peers and teachers

MATERIALS
- *Number Cubes
- Average high temperature data for your city, or resources (such as an almanac or Internet site) for students to research this information

TECHNOLOGY
- e Presentation Lesson 4.11
- e MathTools Spreadsheet and Graphing Tool

TEST PREP
Cumulative Review
Mental Math reviews basic addition and subtraction facts (Lessons 2.1–3.6).

Extended Response
Problem 4

Horizontal Bar Graphs

Context of the Lesson This is the sixth of eight lessons on data collection, organization, and analysis. In this lesson students analyze a horizontal bar graph showing temperature data for a United States city. See page 113B for Math Background for teachers for this lesson.

Planning for Learning ● DIFFERENTIATE INSTRUCTION

INTERVENTION

If . . . students lack the prerequisite skill of naming points on a number line,

Then . . . teach Intervention Lesson 4.C.

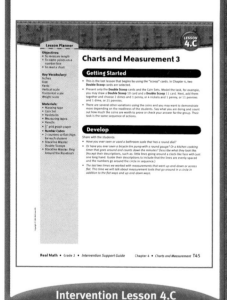

Intervention Lesson 4.C

ENGLISH LEARNER

Preview

If . . . students need language support,

Then . . . use Lesson 4.11 in *English Learner Support Guide* to preview lesson concepts and vocabulary.

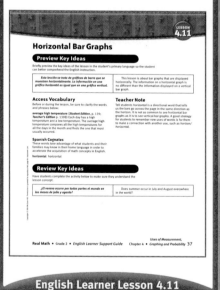

English Learner Lesson 4.11

ENRICH

If . . . students are proficient in the lesson concepts,

Then . . . emphasize exploring *eMathTools.*

PRACTICE

If . . . students would benefit from additional practice,

Then . . . extend Guided Discussion before assigning the student pages.

RETEACH

If . . . students are having difficulty reading a bar graph,

Then . . . extend Guided Discussion before assigning the student pages.

Access Vocabulary
average high temperature Each day has a high temperature and a low temperature. The average high temperature compares all the high temperatures for all the days in the month and finds the one that most usually occurred.

Spanish Cognates
horizontal horizontal

*Manipulative Kit Item

Mental Math 5

 Provide addition and subtraction fact practice with exercises such as the following:

a. 4 + 5 = 9   **b.** 4 + 7 = 11   **c.** 5 + 5 = 10   **d.** 12 − 5 = 7
e. 12 − 6 = 6   **f.** 6 + 5 = 11   **g.** 8 − 2 = 6   **h.** 11 − 5 = 6

1 Develop 20

Tell Students In Today's Lesson They Will
read and interpret a bar graph.

Guided Discussion UNDERSTANDING   Whole Group

Discuss the bar graph on student page 139 and the information from the graph. Begin by explaining that the graph shows the average high temperatures for each month of the year in a U.S. city. Note that although the word *average* is used in this lesson, second-grade students are not ready to fully understand its mathematical meaning (dividing the sum of two or more quantities by the total number of quantities). Rather, explain the meaning of the term in its colloquial sense—the ordinary or usual temperature.

- **How is the bar graph on page 139 different from the bar graph you worked with yesterday?** Bar graphs can be vertical, as in the previous lesson, or horizontal as on this page.
- **What is the average high temperature for April?** The average high temperature for April is about 75°F.
- **What is the average high temperature for February?** The average high temperature for February is between 60°F and 65°F but closer to 60°F.
- **Does the bar graph show the exact temperatures for each day of the month?** No; the bar graph shows the yearly temperature pattern but does not tell the exact temperatures for every day.
- **Do you think it is necessary to know the exact temperatures for each day of each month to understand the temperature pattern for the year? Explain your answer.** Knowing the exact high temperature for each day of each month is not necessary for understanding the temperature pattern for this city. For instance, the graph does not show the exact temperatures for each day of July, but it does show that the high temperature will be around 90°F. It also shows that the high temperature on a day in July will likely be much higher than the high temperature on a day in January, which will be around 59°F.

2 Assign Student Pages 20

Pages 139–140 APPLYING

Write the temperature data you collected for your city on the board, or create handouts you can give the students. Alternatively, you can have the class do the research to find the data. In either case, explain that they are to use the data to complete the table and the horizontal bar graph on page 140.

Before beginning, you will have to decide how to label the horizontal (*x*) axis. That will depend on how wide a range of temperatures you have in your part of the country. For most situations, having 11 increments ranging from 0 to 100 degrees will be appropriate.

Do the first two or three months with the class so they learn how to estimate the length of a bar that falls between two labeled increments. Then allow students to work independently to complete page 139 and the rest of page 140.

As Students Finish

 Allow students to play a game of their choice, or assign games based on needed skill practice.

 **Spreadsheet** and **Graphing Tool** Have students use these tools to re-create the table and bar graph from page 140.

Student Page

Name _____ Date _____

Key Ideas

This bar graph shows the average high temperature for each month in a United States city.

Use the bar graph to answer these questions.

1. What is the average high temperature for April? __75__ °F

2. Which month is usually the coldest in this city? ___January___

3. Which month is usually the warmest? _July or August_

4. **Extended Response** Do you think the temperature ever gets to 100°F in this city? Explain.
   See Reflect in *Teacher's Edition*.

_____

eTextbook This lesson is available in the *eTextbook*.

139

Student Page

LESSON 4.11 · Horizontal Bar Graphs

5. Gather your own data by doing research. Find the average high temperatures for your city or for a city near you for a year. Use this table to record your data.

Month	Average High Temperature °F
January	
February	
March	
April	
May	
June	
July	
August	
September	
October	
November	
December	

Average High Temperatures for the city of _____

6. Transfer the data you collected to the bar graph.

Average High Temperature °F

140 **Real Math • Chapter 4 • Lesson 11**

---

3 Reflect 10

Guided Discussion REASONING

Read and discuss students' responses to student page 140.

- **How was the high temperature pattern for your city different from the city on page 139?** Answers will depend on the location of the city.
- **How were they the same?** Again, the comparison of two cities' temperatures will depend on their locations.
- **In which city would you prefer to live?** Students' responses will be based on personal preference.

Extended Response

Problem 4 Discuss students' answers. Students should realize that the temperature probably does reach 100°F in this city, because the highest average high temperature is 90°F and it will sometimes be hotter or colder than the average.

 Curriculum Connection: Students may be interested in learning about other weather data for your community.

 Cumulative Review: For cumulative review of previously learned skills, see page 147–148.

 Family Involvement: Assign the *Practice, Reteach,* or *Enrichment* activities depending on the needs of your students.

 Concept/Question Board: Have students attempt to answer any unanswered questions on the Concept/Question Board.

 Math Puzzler: How many different ways could you make 50 cents by using 5 or fewer coins? What are the ways? 5 ways: 1 50 cent piece; 2 quarters; 1 quarter, 2 dimes, and 1 nickel; 1 quarter, 1 dime, 3 nickels; 5 dimes.

4 Assess and Differentiate

 Assess Use *eAssess* to record and analyze evidence of student understanding.

A Gather Evidence

Use the Daily Class Assessment Records in *Assessment* or *eAssess* to record daily observations.

Informal Assessment
☑ **Student Pages**

Did the student **APPLYING**
- ❑ apply learning in new situations?
- ❑ contribute concepts?
- ❑ contribute answers?
- ❑ connect mathematics to real-world situations?

Informal Assessment
☑ **Extended Response**

Did the student **UNDERSTANDING**
- ❑ make important observations?
- ❑ extend or generalize learning?
- ❑ provide insightful answers?
- ❑ pose insightful questions?

B Summarize Findings

Analyze and summarize assessment data for each student. Determine which Assessment Follow-Up is appropriate for each student. Use the Student Assessment Record in *Assessment* or *eAssess* to update assessment records.

Assessment page T41

C Assessment Follow-Up • DIFFERENTIATE INSTRUCTION

Based on your observations, use these teaching strategies for assessment follow-up.

INTERVENTION

Review student performance on *Intervention* Lesson 4.C to see if students have mastered prerequisite skills for this lesson.

ENGLISH LEARNER

Review

Use Lesson 4.11 in *English Learner Support Guide* to review lesson concepts and vocabulary.

ENRICH

If . . . students are proficient in the lesson concepts,

Then . . . encourage them to work on the chapter projects or *Enrichment* Lesson 4.11.

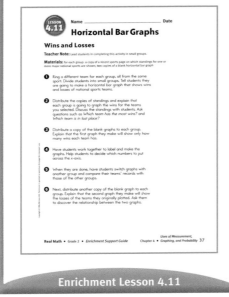

Enrichment Lesson 4.11

PRACTICE

If . . . students would benefit from additional practice,

Then . . . assign *Practice* Lesson 4.11.

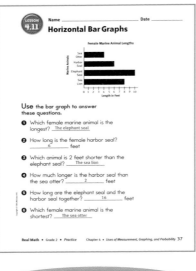

Practice Lesson 4.11

RETEACH

If . . . students are having difficulty reading horizontal bar graphs,

Then . . . reteach the concept using *Reteach* Lesson 4.11.

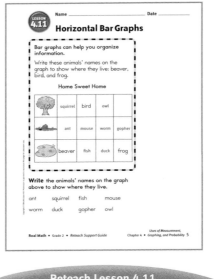

Reteach Lesson 4.11

OBJECTIVES
- To read and interpret line graphs
- To compare the use of bar graphs and line graphs for presenting data
- To informally introduce the concept of using known values to estimate unknown values

NCTM STANDARDS
Data Analysis and Probability
- Representing data using concrete objects, pictures, and graphs
- Describing parts of the data and the set of data as a whole to determine what the data show

Communication
- Organizing and consolidating mathematical thinking through communications
- Communicating mathematical thinking coherently and clearly to peers and teachers

MATERIALS
- *Number Cubes
- blank overhead transparency

TECHNOLOGY
- **Presentation** Lesson 4.12
- **MathTools** Graphing Tool

TEST PREP
Cumulative Review
Mental Math reviews addition chain calculations (Lesson 3.7).

Extended Response
Problems 5 and 9

Graphs on a Grid

Context of the Lesson This is the seventh of eight lessons on data collection, organization, and analysis. In this lesson students learn to read and interpret line graphs and to compare their use to bar graphs.
See page 113B for Math Background for teachers for this lesson.

Planning for Learning ● DIFFERENTIATE INSTRUCTION

INTERVENTION
If . . . students lack the prerequisite skill of naming points on a number line,

Then . . . teach *Intervention* Lesson 4.C.

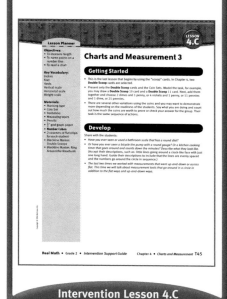

Intervention Lesson 4.C

ENGLISH LEARNER
Preview
If . . . students need language support,

Then . . . use Lesson 4.12 in *English Learner Support Guide* to preview lesson concepts and vocabulary.

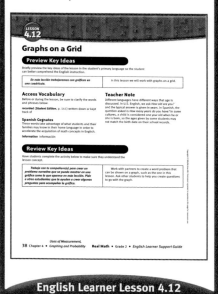

English Learner Lesson 4.12

ENRICH
If . . . students are proficient in the lesson concepts,

Then . . . emphasize exploring *eMathTools*.

PRACTICE
If . . . students would benefit from additional practice,

Then . . . extend Guided Discussion before assigning the student pages.

RETEACH
If . . . students are having difficulty understanding line graphs,

Then . . . extend Guided Discussion before assigning the student pages.

Access Vocabulary
recorded written down or kept track of

Spanish Cognates
information información

---

*Manipulative Kit Item

Mental Math 5

  Present addition chain calculations such as the following:

a. 3 + 3 + 4 = 10   **b.** 2 + 3 + 4 = 9   **c.** 10 + 10 + 5 = 25
d. 4 + 3 + 4 = 11   **e.** 6 + 6 + 2 = 14   **f.** 3 + 4 + 3 + 4 = 14

1 Develop 20

Tell Students In Today's Lesson They Will
read and interpret a line graph.

Guided Discussion UNDERSTANDING   Whole Group

Using an overhead projector transparency of the graph on student page 141 as a guide, help students interpret the line graph showing a boy's growth in centimeters.

Ask students questions such as the following:

■ **What do you think the graph is about?** Look at the labels on either side of the graph to find out that they show Raol's height by age.

Next draw a bar graph on the board or transparency of the same data for comparison.

■ **How are these two graphs similar?** Both of them show Raol's height by age.
■ **How are they different?** One possible answer is that the values on the bar graph are not shown by dots. Other correct answers are possible.

Explain to students that both graphs—the one in the book and the one on the board—present the same information about Raol's growth.

■ **Is one graph better than the other for showing Raol's growth?** Through discussion, help students see that the points on the line graph can be connected by lines that suggest how tall Raol was between birthdays.

2 Assign Student Pages 20

Pages 141–142 APPLYING

Provide a brief explanation about page 142, and then allow students to complete pages 141 and 142 independently.

> **Monitoring Student Progress**
>
> **If . . .** students have difficulty with the analytical questions,
>
> **Then . . .** extra teaching is not essential at this time because upcoming lessons will provide many more opportunities for these types of analysis.

As Students Finish

 Allow students to play a game of their choice, or assign games based on needed skill practice.

 Graphing Tool Have students explore using the same data to create different types of graphs, such as a line graph and bar graph.

Name _____ Date _____

Key Ideas

Information can be recorded on a grid.

This is a graph on a grid. What information do you see on this graph?

Use the graph to answer these questions.

1. Connect the points on the graph.

2. About how tall was Raol when he was 3 years old? __80__ cm

3. About how old was Raol when he was 100 cm tall? __6__

4. About how old was Raol when he was 70 centimeters tall? <u>older than 1 but less than 2—possibly</u>

5. **Extended Response** About how tall 1½ years old will Raol be when he is 8 years old? Explain how you know. <u>possibly about 120 to 130 centimeters; accept all reasonable answers.</u>

Textbook This lesson is available in the *eTextbook*.

LESSON 4.12 • Graphs on a Grid

Max did an experiment to see how long it took for 100 radish seeds to sprout. He planted the seeds and then counted the number that sprouted as of the end of each day. He recorded his results on the following table.

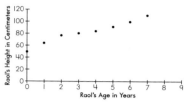

Days	Number Sprouted as of the End of That Day
1	0
2	0
3	5
4	19
5	45
6	70
7	84
8	85
9	85
10	85

Use the table to answer these questions.

6. How many seeds had sprouted by the end of the fifth day? __45__

7. On which day did the most seeds sprout? __5th__

8. How many seeds sprouted on that day? <u>26 seeds sprouted on day 5.</u>

9. **Extended Response** Do you think all 100 seeds will sprout? Write why or why not. <u>See Reflect in *Teacher's Edition*.</u>

---

3 Reflect   10

Guided Discussion REASONING   Whole Group

Call attention to Question 4 on page 141. Allow students to explain how they found their answers. Point out that Raol was more than 1 year old but less than 2 years old and that we can only estimate how much older he was than 1.

Draw students' attention to the bar graph on the board.

■ **Can you tell how tall Raol was at age 5½?** Point out that the bar graph of the same data does not lend itself as well to finding values between the known points.

Extended Response

Problem 5 Explain that we cannot know for sure how tall Raol will be when he is 8 years old, but the general shape of the graph suggests he will continue to grow at about the same rate. Thus, he should be about 120 to 130 centimeters tall.

Problem 9 Students' answers will vary, but students might realize that the remaining seeds will probably not sprout because the number of seeds sprouting has remained stagnant for the last four days.

Cumulative Review: For cumulative review of previously learned skills, see page 147–148.

Family Involvement: Assign the *Practice, Reteach,* or *Enrichment* activities depending on the needs of your students.

Concept/Question Board: Have students attempt to answer any unanswered questions on the Concept/Question Board.

Math Puzzler: The white table is 48 inches tall. The blue table is 48 centimeters tall. How can you tell which table is higher without measuring? The white table is taller. One inch is longer than 1 cm, so 48 inches is longer, or taller, than 48 cm.

4 Assess and Differentiate

 Assess Use *eAssess* to record and analyze evidence of student understanding.

A Gather Evidence

Use the Daily Class Assessment Records in **Assessment** or **eAssess** to record daily observations.

Informal Assessment
☑ **Guided Discussion**

Did the student UNDERSTANDING
❑ make important observations?
❑ extend or generalize learning?
❑ provide insightful answers?
❑ pose insightful questions?

Informal Assessment
☑ **Concept/Question Board**

Did the student APPLYING
❑ apply learning in new situations?
❑ contribute concepts?
❑ contribute answers?
❑ connect mathematics to real-world situations?

B Summarize Findings

Analyze and summarize assessment data for each student. Determine which Assessment Follow-Up is appropriate for each student. Use the Student Assessment Record in **Assessment** or **eAssess** to update assessment records.

Assessment page T41

C Assessment Follow-Up ● DIFFERENTIATE INSTRUCTION

Based on your observations, use these teaching strategies for assessment follow-up.

INTERVENTION

Review student performance on **Intervention** Lesson 4.C to see if students have mastered prerequisite skills for this lesson.

ENGLISH LEARNER

Review

Use Lesson 4.12 in **English Learner Support Guide** to review lesson concepts and vocabulary.

ENRICH

If . . . students are proficient in the lesson concepts,

Then . . . encourage them to work on the chapter projects or **Enrichment** Lesson 4.12.

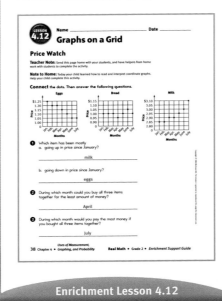

Enrichment Lesson 4.12

PRACTICE

If . . . students would benefit from additional practice,

Then . . . assign **Practice** Lesson 4.12.

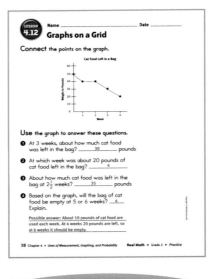

Practice Lesson 4.12

RETEACH

If . . . students are having difficulty connecting points on a grid,

Then . . . have them use a straightedge.

Lesson Planner

OBJECTIVES
- To collect, record, and analyze data
- To predict results

NCTM STANDARDS

Data Analysis and Probability
- Representing data using concrete objects, pictures, and graphs
- Describing parts of the data and the set of data as a whole to determine what the data show

Communication
- Organizing and consolidating mathematical thinking through communications
- Communicating mathematical thinking coherently and clearly to peers and teachers

MATERIALS
*Number Cubes

TECHNOLOGY
e **Presentation** Lesson 4.13
e **MathTools** Spreadsheet

TEST PREP

Cumulative Review
Mental Math reviews chain calculations (Lesson 3.7).

Extended Response
Problem 3

Writing + Math
Journal

Using Probability

Context of the Lesson This is the last of eight lessons on data collection, organization, and analysis. This lesson involves tracking the data of two probability experiments.

See page 113B for Math Background for teachers for this lesson.

Planning for Learning ● DIFFERENTIATE INSTRUCTION

INTERVENTION

If . . . students lack the prerequisite skill of naming points on a number line,

Then . . . teach *Intervention* Lesson 4.C.

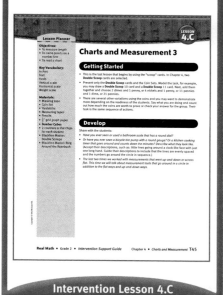

Intervention Lesson 4.C

ENGLISH LEARNER

Preview

If . . . students need language support,

Then . . . use Lesson 4.13 in *English Learner Support Guide* to preview lesson concepts and vocabulary.

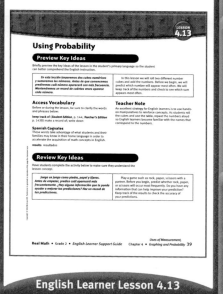

English Learner Lesson 4.13

ENRICH

If . . . students are proficient in the lesson concepts,

Then . . . emphasize chapter projects.

PRACTICE

If . . . students would benefit from additional practice,

Then . . . extend Using Student Pages.

RETEACH

If . . . students are having difficulty understanding probability,

Then . . . extend Using Student Pages.

Access Vocabulary
keep track of make a record of; write down

Spanish Cognates
results resultados

Mental Math 5

 Present students with chain calculations such as the following:

a. 3 + 4 + 4 = 11   **b.** 2 + 3 + 4 − 1 = 8   **c.** 10 + 10 − 5 = 15

d. 4 − 3 + 4 = 5   **e.** 6 + 6 − 2 = 10   **f.** 3 + 4 − 3 = 4

1 Develop 20

Tell Students In Today's Lesson They Will
predict the outcome of an experiment.

Small Group

Using Student Pages MathTools ENGAGING

Use student page 143 as a guide. Divide students into groups of three. Explain that each group will roll a 0–5 cube one hundred times and record the number of times each number comes up. Ask students:

■ **Out of the numbers 0–5, which number do you think will come up most often?** Allow students to make predictions but don't insist they do so. Many students may realize that all numbers are equally likely to be rolled.

Assign students roles. Within each group, one student rolls the cube and calls out the number, one student records a tally mark on the table on page 143, and the third student uses tally marks to keep track of the number of rolls. Students may change roles after about ten rolls.

Model the activity with a demonstration group. Repeat directions several times, making sure that all students are aware of the process. Then direct the rest of the class to begin the activity.

While students begin rolling, prepare a table similar to the following on the board or use *eMathTools: Spreadsheet:*

Number	Group 1	Group 2	Group 3	Group 4	Group 5	Group 6	Totals
0							
1							
2							
3							
4							
5							

After all rolls have been made and recorded on the student pages, enter the data on the table on the board. Discuss the results.

■ **Which number(s) came up most often? Was your prediction true or untrue?** Help students see that although different numbers came up more often for different groups, in general the results show there is about equal likelihood for any number to be rolled.

Using page 144 as a guide, repeat this variation of the Cube Rolling Activity.

Directions: You will roll one 0–5 cube and one 5–10 cube and record the sum of the numbers rolled. Students may still work in groups of three with the student who rolls calling out the sum after each roll. Demonstrate this two or three times.

Before beginning, have students predict and record the sum they think will come up most often.

As in the earlier activity, as students work, prepare a table to record each group's data on the board or use *eMathTools: Spreadsheet Tool.*

After all rolls have been made, enter each group's data on the table on the board. Discuss the results.

■ **What sums appeared most often? What sums appeared least often? Was your prediction true or untrue?** Help students see that not all sums are equally likely. Sums toward the middle of the table tend to come up more often, and those toward the top and the bottom come up least often.

2 Assign Student Pages 20

Page 144 APPLYING

Have students complete Problem 3 and the Journal on page 144 independently.

As Students Finish

 Allow students to play a game of their choice, or assign games based on needed skill practice.

Name _____ Date _____

LESSON 4.13 **Using Probability**

Key Ideas
Some chance events are more likely than others.

Of the numbers 0–5, which number do you think will appear most often as you roll the cube?

My prediction _____   Students should choose one number from 0 to 5.

Do the Cube-Rolling Activity.

1. Roll a 0–5 cube many times.
2. Keep track of the numbers you roll.

	Tallies	Totals	Class Totals
0			
1			
2			
3			
4			
5			

Textbook This lesson is available in the *eTextbook*.

143

LESSON 4.13 · Using Probability

Roll one 0–5 *Number Cube* and one 5–10 *Number Cube*. Find the sum.

What sum do you predict will appear most often?

My Prediction _____

Do the Cube-Rolling Activity.
Keep track of the numbers you roll.

Sum	Tallies	Totals	Class Totals
5			
6			
7			
8			
9			
10			
11			
12			
13			
14			
15			

3. **Extended Response** Which sums appeared most often? Which sums appeared least often? Explain why you think they appeared that way. _____

_____

Writing + Math Journal

How many different ways could you roll a sum of 5? How many different ways could you roll a sum of 10?

---

3 **Reflect**   10

Guided Discussion   **REASONING**   Whole Group

Bring students together, and summarize the results of the activities. Refer to the totals column of the table on the board that shows the sums rolled.

■ **If we wanted to make a graph of these data, would a line graph or a bar graph be more useful?** Through discussion, help students see that a bar graph is more useful because there are no "in between" values between columns.

Extended Response

Problem 3 Discuss students' answers. Answers will depend on which sum appeared most often.

 **Journal**

Students should realize that there is only one way to roll a sum of 5: 0 and 5. However, there are many ways to roll a sum of 10.

 Cumulative Review: For cumulative review of previously learned skills, see page 147–148.

 Family Involvement: Assign the *Practice, Reteach,* or *Enrichment* activities depending on the needs of your students.

 Concept/Question Board: Have students attempt to answer any unanswered questions on the Concept/Question Board.

 Math Puzzler: If you started at 23 and skip-counted aloud by threes, what would be the sixth number you would say? 38

4 **Assess and Differentiate**

 Assess Use *eAssess* to record and analyze evidence of student understanding.

A Gather Evidence

Use the Daily Class Assessment Records in *Assessment* or *eAssess* to record daily observations.

Informal Assessment
☑ **Student Pages**

Did the student **APPLYING**
- ☐ apply learning in new situations?
- ☐ contribute concepts?
- ☐ contribute answers?
- ☐ connect mathematics to real-world situations?

Portfolio Assessment
☑ **Journal**

Did the student **UNDERSTANDING**
- ☐ make important observations?
- ☐ extend or generalize learning?
- ☐ provide insightful answers?
- ☐ pose insightful questions?

B Summarize Findings

Analyze and summarize assessment data for each student. Determine which Assessment Follow-Up is appropriate for each student. Use the Student Assessment Record in *Assessment* or *eAssess* to update assessment records.

Assessment page T41

C Assessment Follow-Up • DIFFERENTIATE INSTRUCTION

Based on your observations, use these teaching strategies for assessment follow-up.

INTERVENTION

Review student performance on *Intervention* Lesson 4.C to see if students have mastered prerequisite skills for this lesson.

ENGLISH LEARNER

Review

Use Lesson 4.13 in *English Learner Support Guide* to review lesson concepts and vocabulary.

ENRICH

If . . . students are proficient in the lesson concepts,

Then . . . encourage them to work on the chapter projects or *Enrichment* Lesson 4.13.

Enrichment Lesson 4.13

PRACTICE

If . . . students would benefit from additional practice,

Then . . . assign *Practice* Lesson 4.13.

Practice Lesson 4.13

RETEACH

If . . . students are having difficulty understanding probability,

Then . . . have them work in pairs to discuss and answer the questions on page 144.

Exploring Problem Solving

Objectives
- To explore Making a Graph as a problem-solving strategy
- To provide practice solving nonroutine problems that involve interpreting data to make decisions

Materials
None

Context of the Lesson While continuing the toy factory theme introduced on page 113I, this lesson provides an opportunity for students to continue to apply what they have been learning about organizing data.

1 Develop 5

Tell Students In Today's Lesson They Will
- organize information about glow-in-the-dark bracelets and necklaces ordered from a toy factory.
- decide which sizes of glow-in-the-dark bracelets and necklaces the factory should make.

Access Prior Knowledge

To help students think about using data to make decisions, ask students to recall times when the class has voted for something. Discuss how voting is a way of expressing a preference and how the results of a vote can be used to help make decisions.

Guided Discussion

Have students look at the order blanks on page 145 as you describe the following situation to them:

The Glow-Shine Toy Factory makes plastic glow-in-the-dark bracelets and necklaces to sell to stores. Up until now, the factory always let stores order any sizes they like, such as 2 inches long, 10 inches long, or 15 inches long. Whatever size was ordered, the factory would make it. The owner of the factory has decided that her workers could make better jewelry if they made only three sizes of bracelets instead of many different sizes. But which sizes should the factory make? The owner wants to make the sizes that most people buy, so she is looking at last month's orders to see which sizes seem to be the most popular. Can you help her figure out which three sizes to make?

Make sure students understand the problem by asking questions such as the following:

- **What kind of jewelry does the Glow-Shine Toy Factory make?** glow-in-the-dark bracelets and necklaces
- **What sizes do they make?** whatever sizes the stores order

---

Exploring Problem Solving

Name _____ Date _____

Listen to the problem. What sizes should the factory make?

How many?	How long?
2	3 inches
2	5 inches
3	7 inches
2	8 inches

How many?	How long?
2	3 inches
1	5 inches
1	8 inches
1	11 inches

How many?	How long?
1	4 inches
2	6 inches
2	7 inches
3	11 inches

How many?	How long?
2	3 inches
1	9 inches
2	10 inches
1	11 inches

How many?	How long?
1	4 inches
3	6 inches
2	11 inches
1	13 inches

Organize this information.

Students should be able to support their decisions.

These are the three sizes the factory should make: _____

Textbook This lesson is available in the *eTextbook*.

145

Exploring Problem Solving

What sizes should the factory make?

How many?	How long?
2	8 inches
1	10 inches
3	15 inches
1	18 inches

How many?	How long?
1	9 inches
3	11 inches
2	15 inches

How many?	How long?
2	14 inches
1	16 inches
3	18 inches
3	20 inches

How many?	How long?
2	8 inches
3	9 inches
2	12 inches
1	14 inches

How many?	How long?
1	8 inches
3	9 inches
2	15 inches
2	20 inches

Organize this information.

Students should be able to support their decisions.

These are the three sizes the factory should make: _____

146   **Real Math • Chapter 4 • Exploring Problem Solving**

- **What does the owner want to do?** make only three sizes of glow-in-the-dark bracelets
- **What information will she use to help her decide which sizes to make?** how many of each size have been ordered in the last month
- **What information does each order form give you?** what sizes were ordered and how many of each size were ordered
- **Did all the stores that placed orders want the same sizes?** No, they ordered lots of different sizes.
- **Can you tell quickly if stores ordered more 6-inch bracelets or more 10-inch bracelets?** no, not quickly, because the information is spread out and mixed up
- **How can you make it easier to see and work with the information on all the order forms?** Help students realize that organizing the information in some way will help.
- **How might you organize the information to help you see which sizes were the most popular?** Suggestions may include making tally marks, making a table, making a bar graph, and making a pictograph.

 Exploring Problem Solving 25

Using Student Pages

Have students work in pairs or small groups to solve the problem. Tell them they may use the grid on page 145 or their own paper to organize the data in whatever way they think will help. As students work on the problem, circulate around the room, providing support as needed.

Students who finish early may solve a similar problem on page 146 that involves deciding the sizes of necklaces rather than bracelets.

 **Reflect** 10

 Knowledge Age Skills

Problem Formulation, Planning, and Strategizing Have groups present how they organized the information, what sizes they decided to make, and why they chose those sizes. See Sample Solutions Strategies.

In discussion, bring out the following points:
- There are different ways to organize information.
- Different people may prefer different ways of organizing information.
- Math can help us make good business decisions and many other kinds of decisions. To use math in this way, we need to think about the meaning of the numbers with which we are working.

- When making decisions in real-life situations, answers may not be clear-cut.
- Different people may look at the same information and come to different conclusions, and both conclusions may be reasonable.

Sample Solutions Strategies

Students might use one or more of the following strategies.

Use Tally Marks
Students might keep track of the number of necklaces ordered by using tally marks to keep track of and display the number of each size ordered.

Make a Bar Graph
Students might use the grid provided or one of their own to create a bar graph to show the number of necklaces of each size ordered.

Make a Pictograph
Students might use pictures to show how many of each size were ordered.

Make a Table
Students might make a table to show the total of each size that was ordered.

 Assess 15

When evaluating student work, focus on whether students thought rationally about the problem. Questions to consider include the following:
- Did the student understand the problem?
- Did the student organize the data in a clear way?
- Was the student able to explain the reasoning behind a decision?
- Did the student listen carefully to other students' explanations?

Cumulative Review

Assign Pages 147–148

Use the Cumulative Review as a review of concepts and skills that students have previously learned.

Here are different ways that you can assign these problems to your students as they work through the chapter:

- With some of the lessons in the chapter, assign a set of cumulative review problems to be completed as practice or for homework.
  Lesson 4.6—Problems 1–6
  Lesson 4.7—Problem 7
  Lesson 4.8—Problem 8
  Lesson 4.9—Problems 9–12
  Lesson 4.10—Problems 13–16
  Lesson 4.11—Problems 17–22
  Lesson 4.12—Problem 23
  Lesson 4.13—Problems 24–26
- At any point during the chapter, assign part or all of the cumulative review problems to be completed as practice or for homework.

Cumulative Review

Problems 1–6 review measurements in meters and centimeters, Lesson 4.3.

Problem 7 reviews near doubles in word problems, Lesson 2.5.

Problem 8 reviews counting applications, Lesson 1.8.

Problems 9–12 review chain calculations, Lesson 3.7.

Problems 13–16 review measurements in yards, feet, and inches, Lesson 4.5.

Problems 17–22 review addition facts, Lesson 2.6.

Problem 23 reviews applications of addition and subtraction, Lesson 3.6.

Problems 24–26 review +9 and +10 addition facts, Lesson 2.3.

Monitoring Student Progress

If . . . students miss more than one problem in a section, ⋮ **Then . . .** refer to the indicated lesson for remediation suggestions.

Cumulative Review

Name _____ Date _____

Measurement—Meters and Centimeters Lesson 4.3

Fill in the blanks.

① 5 m = **500** cm
② 10 m = **1000** cm
③ **4** m = 400 cm
④ **1** **8** m = 100 cm
⑤ **8** m = 800 cm
⑥ **4** m = 400 cm

Near Doubles Lesson 2.5

Write the answer.

⑦ Normie and Tiger each had 6 cat toys. Then Tiger lost 1 toy. Now how many toys do they have altogether? **11**

Counting Applications Lesson 1.8

Write the answer.

⑧ Kalil earned $3 today. Now he has $77. How many dollars did he have yesterday? **74**

Chain Calculations Lessons 3.7

Solve.

⑨
```
  6
  4
+ 3
───
 13
```
⑩
```
  1
  0
+ 8
───
  9
```
⑪
```
  3
  6
+ 4
───
 13
```
⑫
```
 10
  8
+ 0
───
 18
```

Textbook This lesson is available in the *eTextbook*.

147

Cumulative Review

Measurement—Yards, Feet, and Inches Lesson 4.5

Fill in the blanks.

⑬ 1 foot = 12 inches
⑭ **6** feet = 72 inches
⑮ **4** feet = 48 inches
⑯ **5** feet = 60 inches

Remaining Facts and Function Machines Lesson 2.6

Add.

⑰ 9 + 9 = **18**
⑱ 3 + 6 = **9**
⑲ 6 + 9 = **15**
⑳ 7 + 2 = **9**
㉑ 8 + 8 = **16**
㉒ 2 + 9 = **11**

Applications of Addition and Subtraction Lesson 3.6

㉓ **Extended Response** Miguel has $5. He wants to buy a pogo stick for $13. He can earn $2 an hour helping his older sister with her paper route. How many hours must he help with the paper route to have $13? **4 hours** Explain. The pogo stick costs $13. He already has $5. He needs $8 more. He can earn $8 for 4 hours of work. In 1 hour he will have earned $2; in 2 hours, $4; in 4 hours, $8 (2 + 2 + 2 + 2 = 8). The $5 he had plus the $8 he earned gives him $13.

+10 and +9 Addition Facts Lesson 2.3

Add to find the sums.

㉔ 9 + 6 = **15**
㉕ 10 + 3 = **13**
㉖ 9 + 0 = **9**

148

Real Math • Chapter 4

Wrap-Up

1 Discuss 5

Concept/Question Board

Review the Concept/Question Board with students.

- Discuss students' contributions to the Concept side of the Board.
- Have students repose their questions, and lead a discussion to find satisfactory answers.

Chapter Projects APPLYING

Provide an opportunity for students who have worked on one or more of the projects outlined on page 114C to share their work with the class. Allow each student or student group five minutes to present or discuss their projects. For formal assessment, use the rubrics found in **Across the Curriculum Math Connections;** the rubric for **Design a Toy** is on page 47, and the rubric for **Write about the History of Toys** is on page 51. For informal assessment, use the following rubric and questions.

	Exceeds Expectations	Meets Expectations	Minimally Meets Expectations
Applies mathematics in real-world situations:	❑	❑	❑
Demonstrates strong engagement in the activity:	❑	❑	❑

Design a Toy

- What toy did you create?
- What was the length and width of your toy?
- What materials did you use to make your toy?
- What part of your design made your toy move? Explain.
- How did you change the design of your toy to make it work better?
- Is a database a good way to store information about directions? Why or why not?
- If you made your toy again, would you change its length and width? Why or why not?

Write about the History of Toys

- What toy did you write about? Why did you choose that toy?
- What information did you include in your paragraph?
- How did you organize the dates of the toys?
- How is your toy important in the history of American culture?
- How did you format your document?
- If you had to choose another toy, which one would you choose? Why?

Key Ideas Review ✓ UNDERSTANDING

Have students complete the Review questions independently or in small groups. Then discuss each question as a class.

Possible Answers

Problem ① Problems 1–4 review measurement of length. Problem 1 reviews measuring length in nonstandard units. Students should remember that when shorter units are used, more units are required.

Problem ② Students should realize that 9 centimeters is not a good estimate, because the orange line is about half the length of the red line, so the length of the orange line should be about half of 10 centimeters.

Problem ③ The answer is b.

Problem ④ This lesson reviews customary units of length. Answers are shown.

Problem ⑤ Problem 5 reviews tally marks. Students' examples should look similar to the sample, although the number of marks drawn may vary.

Problem ⑥ Problems 6–10 review recording and analyzing data on a graph. The answer is LaDonna.

Problem ⑦ Students should interpret the graph to see that LaDonna read 10 books.

Problem ⑧ Students should remember that the *mode* is the number that appears most often in the data. The answer is 6.

Problem ⑨ Students should remember that the *range* is the lowest and highest numbers that appear in the data. The answer is 3 to 10.

Problem ⑩ Students should add the data to the graph as shown.

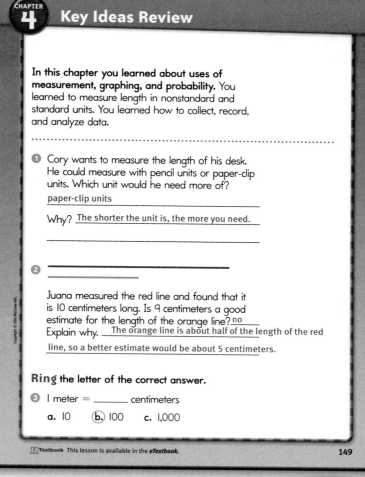

CHAPTER 4 Key Ideas Review

In this chapter you learned about uses of measurement, graphing, and probability. You learned to measure length in nonstandard and standard units. You learned how to collect, record, and analyze data.

① Cory wants to measure the length of his desk. He could measure with pencil units or paper-clip units. Which unit would he need more of?
paper-clip units

Why? The shorter the unit is, the more you need.

② _____

Juana measured the red line and found that it is 10 centimeters long. Is 9 centimeters a good estimate for the length of the orange line? no
Explain why. The orange line is about half of the length of the red line, so a better estimate would be about 5 centimeters.

Ring the letter of the correct answer.

③ I meter = _____ centimeters
   a. 10   **b.** 100   c. 1,000

Textbook This lesson is available in the *eTextbook*. 149

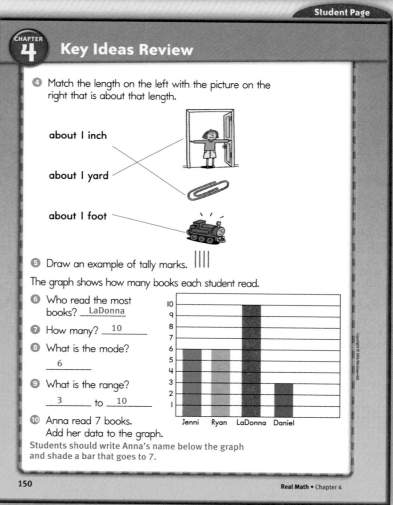

Student Page

CHAPTER 4 Key Ideas Review

④ Match the length on the left with the picture on the right that is about that length.

about 1 inch

about 1 yard

about 1 foot

⑤ Draw an example of tally marks. ||||

The graph shows how many books each student read.

⑥ Who read the most books? LaDonna

⑦ How many? 10

⑧ What is the mode? 6

⑨ What is the range? 3 to 10

⑩ Anna read 7 books. Add her data to the graph.
Students should write Anna's name below the graph and shade a bar that goes to 7.

Jenni Ryan LaDonna Daniel

150   **Real Math** • Chapter 4

Chapter Review

Use the Chapter 4 Review to indicate areas in which each student is having difficulty or in which the class may need help. If students do well on the Chapter 4 Review, you may wish to skip directly to the Chapter Test; if not, you may spend a day or so helping students overcome their individual difficulties before taking the Practice Test.

Next to each set of problems is a list of the lessons in the chapter that covered those concepts. If they need help, students can refer to a specific lesson for additional instruction. You can also use this information to make additional assignments based on the previous lesson concepts.

Have students complete pages 151–152 on their own.

Monitoring Student Progress

Problems 1–3 Lesson 4.10

If . . . students have difficulty with these problems,

Then . . . review bar graphs and how to read them.

Problems 4–5 Lessons 4.2 and 4.4

If . . . students have difficulty with these problems,

Then . . . have them look at rulers to see the differences among centimeters, inches, and feet.

Problems 6–7 Lessons 4.6 and 4.8

If . . . students write an incorrect answer,

Then . . . determine whether the problem is reading the table or understanding the terms *mode* and *range*, and then review accordingly.

Problems 8–12 Lessons 4.3 and 4.5

If . . . students have difficulty with these problems,

Then . . . have them use measuring tools to compare centimeters, inches, feet, and yards.

Name _____ Date _____

Lesson 4.10 Use the bar graph to answer these questions.

Number of Books Read

Jin
Lashaun
Josh

1 2 3 4 5 6 7 8 9 10 11 12 13 14

① Who has read the most books? __Josh__
How many? __14__

② How many books has Lashaun read? __12__

Lessons 4.2 and 4.4 How long? Estimate and then measure.

③

Estimate
in centimeters _____   Actual length
__8__ centimeters

④

Estimate
in inches _____   Actual length
__3__ inches

ⓔTextbook This lesson is available in the *eTextbook*.

Lessons 4.6 and 4.8 Write the number of tally marks. Then use the table to answer the questions below.

Shantrell made this table. She kept track of the number of swimming pool visitors each hour she was there.

Time of Day	Tallies	Number
10 A.M.	‖	2
11 A.M.	卌 ‖‖‖	9
12 P.M.	卌 卌 ‖‖‖	14
1 P.M.	卌 卌 卌 ‖	17
2 P.M.	卌 卌 卌 ‖	16
3 P.M.	卌 卌 卌 ‖	16

⑤ The mode is __16__.

⑥ The range is __2__ to __17__.

Lessons 4.3 and 4.5 Fill in the blanks. Remember, 1 meter = 100 centimeters; 1 foot = 12 inches; 1 yard = 3 feet.

⑦ 5 m = __500__ cm   ⑧ 8 m = __800__ cm

⑨ 1 yard = __36__ inches   ⑩ 2 feet = __24__ inches

⑪ 2 yards = __6__ feet = __72__ inches

Chapter Tests

40

Practice Test

Student Pages 153–156

- The Chapter 4 Practice Test on **Student Edition** pages 153–156 provides an opportunity to formally evaluate students' proficiency with concepts developed in this chapter.
- The content is similar to the Chapter 4 Review, in standardized format.

Problems ㉒ ㉓ and ㉔   **Extended Response**

Students engage in probability experiments to help them understand the nature of fair tools in probability experiments. Encourage students to think about the results of their experiments. They should understand that even though the results of a probability experiment are unpredictable, they may follow certain patterns. For Problem 24, students continue to develop their sense of measurements. They look for objects that are more or less than one meter in length. You may want to encourage students to develop a personal reference for a meter to help them estimate length.

CHAPTER 4 Practice Test

Name _____ Date _____

Use the Venn diagram to answer the questions.

Manuel asked his friends what movies they like.

❶ How many friends like comedies? __15__

❷ How many friends like mysteries? __12__

❸ How many friends like both comedies and mysteries? __7__

❹ How many friends did Manuel ask? __20__

Use the bar graph to answer the questions.

Sports Room Supplies

Footballs	
Basketballs	
Baseballs	
Tennis Balls	

10 15 20 25 30 35 40 45 50 55

❺ What kind of balls are there the fewest of in the sports supply room? __footballs__

❻ How many more baseballs are there than footballs? __30__

❼ What kind of ball is there 30 more of than basketballs? __tennis balls__

Textbook This lesson is available in the **eTextbook**.

153

Student Page

CHAPTER 4 Practice Test

Find the perimeter.

❽ A square has one side that is 4 inches long. What is the perimeter?
- **(a.)** 16 in.
- **b.** 12 in.
- **c.** 8 in.
- **d.** 4 in.

❾ A rectangle has one side that is 8 centimeters long and one side that is 2 centimeters long. What is the perimeter?
- **a.** 32 cm
- **(b.)** 20 cm
- **c.** 16 cm
- **d.** 10 cm

❿ An equilateral triangle has all sides that are 5 feet long. What is the perimeter?
- **a.** 20 ft
- **(b.)** 15 ft
- **c.** 10 ft
- **d.** 5 ft

Ring the measure that is equal.

⓫ 2 ft = _____
- **(a.)** 24 in.
- **b.** 20 in.
- **c.** 2 yd
- **d.** 1 yd

⓬ 3 m = _____
- **a.** 2 yd
- **b.** 3 yd
- **c.** 30 cm
- **(d.)** 300 cm

⓭ 6 ft = _____
- **a.** 4 yd
- **b.** 3 yd
- **(c.)** 2 yd
- **d.** 1 yd

⓮ 500 cm = _____
- **a.** 1 m
- **b.** 2 m
- **(c.)** 5 m
- **d.** 50 m

154

Real Math • Chapter 4

Practice Test

Name _____ Date _____

Use the table to answer the questions.

Children on the Playground

Age	Number of Children
6	16
7	14
8	20

⑮ How many children on the playground are 7 years old?
- a. 36
- b. 20
- c. 16
- **d. 14**

⑯ What is the range of their ages?
- a. 8
- b. 7
- **c. 6 to 8**
- d. 14 to 20

⑰ What is the mode of their ages?
- **a. 8**
- b. 7
- c. 6 to 8
- d. 14 to 20

Solve for each missing term.

⑱ 5 + _____ = 13
- a. 7
- **b. 8**
- c. 9
- d. 10

⑲ 8 + _____ = 16
- a. 6
- b. 7
- **c. 8**
- d. 9

⑳ 13 − _____ = 10
- a. 6
- b. 5
- c. 4
- **d. 3**

㉑ 17 − _____ = 8
- a. 10
- **b. 9**
- c. 8
- d. 7

Student Page

Practice Test

Complete the table, and answer the question.

㉒ Roll a 0–5 *Number Cube* 18 times. Make a tally mark for the number that comes up on each roll. Then write the numbers.

Answers may be about equal and should total 18 rolls.

Number	Tallies	Totals
0		
1		
2		
3		
4		
5		

㉓ **Extended Response** What were the results? Why do you think it came out that way? _____ Possible answers may include the equal number of possible outcomes.

Find objects that are shorter than 1 meter, about 1 meter long, and longer than 1 meter.

㉔ **Extended Response** Draw or write to complete the table.

Accept all reasonable answers.

Shorter than 1 Meter	About 1 Meter	Longer than 1 Meter

Chapter Test ✓ COMPUTING

For further evaluation instead of or in addition to this test, you may wish to have students take the Chapter 4 Test provided in *Assessment*.

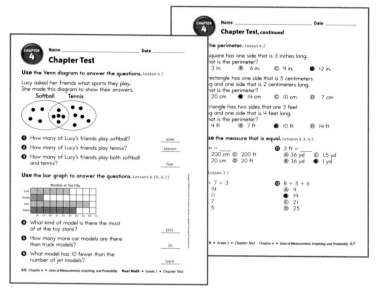

Assessment, pages 66–67

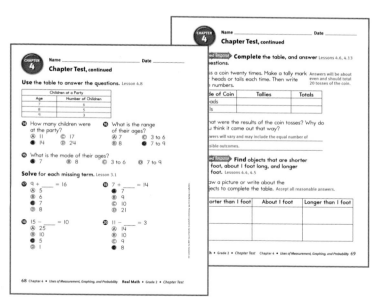

Assessment, pages 68–69

4 Assess and Differentiate

 Assess Use **eAssess** to record and analyze evidence of student understanding.

A Gather Evidence

Use the Daily Class Assessment Records in **Assessment** or **eAssess** to record Informal and Formal Assessments.

Informal Assessment

☑ **Key Ideas Review** UNDERSTANDING

Did the student
- ❑ make important observations?
- ❑ extend or generalize learning?
- ❑ provide insightful answers?
- ❑ pose insightful questions?

Informal Assessment

☑ **Project** APPLYING

Did the student
- ❑ meet the project objectives?
- ❑ communicate clearly?
- ❑ complete the project accurately?
- ❑ connect mathematics to real-world situations?

Formal Assessment

☑ **Chapter Test** COMPUTING

Score the test, and record the results.

B Summarize Findings

Analyze and summarize assessment data for each student. Determine which Chapter Follow-Up is appropriate for each student. Use the Student Assessment Record in **Assessment** or **eAssess** to update assessment records.

C Chapter Follow-Up ● DIFFERENTIATE INSTRUCTION

Based on your observations, use these teaching strategies for chapter follow-up.

ENRICH	PRACTICE	RETEACH	INTERVENTION
If . . . students demonstrate a **secure understanding** of chapter concepts,	If . . . students demonstrate **competent understanding** of chapter concepts,	If . . . students demonstrate **emerging understanding** of chapter concepts,	If . . . students demonstrate **minimal understanding** of chapter concepts,
Then . . . move on to the next chapter.	Then . . . move on to the next chapter.	Then . . . move on to the next chapter, but continue to provide cumulative review.	Then . . . intensive intervention is still needed before they start the next chapter.

Take a Chance

Context of the Thinking Story Ms. Arthur and her class try to find a fair way to determine which five students will go on a tour of Mr. Eng's toy factory.

Lesson Planner

OBJECTIVES
To develop logical thinking while integrating reading skills with mathematics

NCTM STANDARDS

Data Analysis and Probability
- Evaluating inferences and predictions based on data
- Discussing events as likely or unlikely

Problem Solving
- Solving problems that arise in mathematics and in other contexts
- Applying and adapting a variety of appropriate strategies to solve problems

READING STANDARDS
- Listening for details
- Drawing conclusions
- Evaluating information
- Making inferences

Using the Thinking Story

The Thinking Story may be used at any time throughout the chapter. Read the Thinking Story "Take a Chance" to your class. As you read the story, give students time to think about each question, but not so much that they forget the point being made.

TAKE A CHANCE

One day Ms. Arthur announced to her class, "I have good news for you. Mr. Eng has invited all of you to visit his famous toy factory."

The children cheered. They wanted to see this factory, which was known for producing the world's most beautiful stuffed animals.

"But," said Ms. Arthur, "it's a small factory, and Mr. Eng can take only five children at a time. We have to decide which children can go this week. The rest can go later." Everyone's hand went up. All the children wanted to go the first week.

"I see. All of you want to go this week," Ms. Arthur said. "We'll have to work out a fair way of deciding which children get to go first."

What are some fair ways to decide? **Possible answers include drawing names out of a box or hat.**

"I know a fair way," said Ferdie. "Let's have a race around the school yard. The five children who run the fastest should be the ones who get to go."

"I like that idea too," said Marcus.

Do you think that is a fair way to decide? **no**

Can you think of a reason that Ferdie and Marcus would like that idea? **They are probably fast runners.**

"That's not a fair way," said Manolita. "Ferdie and Marcus want to do it that way because they know they're the fastest runners and they'll be sure to get to go first."

Who do you think one of the winners would be if they did it that way? **Ferdie or Marcus**

Ms. Arthur said, "I believe a fair way is one that gives everyone an equal chance of being picked."

Can you think of a way that would give every child in the class an equal chance of being picked? **Answers may vary. Possible answers include drawing names out of a box or hat.**

Finally the class decided that the fairest way would be for the children to write their names on slips of paper, put the slips into a box and mix them up, and then draw five names. So Ms. Arthur passed out slips of paper (all the same size), and the children wrote their names on them. She collected the slips in a box. Then she mixed up the slips, held the box above Willy's head, and asked him to take out five slips.

"That's not fair," one of the children said. "Willy will be sure to pull out his own name."

Is that true? **no**

Why or why not? **He can't see inside the box.**

"I can't see what the names are," Willy said. "So there isn't any way I can be sure to get my own name—though I wish there were."

Willy carefully drew five slips from the box and handed them to Ms. Arthur. Looking at the slips of paper one by one she said, "The five lucky children are Ivan, … Ferdie, … Willy, … Sumi, … and Ferdie!"

There were angry shouts from the children that Ferdie had cheated.

"No, I didn't," said Ferdie. "I'm just lucky, I guess."

Could it be luck that Ferdie's name was drawn twice? no

How could it have happened? He must have put more than one slip of paper into the box.

"We'll have to look into this matter," said Ms. Arthur, sounding a bit angry. She dumped the slips of paper onto a table and spread them out.

"This is very strange," she said. "Every other child's name is here once, but there are ten slips of paper with Ferdie's name on them. Ferdie, what do you have to say for yourself?"

"I was at the end of the row," Ferdie said, "and there were ten pieces of paper left when they got to me, so I wrote my name on all of them. I don't see anything wrong with that."

Do you see anything wrong with it? He had a greater chance of being picked than the other students.

"Remember," Ms. Arthur said, "that a fair way is one that gives every child an equal chance. Did you all have an equal chance of winning?"

Can you explain why Ferdie had more of a chance to win than the others? His name is on ten slips of paper; the other students only have one.

"We all had an equal chance—except Ferdie," Manolita said. "He had lots more chances to win than the rest of us because lots of the pieces of paper had his name on them."

Ferdie looked sad. "I didn't think about that," he said. "I just wanted to be sure I still had a chance in case my name got stuck on the bottom of the box or something. I'm sorry."

"We've learned something about fair choosing," Ms. Arthur said, "and I believe you weren't trying to cheat, Ferdie. But we still have the problem of choosing the names fairly now."

"That's easy," Ferdie said. "Just put the names back into the box, all but mine, and pull out another name. That way we'll pick the last person fair and square."

Does that sound like a fair way to finish the choosing? no

Why or why not? Ferdie's name was not picked fairly.

Copyright © SRA/McGraw-Hill.

Most of the children thought that was a fair way, but not Manolita. "That means that Ferdie gets to go," she said, "because his name is already one of the first four. But if he had done it right, like the rest of us, maybe his name wouldn't have been picked. Maybe my name would have been picked instead."

What do you think of Manolita's argument? **It makes sense.**

"That's good thinking, Manolita," said Ms. Arthur. "I'm afraid that Ferdie had an unfair advantage when his name was picked both times. So the way we'll handle it is that Ivan, Willy, and Sumi get to go, and then we'll draw two more names to decide who the other two will be."

"Then I won't have any chance at all!" Ferdie wailed.

Why does Ferdie think he won't have any chance? **He thinks his name won't be in the box.**

"Yes, you will," said Ms. Arthur, as she dropped one of the slips with Ferdie's name on it into the box and mixed it in with the others. "You won't have as good a chance as the others, because they all had a chance against Ivan, Willy, and Sumi. But you still have a chance."

Willy drew two more names. They were Susan and Mario.

"Don't feel bad," Manolita said to Ferdie. "You might get to go to the toy factory next week."

THE END

Copyright © SRA/McGraw-Hill.

Guided Discussion

As students answer the questions in the story, ask them to communicate how they chose their answers. Allow students to debate the answers if necessary. There are some aspects of this story that you may not choose to discuss with students but of which you should be aware. Ferdie did not have ten times the chance of being chosen just because he put his name in ten times. The probabilities depend on the size of the class; and for a class of normal size, Ferdie would have about five times the chance of being chosen than the other students had. The way it worked out at the end, he had only two-fifths the chance of being chosen because the others had a chance on five draws, whereas he had a chance on only two. Ms. Arthur could have done the whole drawing over again, with each student's name in the box once, but that would have been upsetting to Ivan, Willy, and Sumi, who had been chosen fairly the first time.

Using Student Pages 157–158

Have students follow the instructions and complete the **Student Edition** activities. Read the instructions aloud if students are having difficulty.

Lesson Study

Reflect on each of the lessons you taught in this chapter. Rate each one on the following scale, and then consider ways to maintain or improve positive teaching experiences in the future.

Lessons	Very Effective	Effective	Less Effective	What Worked	Ways to Improve
4.1 Measuring Using Nonstandard Units					
4.2 Measuring Length—Centimeters					
4.3 Measurement—Meters and Centimeters					
4.4 Measuring Length—Inches					
4.5 Measurement—Yards, Feet, and Inches					
4.6 Collecting and Recording Data					
4.7 Venn Diagrams					
4.8 Range and Mode					
4.9 Pictographs					
4.10 Vertical Bar Graphs					
4.11 Horizontal Bar Graphs					
4.12 Graphs on a Grid					
4.13 Using Probability					

Two-Digit Addition

Teaching for Understanding

In this chapter students are introduced to the algorithm for two-digit addition. Students learn the algorithm by using a variety of manipulatives, including craft sticks, fingers, and play money, to understand the base-ten system and model the addition. Students then begin to write the algorithm to record what they did with the manipulatives.

Prerequisite Skills and Concepts

- Addition Facts
- Place Value to 100
- Interpreting Addition Word Problems

Two-Digit Addition Skills Trace

Before Grade 2	Grade 2	After Grade 2
Grades K–1 Informally and formally introduced two-digit addition using manipulatives	**This chapter** develops fluency with computational strategies for two-digit addition. **Chapter 9** will introduce three-digit addition.	Review and mastery of two-digit addition Formal introduction of larger numbers and decimals

Problem Solving

Problem solving is in every lesson. This chapter includes the following:

CHAPTER INTRODUCTION Students use organization strategies to more easily count the number of ice-cream spoons needed for a picnic. (pp. 159I–160C)

EXPLORING PROBLEM SOLVING The first lesson provides nonroutine problem solving in which students practice regrouping to determine whether there are enough juice boxes for everyone at a picnic (pp. 171–172, 172A). The second lesson provides practice interpreting whether an answer is reasonable as students make tug-of-war teams that have the same number of children (pp. 189–190, 190A).

THINKING STORY In "Sharing with Cousin Trixie" students use whole-number computations to help the characters determine fair ways to share a number of objects and a single object (pp. 201A–201E, 201–202).

Games

Develop reasoning skills, and provide extensive practice.

- **Get to 100 by Tens or Ones Game** (Lesson 5.1)
- **Roll a Problem Game** (Lesson 5.8)

Math Background

Two-Digit Addition

Addition Algorithm

- The algorithm, or step-by-step procedure, introduced in this chapter is efficient and the most widely used algorithm for adding multidigit numbers, but there are others. Learning this algorithm is important because after it is learned, it allows students to add routinely and without having to think unnecessarily about the procedure. This allows students to think about other more important aspects of the problem they happen to be solving.

- However, using this procedure as a preferred method is not the goal of school mathematics. Rather, the goal of school mathematics is to develop sufficient number sense so students can do many calculations mentally, without resorting to paper and pencil (or calculators) but with the knowledge that they have a standby method—the algorithm—that will work if mental calculations become too difficult.

- This is why we develop facility with mental arithmetic in every lesson—even while we are developing proficiency with the algorithm.

Paper Explorer

- The Paper Explorer was introduced in Chapter 2 to model single-digit addition. It is used in this chapter to reinforce concepts related to place value and renaming. Manipulating counters on the Paper Explorer allows students to notice that procedures for adding tens are essentially the same as those for adding units (ones). This concept becomes important as students notice that when adding (or subtracting) multidigit numbers, the procedures are the same in each column. Thus adding two-digit numbers is little different than adding three- or four-digit numbers or even greater numbers.

- As students use the Paper Explorer, place emphasis on having them move the counters so the counters match the already given sums rather than having students determine the sums. Students will get frustrated if they are asked to determine sums and then make a wrong move and get the wrong answer. This is especially true if students already know the correct sum. The idea here is to explore the relationships rather than calculate sums.

Manipulatives

- Concepts of regrouping and addition are developed in this chapter using craft sticks in bundles of ten and play money ($1 and $10 bills) as concrete models. Two different manipulatives are used to represent two-digit numbers to make it less likely that students will become dependent on any single manipulative. This will also make it easier to move to the abstract—that is, work with two- and three-digit numbers without the need for manipulatives later in the year.

- The use of base-ten manipulatives (such as bundled craft sticks and base-ten blocks) in this chapter is important because it leads to an understanding of place value and to why the addition algorithm works. It is, therefore, important to be alert to those students who might have memorized the rules for an algorithm and can produce correct answers, but who have little or no understanding of why the procedures work. Those students will be at a severe disadvantage in future work in mathematics, so it is important that you identify such students and devise ways to make the use of manipulatives meaningful and appealing to them.

- At the same time, you will have students who develop these understandings early and no longer need manipulatives for the kind of exercises in these lessons. Such students should not be forced to use manipulatives if they are able to solve the problems efficiently without them.

What Research Says
About Multidigit Addition

How Children Develop Multidigit Addition Strategies

"Proficiency with multidigit computation is more heavily influenced by instruction than single-digit computation is. Many features of multidigit procedures are not part of children's everyday experience and need to be learned in the classroom. . . . Children can and do devise or invent algorithms for carrying out multidigit computations. Opportunities to construct their own procedures provide students with opportunities to make connections between the strands of proficiency. Procedural fluency is built directly on their understanding."

Kilpatrick, J., J. Swafford, and B. Findell, eds. *Adding It Up: Helping Children Learn Mathematics.* Washington, D.C.: National Research Council/National Academy Press, 2001, p. 197.

Learning Trajectories for Multidigit Addition

Learning single-digit addition and subtraction is generally characterized as "learning math facts." It is assumed that children must memorize these facts, yet research has shown that addition and subtraction have their roots in counting, counting on, number sense, the ability to compose and decompose numbers, and place value. Key steps in the learning trajectory for measurement from the 2nd grade range are described below. For the complete trajectory, see Appendix B.

Level Name	Description
Numbers-in-Numbers +/−	Evidence of the advancement in adding is when a child recognizes that a number is part of a whole and can solve problems when the start is unknown (_ + 4 = 9) with counting strategies.
Deriver +/−	At the next level a child can use flexible strategies and derived combinations (for example, "7 + 7 is 14, so 7 + 8 is 15") to solve all types of problems.
Problem Solver +/−	As children develop their addition and subtraction abilities, they can solve all types of problems by using flexible strategies and many known combinations.
Multidigit +/−	Further development is evidenced when children can use composition of tens and all previous strategies to solve multidigit +/− problems.

Clements, D. H., J. Sarama, & A.-M. DiBiase, eds. *Engaging Young Children in Mathematics: Standards for Early Childhood Mathematics Education.* Mahwah, NJ: Lawrence Erlbaum Associates, 2004.

Research-Based Teaching Strategies

In order to become proficient with multidigit addition and subtraction, children need to apply their knowledge and skills related to place value and base-ten number structure. A range of strategies may be used by a child in performing the computations required for solving the multidigit addition or subtraction problem.

Algorithms are the step-by-step procedures commonly used for addition, subtraction, multiplication or division of numbers. Developing proficiency in the use of standard algorithms for addition or subtraction of multidigit numbers requires both conceptual knowledge and procedural fluency.

Research has shown that students benefit from learning and practicing a variety of different approaches to solving multidigit addition or subtraction problems. Some approaches may require modeling the problem with physical materials or manipulatives, in addition to the use of symbols or words. Other instructional practices will focus upon the application of forms of the standard algorithms. The use of a variety of approaches or strategies for solving multidigit addition and subtraction problems will result in the development of richer understanding of place value and computation procedures.

Kilpatrick, J., J. Swafford, and B. Findell, eds. *Adding It Up: Helping Children Learn Mathematics.* Washington, D.C.: National Research Council/National Academy Press, 2001, pp. 195–199.

RESEARCH IN ACTION

Place value Chapter 5 reinforces the development of conceptual understandings of place value based upon the students' use of base-ten concepts, language associated with the base-ten number system, and the written expressions of base-ten numbers.

Reasonableness In Chapter 5 students will develop strategies for determining the reasonableness of answers to addition problems.

Vocabulary

ones place (Lesson 5.1) the right digit in a two-digit number

tens place (Lesson 5.1) the left digit in a two-digit number

English Learner

Cognates

For English learners, a quick way to acquire new English vocabulary is to build on what is known in the primary language.

English	Spanish
digit	dígito
exercise	ejercicio
regroup	reagrupar
cents	centavos
to combine	combinar
to practice	practicar
more practice	más práctica
applications	aplicaciones
to group	agrupar
explorer	explorador
paper	papel
multidigit	multidígito

Access Vocabulary

English learners may understand words in different contexts or not understand idioms. Review chapter vocabulary for this concern. For example:

dime	a silver coin worth ten cents
penny	a copper coin worth one cent
exercises	practice to make you better at a skill
regroup	to rearrange existing sets of objects to form them into new groups
ice-cream scoop	a ball of ice cream formed by a special spoon
combine	to join or add together
rubber band	a stretchy ring used to hold things together
here is one way	This is a possible process, but there are other ways.
price tag	a label with the price of an object for sale
shortcut	a way to arrive at a destination or answer using fewer steps
counters	small, round, plastic discs used for counting
multidigit	more than one digit

Chapter Planner

Lessons	Objectives	NCTM Standards	State Standards
5.1 Place Value pp. 161A–162A 45–60 minutes	To review place value for numbers less than 100 and to introduce place value of three- and four-digit numbers	Number and Operations, Communication	
5.2 Adding Tens pp. 163A–164A 45–60 minutes	To develop an understanding of the relationship between adding tens and adding ones and to introduce the names of multiples of ten between 100 and 200	Number and Operations, Communication	
5.3 Regrouping for Addition pp. 165A–166A 45–60 minutes	To practice using craft sticks or other base-ten materials to represent two-digit numbers and to convert numbers written in nonstandard form to standard form	Number and Operations, Problem Solving	
5.4 Adding Two-Digit Numbers pp. 167A–168A 45–60 minutes	To continue to provide experience in adding two-digit numbers and to recognize situations that require addition	Number and Operations, Representation	
5.5 More Adding Two-Digit Numbers pp. 169A–170A 45–60 minutes	To add two-digit numbers with sums equal to a multiple of ten	Number and Operations, Problem Solving	
5.6 Practice with Two-Digit Addition pp. 175A–176A 45–60 minutes	To add two digit-numbers that have a sum that is not a multiple of ten and to begin to develop a written form for recording the addition process	Numbers and Operations, Representation	
5.7 More Practice Adding Two-Digit Numbers pp. 177A–178A 45–60 minutes	To teach students an algorithm for adding two-digit numbers and to give practice in using the algorithm	Number and Operations, Connections	
5.8 Applications of Two-Digit Addition pp. 179A–180A 45–60 minutes	To introduce problems that require two-digit addition and to introduce the Roll a Problem Game	Number and Operations, Problem Solving	
5.9 Grouping by Tens pp. 181A–182A 45–60 minutes	To introduce grouping addends to make sums of ten or multiples of ten as a shortcut for addition	Number and Operations, Problem Solving	
5.10 Addition Shortcuts pp. 183A–184A 45–60 minutes	To introduce regrouping addends to make one of the addends a multiple of ten as a shortcut for addition	Number and Operations, Problem Solving	
5.11 The Paper Explorer–Adding Tens pp. 185A–186A 45–60 minutes	To introduce the Paper Explorer as a model for adding two-digit numbers	Number and Operations, Representation	
5.12 The Paper Explorer–Multidigit Addition pp. 187A–188A 45–60 minutes	To continue to use the Paper Explorer as a model for adding two-digit numbers	Number and Operations, Representation	

Vocabulary	Manipulatives and Materials	Games to reinforce skills and concepts
• ones place • tens place	• *Number Cubes* • Craft sticks and rubber bands • Play money • Overhead bills and coins • Base-ten blocks	**Get to 100 by Tens or Ones Game**
	• *Number Cubes* • Play money • Overhead bills and coins	**Get to 100 by Tens or Ones Game**
	• *Number Cubes* • Craft sticks and rubber bands or other base-ten materials	**Yard Sale Game**
	• *Number Cubes* • Craft sticks and rubber bands or other base-ten materials	
	• *Number Cubes* • Craft sticks and rubber bands or other base-ten materials • Play money ($10 and $1 bills)	
	• *Number Cubes* • Craft sticks and rubber bands or other base-ten materials	
	• *Number Cubes* • Craft sticks and rubber bands or other base-ten materials	**Roll a 15 Game**
	• *Number Cubes* • Craft sticks and rubber bands or other base-ten materials	
	• *Number Cubes* • Base-ten blocks	
	• *Number Cubes* • Craft sticks and rubber bands, base-ten blocks, or interlocking cubes • Counters	
	• *Number Cubes* • Overhead transparency of the Paper Explorer on *Practice* page 122 • Counters or pawns	
	• *Number Cubes* • Overhead transparency of the Paper Explorer on *Practice* page 123 • Counters	

Additional Resources

Differentiated Instruction

Intervention Support Guide Provides instruction for the following prerequisite skills:

- Lesson 5.A Place Value and Addition—1
- Lesson 5.B Place Value and Addition—2
- Lesson 5.C Place Value and Addition—3

Enrichment Support Guide Extends lesson concepts

Practice Reinforces lesson skills and concepts

Reteach Support Guide Provides alternate instruction for lesson concepts

English Learner Support Guide Previews and reviews lesson concepts and vocabulary for English learners

Technology

The following electronic resources are available:

ⓔ **Planner** Lessons 5.1–5.12

ⓔ **Presentation** Lessons 5.1–5.12

ⓔ **Textbook** Lessons 5.1–5.12

ⓔ **Assess** Lessons 5.1–5.12

ⓔ **MathTools** *Base Ten Lessons* 5.1, 5.3, 5.6
  Coins and Money Lesson 5.1
  Sets Former Lesson 5.9

Building Blocks *Number Compare 4* Lesson 5.1
  School Supply Shop Lesson 5.2
  Book Stacks Lesson 5.3
  Number Snapshots 10 Lesson 5.4
  Figure the Fact: Two-Digit Adding Lessons 5.5, 5.6
  Math-O-Scope Lesson 5.7
  Word Problems with Tools 4 Lesson 5.8

Assessment
Informal Assessment rubrics at the end of each lesson provide daily evaluation of student math proficiency.

Overview

Chapter Planner, continued

Problem Solving	When to Use	Objectives	NCTM Standards	Skills Covered
Chapter Introduction (pp. 159I–160C) 15–30 minutes	Use after the Chapter 5 Pretest.	To introduce chapter concepts in a problem-solving setting	Problem Solving, Communication	Counting, Two-digit addition
Exploring Problem Solving (pp. 171–172, 172A) 30–45 minutes	Use anytime during the chapter.	To explore methods of solving nonroutine problems	Problem Solving, Communication	Two-digit addition
Exploring Problem Solving (pp. 189–190, 190A) 45–60 minutes	Use anytime during the chapter.	To explore methods of solving nonroutine problems	Problem Solving, Communication	Two-digit addition
Thinking Story–Sharing with Cousin Trixie (pp. 201A–201E, 201–202) 20–30 minutes	Use anytime during the chapter.	To develop logical reasoning while integrating reading skills with mathematics	Number and Operations, Connections	Counting, Division applications

Review	When to Use	Objectives	NCTM Standards	Skills Covered
Cumulative Review (p. 173–174) 15–30 minutes	Use anytime after Lesson 5.5.	To review concepts and skills taught earlier in the year	Number and Operations	Addition strategies
Cumulative Review (p. 191–192) 15–30 minutes	Use anytime after Lesson 5.12.	To review concepts and skills taught earlier in the year	Number and Operations	Addition strategies
Chapter 5 Review (pp. 195A, 195–196) 30–45 minutes	Use after Lesson 5.12.	To review concepts and skills taught in the chapter	Number and Operations	Addition strategies

Assessment	When to Use	Objectives	NCTM Standards	Skills Covered
Informal Assessment Rubrics (pp. 162A–188A) 5 minutes per student	Use at the end of each lesson.	To provide daily evaluation of math proficiency	Number and Operations, Communication	Computing, Understanding, Reasoning, Applying, Engaging
Pretest (*Assessment* pp. 71–72) 15–30 minutes	Use prior to Chapter 5.	To provide assessment of prerequisite and chapter topics	Number and Operations, Problem Solving	Computing, Understanding, Reasoning, Applying, Engaging
Individual Oral Assessment (p. 174A) 5 minutes per student	Use after Lesson 5.5.	To provide alternate means of assessing students' progress	Number and Operations	Two-digit addition
Mastery Checkpoint (*Assessment* p. T58) 5 minutes per student	Use after Lesson 5.10.	To provide assessment of mastery of key skills	Number and Operations	Two-digit addition
Chapter 5 Practice Test (pp. 197–198, 199–200) 30–45 minutes	Use after or in place of the Chapter 5 Review.	To provide assessment or additional practice with the chapter concepts	Number and Operations, Problem Solving	Two-digit addition
Chapter 5 Test (*Assessment* pp. 79–82) 30–45 minutes	Use after or in place of the Chapter 5 Review.	To provide assessment of the chapter concepts	Number and Operations, Problem Solving	Two-digit addition

Technology Resources and Support

Visit SRAonline.com for online versions of the **Real Math** eSuite.

Technology for Teachers

e Presentation	Lessons 5.1–5.12 Use the **ePresentation** to present chapter content interactively.
e Planner	Use the Chapter and Lesson Planners to outline activities and time frames for Chapter 5
e Assess	Students can take the following assessments in **eAssess:** • Chapter Pretest • Mastery Checkpoint **Lesson 5.10** • Chapter Test Teachers can record results and print reports for all assessments in this chapter.
e MathTools	**Base Ten Lessons** 5.1, 5.3, 5.6 **Coins and Money** Lesson 5.1 **Sets Former** Lesson 5.9

Technology for Students

e Textbook	An electronic, interactive version of the **Student Edition** is available for all lessons in Chapter 5.
e MathTools	**Base Ten Lessons** 5.1, 5.3, 5.6 **Coins and Money** Lesson 5.1 **Sets Former** Lesson 5.9
TECH KNOWLEDGE	**TechKnowledge** Level 2 provides lessons that specifically teach the Unit 10 Internet, Unit 3 Word Processing, and Unit 1 Computer Basics applications that students can use in this chapter's project.
Building Blocks	**Number Compare 4** Lesson 5.1 **School Supply Shop** Lesson 5.2 **Book Stacks** Lesson 5.3 **Number Snapshots 10** Lesson 5.4 **Figure the Fact: Two-Digit Adding** Lessons 5.5, 5.6 **Math-O-Scope** Lesson 5.7 **Word Problems with Tools 4** Lesson 5.8

Two-Digit Addition

1 Introduce Chapter 5

Chapter Objectives

Explain to students that in this chapter they will build on what they already know about addition. Explain that in this chapter they will

- use addition to combine numbers.
- use the Commutative Law.
- use function machines.

Pretest COMPUTING

Administer the Pretest on **Assessment** pages 71 and 72.

The Pretest covers the following skills and topics from this chapter:

- Place value (Problems 1–3)
- Adding 9 and 10 (Problems 4–6)
- Missing addends (Problems 7–10)
- Bar graphs (Problems 11–13)
- Adding tens (Problems 14–17)
- Adding two-digit numbers with and without regrouping (Problems 18–21)
- Adding multiple addends (Problems 22–25)

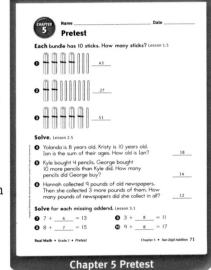

Chapter 5 Pretest

Access Prior Knowledge ✓ UNDERSTANDING

Have students look at the photograph on page 159 and talk about picnics they have attended. Focus on picnics such as school picnics where there are a lot of people. Encourage students to talk about some of the things people take on picnics and how they know they have enough for everyone. Ask them what they do besides eat when they go on a picnic. Guide the conversation by asking questions such as the following:

■ **When do people like to have picnics?** when it's warm enough to enjoy being outside
■ **Why might people decide to have a picnic?** to have fun; to celebrate a special occasion; to get together with other people
■ **Besides eating, what are some of the things people do to have fun on a picnic?** They might play games or have races; they might go hiking or fishing.

2 Exploring Problem Solving

Tell Students In Today's Lesson They Will

organize ice-cream spoons for a picnic.

Materials

Craft sticks or other countable objects (50–70 per group)

Strategy Building

Have students look at the illustration on page 160. Ask questions such as the following:

■ **What are the people doing?** They are gathered around a picnic table.
■ **What do you see on the picnic table?** a pile of wooden spoons
■ **Can you tell how many spoons there are?** no
■ **Would it be easy to count these spoons?** No; there are a lot of them.
■ **If you were at the picnic counting the spoons, how could you keep track of how many you have already counted?** Accept all reasonable responses such as the following: I could put them in groups, every minute I could write down how many I have counted, and so on.

Using Student Pages

Present this problem:

Four second-grade classes are planning a picnic in a park near their school. As a special treat, their teachers have ordered individual cups of ice cream for dessert. The teachers have some wooden spoons, but they are not sure if they have one for every student. They want to organize the spoons to make it easier to see how many they have and to keep track of them. Can you help?

Show the students a big pile of craft sticks (or other objects) and tell them that these stand for the wooden spoons. Give each small group of students a bunch (about 50 to 70). Tell students that they will need to organize the spoons so they can count them more easily and prove that they have counted correctly. Explain that afterward each group will present

- how many spoons they have.
- how they know they counted correctly.
- how they organized the spoons to make them easy for others to count.

Extension

Tell students that there are 23 students in each of the classes going on the picnic. Ask students if their group has enough spoons for all the students in the four classes.

CHAPTER 5 Two-Digit Addition

In This Chapter You Will Learn
- to use addition to combine numbers.
- the Commutative Law.
- about function machines.

159

💡 Problem Solving

Name _____ Date _____

Listen to the problem.

There are _____ spoons. Answers will depend on how many you give to the group.

This is how I organized them.

160   Real Math • Chapter 5

Concept/Question Board APPLYING

Questions

Have students think of and write three questions they have about two-digit addition and how it can be used. Then have them select one question to post on the Question side of the Board.

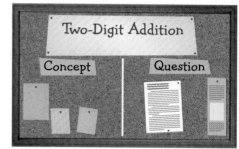

Concepts

As students work through the chapter, have them collect examples of how two-digit addition is used in everyday situations. For each example, have them write a problem that relates to the item(s). Have them display their examples on the Concept side of the Board. Suggest the following:

- budgets
- machines

Answers

Throughout the chapter, have students post answers to the questions and solutions to the problems on the Board.

3 Reflect   20

Effective Communication

Have groups present their results. In discussion, bring out these points:

- Forming groups that are easy to count (2s, 5s, 10s, 25s) makes it easier to check your counting if you lose track of where you are.
- Counting by tens is more efficient than counting by most other numbers because we are used to tens and our number system is based on ten.
- When people work in groups, they can organize and divide the work so each person does his or her part.

Sample Solutions Strategies

Students might use one or more of the following strategies to count the spoons.

Grouping/Skip Counting

Students might put their spoons into groups that are easy to count.

Make a Table

Students might make a tally mark for each spoon as they count them.

Use a Model or Diagram

Students might check off a numbered square on a 100 Table for each spoon they count.

Home Connection

At this time, you may want to send home the letter on pages 18–21 of *Home Connection.* This letter describes what students will be learning and what activities they can do at home to support their work in school.

Home Connection
page 18

4 Assess and Differentiate

 Assess Use *eAssess* to record and analyze evidence of student understanding.

A Gather Evidence

Use the Daily Class Assessment Records in **Assessment** or *eAssess* to record Informal and Formal Assessments.

Informal Assessment
☑ **Access Prior Knowledge**
Did the student   **UNDERSTANDING**
- ❏ make important observations?
- ❏ extend or generalize learning?
- ❏ provide insightful answers?
- ❏ pose insightful questions?

Informal Assessment
☑ **Concept/Question Board**
Did the student   **APPLYING**
- ❏ apply learning in new situations?
- ❏ contribute concepts?
- ❏ contribute answers?
- ❏ connect mathematics to real-world situations?

Formal Assessment
☑ **Pretest**  **COMPUTING**
- ❏ Place value (Problems 1–3)
- ❏ Adding 9 and 10 (Problems 4–6)
- ❏ Missing addends (Problems 7–10)
- ❏ Bar graphs (Problems 11–13)
- ❏ Adding tens (Problems 14–17)
- ❏ Adding two-digit numbers with and without regrouping (Problems 18–21)
- ❏ Adding multiple addends (Problems 22–25)

B Summarize Findings

Analyze and summarize assessment data for each student. Determine which Assessment Follow-Up is appropriate for each student. Use the Student Assessment Record in **Assessment** or *eAssess* to update assessment records.

C Assessment Follow-Up ● DIFFERENTIATE INSTRUCTION

Based on your observations of each student, use these teaching strategies for a general approach to the chapter. Look for specific Differentiate Instruction and Monitoring Student Progress strategies in each lesson that relate specifically to the lesson content.

ENRICH	PRACTICE	RETEACH	INTERVENTION	ENGLISH LEARNER
If . . . students demonstrate a **secure understanding** of chapter concepts, **Then . . .** move quickly through the chapter or use *Enrichment* Lessons 5.1–5.12 as assessment follow-up to extend and apply understanding.	**If . . .** students grasp chapter concepts with **competent understanding, Then . . .** use *Practice* Lessons 5.1–5.12 as lesson follow-up to develop fluency.	**If . . .** students have prerequisite understanding but demonstrate **emerging understanding** of chapter concepts, **Then . . .** use *Reteach* Lessons 5.2 and 5.3 to reteach lesson concepts.	**If . . .** students are not competent with prerequisite skills, **Then . . .** use *Intervention* Lessons 5.A–5.C before each lesson to develop fluency with prerequisite skills.	Use *English Learner Support Guide* Lessons 5.1–5.12 for strategies to preteach lesson vocabulary and concepts.

Math Across the Curriculum

Preview the chapter projects with students. Assign projects or have students choose from the projects to extend and enrich concepts in this chapter.

Take an Online Field Trip 4 weeks

SOCIAL STUDIES WebQuest

MATH OBJECTIVE
To reinforce studies of two-digit addition by calculating numbers of animals and plants

SOCIAL STUDIES OBJECTIVE
To reinforce studies of United States geography by researching national parks

TECHNOLOGY OBJECTIVE
To use basic computer skills to create, save, and print files

Have students use technology to research parks according to geography and activities offered.

For this project, students use the Internet to investigate the geography, animal and plant life, and activities and features of national parks.

For specific step-by-step instructions for this project, see **Across the Curriculum Math Connections** pages 52–57.

Take an Online Field Trip

Activity 1

Careers in Math

Environmental scientists use their knowledge of Earth to protect the environment, locate natural resources, and predict geological hazards. Environmental scientists use mathematical modeling, systems analysis, thermodynamics, and computer techniques to analyze and report measurements and observations. The scientists then make recommendations on the best ways to clean and preserve the environment.

Knowledge Age Skills

High-Level Responsibility Students take on decision-making roles for the family.

Problem Formulation, Planning, and Strategizing Students find national parks that would be appealing for a family vacation.

TechKnowledge Level 2 provides lessons that specifically teach the Unit 10 Internet, Unit 3 Word Processing, and Unit 1 Computer Basics applications that students can use in this project.

Track Bird Sightings 1 week

SCIENCE

MATH OBJECTIVE
To reinforce studies of addition with two-digit numbers by adding numbers of birds

SCIENCE OBJECTIVE
To reinforce studies of animals by observing birds and recording observations

TECHNOLOGY OBJECTIVE
To enter data about birds into a computer spreadsheet

Have students use mathematics to record information about birds in a spreadsheet. To broaden the science concept, have students include additional categories about the birds they observe.

As part of the project, students should consider the following issues:

- environments in which birds are likely to be found
- whether certain species of birds tend to stay in groups, pairs, or alone
- why birds act in certain ways

Track Bird Sightings

Activity 2

Careers in Math

Ornithologists are zoologists who specifically study birds. Some ornithologists collect and analyze data to determine how uses of land and water by birds affect the environment. They collect and analyze data on feeding habits, population growth, diseases, and social interactions among birds, including mating and parenting habits. Some ornithologists study birds in their natural habitats, while others work in nature preserves and zoos.

For specific step-by-step instructions for this project, see **Across the Curriculum Math Connections** pages 58–61.

Knowledge Age Skills

Effective Communication Students communicate observations of birds in clear and convincing descriptions.

Problem Formulation, Planning, and Strategizing Students research and identify different species of birds.

Lesson Planner

OBJECTIVES
- To review place value for numbers less than 100
- To review counting money
- To introduce place value of three- and four-digit numbers

NCTM STANDARDS
Number and Operations
- Using models to develop understanding of place value
- Developing a sense of whole numbers and representing and using them in flexible ways
- Connecting number words to the quantities they represent

Communication
- Analyzing and evaluating mathematical thinking and strategies of others
- Communicating mathematical thinking clearly

MATERIALS
- *Number Cubes
- *Craft sticks and rubber bands
- *Play money
- *Overhead bills and coins
- *Base-ten blocks (optional)

TECHNOLOGY
- e Presentation Lesson 5.1
- e MathTools Base Ten, Coins and Money
- Building Blocks Number Compare 4

TEST PREP
Cumulative Review
Mental Math reviews one-digit addition (Lessons 2.1–2.9).

Place Value

Context of the Lesson The twelve lessons in this chapter are intended to lead to mastery of the two-digit addition algorithm. This is the first of two lessons reviewing the base-ten system of numbers. Craft sticks, fingers, and play money are used as base-ten materials, but other base-ten materials may be substituted. Using more than one representation makes it less likely that students will become dependent on any single manipulative. This will also make it easier to transition to working with two- and three-digit numbers without the need for manipulatives later in the year.

See page 159B for Math Background for teachers for this lesson.

Planning for Learning ● DIFFERENTIATE INSTRUCTION

INTERVENTION
If . . . students lack the prerequisite skill of knowing addition facts,

Then . . . teach **Intervention** Lesson 5.A.

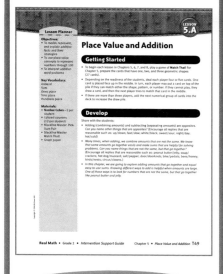

Intervention Lesson 5.A

ENGLISH LEARNER
Preview

If . . . students need language support,

Then . . . use Lesson 5.1 in **English Learner Support Guide** to preview lesson concepts and vocabulary.

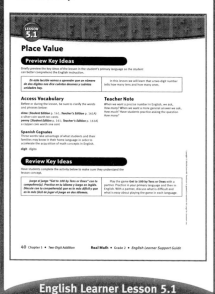

English Learner Lesson 5.1

ENRICH
If . . . students are proficient in the lesson concepts,

Then . . . emphasize game variations.

PRACTICE
If . . . students would benefit from additional practice,

Then . . . extend the game demonstration before assigning the student pages.

RETEACH
If . . . students are having difficulty understanding place value,

Then . . . extend Guided Discussion before assigning the student pages.

Vocabulary
Review from Lesson 1.5:

ones place

tens place

Access Vocabulary
dime a silver coin worth ten cents

penny a copper coin worth one cent

Spanish Cognates
digit dígito

*Manipulative Kit Item

Mental Math 5

  Review Present an addition fact drill. Write a statement on the board, and have students show answers with **Number Cubes.** Possible examples include the following:

a. $4 + 6 = 10$ **b.** $5 + 5 = 10$ **c.** $3 + 6 = 9$
d. $4 + 7 = 11$ **e.** $1 + 8 = 9$ **f.** $6 + 5 = 11$
g. $4 + 5 = 9$ **h.** $2 + 7 = 9$ **i.** $9 + 2 = 11$

1 Develop 20

Tell Students In Today's Lesson They Will
learn about place value.

Whole Group

Guided Discussion  MathTools ENGAGING

1. Call five volunteers to the front of the class. Ask them to show how to represent the number 43 with their fingers. Four students should hold up all ten fingers, and the fifth student should hold up three fingers.

2. Use crafts sticks or **eMathTools: Base Ten** to complete the following activity. Show the class ten craft sticks held together by a rubber band.

■ **How many craft sticks do you think there are in this bundle?** ten

Remove the rubber band, and ask a student to count to make sure the answer really is ten. Repeat with several bundles of ten sticks.

Hold up four bundles of ten sticks in one hand and three single sticks in the other.

■ **How many sticks am I holding?** 43
■ **How did you figure out there are 43 sticks?** because four bundles of ten sticks is forty, plus three single sticks

Write 43 on the board. Explain that the 4 is in the tens place, meaning there are 4 tens, and the 3 is in the ones place, meaning there are 3 ones. You might wish to illustrate this using a table such as the following:

thousands	hundreds	tens	ones
		4	3

Repeat this procedure with other numbers, going up to 1,000. (For numbers greater than 100 you may wish to use base-ten blocks rather than craft sticks.) After students identify the number of sticks, ask what number should be written in each place, and write the number on the board.

Then reverse the procedure, giving students a number and asking how many bundles of ten sticks and how many single sticks you would use to represent it.

3. Ask students how they would represent the number 43 using dimes and pennies. Then select the appropriate coins, one at a time, using play money or **eMathTools: Coins and Money** while counting aloud. Repeat the procedure with several other numbers.

Then ask students how they would represent the number 43 using $10 bills and $1 bills. As with the coins, place the appropriate bills down or use **eMathTools: Coins and Money,** while counting aloud.

Skill and Strategy Building COMPUTING Whole Group

Game   **Get to 100 by Tens or Ones Game**

Introduce and demonstrate the **Get to 100 by Tens or Ones Game** by playing at the overhead projector with a volunteer and the overhead bills and coins. Game rules are on student page 162.

Game Variation
Play using only $10 bills.

2 Assign Student Pages 25

Pages 161–162 UNDERSTANDING

Have students complete page 161 independently. Then have students play the **Get to 100 by Tens or Ones Game** in pairs. Observe students' abilities when playing, and suggest they play the variation of the game as appropriate.

Monitoring Student Progress

If . . . students are having difficulty seeing the relationship between single units and tens,

Then . . . have students work related problems with base-ten materials. For example, $3 + 5$, and $30 + 50$.

As Students Finish

Game ✓ Get to 100 by Tens or Ones Game

Building **B**locks *Number Compare 4*

LESSON 5.1 Place Value

Name _____ Date _____

Key Ideas

A two-digit number tells how many tens and how many ones. 34 means 3 tens and 4 ones.

Each bundle has 10 sticks. There are 3 bundles of 10 and 4 single sticks. There are 34 sticks.

A dime is worth 10¢. A penny is worth 1¢. There are 3 dimes and 4 pennies. There is 34¢.

How many craft sticks? Write your answers.

① **36**   ③ **70**

② **17**   ④ **47**

How many cents? Write your answers.

⑤ **32**¢

⑥ **51**¢

Textbook This lesson is available in the *eTextbook.*

161

Game

Counting and Strategies Practice

Get to 100 by Tens or Ones Game

Players: Two

Materials: 20 play $10 bills, 20 play $1 bills, paper and pencil for each player

HOW TO PLAY

❶ The $10 bills and $1 bills are divided equally between the two players.

❷ Beginning with Player One, the players take turns placing one or two bills in the middle of the playing area. If a player runs out of one kind of bill, he or she must use the other kind.

❸ Each player keeps a running total of the amount of money put down by counting aloud as each bill is placed. The players should keep written records only if necessary.

❹ The player who is first to reach 100 or more wins.

---

3 Reflect   10

Whole Group

Guided Discussion    MathTools   REASONING

Draw five pennies and three dimes on the board or use *eMathTools: Coins and Money.* Tell the class that sometimes students mistakenly say that these coins show 53 cents. Ask students the following questions:

■ **Why do you think students make this mistake?** because they are getting the values of pennies and dimes confused

■ **What would you do to help a friend who made this mistake?** Explain that because dimes are worth ten cents and pennies are worth one cent, the number of dimes is the number that belongs in the tens place, and the number of pennies is the number that belongs in the ones place.

RESEARCH IN ACTION

"Children's place value ideas gradually develop from (a) perceiving numbers in terms of a unit of one and counting by ones or counting on by ones; to (b) counting by groups or counting on by groups, such as groups of twos, five, or tens; to (c) working separately with the tens and ones that compose numbers; to (d) finally coordinating and flexibly adjusting between tens and ones within numbers."

Campbell, Patricia F. "Connecting Instructional Practice to Student Thinking." *Teaching Children Mathematics,* October 1997.

Cumulative Review: For cumulative review of previously learned skills, see page 173–174.

Family Involvement: Assign the *Practice, Reteach,* or *Enrichment* activities depending on the needs of your students.

Having students play an appropriate variation of the **Get to 100 by Tens or Ones Game** will also be beneficial.

Concept/Question Board: Have students look for additional examples using multidigit addition and post them on the Concept/Question Board.

Math Puzzler: There are 20 red crayons and 40 blue crayons in box one. There are 50 blue crayons in box two. Which box has more crayons? How many more? box 1; 10 more

Assess and Differentiate

 **Assess** Use **eAssess** to record and analyze evidence of student understanding.

A Gather Evidence

Use the Daily Class Assessment Records in **Assessment** or **eAssess** to record daily observations.

Performance Assessment
☑ **Game**

Did the student **COMPUTING**
- ❏ respond accurately?
- ❏ respond quickly?
- ❏ respond with confidence?
- ❏ self-correct?

Informal Assessment
☑ **Guided Discussion**

Did the student **REASONING**
- ❏ provide a clear explanation?
- ❏ communicate reasons and strategies?
- ❏ choose appropriate strategies?
- ❏ argue logically?

B Summarize Findings

Analyze and summarize assessment data for each student. Determine which Assessment Follow-Up is appropriate for each student. Use the Student Assessment Record in **Assessment** or **eAssess** to update assessment records.

Assessment page T41

C Assessment Follow-Up • DIFFERENTIATE INSTRUCTION

Based on your observations, use these teaching strategies for assessment follow-up.

INTERVENTION

Review student performance on **Intervention** Lesson 5.A to see if students have mastered prerequisite skills for this lesson.

ENGLISH LEARNER

Review

Use Lesson 5.1 in **English Learner Support Guide** to review lesson concepts and vocabulary.

ENRICH

If . . . students are proficient in the lesson concepts,

Then . . . encourage them to work on the chapter projects or **Enrichment** Lesson 5.1.

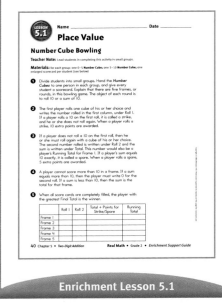

Enrichment Lesson 5.1

PRACTICE

If . . . students would benefit from additional practice,

Then . . . assign **Practice** Lesson 5.1.

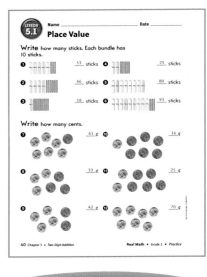

Practice Lesson 5.1

RETEACH

If . . . students are having difficulty understanding place value,

Then . . . have them use base-ten blocks to make models that show place values.

Lesson Planner

OBJECTIVES
- To develop an understanding of the relationship between adding ones and adding tens
- To introduce the names of multiples of ten between 100 and 200
- To practice adding tens and multiples of ten

NCTM STANDARDS
Number and Operations
- Counting with understanding and recognizing "how many" in sets of objects
- Using multiple models to develop initial understanding of place value and the base-ten number system
- Developing understanding of the relative position and magnitude of whole numbers
- Developing and using strategies for addition
- Developing fluency with basic number combinations for addition

Communication
- Organizing and consolidating mathematical thinking through communication
- Communicating mathematical thinking coherently and clearly to peers, teachers, and others

MATERIALS
- *Number Cubes
- *Play money
- *Overhead bills and coins

TECHNOLOGY
- ⒺPresentation Lesson 5.2
- Building Blocks School Supply Shop

TEST PREP
Cumulative Review
Mental Math reviews coins (Lesson 1.5).

Writing + Math
Journal

*Manipulative Kit Item

Adding Tens

Context of the Lesson This is the second of two lessons reviewing the base-ten system of numbers. Understanding of the base-ten system of numeration leads to development of the two-digit addition algorithm later in this chapter.

See page 159B for Math Background for teachers for this lesson.

Planning for Learning ● DIFFERENTIATE INSTRUCTION

INTERVENTION
If . . . students lack the prerequisite skill of knowing addition facts,

Then . . . teach Intervention Lesson 5.A.

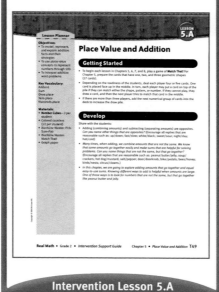

Intervention Lesson 5.A

ENGLISH LEARNER
Preview

If . . . students need language support,

Then . . . use Lesson 5.2 in *English Learner Support Guide* to preview lesson concepts and vocabulary.

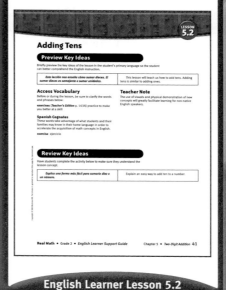

English Learner Lesson 5.2

ENRICH
If . . . students are proficient in the lesson concepts,

Then . . . emphasize additional game time.

PRACTICE
If . . . students would benefit from additional practice,

Then . . . extend Guided Discussion before assigning the student pages.

RETEACH
If . . . students are having difficulty understanding adding tens,

Then . . . extend Guided Discussion before assigning the student pages.

Access Vocabulary
exercises practice to make you better at a skill

Spanish Cognates
exercise ejercicio

Mental Math 5

  Form amounts of money using the overhead coins, and have students use **Number Cubes** to show the numerical equivalents. Possible examples include the following:

a. five dimes and three pennies 53
b. eight dimes and nine pennies 89
c. four dimes and five pennies 45
d. five dimes and two pennies 52
e. six dimes and one penny 61
f. four dimes and two pennies 42
g. six dimes and seven pennies 67
h. two dimes and two pennies 22

1 Develop 20

Tell Students In Today's Lesson They Will
practice adding tens.

Guided Discussion UNDERSTANDING
Whole Group

Have students count in unison from 1 through 20 as you write the numbers on the board. Then have them count by tens as you write the numbers beside the corresponding units numbers. In the second column, when you get to 100, stop and ask how to write the next number and how to say it. Discuss the fact that it is 11 tens and is written with a 0 after an 11. Ask a question such as the following:

■ **How is that number usually read?** one hundred ten or one hundred and ten

Repeat for 120, and so on.

Then ask if anyone can give the answer to the problem 30 + 50. If a student can, have him or her explain how to get the answer (3 tens plus 5 tens equals 8 tens). Do several more exercises. Then do several similar exercises written in vertical form.

2 Assign Student Pages 25

Pages 163–164 COMPUTING

Have students complete pages 163 and 164 individually or in small groups.

Monitoring Student Progress

If . . . students are having difficulty seeing the relationship between ones and tens,	**Then . . .** have students form a two-digit number with their **Number Cubes.** Then ask questions such as: *If you add ten to this number, which cube must be changed? If you add one to this number, which cube must be changed?*

As Students Finish

Game **Get to 100 by Tens or Ones Game** (Introduced in Lesson 5.1)

Building Blocks *School Supply Shop*

RESEARCH IN ACTION

"The beauty and seeming simplicity of the base-ten number system can contribute greatly to the students' acquisition of mathematical power as well as their ability to view mathematics as a sense-making endeavor. However, such an appreciation does not develop unnurtured for most students. It results only if we present frequent opportunities over an extended time for students to construct understanding of place value, a concept that is difficult and slow to develop for most students."

Sowder, Judith and Bonnie Schappelle. "Number Sense-Making."
Arithmetic Teacher, February 1994.

LESSON 5.2 Adding Tens

Key Ideas

Adding tens is similar to adding ones.

$3 + 5 = 8$

3 tens + 5 tens = 8 tens

$30 + 50 = 80$

Add. Counting by tens will help you do these without using paper and pencil.

① $10 + 0 = \underline{10}$

② $10 + 10 = \underline{20}$

③ $10 + 10 + 10 = \underline{30}$

④ $20 + 10 = \underline{30}$

⑤ $10 + 10 + 10 + 10 = \underline{40}$

⑥ $30 + 10 = \underline{40}$

⑦ $10 + 10 + 10 + 10 + 10 = \underline{50}$

⑧ $40 + 10 = \underline{50}$

⑨ $10 + 10 + 10 + 10 + 10 + 10 = \underline{60}$

⑩ $50 + 10 = \underline{60}$

⑪ $10 + 10 + 10 + 10 + 10 + 10 + 10 = \underline{70}$

⑫ $60 + 10 = \underline{70}$

Textbook This lesson is available in the *eTextbook*.

163

LESSON 5.2 · Adding Tens

Add. The exercises in one column will help you solve the exercises in the other column.

⑬ $3 + 5 = \underline{8}$ ⑭ $30 + 50 = \underline{80}$

⑮ $5 + 2 = \underline{7}$ ⑯ $50 + 20 = \underline{70}$

⑰ $8 + 7 = \underline{15}$ ⑱ $80 + 70 = \underline{150}$

⑲ $\begin{array}{r} 8 \\ + 4 \\ \hline 12 \end{array}$ ⑳ $\begin{array}{r} 80 \\ + 40 \\ \hline 120 \end{array}$ ㉑ $\begin{array}{r} 7 \\ + 3 \\ \hline 10 \end{array}$ ㉒ $\begin{array}{r} 70 \\ + 30 \\ \hline 100 \end{array}$

 Journal

Describe how knowing the sum of $6 + 3$ can help you know the sum of $60 + 30$.

164   **Real Math** • Chapter 5 • Lesson 2

 Reflect 10

Guided Discussion REASONING

Whole Group

Using student page 164 as a guide, have student volunteers explain in their own words how the exercises in the right and left columns are related.

 **Journal** ✓

Students should explain that $60 + 30$ is the same as 6 tens + 3 tens. Because students know that $6 + 3 = 9$, then they also know that 6 tens + 3 tens = 9 tens, or $60 + 30 = 90$.

Cumulative Review: For cumulative review of previously learned skills, see page 173–174.

Family Involvement: Assign the *Practice, Reteach,* or *Enrichment* activities depending on the needs of your students.

Having students play an appropriate variation of the **Get to 100 by Tens or Ones Game** will also be beneficial.

Concept/Question Board: Have students look for additional examples using multidigit addition and post them on the Concept/Question Board.

Math Puzzler: Which is greater, 4 tens and 5 or 5 tens and 4? How can you tell? 5 tens and 4 is greater; because there are more tens or because 54 is greater than 45.

Assess and Differentiate

 Assess Use *eAssess* to record and analyze evidence of student understanding.

A Gather Evidence

Use the Daily Class Assessment Records in *Assessment* or *eAssess* to record daily observations.

Informal Assessment
☑ **Guided Discussion**

Did the student **UNDERSTANDING**
- ❑ make important observations?
- ❑ extend or generalize learning?
- ❑ provide insightful answers?
- ❑ pose insightful questions?

Portfolio Assessment
☑ **Journal**

Did the student **REASONING**
- ❑ provide a clear explanation?
- ❑ communicate reasons and strategies?
- ❑ choose appropriate strategies?
- ❑ argue logically?

B Summarize Findings

Analyze and summarize assessment data for each student. Determine which Assessment Follow-Up is appropriate for each student. Use the Student Assessment Record in *Assessment* or *eAssess* to update assessment records.

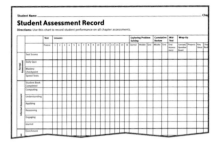

Assessment page T41

C Assessment Follow-Up ● DIFFERENTIATE INSTRUCTION

Based on your observations, use these teaching strategies for assessment follow-up.

INTERVENTION

Review student performance on *Intervention* Lesson 5.A to see if students have mastered prerequisite skills for this lesson.

ENGLISH LEARNER

Review

Use Lesson 5.2 in *English Learner Support Guide* to review lesson concepts and vocabulary.

ENRICH

If . . . students are proficient in the lesson concepts,

Then . . . encourage them to work on the chapter projects or *Enrichment* Lesson 5.2.

Enrichment Lesson 5.2

PRACTICE

If . . . students would benefit from additional practice,

Then . . . assign *Practice* Lesson 5.2.

Practice Lesson 5.2

RETEACH

If . . . students are having difficulty understanding adding tens,

Then . . . assign *Reteach* Lesson 5.2.

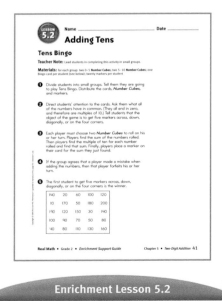

Reteach Lesson 5.2

Lesson Planner

OBJECTIVES

- To practice using craft sticks or other base-ten materials to represent two-digit numbers
- To teach students to convert numbers written in nonstandard form to standard form

NCTM STANDARDS

Number and Operations

- Using multiple models to develop initial understanding of place value and the base-ten number system
- Developing understanding of the relative position and magnitude of whole numbers
- Developing a sense of whole numbers and representing and using them in flexible ways, including relating, composing, and decomposing numbers
- Developing and using strategies for addition
- Developing fluency with basic number combinations for addition
- Using a variety of methods and tools to compute, including objects, mental computation, estimation, paper and pencil, and calculators

Problem Solving

- Building new mathematical knowledge through problem solving
- Applying and adapting a variety of appropriate strategies to solve problems

MATERIALS

- *Number Cubes
- *Craft sticks and rubber bands or other base-ten materials

TECHNOLOGY

- e Presentation Lesson 5.3
- e MathTools Base Ten
- Building Blocks Book Stacks

TEST PREP

Cumulative Review (Review)

Mental Math reviews adding tens (Lesson 5.2).

Regrouping for Addition

Context of the Lesson This is the first of five lessons that introduces the algorithm, or step-by-step procedure, for addition of two-digit numbers. In this lesson students learn to convert numbers represented by base-ten materials and written in nonstandard form (such as *3 bundles of ten sticks and 7 single sticks*) into standard form (37). This skill is necessary for the addition of two two-digit numbers.

See page 159B for Math Background for teachers for this lesson.

Planning for Learning ● DIFFERENTIATE INSTRUCTION

INTERVENTION

If . . . students lack the prerequisite skill of knowing addition facts,

Then . . . teach *Intervention* Lesson 5.A.

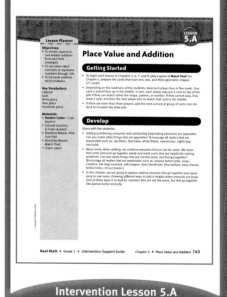

Intervention Lesson 5.A

ENGLISH LEARNER

Preview

If . . . students need language support,

Then . . . use Lesson 5.3 in *English Learner Support Guide* to preview lesson concepts and vocabulary.

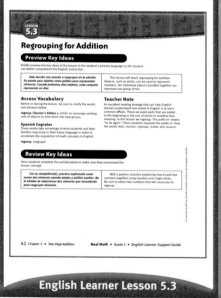

English Learner Lesson 5.3

ENRICH

If . . . students are proficient in the lesson concepts,

Then . . . emphasize exploring *eMathTools.*

PRACTICE

If . . . students would benefit from additional practice,

Then . . . extend Skill Practice before assigning the student pages.

RETEACH

If . . . students are having difficulty understanding regrouping for addition,

Then . . . extend Guided Discussion before assigning the student pages.

Access Vocabulary
regroup to rearrange existing sets of objects to form them into new groups

Spanish Cognates
regroup reagrupar

---

*Manipulative Kit Item

Mental Math 5

  Write addition statements on the board as students find, hide, and show the sums. Use examples in which the addends are multiples of ten. Possible examples include the following:

a. 20 + 50 = 70   **b.** 30 + 40 = 70   **c.** 70 + 50 = 120
d. 30 + 30 = 60   **e.** 10 + 20 = 30   **f.** 90 + 10 = 100
g. 60 + 80 = 140   **h.** 30 + 10 = 40   **i.** 20 + 20 = 40

1 Develop 15

Tell Students In Today's Lesson They Will

represent numbers with craft sticks.

Whole Group

Guided Discussion MathTools UNDERSTANDING

With the class watching, place sticks on a desk, or use *eMathTools: Base Ten,* to form various two-digit numbers, and have the class find, hide, and show the number represented with their **Number Cubes.** For example, place the following:

3 bundles of 10 and 7   37

5 bundles of 10 and 6   56

1 bundle of 10 and 7   17

Next, place 2 bundles of 10 and 15 single sticks on a desk. Say that you have 2 bundles of 10 and 15 more.

- **How many is that?** 35
- **How could you show that fact with the sticks?** by regrouping the sticks into 3 tens and 5 single sticks

Give several exercises that have more than 10 loose sticks, but include some that have fewer than 10. Have students regroup the sticks.

Skill Practice COMPUTING

Whole Group

 Give exercises in which you show groupings of craft sticks in which some of the single sticks should be regrouped as a bundle of ten. Students should show their answers with **Number Cubes.** Give exercises such as the following:

a. 7 tens and 15 85   **b.** 4 tens and 17 57
c. 5 tens and 10 60   **d.** 8 tens and 14 94
e. 2 tens and 12 32   **f.** 9 tens and 10 100

2 Assign Student Pages 30

Pages 165–166   UNDERSTANDING

Have students complete pages 165 and 166. Students may use craft sticks or other base-ten materials as they complete these pages.

Monitoring Student Progress

| **If . . .** students are having difficulty with regrouping, | **Then . . .** use craft sticks to model the exercises, taking turns as you give the student an exercise, and then allow the student to give you an exercise. |

As Students Finish

Game **Yard Sale Game** (Introduced in Lesson 1.5)

Building Blocks *Book Stacks*

MathTools *Base Ten* Have students explore base-ten groupings.

Student Page

Name _____ Date _____

LESSON 5.3 **Regrouping for Addition**

Key Ideas

Two bundles of ten and 14 craft sticks can be regrouped as 3 bundles of ten and 4 craft sticks, or 34.

Write the standard name for each of these.

1. 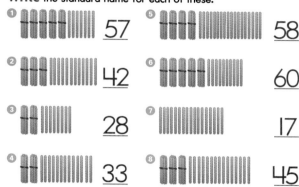 **57**
2. **42**
3. **28**
4. **33**
5. **58**
6. **60**
7. **17**
8. **45**

Textbook This lesson is available in the *eTextbook*.

165

Student Page

LESSON 5.3 • Regrouping for Addition

Write the standard name for each of these.
Use craft sticks if you need help.

9. 6 tens and 8 = **68**
10. 8 tens and 19 = **99**
11. 1 ten and 8 = **18**
12. 7 tens and 16 = **86**
13. 8 tens and 0 = **80**
14. 0 tens and 8 = **8**
15. 1 ten and 14 = **24**
16. 4 tens and 18 = **58**

166   **Real Math • Chapter 5 • Lesson 3**

3 Reflect   10

Guided Discussion   REASONING   Whole Group

As a brief preview of what is coming in the next lessons, set up a two-digit addition exercise, and allow students to discuss how to find the sum. A possible example includes the following:

Place 3 groups of 10 and 7 single craft sticks on a desk, and separately place 4 groups of 10 and 5 single sticks. Have students tell you how many sticks are in each group. 37 and 45

Now ask how many sticks there are altogether. Through discussion and demonstration, show how you can combine the tens to get 7 groups of 10, and combine the single sticks to get 12 single sticks.

Finally ask, *What is another name for 7 tens and 12?* Help students to see that they can put a rubber band around 10 of the single sticks, so the answer is 8 tens and 2 or 82. Thus, 37 + 45 = 82.

 Cumulative Review: For cumulative review of previously learned skills, see page 173–174.

 Family Involvement: Assign the *Practice, Reteach,* or *Enrichment* activities depending on the needs of your students.

Have students play the **Yard Sale Game** with a helper at home.

 Concept/Question Board: Have students look for additional examples using multidigit addition and post them on the Concept/Question Board.

 Math Puzzler: Henry bought two pens that cost 50¢ each. Aiko bought one pen for 80¢. Who spent more money? How much more? Henry; he spent 20¢ more.

4 Assess and Differentiate

 Assess Use *eAssess* to record and analyze evidence of student understanding.

A Gather Evidence

Use the Daily Class Assessment Records in *Assessment* or *eAssess* to record daily observations.

Informal Assessment
☑ **Mental Math**

Did the student `COMPUTING`
- ❏ respond accurately?
- ❏ respond quickly?
- ❏ respond with confidence?
- ❏ self-correct?

Informal Assessment
☑ **Student Pages**

Did the student `UNDERSTANDING`
- ❏ make important observations?
- ❏ extend or generalize learning?
- ❏ provide insightful answers?
- ❏ pose insightful questions?

B Summarize Findings

Analyze and summarize assessment data for each student. Determine which Assessment Follow-Up is appropriate for each student. Use the Student Assessment Record in *Assessment* or *eAssess* to update assessment records.

Assessment page T41

C Assessment Follow-Up ● DIFFERENTIATE INSTRUCTION

Based on your observations, use these teaching strategies for assessment follow-up.

INTERVENTION	ENRICH	PRACTICE	RETEACH
Review student performance on *Intervention* Lesson 5.A to see if students have mastered prerequisite skills for this lesson.	**If . . .** students are proficient in the lesson concepts, **Then . . .** encourage them to work on the chapter projects or *Enrichment* Lesson 5.3.	**If . . .** students would benefit from additional practice, **Then . . .** assign *Practice* Lesson 5.3.	**If . . .** students are having difficulty understanding regrouping, **Then . . .** assign *Reteach* Lesson 5.3.

ENGLISH LEARNER

Review

Use Lesson 5.3 in *English Learner Support Guide* to review lesson concepts and vocabulary.

Enrichment Lesson 5.3

Practice Lesson 5.3

Reteach Lesson 5.3

OBJECTIVES
- To provide an initial experience in adding two-digit numbers
- To continue to provide experience in recognizing situations that require addition

NCTM STANDARDS

Number and Operations
- Using multiple models to develop initial understanding of place value and the base-ten number system
- Developing understanding of the relative position and magnitude of whole numbers
- Developing a sense of whole numbers and representing and using them in flexible ways, including relating, composing, and decomposing numbers
- Developing and using strategies for addition
- Developing fluency with basic number combinations for addition
- Using a variety of methods and tools to compute, including objects, mental computation, estimation, paper and pencil, and calculators

Representation
- Creating and using representations to organize, record, and communicate mathematical ideas
- Selecting, applying, and translating among mathematical representations to solve problems

MATERIALS
- *Number Cubes
- *Craft sticks and rubber bands or other base-ten materials

TECHNOLOGY
ePresentation Lesson 5.4
Building Blocks Number Snapshots 10

TEST PREP
Cumulative Review
Mental Math reviews adding two-digit numbers (Lesson 5.3).

*Manipulative Kit Item

Adding Two-Digit Numbers

Context of the Lesson This is the second of five lessons that introduces the algorithm for addition of two-digit numbers. This lesson is designed to help students understand clearly what addition is and how they can find sums through inefficient but correct methods that they already understand (such as the use of base-ten materials). The methods used in this lesson and the next two may be difficult for students, but experience has shown that they lead to a much quicker understanding and mastery of the complete addition algorithm, which will begin to be introduced in Lesson 5.7.

See page 159B for Math Background for teachers for this lesson.

Planning for Learning ● DIFFERENTIATE INSTRUCTION

INTERVENTION

If . . . students lack the prerequisite skill of knowing addition facts,

Then . . . teach **Intervention** Lesson 5.A.

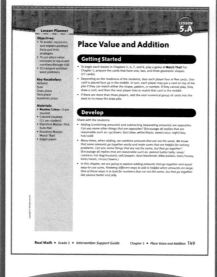

Intervention Lesson 5.A

ENGLISH LEARNER

Preview

If . . . students need language support,

Then . . . use Lesson 5.4 in **English Learner Support Guide** to preview lesson concepts and vocabulary.

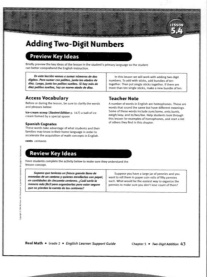

English Learner Lesson 5.4

ENRICH

If . . . students are proficient in the lesson concepts,

Then . . . emphasize additional game time.

PRACTICE

If . . . students would benefit from additional practice,

Then . . . extend Guided Discussion before assigning the student pages.

RETEACH

If . . . students are having difficulty understanding adding two-digit numbers,

Then . . . extend Guided Discussion before assigning the student pages.

Access Vocabulary
ice-cream scoop a ball of ice cream formed by a special spoon

Spanish Cognates
cents centavos

Mental Math 5

  Write addition statements on the board as students find, hide, and show the sums. Use examples in which at least one of the numbers is a multiple of ten. Possible examples include the following:

a. 35 + 40 = 75 **b.** 75 + 20 = 95 **c.** 25 + 50 = 75
d. 45 + 20 = 65 **e.** 25 + 20 = 45 **f.** 75 + 10 = 85
g. 65 + 30 = 95 **h.** 90 + 10 = 100 **i.** 0 + 0 = 0
j. 0 + 50 = 50 **k.** 50 + 20 = 70 **l.** 30 + 45 = 75

1 Develop 20

Tell Students In Today's Lesson They Will
practice two-digit addition with craft sticks.

Guided Discussion REASONING
Whole Group

1. Have a group of five volunteers come to the front of the room. Have four volunteers hold up all ten fingers and the fifth volunteer hold up eight fingers. Then have a group of four more volunteers join the first group. Have three of the new volunteers hold up all ten fingers and the fourth volunteer hold up five fingers.

   Point out that it would be easier to count fingers if all students holding up ten fingers were standing together so you could count by tens. Count to confirm that seven tens and thirteen fingers are being held up. Help students see that it would be even easier to count fingers if the student holding up eight fingers turned up two more and the student holding up five fingers turned down two, resulting in eight tens and three.

2. Count four bundles of sticks and then eight single sticks. Ask students how many sticks you have, and discuss how they know. Ask how many sticks you would have if you took three more bundles of ten and five more single sticks. Let students work on this while you actually take three more bundles of ten and five single sticks. When someone has an answer, ask how he or she got it. The answer seven tens and thirteen is good, but ask for the standard form. Ask if you could make another bundle of ten from the thirteen—then how many bundles of ten would there be? eight How many single sticks would be left over? three

2 Assign Student Pages 25

Pages 167–168 UNDERSTANDING

Have students complete pages 167 and 168 individually or in small groups. Students should use craft sticks or other base-ten materials. Because they are not expected to use a standard algorithm at this time, the horizontal format of these exercises should not trouble them.

Monitoring Student Progress

| If . . . students are having trouble with two-digit addition, | Then . . . the most efficient approach is to make up a problem together with the student, and then use base-ten materials to model the problem. |

As Students Finish

 Give a choice of games from among those previously introduced, or assign games based on individual needs.

Building Blocks *Number Snapshots 10*

RESEARCH IN ACTION

"Proficiency with multidigit computation is more heavily influenced by instruction than single-digit computation is. Many features of multidigit procedures are not part of children's everyday experience and need to be learned in the classroom. . . . Children can and do devise or invent algorithms for carrying out multidigit computations. Opportunities to construct their own procedures provide students with opportunities to make connections between the strands of proficiency. Procedural fluency is built directly on their understanding."

Kilpatrick, J., J. Swafford, and B. Findell, eds. *Adding It Up: Helping Children Learn Mathematics.* Washington, D.C.: National Research Council/Academy Press, 2001, p. 197.

LESSON 5.4 Adding Two-Digit Numbers

Key Ideas

To add with craft sticks, put bundles of ten together. Put single sticks together. Then make a new bundle if you have enough single sticks.

$48 + 35 =$ ____

1. two groups

2. combine groups

3. regroup

$48 + 35 = 83$

Use craft sticks or other objects to help add.

❶ $50 + 23 = \underline{73}$
There are $\underline{73}$ sticks.

❷ $35 + 29 = \underline{64}$
There are $\underline{64}$ sticks.

Copyright © SRA/McGraw Hill.

Textbook This lesson is available in the *eTextbook*.   167

LESSON 5.4 · Adding Two-Digit Numbers

Use craft sticks or other objects to help add.

❸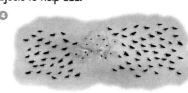
$28 + 24 = \underline{52}$
There are $\underline{52}$ scoops.

❹
$34 + 48 = \underline{82}$
There are $\underline{82}$ ants.

How many cents?

❺
$34 + 47 = \underline{81}$ There are $\underline{81}$ cents.

❻
$58 + 35 = \underline{93}$ There are $\underline{93}$ cents.

Do these exercises. Use any objects you want to help add.

❼ $17 + 18 = \underline{35}$ ❿ $23 + 15 = \underline{38}$

❽ $82 + 17 = \underline{99}$ ⓫ $13 + 68 = \underline{81}$

❾ $26 + 37 = \underline{63}$ ⓬ $53 + 42 = \underline{95}$

Copyright © SRA/McGraw Hill.

168   **Real Math** • Chapter 5 • Lesson 4

---

3 Reflect   10 ⏱

Guided Discussion ✓ REASONING   Whole Group

Write the following two word problems on the board:

Malcolm drove 54 miles to visit a friend. He drove 37 more miles to visit another friend. How many miles did Malcolm drive?

Lola picked 54 tomatoes from her garden on Monday. She picked 37 more tomatoes on Tuesday. How many tomatoes did Lola pick on both days?

Through discussion, have students decide on an equation for each problem and write them on the board. Point out that, although the problems are different, both can be solved by identical equations.

Finally, have students use sticks to find the sums for both problems as you point out that in one problem, each stick represents 1 mile, while in the other problem each stick represents 1 tomato.

REAL WORLD **Curriculum Connection:** Students may be interested in researching how many scoops were in the world's tallest ice-cream cone.

Review **Cumulative Review:** For cumulative review of previously learned skills, see page 173–174.

Family Involvement: Assign the *Practice, Reteach,* or *Enrichment* activities depending on the needs of your students.

Concept/Question Board: Have students look for additional examples using multidigit addition and post them on the Concept/Question Board.

Math Puzzler: What is a two-digit number in which the sum of its digits is 15 and the difference is 3? 96 or 69

Assess and Differentiate

 Assess Use *eAssess* to record and analyze evidence of student understanding.

A Gather Evidence

Use the Daily Class Assessment Records in *Assessment* or *eAssess* to record daily observations.

Informal Assessment
☑ **Mental Math**

Did the student **COMPUTING**
- ❑ respond accurately?
- ❑ respond quickly?
- ❑ respond with confidence?
- ❑ self-correct?

Informal Assessment
☑ **Guided Discussion**

Did the student **REASONING**
- ❑ provide a clear explanation?
- ❑ communicate reasons and strategies?
- ❑ choose appropriate strategies?
- ❑ argue logically?

B Summarize Findings

Analyze and summarize assessment data for each student. Determine which Assessment Follow-Up is appropriate for each student. Use the Student Assessment Record in *Assessment* or *eAssess* to update assessment records.

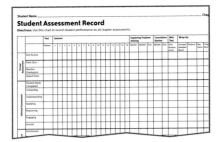

Assessment page T41

C Assessment Follow-Up ● DIFFERENTIATE INSTRUCTION

Based on your observations, use these teaching strategies for assessment follow-up.

INTERVENTION	ENRICH	PRACTICE	RETEACH
Review student performance on *Intervention* Lesson 5.A to see if students have mastered prerequisite skills for this lesson.	**If . . .** students are proficient in the lesson concepts, **Then . . .** encourage them to work on the chapter projects or *Enrichment* Lesson 5.4.	**If . . .** students would benefit from additional practice, **Then . . .** assign *Practice* Lesson 5.4.	**If . . .** students are having difficulty adding two-digit numbers, **Then . . .** have students say each step aloud.

ENGLISH LEARNER

Review

Use Lesson 5.4 in *English Learner Support Guide* to review lesson concepts and vocabulary.

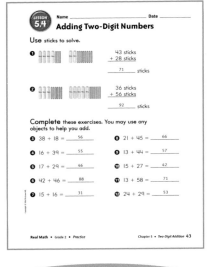

Enrichment Lesson 5.4

Practice Lesson 5.4

Lesson Planner

OBJECTIVES
- To teach students to add two-digit numbers with sums equal to a multiple of ten
- To continue to provide experience in the recognition of situations that require addition

NCTM STANDARDS
Number and Operations
- Using multiple models to develop initial understanding of place value and the base-ten number system
- Developing understanding of the relative position and magnitude of whole numbers
- Developing a sense of whole numbers and representing and using them in flexible ways, including relating, composing, and decomposing numbers
- Developing and using strategies for addition
- Developing fluency with basic number combinations for addition
- Using a variety of methods and tools to compute, including objects, mental computation, estimation, paper and pencil, and calculators

Problem Solving
- Building new mathematical knowledge through problem solving
- Applying and adapting a variety of appropriate strategies to solve problems

MATERIALS
- *Number Cubes
- *Craft sticks and rubber bands or other base-ten materials
- *Play money ($10 and $1 bills)

TECHNOLOGY
ⓔ **Presentation** Lesson 5.5

Building **B**locks **Figure the Fact: Two-Digit Adding**

TEST PREP
Cumulative Review
Mental Math reviews two-digit addition (Lesson 5.4).

More Adding Two-Digit Numbers

Context of the Lesson This is the third of five lessons that introduce the algorithm for addition of two numbers. This lesson continues to use base-ten materials to introduce students to the algorithm. The use of base-ten manipulatives is important because it leads to an understanding of place value and to why the addition algorithm works. Students who simply memorize an algorithm can produce correct answers but have little understanding of why the procedures work, which will lead to a disadvantage in future work in mathematics.

See page 159B for Math Background for teachers for this lesson.

Planning for Learning ● DIFFERENTIATE INSTRUCTION

INTERVENTION
If . . . students lack the prerequisite skill of understanding place value to 100,

Then . . . teach *Intervention* Lesson 5.B.

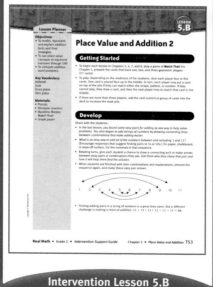

Intervention Lesson 5.B

ENGLISH LEARNER
Preview

If . . . students need language support,

Then . . . use Lesson 5.5 in *English Learner Support Guide* to preview lesson concepts and vocabulary.

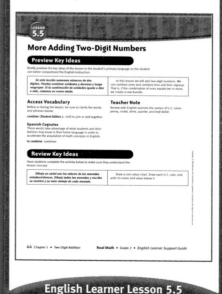

English Learner Lesson 5.5

ENRICH
If . . . students are proficient in the lesson concepts,

Then . . . emphasize additional game time.

PRACTICE
If . . . students would benefit from additional practice,

Then . . . extend Skill Building before assigning the student pages.

RETEACH
If . . . students are having difficulty understanding adding two-digit numbers,

Then . . . extend Skill Building before assigning the student pages.

Access Vocabulary
combine to join or add together

Spanish Cognates
to combine combinar

*Manipulative Kit Item

Mental Math 5

Write addition statements on the board as students find, hide, and show the sums. Use examples in which at least one of the numbers is a multiple of ten. Possible examples include the following:

a. 30 + 25 = 55 **b.** 55 + 20 = 75 **c.** 75 + 20 = 95
d. 25 + 20 + 5 = 50 **e.** 10 + 25 = 35 **f.** 50 + 25 = 75
g. 50 + 20 = 70 **h.** 75 + 10 = 85 **i.** 80 + 20 = 100
j. 10 + 80 = 90 **k.** 20 + 75 = 95 **l.** 40 + 55 = 95

1 Develop 20

Tell Students In Today's Lesson They Will

continue practicing two-digit addition.

Skill Building **APPLYING**

Small Group

Present problems in which the sum of the ones digits is ten, and have students find the sums and discuss their solutions in small groups. All the problems should have sums less than or equal to 100. The students should have craft sticks or other base-ten materials to work with as they solve the problems, or they may use fingers to solve if there are enough students in the group. Possible examples include the following:

- **Pedro baked 28 cookies in one pan and 22 cookies in another. How many cookies did he bake?** 50
- **One package weighs 35 pounds. Another package weighs 25 pounds. How much do they weigh altogether?** 60 pounds
- **Ying had $17. She earned $13. How much money does she have now?** $30

2 Assign Student Pages 25

Pages 169–170 **UNDERSTANDING**

Have students complete pages 169 and 170 individually. Allow students to work with base-ten materials.

Monitoring Student Progress

If . . . students have difficulty adding two-digit numbers,

Then . . . continue to offer help with base-ten manipulatives.

As Students Finish

Game Give a choice of games from among those previously introduced, or assign games based on individual needs.

Building Blocks *Figure the Fact: Two-Digit Adding*

RESEARCH IN ACTION

"A number of researchers have argued that mental arithmetic—calculating the solution to multidigit arithmetic problems mentally without the use of pencil and paper—can lead to deeper insights into the number system. . . . Mental arithmetic, or mental math, can provide opportunities for students to practice and use numbers and operations in ways that promote making sense of the mathematics and reveal further insights into the properties of numbers and operations."

Kilpatrick, J., J. Swafford, and B. Findell, eds. *Adding It Up: Helping Children Learn Mathematics.* Washington, D.C.: National Research Council/National Academy Press, 2001, p. 214.

Name _____ Date _____

LESSON 5.5 More Adding Two-Digit Numbers

Key Ideas

To add two-digit numbers, you can combine tens, combine ones, and then regroup.

$$\begin{array}{r} 31 \\ + 19 \\ \hline \end{array}$$

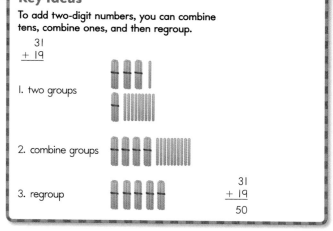

1. two groups

2. combine groups

3. regroup

$$\begin{array}{r} 31 \\ + 19 \\ \hline 50 \end{array}$$

Use craft sticks or other objects to help add.

❶  46 sticks

24 sticks

$$\begin{array}{r} 46 \\ + 24 \\ \hline 70 \end{array}$$

Textbook This lesson is available in the *eTextbook*.

169

LESSON 5.5 · More Adding Two-Digit Numbers

Use craft sticks or other objects to help add.

❷  27 books

23 books

$$\begin{array}{r} 27 \\ + 23 \\ \hline 50 \end{array}$$

❸   45¢

 25¢

$$\begin{array}{r} 45 \\ + 25 \\ \hline 70 \end{array}$$

Add.

❹ $\begin{array}{r} 14 \\ + 36 \\ \hline 50 \end{array}$	❺ $\begin{array}{r} 17 \\ + 13 \\ \hline 30 \end{array}$	❻ $\begin{array}{r} 24 \\ + 56 \\ \hline 80 \end{array}$
❼ $\begin{array}{r} 49 \\ + 31 \\ \hline 80 \end{array}$	❽ $\begin{array}{r} 49 \\ + 32 \\ \hline 81 \end{array}$	❾ $\begin{array}{r} 49 \\ + 33 \\ \hline 82 \end{array}$
❿ $\begin{array}{r} 52 \\ + 8 \\ \hline 60 \end{array}$	⓫ $\begin{array}{r} 35 \\ + 35 \\ \hline 70 \end{array}$	⓬ $\begin{array}{r} 73 \\ + 7 \\ \hline 80 \end{array}$

---

3 Reflect   10

Guided Discussion REASONING   Whole Group

Demonstrate how you can use play money ($1 bills and $10 bills) to model one of the problems on student page 169 or 170.

Then initiate a discussion that allows students to tell which model, the sticks or the play money, is most helpful. Possible explanations might include the idea that with sticks it is easier to see that a bundle of ten sticks represents 10. It is harder to think of a $10 bill representing ten $1 bills. Some students might say that the play money is more like real life.

Conclude the discussion by pointing out that both the sticks and the play money may be used correctly as models for adding two-digit numbers.

Cumulative Review: For cumulative review of previously learned skills, see page 173–174.

Family Involvement: Assign the *Practice, Reteach,* or *Enrichment* activities depending on the needs of your students.

Concept/Question Board: Encourage students to continue to post questions, answers, and examples on the Concept/Question Board.

Math Puzzler: There are 130 animals in a shelter: 80 are dogs, 10 are rabbits, and the rest are cats. How many are cats? 40

4 Assess and Differentiate

 Assess Use **eAssess** to record and analyze evidence of student understanding.

A Gather Evidence

Use the Daily Class Assessment Records in **Assessment** or **eAssess** to record daily observations.

Informal Assessment
☑ Student Pages

Did the student UNDERSTANDING
- ☐ make important observations?
- ☐ extend or generalize learning?
- ☐ provide insightful answers?
- ☐ pose insightful questions?

Informal Assessment
☑ Concept/Question Board

Did the student APPLYING
- ☐ apply learning in new situations?
- ☐ contribute concepts?
- ☐ contribute answers?
- ☐ connect mathematics to real-world situations?

B Summarize Findings

Analyze and summarize assessment data for each student. Determine which Assessment Follow-Up is appropriate for each student. Use the Student Assessment Record in **Assessment** or **eAssess** to update assessment records.

Assessment page T41

C Assessment Follow-Up • DIFFERENTIATE INSTRUCTION

Based on your observations, use these teaching strategies for assessment follow-up.

INTERVENTION

Review student performance on **Intervention** Lesson 5.B to see if students have mastered prerequisite skills for this lesson.

ENGLISH LEARNER

Review

Use Lesson 5.5 in **English Learner Support Guide** to review lesson concepts and vocabulary.

ENRICH

If . . . students are proficient in the lesson concepts,

Then . . . encourage them to work on the chapter projects or **Enrichment** Lesson 5.5.

Enrichment Lesson 5.5

PRACTICE

If . . . students would benefit from additional practice,

Then . . . assign **Practice** Lesson 5.5.

Practice Lesson 5.5

RETEACH

If . . . students are still having difficulty adding two-digit numbers,

Then . . . it is possible they need to review the basic addition facts to speed up their computation.

Exploring Problem Solving

Name _____ Date _____

Listen to the problem.

Tanya is acting out the problem.

171

Objectives

- To explore the Act It Out and Make a Diagram strategies
- To provide practice with regrouping
- To provide practice in presenting solutions to nonroutine problems

Materials

Countable objects (about 60 per group)

Context of the Lesson Reasoning and problem solving are prevalent in every *Real Math* lesson. This lesson and other special problem-solving lessons allow more time for students to share and compare their strategies. While continuing the park and picnic theme, this lesson provides an additional opportunity for students to apply their developing skills with regrouping and adding two-digit numbers.

 **Develop** 5

Tell Students In Today's Lesson They Will

determine if there are enough juice boxes for everyone at a picnic.

Guided Discussion

Have students look at the picture on page 171 as you read the following problem to them:

On a field trip to a museum, two second-grade classes are going to have a picnic in a nearby park. There are 24 children in one of the classes and 25 in the other. Eight children have brought packs of juice boxes for the picnic. The boxes come in packs of 10, but as you can see in the picture, some of the boxes from each 10-pack have been left at home. The teachers want to know whether there are enough juice boxes for each child to have one. Use the information in the picture to find out.

To be sure students understand the problem, ask questions such as the following:

- **Where are the children going?** on a field trip to a museum
- **Why are they bringing juice boxes?** for their picnic lunch
- **What is the problem asking you to do?** to figure out if they have enough boxes of juice for every child to have one
- **How many juice boxes are in the first pack in the picture?** 7
- **How many boxes are in the second pack?** 8
- **How would you figure out if there are enough boxes of juice?** Allow students to offer approaches. See Sample Solutions Strategies under Reflect.

Tell students that they are going to have a chance to solve the problem, but first they will look at how two other children are trying to solve it.

Gilbert is making a diagram to solve the problem.

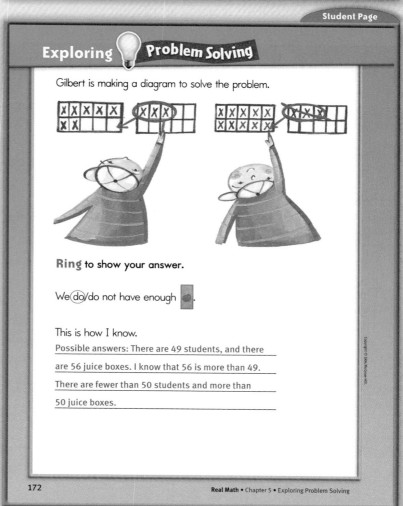

Ring to show your answer.

We do/do not have enough .

This is how I know.

Possible answers: There are 49 students, and there
are 56 juice boxes. I know that 56 is more than 49.
There are fewer than 50 students and more than
50 juice boxes.

172

Using Student Pages

Analyzing Sample Solution 1

Have students look at the picture on page 171 of Tanya solving the problem. Ask questions about her strategy, such as the following:

- **Look at the first picture. What do you think the cubes stand for?** juice boxes
- **What has Tanya done with the cubes?** She has arranged them to match the number of boxes in each pack.
- **What is she doing in the second picture?** She is breaking off 3 cubes from the group of 5.
- **What is she doing in the third picture?** adding those 3 cubes to the group of 7 cubes to make 10
- **Why do you think she did that?** It is easier to work with groups of 10 than with groups of different numbers.
- **What do you think she will do next?** She might take the 2 cubes that are left over from the group of 5 and add them to the group of 8 to make another 10.
- **How will this help her solve the problem?** When she has regrouped the cubes to form as many groups of 10 as she can, it will be easier to see how many cubes she has altogether.

Analyzing Sample Solution 2

Tell students that Gilbert is using a different strategy to try to solve the problem. Have students look at the picture on page 172 of Gilbert's approach. Ask questions such as the following:

- **Look at the first picture. What do the Xs stand for?** juice boxes
- **What has Gilbert done to begin to solve the problem?** He has drawn a diagram to show how many juice boxes are in each group. He has included the empty boxes that show how many more he would need to have a full 10-pack. He has ringed 3 boxes from a group of 5 and drawn an arrow to the 3 empty places in the group of 7.
- **What has he done in the second picture?** He has crossed out the 3 boxes he had ringed and is redrawing them in the first group.
- **So far, how is Gilbert's method like Tanya's, and how is it different?** Like Tanya, Gilbert is using something to stand for the juice boxes so he can show how many are in each pack. Also, he is making groups of 10. Gilbert's method differs in that he is using a picture instead of using objects to keep track of what he is doing.
- **What do you think he will do next?** He will probably continue to move boxes into different groups to make full 10-packs.
- **How will you work on this problem?** Allow students to share what they like about Tanya's and Gilbert's strategies and what they would do differently.

Have students work on the problem individually or in pairs. They may use Tanya's strategy, Gilbert's strategy, or one of their own. Provide support as needed, remembering to suggest approaches rather than show them the answer. Remind students to check their answers.

 **Knowledge Age Skills**

Problem Formulation, Planning, and Strategizing Ask students to share their solutions and their strategies. In discussion bring out the following points:

- Different strategies can be used to solve the same problem.
- Different people may prefer different strategies for solving problems.
- There are different ways to add a group of numbers.
- A good way to check your answer is to do the same problem using a different strategy.

Sample Solutions Strategies

Students might use one or more of the following strategies to solve the problem.

Act It Out

Students might use cubes or other similar materials to create groups equal to the groups in the problem and then combine them and count them. They may or may not group them into tens.

Write a Number Sentence

Students might write the number in each pack and then write one or more number sentences to find the total. For example,

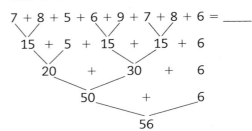

$$7 + 8 + 5 + 6 + 9 + 7 + 8 + 6 = \underline{\quad}$$

Use Approximation

Students might realize that $24 + 25$ is less than 50 because $25 + 25 = 50$, so they might stop adding the juice boxes when they reach 50, knowing that there must be enough.

When evaluating student work, focus not only on the correctness of the answer but also on whether the student thought rationally about the problem. Questions to consider include the following:

- Did the student understand the problem?
- Did the student understand the Sample Solutions Strategies?
- Was the student able to compare the number of children to the number of juice boxes?
- If the student regrouped, was the regrouping done correctly?
- Was the student able to explain his or her strategy?

Cumulative Review

Assign Pages 173–174

Use the Cumulative Review as a review of concepts and skills that students have previously learned.

Here are different ways that you can assign these problems to your students as they work through the chapter:

- With some of the lessons in the chapter, assign a set of cumulative review problems to be completed as practice or for homework.
  Lesson 5.1—Problems 1–3
  Lesson 5.2—Problems 4–6
  Lesson 5.3—Problems 7–12
  Lesson 5.4—Problems 13–16
  Lesson 5.5—Problems 17–20
- At any point during the chapter, assign part or all of the cumulative review problems to be completed as practice or for homework.

Cumulative Review

Problems 1–3 review counting on a number line, Lesson 1.7.

Problems 4–6 review collecting and recording data, Lesson 4.6.

Problems 7–12 review adding tens, Lesson 5.2.

Problems 13–16 review horizontal bar graphs, Lesson 4.11.

Problems 17–20 review regrouping items to make addition easier, Lesson 5.3.

Monitoring Student Progress

If . . . students miss more than one problem in a section,

Then . . . refer to the indicated lesson for remediation suggestions.

Cumulative Review

Name _____ Date _____

Counting on a Number Line Lesson 1.7

Solve using the number line. Ring each answer.

❶ 67 + 1
62 63 64 65 66 67 ⑥⑧ 69 70 71 72

❷ 20 − 1
14 15 16 17 18 ⑲ 20 21 22 23 24

❸ 41 − 2
35 36 37 38 ㉛ 40 41 42 43 44 45

Collecting and Recording Data Lesson 4.6

Use the table to answer the questions.

How Students Get to School	Number of Students
bus	卌 卌
car	卌
bike	IIII
walk	卌 II

❹ How many students walk to school? __7__

❺ How many students ride the bus? __10__

❻ How many students get to school on wheels? __19__

Adding Tens Lesson 5.2

Complete the following addition exercises.

❼ 10 + 10 + 10 + 10 + 10 = **50** ❿ 40 + 10 = **50**

❽ 10 + 10 + 10 + 10 + 10 + 10 = **60** ⓫ 50 + 10 = **60**

❾ 10 + 10 + 10 + 10 + 10 + 10 + 10 = **70** ⓬ 60 + 10 = **70**

Textbook This lesson is available in the *eTextbook*. 173

Cumulative Review

Horizontal Bar Graphs Lesson 4.11

Use the bar graph to answer the questions.

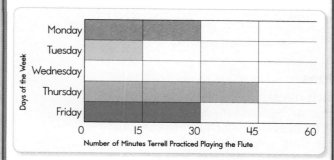

Days of the Week — Monday, Tuesday, Wednesday, Thursday, Friday
0   15   30   45   60
Number of Minutes Terrell Practiced Playing the Flute

⓭ How many minutes did Terrell practice on Tuesday? __15__

⓮ How many minutes did Terrell practice on Wednesday? __0__

⓯ On which days did Terrell practice for the same number of minutes? __Monday and Friday__

⓰ How many minutes did Terrell practice on Saturday? __can't tell__

Regrouping for Addition Lesson 5.3

How many sticks?

⓱ **54**   ⓳ **90**

⓲ **63**   ⓴ **4**

174 **Real Math • Chapter 5**

Individual Oral Assessment

Purpose of the Test

The Individual Oral Assessment is designed to measure students' growing knowledge of chapter concepts. It is administered individually to each student, and it requires oral responses from each student. The test takes about five minutes to complete. See **Assessment** for detailed instructions for administering and interpreting the test, and record students' answers on the Student Assessment Recording Sheet.

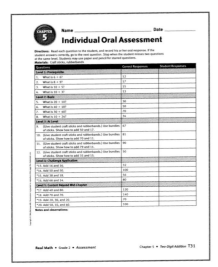

Assessment page T31

Directions

Read each question to the student, and record his or her oral response. If the student answers correctly, go to the next question. Stop when the student misses two questions at the same level. Students may use paper and pencil for Questions 13–20 only.

Materials

Craft sticks and rubber bands, paper and pencil

Questions

Level 1: Prerequisite
1. What is 6 + 6? 12
2. What is 8 + 9? 17
3. What is 10 + 5? 15
4. What is 10 + 3? 13

Level 2: Basic
5. What is 20 + 10? 30
6. What is 40 + 10? 50
7. What is 30 + 40? 70
8. What is 10 + 24? 34

Level 3: At Level
9. Use bundles of sticks. Show how to add 50 and 17. 67
10. Use bundles of sticks. Show how to add 70 and 11. 81
11. Use bundles of sticks. Show how to add 79 and 11. 90
12. Use bundles of sticks. Show how to add 35 and 15. 50

Level 4: Challenge Application
13. Use paper and pencil. Add 16 and 16. 32
14. Use paper and pencil. Add 50 and 50. 100
15. Use paper and pencil. Add 38 and 18. 56
16. Use paper and pencil. Add 66 and 14. 80

Level 5: Content Beyond Mid-Chapter
17. Use paper and pencil. Add 40 and 80. 120
18. Use paper and pencil. Add 70 and 70. 140
19. Use paper and pencil. Add 20, 30, and 20. 70
20. Use paper and pencil. Add 50, 10, and 40. 100

OBJECTIVES
- To provide more practice solving problems that involve adding two-digit numbers
- To add two-digit numbers that have a sum that is not a multiple of ten
- To begin to develop a written form for recording the addition process

NCTM STANDARDS
Number and Operations
- Using multiple models to develop initial understanding of place value and the base-ten number system
- Developing understanding of the relative position and magnitude of whole numbers
- Developing a sense of whole numbers and representing and using them in flexible ways, including relating, composing, and decomposing numbers
- Developing and using strategies for addition
- Developing fluency with basic number combinations for addition
- Using a variety of methods and tools to compute, including objects, mental computation, estimation, paper and pencil, and calculators

Representation
- Creating and using representations to organize, record, and communicate mathematical ideas
- Selecting, applying, and translating among mathematical representations to solve problems

MATERIALS
- *Number Cubes
- *Craft sticks and rubber bands or other base-ten materials

TECHNOLOGY
Presentation Lesson 5.6
Building Blocks Figure the Fact: Two-Digit Adding

TEST PREP
Cumulative Review
Mental Math reviews two-digit addition (Lesson 5.5).

*Manipulative Kit Item

Practice with Two-Digit Addition

Context of the Lesson This is the fourth of five lessons leading to mastery of the algorithm for two-digit addition. This lesson provides further practice in solving problems that involve the sum of two two-digit numbers. There is no attempt to introduce the standard algorithm in this lesson although some students may begin to discover it for themselves.

See page 159B for Math Background for teachers for this lesson.

Planning for Learning ● DIFFERENTIATE INSTRUCTION

INTERVENTION
If . . . students lack the prerequisite skill of understanding place value to 100,

Then . . . teach **Intervention** Lesson 5.B.

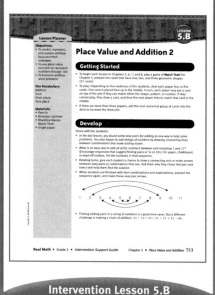

Intervention Lesson 5.B

ENGLISH LEARNER
Preview
If . . . students need language support,

Then . . . use Lesson 5.6 in **English Learner Support Guide** to preview lesson concepts and vocabulary.

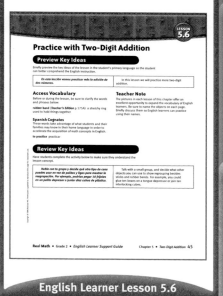

English Learner Lesson 5.6

ENRICH
If . . . students are proficient in the lesson concepts,

Then . . . emphasize exploring **eMathTools**.

PRACTICE
If . . . students would benefit from additional practice,

Then . . . extend Skill Building before assigning the student pages.

RETEACH
If . . . students are having difficulty understanding two-digit addition,

Then . . . extend Skill Building before assigning the student pages.

Access Vocabulary
rubber band a stretchy ring used to hold things together

Spanish Cognates
to practice practicar

Mental Math 5

Write addition statements on the board as students find, hide, and show the sums. Use examples in which at least one of the numbers is a multiple of ten. Possible examples include the following:

a. 30 + 56 = 86   **b.** 26 + 30 = 56   **c.** 16 + 20 = 36

d. 36 + 0 = 36   **e.** 45 + 40 = 85   **f.** 45 + 20 = 65

g. 65 + 30 = 95   **h.** 65 + 10 = 75   **i.** 60 + 40 = 100

1 Develop 20

Tell Students In Today's Lesson They Will

do two-digit addition with pencil and paper.

Skill Building   APPLYING

Whole Group

Using the photos and captions at the top of student page 175, demonstrate how to correlate the manipulation of fingers or sticks with the written notation shown in expanded form. It's important that you go back and forth between the manipulative form and the written form so that students see the relationship between them. Many students will not see this if you do not do both together.

Next, present one or two addition word problems and allow students to find the sums using sticks or other base-ten materials while, at the same time, writing the problem using expanded notation.

2 Assign Student Pages 25

Pages 175–176 UNDERSTANDING

Have students complete pages 175 and 176 individually. Allow students to work with base-ten materials, but do not insist if you believe students truly understand the procedures and have not just memorized rules. Have students rewrite the problems on student page 176 in vertical and expanded form.

Monitoring Student Progress

| **If . . .** students have difficulty adding with two-digit numbers, | **Then . . .** continue to offer help with base-ten materials. |

As Students Finish

Game Give a choice of games from among those previously introduced, or assign games based on individual needs.

Building Blocks *Figure the Fact: Two-Digit Adding*

e MathTools *Base Ten* Have students explore base-ten groupings.

Name _____ Date _____

LESSON 5.6 Practice with Two-Digit Addition

Key Ideas

When you use craft sticks to add, you can write what you did.

1. 2 tens and 8
   + 3 tens and 5

2. 5 tens and 13

3. 6 tens and 3

Use craft sticks to add. Write what you did.

① 4 tens and 4
  + 3 tens and 6
  7 tens and 10
  or
  8 tens

③ 8 tens and 6
  + 0 tens and 7
  8 tens and 13
  or
  9 tens and 3

② 3 tens and 9
  + 1 ten and 0
  4 tens and 9

④ 4 tens and 5
  + 5 tens and 3
  9 tens and 8

Textbook This lesson is available in the *eTextbook*.

175

LESSON 5.6 · Practice with Two-Digit Addition

Add. You may use craft sticks or other objects to help.

⑤

27 + 16 = __43__
There are __43__ pretzels.

⑥

40 + 32 = __72__
There are __72__ peanuts.

⑦

35 + 35 = __70__
There are __70__ cups.

⑧

30 + 31 = __61__
There are __61__ days.

176   **Real Math** • Chapter 5 • Lesson 6

---

3 **Reflect**   10

Guided Discussion REASONING   Whole Group

Write the following incorrect number sentence on the board:

$35 + 47 = 712$

Through discussion, ask the following three questions:

■ **How do you know that 712 is the wrong answer?** Some students might explain that the correct procedures were not followed, while others might argue that the sum of 712 is contrary to reason, since $50 + 50 = 100$, and this sum must clearly be less than 100.

■ **What mistake was made?** writing the sum of the units column as a two-digit number and the sum of the tens in the hundreds place

■ **If your friend made this mistake, how would you help him or her?** Answers will vary, but most students will insist on teaching the correct procedures. A good answer might be to use manipulatives to show how.

 Cumulative Review: For cumulative review of previously learned skills, see page 191–192.

 Family Involvement: Assign the *Practice, Reteach,* or *Enrichment* activities depending on the needs of your students.

 Concept/Question Board: Encourage students to continue to post questions, answers, and examples on the Concept/Question Board.

 Math Puzzler: Brad's bedtime is 3 hours after he finishes dinner. He takes 1 hour to eat dinner. Brad's dinner is served at 5 P.M. What time is his bedtime? 9 P.M.

Assess and Differentiate

 Assess Use **eAssess** to record and analyze evidence of student understanding.

A Gather Evidence

Use the Daily Class Assessment Records in **Assessment** or **eAssess** to record daily observations.

Informal Assessment
☑ **Mental Math**

Did the student COMPUTING
- ❏ respond accurately?
- ❏ respond quickly?
- ❏ respond with confidence?
- ❏ self-correct?

Informal Assessment
☑ **Skill Building**

Did the student APPLYING
- ❏ apply learning in new situations?
- ❏ contribute concepts?
- ❏ contribute answers?
- ❏ connect mathematics to real-world situations?

B Summarize Findings

Analyze and summarize assessment data for each student. Determine which Assessment Follow-Up is appropriate for each student. Use the Student Assessment Record in **Assessment** or **eAssess** to update assessment records.

Assessment page T41

C Assessment Follow-Up • DIFFERENTIATE INSTRUCTION

Based on your observations, use these teaching strategies for assessment follow-up.

INTERVENTION	ENRICH	PRACTICE	RETEACH
Review student performance on **Intervention** Lesson 5.B to see if students have mastered prerequisite skills for this lesson.	**If . . .** students are proficient in the lesson concepts, **Then . . .** encourage them to work on the chapter projects or **Enrichment** Lesson 5.6.	**If . . .** students would benefit from additional practice, **Then . . .** assign **Practice** Lesson 5.6.	**If . . .** students continue to make errors when adding two-digit numbers, **Then . . .** have them repeat Guided Discussion from Reflect with other incorrect examples, and answer the questions in small groups.

ENGLISH LEARNER
Review

Use Lesson 5.6 in **English Learner Support Guide** to review lesson concepts and vocabulary.

Enrichment Lesson 5.6

Practice Lesson 5.6

OBJECTIVES
- To teach those students who have not yet discovered it, an algorithm for adding two-digit numbers
- To give practice in using the algorithm for adding two-digit numbers

NCTM STANDARDS
Number and Operations
- Using multiple models to develop initial understanding of place value and the base-ten number system
- Developing understanding of the relative position and magnitude of whole numbers
- Developing a sense of whole numbers and representing and using them in flexible ways, including relating, composing, and decomposing numbers
- Developing and using strategies for addition
- Developing fluency with basic number combinations for addition
- Using a variety of methods and tools to compute, including objects, mental computation, estimation, paper and pencil, and calculators

Connections
- Recognizing and using connections among mathematical ideas
- Understanding how mathematical ideas interconnect and build on one another to produce a coherent whole

MATERIALS
- *Number Cubes
- *Craft sticks and rubber bands or other base-ten materials

TECHNOLOGY
e Presentation Lesson 5.7
Building Blocks Math-O-Scope

TEST PREP
Cumulative Review (Review)
Mental Math reviews two-digit addition (Lesson 5.6).

More Practice Adding Two-Digit Numbers

Context of the Lesson This is the last of five lessons that introduces the algorithm for two-digit addition. In this lesson the algorithm, or step-by-step procedure, is introduced. The algorithm introduced here is efficient and widely used for adding multidigit numbers, although there are others. Learning the algorithm is important because once learned, students can add routinely without having to think about the procedure, which allows students to think about other more important aspects of the problem they happen to be solving.

See page 159B for Math Background for teachers for this lesson.

Planning for Learning ● DIFFERENTIATE INSTRUCTION

INTERVENTION
If . . . students lack the prerequisite skill of understanding place value to 100,

Then . . . teach *Intervention* Lesson 5.B.

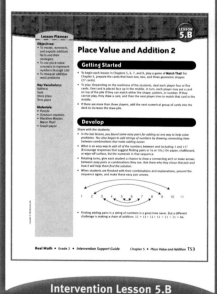

Intervention Lesson 5.B

ENGLISH LEARNER
Preview

If . . . students need language support,

Then . . . use Lesson 5.7 in *English Learner Support Guide* to preview lesson concepts and vocabulary.

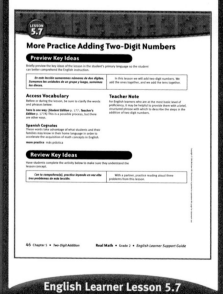

English Learner Lesson 5.7

ENRICH
If . . . students are proficient in the lesson concepts,

Then . . . emphasize additional game time.

PRACTICE
If . . . students would benefit from additional practice,

Then . . . extend Guided Discussion before assigning the student pages.

RETEACH
If . . . students are having difficulty understanding two-digit addition,

Then . . . extend Guided Discussion before assigning the student pages.

Access Vocabulary
here is one way This is a possible process, but there are other ways.

Spanish Cognates
more practice más práctica

Mental Math 5

Review

Write addition statements on the board as students find, hide, and show the sums. Use examples in which at least one of the numbers is a multiple of ten. Possible examples include the following:

a. 27 + 30 = 57 **b.** 27 + 40 = 67 **c.** 27 + 41 = 68
d. 41 + 27 = 68 **e.** 41 + 30 = 71 **f.** 41 + 29 = 70

1 Develop 20

Tell Students In Today's Lesson They Will

learn the procedure for adding two-digit numbers.

Guided Discussion  UNDERSTANDING   Whole Group

Have two groups of volunteers come to the front of the room and hold up fingers as follows: In the first group three students hold up all ten fingers, and one student holds up four fingers; in the second group five students hold up all ten fingers, and one student holds up eight fingers. The class should make suggestions on how to combine the two groups. In the process students holding up four and eight fingers should be combined to make two and ten fingers (ask one student to hold up two more fingers and the other to turn down two fingers). The student who is now holding up ten fingers should stand with the other students holding up ten. It should now be easy to see that there are 9 tens and 2 fingers showing.

Now show how to record what was just done with fingers.

Write this on the board:

```
  34            3 tens and 4
+ 58          + 5 tens and 8
```

Ask if anyone sees a connection between the two. Ask a volunteer to come to the board and show how to get the sum. Encourage students to find how many tens there will be and how many ones left over. If a student gets 8 tens and 12, ask what can be done with the 12. Say, *Does the 1 in the 12 stand for 1 ten? Then there are 9 tens and 2.* Ask a student to tell how that number is usually read. ninety-two Encourage students to explain each step. Show them how they can record the steps by placing the 2 from the 12 in the units column and showing the 1 ten in the tens column for either form of the exercise. Present several similar exercises, encouraging students to explain each step and to record the steps.

2 Assign Student Pages 25

Pages 177–178 UNDERSTANDING

Have students do the exercises on student page 178. Before beginning, ask students if they think they will need help. Work with those students, using base-ten materials, if necessary, while the rest of the class works independently. Students may refer to the worked example on student page 177. At this time, most students should not need base-ten materials.

Monitoring Student Progress

If . . . students have faulty understanding of place value,	Then . . . you will need to concentrate on that before giving help with executing the algorithm. For these students, effective teaching will be to give two-digit numbers and have students form those amounts using base-ten materials. Try to use at least two different materials, sticks and play money, for example.
If . . . students have faulty execution of the algorithm,	Then . . . individual or small group tutoring in which you correlate the manipulation of the base-ten materials with the written format will be useful.

As Students Finish

Have students play any of the games previously introduced. **The Roll a 15 Game** (introduced in Lesson 2.7) is a good choice.

Building Blocks *Math-O-Scope*

Name _____ Date _____

LESSON 5.7 More Practice Adding Two-Digit Numbers

Key Ideas

Here is one way to add two two-digit numbers.

$34 + 58 =$ _____

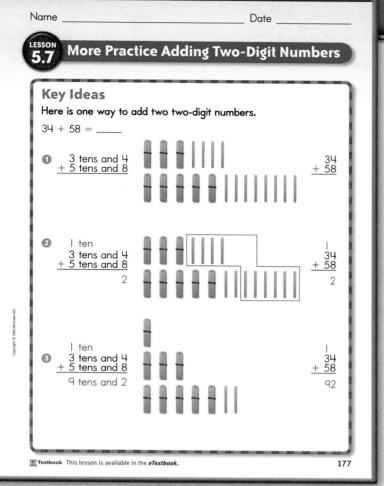

① 3 tens and 4
+ 5 tens and 8

34
+ 58

② 1 ten
3 tens and 4
+ 5 tens and 8
——
2

34
+ 58
——
2

③ 1 ten
3 tens and 4
+ 5 tens and 8
——
9 tens and 2

34
+ 58
——
92

Textbook This lesson is available in the *eTextbook*.   177

LESSON 5.7 · More Practice Adding Two-Digit Numbers

Add.

① 89
+ 7
——
96

② 19
+ 46
——
65

③ 15
+ 15
——
30

④ 25
+ 25
——
50

⑤ 45
+ 45
——
90

⑥ 94
+ 6
——
100

⑦ 0
+ 73
——
73

⑧ 30
+ 57
——
87

⑨ 89
+ 1
——
90

⑩ 37
+ 45
——
82

⑪ 38
+ 45
——
83

⑫ 39
+ 45
——
84

---

3 Reflect   10

Guided Discussion REASONING   Whole Group

As in the previous lesson, write an incorrect number statement on the board, and discuss what is wrong and how to help a friend who made the mistake.

A possible example includes the following:

$29 + 62 = 811$

Through discussion, ask the following three questions:

■ **How do you know that 811 is the wrong answer?** Some students might explain that the correct procedures were not followed, while others might argue that the sum of 811 is much too great and is contrary to reason.

■ **What mistake was made?** Possible answer: Writing the sum of the ones in the ones and tens columns and putting the sum of the tens in the hundreds column.

■ **If your friend made this mistake, how would you help him or her?** Answers will vary, but most students will insist on teaching the correct procedures.

 Cumulative Review: For cumulative review of previously learned skills, see page 191–192.

 Family Involvement: Assign the **Practice, Reteach,** or **Enrichment** activities depending on the needs of your students.

 Concept/Question Board: Encourage students to continue to post questions, answers, and examples on the Concept/Question Board.

 Math Puzzler: A bookcase is 2 meters tall. A chest of drawers is 300 centimeters tall. Which is taller? How can you tell? The chest of drawers is taller, because the bookcase is only 200 centimeters tall.

Assess and Differentiate

 Assess Use *eAssess* to record and analyze evidence of student understanding.

A Gather Evidence

Use the Daily Class Assessment Records in *Assessment* or *eAssess* to record daily observations.

Informal Assessment

✓**Guided Discussion**

Did the student **UNDERSTANDING**

- ❏ make important observations?
- ❏ extend or generalize learning?
- ❏ provide insightful answers?
- ❏ pose insightful questions?

Informal Assessment

✓**Concept/Question Board**

Did the student **APPLYING**

- ❏ apply learning in new situations?
- ❏ contribute concepts?
- ❏ contribute answers?
- ❏ connect mathematics to real-world situations?

B Summarize Findings

Analyze and summarize assessment data for each student. Determine which Assessment Follow-Up is appropriate for each student. Use the Student Assessment Record in *Assessment* or *eAssess* to update assessment records.

Assessment page T41

C Assessment Follow-Up ● DIFFERENTIATE INSTRUCTION

Based on your observations, use these teaching strategies for assessment follow-up.

INTERVENTION	ENRICH	PRACTICE	RETEACH
Review student performance on *Intervention* Lesson 5.B to see if students have mastered prerequisite skills for this lesson.	**If . . .** students are proficient in the lesson concepts, **Then . . .** encourage them to work on the chapter projects or *Enrichment* Lesson 5.7.	**If . . .** students would benefit from additional practice, **Then . . .** assign *Practice* Lesson 5.7.	**If . . .** students are having difficulty understanding the algorithm for two-digit addition, **Then . . .** have them continue to practice the algorithm.

ENGLISH LEARNER

Review

Use Lesson 5.7 in *English Learner Support Guide* to review lesson concepts and vocabulary.

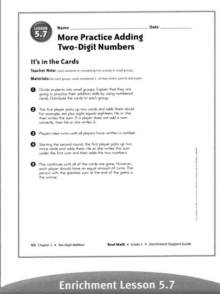

Enrichment Lesson 5.7

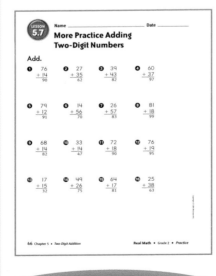

Practice Lesson 5.7

Lesson Planner

OBJECTIVES
- To introduce realistic problems, some of which require two-digit addition
- To introduce the **Roll a Problem Game,** which gives practice with addition, place value, and probability

NCTM STANDARDS
Number and Operations
- Using multiple models to develop initial understanding of place value and the base-ten number system
- Developing understanding of the relative position and magnitude of whole numbers
- Developing a sense of whole numbers and representing and using them in flexible ways, including relating, composing, and decomposing numbers
- Developing and using strategies for addition
- Developing fluency with basic number combinations for addition
- Using a variety of methods and tools to compute, including objects, mental computation, estimation, paper and pencil, and calculators

Problem Solving
- Building new mathematical knowledge through problem solving
- Applying and adapting a variety of appropriate strategies to solve problems

MATERIALS
- blank overhead transparency
- *Craft sticks and rubber bands or other base-ten materials

TECHNOLOGY
e Presentation Lesson 5.8

Building Blocks Word Problems with Tools 4

TEST PREP
Cumulative Review (Review)
Mental Math reviews two-digit addition (Lesson 5.7).

*Manipulative Kit Item

Applications of Two-Digit Addition

Context of the Lesson This lesson provides applications for which students can sometimes use the two-digit addition algorithm learned in the previous lesson. This lesson also introduces the **Roll a Problem Game,** which will be used throughout the program in many different contexts.

See page 159B for Math Background for teachers for this lesson.

Planning for Learning ● DIFFERENTIATE INSTRUCTION

INTERVENTION	ENGLISH LEARNER	ENRICH
If . . . students lack the prerequisite skill of understanding place value to 100, **Then . . .** teach *Intervention* Lesson 5.B.	Preview **If . . .** students need language support, **Then . . .** use Lesson 5.8 in *English Learner Support Guide* to preview lesson concepts and vocabulary.	**If . . .** students are proficient in the lesson concepts, **Then . . .** emphasize additional game time.

ENRICH

If . . . students are proficient in the lesson concepts,

Then . . . emphasize additional game time.

PRACTICE

If . . . students would benefit from additional practice,

Then . . . extend Skill and Strategy Building before assigning the student pages.

RETEACH

If . . . students are having difficulty understanding applications of two-digit addition,

Then . . . extend Guided Discussion before assigning the student pages.

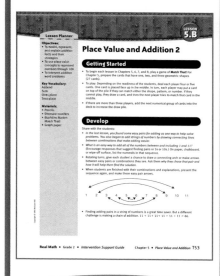

Intervention Lesson 5.B

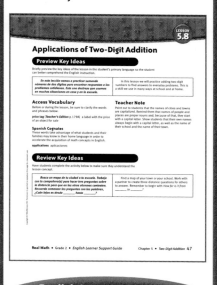

English Learner Lesson 5.8

Access Vocabulary
price tag a label with the price of an object for sale

Spanish Cognates
applications aplicaciones

Mental Math 5

Write a number expression on the board and say it. Students show thumbs-up if the sum is greater than 100, thumbs-down if less than 100, and open hand if exactly 100. Possible examples include the following:

a. 51 + 57 up

b. 49 + 37 down

c. 25 + 75 open hand

d. 25 + 74 down

e. 25 + 76 up

f. 40 + 60 open hand

1 Develop 25

Tell Students In Today's Lesson They Will

solve word problems.

Whole Group

Skill and Strategy Building ENGAGING

 Roll a Problem Game

Introduce and play the **Roll a Problem Game.**

Materials: 5–10 Number Cube, a game form for each student

How to Play:

1. Write the outline of a two-digit addition problem (such as those at the bottom of student page 179) on an overhead transparency.

2. Have students notice the first outline at the bottom of student page 179.

3. Turn off the light on the overhead projector so students cannot see your numbers as you write them.

4. Roll a **5–10 Number Cube.** Call the number, and have students write it in one of the spaces on the first outline in the student book. (If a 10 is rolled, do not count it and roll again.) You write the number in one of your spaces as well.

5. Roll again, and have students write the number in one of the three remaining spaces. Continue in this way. After all spaces have been filled, four in this case, turn on the overhead light so students can see the number you made.

6. Without calculating with paper and pencil, ask students to raise their hands if they think they have a sum that is greater than yours.

7. Select a student whose hand is raised, and ask him or her to write his or her problem on the board and to explain why its sum is greater than your sum.

8. In a similar manner, ask other students if they have a still greater sum. If so, have them write their problem on the board and explain why it is greater. Continue until you have the greatest sum and can declare a winner or winners. After declaring a winner, ask if anybody can see a way to get a greater sum. If so, try it and see.

You should have time to do three or four rounds of this game in about fifteen minutes.

As the game proceeds, walk around noting students who place their numbers without regard to place value, for example, a student who always places the first number rolled in the ones place. If the placement of numbers does not improve through game repetition, such students will need remedial work.

Guided Discussion APPLYING
Small Group

Present word problems, some of which require adding two-digit numbers and some of which do not. Have students discuss the problems and their solutions. After a while, have students make up and present problems to each other in small groups. Some suggested problems include the following:

■ **Max is thinking of buying four things. They cost 38¢, 59¢, 26¢, and 34¢. (Write the numbers on the board.) Which of these things can he buy if he has only $1 (100 cents) to spend?** He can buy the second item and any one of the others, or he can buy all three of the others.

■ **Shandi, who is 27 years old, wants to buy a book that costs $45. Does she have enough money?** cannot tell as there is insufficient information

■ **Evan and Beth each have $25. If they combine their money can they buy 3 CDs that cost $15 each?** yes **Can they buy 4?** no **Why?** Three CDs will cost $45; 4 will cost $60. They have only $50 between them.

2 Assign Student Pages 20

Pages 179–180 UNDERSTANDING

Have students complete the problems at the top of page 179 and on page 180 independently.

As Students Finish

 Give a choice of games from among those previously introduced, or assign games based on individual needs.

Building Blocks *Word Problems with Tools 4*

LESSON **5.8** **Applications of Two-Digit Addition**

Key Ideas

Being able to add two-digit numbers is useful for solving different kinds of problems.

Figure out how much each pair of items costs.

① pen and pencil __41__ ¢
② 2 pens __58__ ¢
③ 2 pencils __24__ ¢

29¢

12¢

Game Play the **Roll a Problem Game.**

Textbook This lesson is available in the *eTextbook.*

179

Student Page

LESSON 5.8 • Applications of Two-Digit Addition

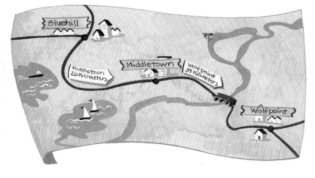
Bluehill
Middletown 26 kilometers
Middletown
Wolfpoint 39 kilometers
Wolfpoint

Use the map to answer the questions.

④ How far is it from Bluehill to Middletown to Wolfpoint? __65__ kilometers

⑤ How many people live in Bluehill? __can't tell__

⑥ How far is it from Wolfpoint to Middletown to Bluehill? __65__ kilometers

⑦ How far is it from Bluehill to Middletown and back to Bluehill? __52__ kilometers

⑧ **Extended Response** About how far is it from Wolfpoint to Bluehill if you go in a straight line in an airplane? Explain. __Accept all reasonable__ explanations that are less than 65 kilometers and more than 50 kilometers.

180 **Real Math** • Chapter 5 • Lesson 8

---

3 Reflect 10

Guided Discussion **UNDERSTANDING** Whole Group

Spend a few minutes allowing students to make up problems for the class to discuss and solve. Try to include some problems for which there is either too much information or too little information.

SOCIAL STUDIES **Curriculum Connection:** Students might be interested in solving problems similar to those on page 180 using a local map.

Review **Cumulative Review:** For cumulative review of previously learned skills, see page 191–192.

Family Involvement: Assign the *Practice, Reteach,* or *Enrichment* activities depending on the needs of your students.

Concept/Question Board: Encourage students to continue to post questions, answers, and examples on the Concept/Question Board.

Math Puzzler: Suppose you buy a pencil for 10¢ and an eraser for 20¢. If you pay for them with two quarters how much change will you get? 20¢

4 Assess and Differentiate

 Assess Use *eAssess* to record and analyze evidence of student understanding.

A Gather Evidence

Use the Daily Class Assessment Records in *Assessment* or *eAssess* to record daily observations.

Informal Assessment
☑ **Mental Math**

Did the student COMPUTING
- ❑ respond accurately?
- ❑ respond quickly?
- ❑ respond with confidence?
- ❑ self-correct?

Performance Assessment
☑ **Skill and Strategy Building**

Did the student ENGAGING
- ❑ pay attention to others' contributions?
- ❑ contribute information and ideas?
- ❑ improve on a strategy?
- ❑ reflect on and check the accuracy of his or her work?

B Summarize Findings

Analyze and summarize assessment data for each student. Determine which Assessment Follow-Up is appropriate for each student. Use the Student Assessment Record in *Assessment* or *eAssess* to update assessment records.

Assessment page T41

C Assessment Follow-Up • DIFFERENTIATE INSTRUCTION

Based on your observations, use these teaching strategies for assessment follow-up.

INTERVENTION

Review student performance on *Intervention* Lesson 5.B to see if students have mastered prerequisite skills for this lesson.

ENGLISH LEARNER

Review

Use Lesson 5.8 in *English Learner Support Guide* to review lesson concepts and vocabulary.

ENRICH

If . . . students are proficient in the lesson concepts,

Then . . . encourage them to work on the chapter projects or *Enrichment* Lesson 5.8.

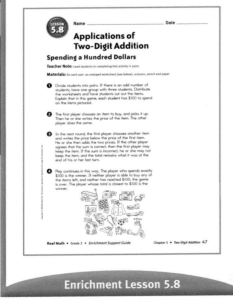

Enrichment Lesson 5.8

PRACTICE

If . . . students would benefit from additional practice,

Then . . . assign *Practice* Lesson 5.8.

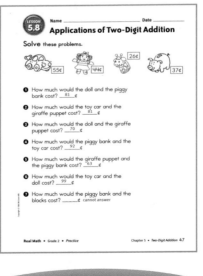

Practice Lesson 5.8

RETEACH

If . . . students are having difficulty solving application problems,

Then . . . have them think aloud with a partner to find the number sentence that will solve each problem.

OBJECTIVES
To introduce a computational shortcut—grouping addends to make tens or multiples of ten

NCTM STANDARDS

Number and Operations
- Using multiple models to develop initial understanding of place value and the base-ten number system
- Developing understanding of the relative position and magnitude of whole numbers
- Developing a sense of whole numbers and representing and using them in flexible ways, including relating, composing, and decomposing numbers
- Developing and using strategies for addition
- Developing fluency with basic number combinations for addition
- Using a variety of methods and tools to compute, including objects, mental computation, estimation, paper and pencil, and calculators

Problem Solving
- Building new mathematical knowledge through problem solving
- Applying and adapting a variety of appropriate strategies to solve problems

MATERIALS
- *Number Cubes

TECHNOLOGY
- e Presentation Lesson 5.9
- e MathTools Sets Former

TEST PREP
Cumulative Review
Mental Math reviews two-digit addition (Lesson 5.8).

Grouping by Tens

Context of the Lesson This is the first of two lessons meant to provide students with strategies for solving addition problems more efficiently. These strategies can be useful for avoiding tedious computations. In this lesson students practice grouping addends that make sums of ten.

See page 159B for Math Background for teachers for this lesson.

Planning for Learning ● DIFFERENTIATE INSTRUCTION

INTERVENTION	ENGLISH LEARNER	ENRICH
If . . . students lack the prerequisite skill of interpreting addition word problems,	Preview	**If . . .** students are proficient in the lesson concepts,
Then . . . teach **Intervention** Lesson 5.C.	**If . . .** students need language support,	**Then . . .** emphasize exploring **eMathTools**.
	Then . . . use Lesson 5.9 in **English Learner Support Guide** to preview lesson concepts and vocabulary.	

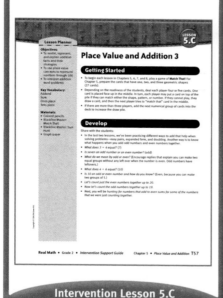

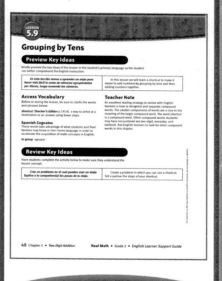

Intervention Lesson 5.C

English Learner Lesson 5.9

PRACTICE

If . . . students would benefit from additional practice,

Then . . . extend Skill Practice before assigning the student pages.

RETEACH

If . . . students are having difficulty understanding grouping by tens,

Then . . . extend Guided Discussion before assigning the student pages.

Access Vocabulary
shortcut a way to arrive at a destination or answer using fewer steps

Spanish Cognates
to group agrupar

Mental Math 5

THUMBS UP Write a number expression on the board and say it. Students show thumbs-up if the answer is greater than 100, thumbs-down if less than 100, and open hand if exactly 100. Possible examples include the following:

a. 41 + 67 up

b. 39 + 47 down

c. 22 + 74 down

d. 51 + 49 open hand

e. 25 + 79 up

f. 20 + 80 open hand

1 Develop 20

Tell Students In Today's Lesson They Will
learn a shortcut to help add mentally.

Guided Discussion UNDERSTANDING Whole Group

Write 10 + 10 + 10 + 10 = on the board. Ask students to calculate the sum of the problem without paper and pencil. 40

Then write 3 + 7 + 4 + 6 + 5 + 5 + 2 + 8 =. Ask how to add these numbers without paper and pencil. Guide students to see that if they group the addends into sums of ten, the answer is the same as the answer to the first problem. 40

Skill Practice COMPUTING Whole Group

 Write several more exercises that include sums of ten in the addends. Remind students that they can add the numbers in any order. Have students find, hide, and show their answers. Possible examples include the following:

a. 6 + 5 + 4 + 5 = 20

b. 8 + 5 + 3 + 7 + 5 + 2 = 30

c. 10 + 10 + 5 + 3 + 7 + 5 = 40

d. 6 + 5 + 3 + 7 + 5 + 4 = 30

Now include a few exercises in which one of the addends does not have a match that makes ten. Possible examples include the following:

e. 3 + 1 + 7 + 5 + 5 = 21

f. 6 + 7 + 4 + 3 + 4 = 24

g. 3 + 5 + 5 + 1 + 7 = 21

2 Assign Student Pages 25

Pages 181–182 APPLYING

Have students complete pages 181–182 individually. Invite volunteers to share their answers.

As Students Finish

Game Give a choice of games from among those previously introduced, or assign games based on individual needs.

 MathTools **Sets Former** Have students practice combining smaller sets to form sets of ten.

LESSON 5.9 Grouping by Tens

Key Ideas
Finding numbers that add to 10 can make a shortcut.

$3 + 4 + 7 + 6 =$ _____

$3 + 7 = 10$ and $4 + 6 = 10$

$10 + 10 = 20$

Add. Use shortcuts if you can.

1. $1 + 3 + 7 + 9 = 20$
2. $6 + 7 + 4 = 17$
3. $1 + 3 + 5 + 7 + 9 = 25$
4. $6 + 7 + 4 + 3 = 20$
5. $4 + 2 + 6 + 8 + 3 + 7 = 30$
6. $8 + 2 + 9 + 1 + 7 + 3 + 6 + 4 + 10 = 50$
7. $4 + 6 + 7 + 3 + 5 + 5 + 9 + 1 = 40$
8. $1 + 2 + 3 + 4 + 5 + 6 + 7 + 8 + 9 = 45$
9. $7 + 3 + 1 + 9 + 5 + 5 + 3 = 33$
10. $5 + 6 + 5 + 4 + 1 + 9 + 7 = 37$

Textbook This lesson is available in the *eTextbook*.

181

LESSON 5.9 · Grouping by Tens

Add. Use shortcuts if you can.

11. $4 + 1 + 3 + 2 + 5 + 0 + 2 + 3 = 20$
12. $10 + 9 + 8 + 2 + 1 + 10 = 40$
13. $2 + 4 + 6 + 8 + 10 = 30$
14. $20 + 40 + 60 + 80 + 100 = 300$
15. $21 + 19 + 32 + 18 = 90$
16. $9 + 1 + 10 + 19 + 1 + 30 = 70$
17. $42 + 8 + 5 + 6 + 5 + 4 = 70$

18. Susan worked for five weeks during the summer. The table shows how much she earned each week. How much did she earn in those five weeks? Write the answer in the table.

Week	Dollars Earned
1	41
2	72
3	14
4	28
5	59
Total	214

182   **Real Math • Chapter 5 • Lesson 9**

---

3 Reflect   10

Guided Discussion ENGAGING   Small Group

1. Discuss Problem 18 on page 182. Allow students to explain how they were able to find the total amount of money earned. Accept all correct answers, but focus attention on those strategies that involved finding a shortcut.

2. Have students make up a problem with four or more addends that they can answer easily without using pencil and paper. Have students exchange and mentally solve each other's problems.

Cumulative Review: For cumulative review of previously learned skills, see page 191–192.

Family Involvement: Assign the **Practice, Reteach,** or **Enrichment** activities depending on the needs of your students.

Concept/Question Board: Have students attempt to answer any unanswered questions on the Concept/Question Board.

Math Puzzler: Fruit rolls cost $1 for three. How many fruit rolls can you buy if you have $3? 9

Assess and Differentiate

 Assess Use **eAssess** to record and analyze evidence of student understanding.

A Gather Evidence

Use the Daily Class Assessment Records in **Assessment** or **eAssess** to record daily observations.

Informal Assessment
☑ **Mental Math**

Did the student **COMPUTING**
❑ respond accurately?
❑ respond quickly?
❑ respond with confidence?
❑ self-correct?

Informal Assessment
☑ **Skill Practice**

Did the student **COMPUTING**
❑ respond accurately?
❑ respond quickly?
❑ respond with confidence?
❑ self-correct?

B Summarize Findings

Analyze and summarize assessment data for each student. Determine which Assessment Follow-Up is appropriate for each student. Use the Student Assessment Record in **Assessment** or **eAssess** to update assessment records.

Assessment page T41

C Assessment Follow-Up ● DIFFERENTIATE INSTRUCTION

Based on your observations, use these teaching strategies for assessment follow-up.

INTERVENTION	ENRICH	PRACTICE	RETEACH
Review student performance on **Intervention** Lesson 5.C to see if students have mastered prerequisite skills for this lesson.	**If . . .** students are proficient in the lesson concepts, **Then . . .** encourage them to work on the chapter projects or **Enrichment** Lesson 5.9.	**If . . .** students would benefit from additional practice, **Then . . .** assign **Practice** Lesson 5.9.	**If . . .** students are having difficulty mentally grouping by tens to add, **Then . . .** have them connect pairs of addends with sums of ten.

ENGLISH LEARNER
Review

Use Lesson 5.9 in **English Learner Support Guide** to review lesson concepts and vocabulary.

Enrichment Lesson 5.9

LESSON 5.9 Name _____ Date _____
Grouping by Tens

Number 10 Search Puzzler

Teacher Note: Send this page home with your students, and have helpers from home work with students to complete this activity.

Note to Home: Today your child learned about grouping by ten for mental addition. Help your child complete this activity.

This is a number search. It is like a word search, except that you are looking for a group of numbers instead of words. The groups of numbers you are looking for are those that add to 10. There may be two numbers in a group, such as 9 and 1, or there may be three numbers in a group, such as 6, 2, and 2.

Ring each group of numbers that add to 10. There are exactly thirteen groups of numbers that add to 10. The groups of numbers go only across and down. Do not circle diagonally. The first one has been done for you.
NOTE: Once you have circled a group of numbers, you may not use any of the numbers in that group again. You might want to color each of the numbers after you circle them.

48 Chapter 5 • Two-Digit Addition   **Real Math** • Grade 2 • Enrichment Support Guide

Practice Lesson 5.9

LESSON 5.9 Name _____ Date _____
Grouping by Tens

Add. Use shortcuts if you can.

❶ $8 + 6 + 4 =$ ___18___

❷ $3 + 5 + 5 + 7 =$ ___20___

❸ $9 + 3 + 1 + 7 + 6 =$ ___26___

❹ $2 + 1 + 8 + 9 + 5 =$ ___25___

❺ $5 + 4 + 1 + 10 + 3 =$ ___23___

❻ $5 + 5 + 5 + 5 + 3 + 7 =$ ___30___

❼ $10 + 6 + 3 + 4 + 7 + 5 =$ ___35___

❽ $6 + 3 + 5 + 5 + 7 + 4 + 8 =$ ___38___

❾ $2 + 15 + 8 + 15 + 10 + 10 + 5 =$ ___65___

❿ $24 + 6 + 3 + 2 + 8 + 7 =$ ___50___

⓫ $60 + 20 + 40 + 30 + 70 + 80 =$ ___300___

⓬ $10 + 50 + 20 + 70 + 30 + 50 + 90 + 80 =$ ___400___

48 Chapter 5 • Two-Digit Addition   **Real Math** • Grade 2 • Practice

Lesson Planner

OBJECTIVES
To introduce and study a computational shortcut for adding two-digit numbers

NCTM STANDARDS

Number and Operations
- Using multiple models to develop initial understanding of place value and the base-ten number system
- Developing understanding of the relative position and magnitude of whole numbers
- Developing a sense of whole numbers and representing and using them in flexible ways, including relating, composing, and decomposing numbers
- Developing and using strategies for addition
- Developing fluency with basic number combinations for addition
- Using a variety of methods and tools to compute, including objects, mental computation, estimation, paper and pencil, and calculators

Problem Solving
- Building new mathematical knowledge through problem solving
- Applying and adapting a variety of appropriate strategies to solve problems

MATERIALS
- *Number Cubes

TECHNOLOGY
e Presentation Lesson 5.10

TEST PREP
Cumulative Review
Mental Math reviews grouping by tens (Lesson 5.9).

Extended Response
Problem 13

*Manipulative Kit Item

Addition Shortcuts

Context of the Lesson This lesson continues to provide students with strategies for solving addition problems more efficiently. In this lesson students learn that addends can be regrouped to make one of the addends a multiple of ten. The shortcut studied in this lesson will help students better understand why using the Paper Explorer for multidigit addition (covered in the next two lessons) works.

See page 159B for Math Background for teachers for this lesson.

Planning for Learning ● DIFFERENTIATE INSTRUCTION

INTERVENTION

If . . . students lack the prerequisite skill of interpreting addition word problems,

Then . . . teach *Intervention* Lesson 5.C.

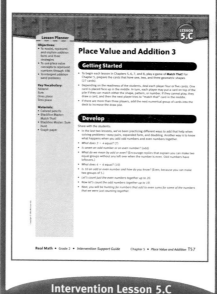

Intervention Lesson 5.C

ENGLISH LEARNER

Preview

If . . . students need language support,

Then . . . use Lesson 5.10 in *English Learner Support Guide* to preview lesson concepts and vocabulary.

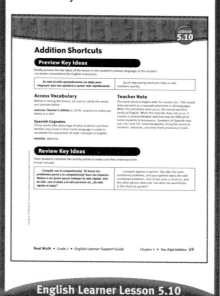

English Learner Lesson 5.10

ENRICH

If . . . students are proficient in the lesson concepts,

Then . . . emphasize chapter projects.

PRACTICE

If . . . students would benefit from additional practice,

Then . . . extend Skill Practice before assigning the student pages.

RETEACH

If . . . students are having difficulty understanding addition shortcuts,

Then . . . extend Guided Discussion before assigning the student pages.

Access Vocabulary
exercise practice to make you better at a skill

Spanish Cognates
exercise ejercicio

Mental Math 5

 Write addition statements on the board, one at a time, as students find, hide, and show the sums. Use examples in which addends can be grouped by tens. Possible examples include the following:

a. $5 + 5 + 4 + 6 = 20$

b. $1 + 3 + 5 + 7 + 9 = 25$

c. $1 + 3 + 7 + 9 = 20$

d. $6 + 7 + 4 + 3 = 20$

e. $6 + 7 + 4 = 17$

f. $4 + 6 + 2 + 8 + 3 + 7 = 30$

1 Develop 20

Tell Students In Today's Lesson They Will

learn another shortcut to help add without pencil and paper.

Guided Discussion REASONING Whole Group

Describe a situation similar to the one illustrated in the Key Ideas box on student page 183, in which moving objects from one group to another group does not change the total number of objects. For example, say there were two containers of apples, one containing 35 apples and one containing 39 apples. Illustrate the containers on the board, and label them. Ask how many apples there are altogether, and allow students to calculate the answer with paper and pencil.

Then announce that you know a shortcut to find the sum. Ask if the total number of apples would change if you moved one of the apples to the other container. When students are satisfied that the total number will not change, revise the illustration on the board as follows: Cross out the old labels, and relabel the containers as 34 and 40. Point out that it is much easier to add $40 + 34$ than it is to add $39 + 35$.

Now give the students one or two exercises, and ask if they can find the sums without using paper and pencil. Allow students to explain the procedures they used. Possible examples include the following:

$29 + 64 = 30 + 63$, or 93

$39 + 55 = 40 + 54$, or 94

Skill Practice COMPUTING Whole Group

 Present two-digit addition exercises that students can do mentally. Have students show sums with their **Number Cubes.** Possible examples include the following:

a. $34 + 49 = 83$

b. $23 + 29 = 52$

c. $75 + 19 = 94$

d. $24 + 39 = 63$

Monitoring Student Progress

If . . . students insist on using paper and pencil or appear to be doing so by imagining that they are writing the numbers,

Then . . . individual or small-group tutoring may be useful but need not be extensive. Students will have many opportunities to develop these understandings. Also students should not be penalized for getting the correct answers without using the shortcut.

2 Assign Student Pages 25

Pages 183–184 UNDERSTANDING

Have students complete pages 183 and 184 independently. Correct the problems with the class. Notice that on page 184 not all the exercises can be easily completed using the shortcuts learned in this lesson. Be alert, however, to students who can extend what they have learned to exercises such as

28 + 37 =

and change the exercise to

30 + 35 =

These students should be commended, but don't expect all students to see this at this time.

As Students Finish

 Give a choice of games from among those previously introduced, or assign games based on individual needs.

Student Page

Name _____ Date _____

LESSON 5.10 Addition Shortcuts

Key Ideas

Moving objects from one group to another does not change the number of objects. This idea can be used to find shortcuts for addition.

Move 1 apple.

$17 + 19 = 36$ $16 + 20 = 36$

Add. Use shortcuts if you can.

1. $56 + 29 = 85$
4. $38 + 42 = 80$
2. $63 + 19 = 82$
5. $38 + 47 = 85$
3. $54 + 39 = 93$
6. $28 + 32 = 60$

Textbook This lesson is available in the *eTextbook*.

183

Student Page

LESSON 5.10 · Addition Shortcuts

Add. Use shortcuts if you can.

7. $28 + 37 = 65$
10. $46 + 39 = 85$
8. $73 + 19 = 92$
11. $46 + 38 = 84$
9. $23 + 19 = 42$
12. $46 + 37 = 83$

13. **Extended Response** Laura and Anna decided to put their model car collections into one large collection. Anna had 49 cars. Laura had 37 cars. Then they bought 3 more cars together. Now how many cars are in their collection? __89__ Explain how you solved the problem. __See Reflect.__

_____

_____

184   **Real Math** • Chapter 5 • Lesson 10

---

3 Reflect   10

Guided Discussion **REASONING**   Whole Group

Call attention to the extended response question on page 184, and allow students to explain their solutions. Accept all correct solutions, but focus discussion on any shortcuts used. You are likely to see three solutions, as follows:

1. $49 + 37 + 3 = 89$
2. $49 + 37 = 50 + 36$, or 86
   $86 + 3 = 89$
3. $37 + 3 = 40$
   $40 + 49 = 89$

☑ Use Mastery Checkpoint 7 found in **Assessment** to evaluate student mastery of two-digit addition. By this time, students should be able to correctly answer eighty percent of the Mastery Checkpoint items.

Extended Response ▶

Problem 13 Students will likely have one of three solutions. See the Guided Discussion above for a detailed explanation.

Cumulative Review: For cumulative review of previously learned skills, see page 191–192.

Family Involvement: Assign the **Practice, Reteach,** or **Enrichment** activities depending on the needs of your students.

Concept/Question Board: Have students attempt to answer any unanswered questions on the Concept/Question Board.

Math Puzzler: You had 75¢ on Monday. You spent 20¢ on Tuesday and 32¢ on Wednesday. Can you still buy a 25¢ granola bar? Why? no; because you have only 23¢ left

4 Assess and Differentiate

 e Assess Use *eAssess* to record and analyze evidence of student understanding.

A Gather Evidence

Use the Daily Class Assessment Records in *Assessment* or *eAssess* to record daily observations.

Formal Assessment

✓ **Mastery Checkpoint**

Did the student
- ❑ use correct procedures?
- ❑ respond with at least 80% accuracy?

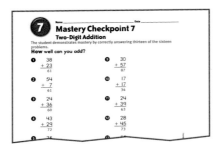

7 Mastery Checkpoint 7
Two-Digit Addition
The student demonstrates mastery by correctly answering thirteen of the sixteen problems.
How well can you add?

Assessment page T58

B Summarize Findings

Analyze and summarize assessment data for each student. Determine which Assessment Follow-Up is appropriate for each student. Use the Student Assessment Record in *Assessment* or *eAssess* to update assessment records.

Assessment page T41

C Assessment Follow-Up • DIFFERENTIATE INSTRUCTION

Based on your observations, use these teaching strategies for assessment follow-up.

INTERVENTION	ENRICH	PRACTICE	RETEACH
Review student performance on *Intervention* Lesson 5.C to see if students have mastered prerequisite skills for this lesson.	**If . . .** students are proficient in the lesson concepts, **Then . . .** encourage them to work on the chapter projects or *Enrichment* Lesson 5.10.	**If . . .** students would benefit from additional practice, **Then . . .** assign *Practice* Lesson 5.10.	**If . . .** students are having difficulty remembering shortcuts for addition, **Then . . .** have them say the shortcuts aloud to another student and take turns reciting them until both students remember the possible problem-solving methods.

ENGLISH LEARNER

Review

Use Lesson 5.10 in *English Learner Support Guide* to review lesson concepts and vocabulary.

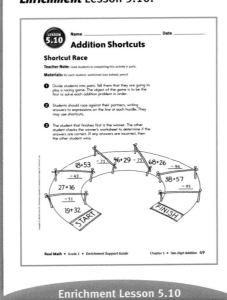

Enrichment Lesson 5.10

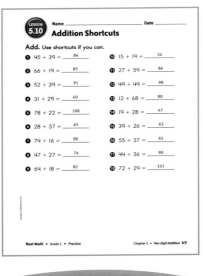

Practice Lesson 5.10

Lesson Planner

OBJECTIVES
- To develop the Paper Explorer as a model for helping students devise strategies for adding two-digit numbers
- To reinforce the idea that adding tens is essentially the same as adding units

NCTM STANDARDS
Number and Operations
- Using multiple models to develop initial understanding of place value and the base-ten number system
- Developing understanding of the relative position and magnitude of whole numbers
- Developing a sense of whole numbers and representing and using them in flexible ways, including relating, composing, and decomposing numbers
- Developing and using strategies for addition
- Developing fluency with basic number combinations for addition
- Using a variety of methods and tools to compute, including objects, mental computation, estimation, paper and pencil, and calculators

Representation
- Creating and using representations to organize, record, and communicate mathematical ideas
- Selecting, applying, and translating among mathematical representations to solve problems

MATERIALS
- Overhead transparency of the Paper Explorer on *Practice* page 122
- *Number Cubes
- *Counters or pawns

TECHNOLOGY
ePresentation Lesson 5.11

TEST PREP
Cumulative Review
- Mental Math reviews adding tens (Lesson 5.2).
- Problem 9 reviews perimeter (Lesson 2.8).

*Manipulative Kit Item

The Paper Explorer— Adding Tens

Context of the Lesson This is the first of two lessons in this chapter in which students use the Paper Explorer for addition. Students were introduced to the Paper Explorer in Lesson 2.9 and used it for adding ones. In this lesson students use the Paper Explorer to add multidigit numbers that are multiples of ten. In the next lesson students will add multidigit numbers that are not multiples of ten. As noted in Lesson 2.9, using the Paper Explorer requires some manual dexterity. Some students may have difficulty and will need time for more practice.

See page 159B for Math Background for teachers for this lesson.

Planning for Learning • DIFFERENTIATE INSTRUCTION

INTERVENTION

If . . . students lack the prerequisite skill of interpreting addition word problems,

Then . . . teach *Intervention* Lesson 5.C.

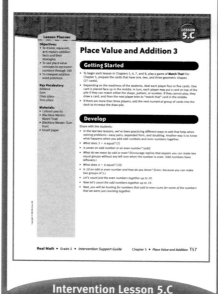

Intervention Lesson 5.C

ENGLISH LEARNER

Preview

If . . . students need language support,

Then . . . use Lesson 5.11 in *English Learner Support Guide* to preview lesson concepts and vocabulary.

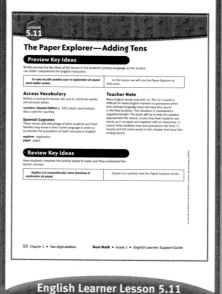

English Learner Lesson 5.11

ENRICH

If . . . students are proficient in the lesson concepts,

Then . . . emphasize chapter projects.

PRACTICE

If . . . students would benefit from additional practice,

Then . . . extend Guided Discussion before assigning the student pages.

RETEACH

If . . . students are having difficulty understanding the Paper Explorer,

Then . . . extend Guided Discussion before assigning the student pages.

Access Vocabulary
counters small round plastic discs used for counting

Spanish Cognates
explorer explorador

paper papel

Mental Math 5

Do an exercise in which you present statements that involve adding tens. Make sure the sums are all less than 100. Possible examples include the following:

a. 30 + 10 = 40   **b.** 50 + 30 = 80   **c.** 80 + 20 = 100
d. 80 + 10 = 90   **e.** 20 + 70 = 90   **f.** 30 + 30 = 60
g. 30 + 40 = 70   **h.** 20 + 60 = 80   **i.** 60 + 20 = 80

1 Develop 20

Tell Students In Today's Lesson They Will
use the Paper Explorer to add tens.

Guided Discussion UNDERSTANDING   Whole Group

Use a tens Paper Explorer overhead transparency (see **Practice** page 122). Write 80 + 50 = ___ on the transparency, and tell students that you can find the sum using the Paper Explorer. Demonstrate by placing one counter in the 80 box and one in the 50 box on the Paper Explorer. Moving both counters simultaneously, move the counters one box in opposite directions so that they are in the 90 and 40 boxes. Say, *80 plus 50 is the same as 90 + 40* as you move the counters.

Help students see that, like the ones Paper Explorer in Chapter 2, moving the counters on the Paper Explorer in the opposite directions did not change the total value on the calculator.

Next, move the counters on the Explorer in opposite directions, saying *90 plus 40 is the same as 100 plus 30* as you do so.

Briefly discuss what you have done. Most students will notice that the procedure you used is essentially the same as the ones Paper Explorer. Some students may also notice that moving the counters in opposite directions is the same as adding a number to one addend and subtracting the same number from the second addend. In both situations the sum remains the same.

2 Assign Student Pages 25

Pages 185–186   UNDERSTANDING

Have students turn their books so the Paper Explorer on page 185 runs horizontally across the page and the problems to be worked are under the Explorer.

Do the first exercise together with students, having them move the counters at the same time as they whisper the exercises. For example, *70 + 50 is the same as 80 + 40, which is the same as 90 + 30, which is the same as 100 + 20 = 120.* Then write the corresponding exercises on the board.

Allow students to complete the exercises on their own as you circulate and help. Make sure students see this exercise as an exploration rather than a calculation device.

Emphasize the following rules:

- To keep the sum the same, move counters in opposite directions.
- A counter in the zero box may be removed without changing the sum.

As students finish the Paper Explorer page, they should complete the problems on student page 186 independently.

Monitoring Student Progress

If . . . students are having difficulty getting the correct sums on the Paper Explorer,	**Then . . .** they are likely having difficulty moving the counters simultaneously. These students should be helped by reassuring them that they can do it, by having students go more slowly, and by having them whisper the sums as they make their moves. As students will not be using the Paper Explorer as a regular part of the curriculum, extensive extra teaching and practice is not essential.
If . . . students enjoyed using this device and appear to be interested in why it works,	**Then . . .** you might consider challenging them to see if they can subtract on the Explorer. (This will be covered in Lesson 6.5.)

As Students Finish

 Give a choice of games from among those previously introduced, or assign games based on individual needs.

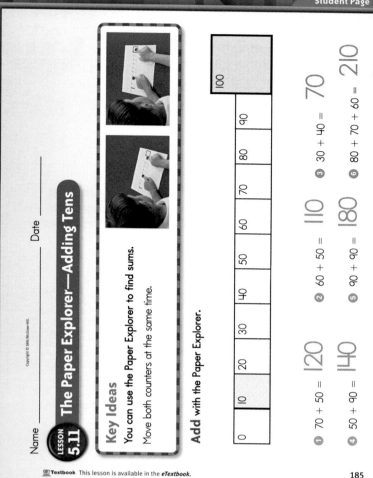

Name _____

Date _____

LESSON
5.11

The Paper Explorer—Adding Tens

Key Ideas
You can use the Paper Explorer to find sums.

Move both counters at the same time.

Add with the Paper Explorer.

| 0 | 10 | 20 | 30 | 40 | 50 | 60 | 70 | 80 | 90 | 100 |

① 70 + 50 = **120**
② 60 + 50 = **110**
③ 30 + 40 = **70**

④ 50 + 90 = **140**
⑤ 90 + 90 = **180**
⑥ 80 + 70 + 60 = **210**

185

LESSON 5.11 • The Paper Explorer—Adding Tens

REAL WORLD **Solve** these problems.

⑦ Tanisha had 10¢. Then she earned 60¢ for running an errand. Now how much money does Tanisha have? __70__ ¢

⑧ Each bottle contains 20 ounces of juice. Ethan bought 3 bottles. How many ounces of juice did he buy? __60__ ounces

Review ⑨ Dexter Park is shaped like a rectangle. One side is 40 meters long, and the other side is 30 meters long. What is the perimeter of Dexter Park? __140__ meters

⑩ Sara is 10 years old. How old will she be in 40 years? __50__ years

⑪ Mark and his mother rode the bus 50 blocks to the library. Then they rode 40 blocks to the supermarket, and then they rode 30 blocks home. How many blocks did they ride the bus? __120__

---

3 Reflect
10

Guided Discussion REASONING
Whole Group

Review students' answers to the word problems on student page 186, and allow students to explain their solutions. Then ask students which of the problems can be solved using the Paper Explorer. Show students how to use the Paper Explorer to find sums with 3 or 4 addends (Problems 8, 9, and 11).

For example, for Problem 11, to add 50 + 40 + 30 place counters on the 30, 40, and 50 boxes. Then choose any two of the numbers (the order of addition makes no difference) to add. For example:

Move and say, *50 + 40 is the same as 60 + 30* and stop. Now you have one marker on 60 and two markers on 30.

Next add the 60 and 30, moving the counters and saying, *60 + 30 is the same as 70 + 20, which is the same as 80 + 10, which is the same as 90 + 0.* You can remove the counter on zero because it does not change the sum. Now there is one counter in the 90 box and one counter in the 30 box.

Now add the 90 and 30 by moving those counters in the opposite direction to 100 and 20. Thus, the sum of 50 + 40 + 30 is 120.

 Curriculum Connection: Discuss with students whether they have recently solved any real-world problems similar to those on page 186.

 Cumulative Review: For cumulative review of previously learned skills, see page 191–192.

 Family Involvement: Assign the *Practice, Reteach,* or *Enrichment* activities depending on the needs of your students.

 Concept/Question Board: Have students attempt to answer any unanswered questions on the Concept/Question Board.

 Math Puzzler: The sum of the numbers that the two hands of a clock are pointing to is 6. If both hands are pointing to the same number, what time is it? 3:15

4 Assess and Differentiate

 Assess Use **eAssess** to record and analyze evidence of student understanding.

A Gather Evidence

Use the Daily Class Assessment Records in **Assessment** or **eAssess** to record daily observations.

Informal Assessment
 Student Pages

Did the student **UNDERSTANDING**
- ❑ make important observations?
- ❑ extend or generalize learning?
- ❑ provide insightful answers?
- ❑ pose insightful questions?

Informal Assessment
☑ **Concept/Question Board**

Did the student **APPLYING**
- ❑ apply learning in new situations?
- ❑ contribute concepts?
- ❑ contribute answers?
- ❑ connect mathematics to real-world situations?

B Summarize Findings

Analyze and summarize assessment data for each student. Determine which Assessment Follow-Up is appropriate for each student. Use the Student Assessment Record in **Assessment** or **eAssess** to update assessment records.

Assessment page T41

C Assessment Follow-Up • DIFFERENTIATE INSTRUCTION

Based on your observations, use these teaching strategies for assessment follow-up.

INTERVENTION

Review student performance on **Intervention** Lesson 5.C to see if students have mastered prerequisite skills for this lesson.

ENGLISH LEARNER

Review

Use Lesson 5.11 in **English Learner Support Guide** to review lesson concepts and vocabulary.

ENRICH

If . . . students are proficient in the lesson concepts,

Then . . . encourage them to work on the chapter projects or **Enrichment** Lesson 5.11.

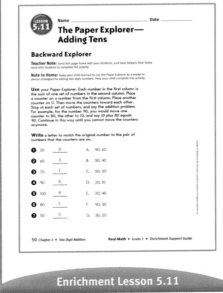

Enrichment Lesson 5.11

PRACTICE

If . . . students would benefit from additional practice,

Then . . . assign **Practice** Lesson 5.11.

Practice Lesson 5.11

RETEACH

If . . . students are having difficulty adding two-digit numbers,

Then . . . have them use estimation and check their answers on a calculator.

Lesson Planner

OBJECTIVES
To continue to develop the Paper Explorer as a model for helping students devise strategies for adding two-digit numbers

NCTM STANDARDS
Number and Operations
- Using multiple models to develop initial understanding of place value and the base-ten number system
- Developing understanding of the relative position and magnitude of whole numbers
- Developing a sense of whole numbers and representing and using them in flexible ways, including relating, composing, and decomposing numbers
- Developing and using strategies for addition
- Developing fluency with basic number combinations for addition
- Using a variety of methods and tools to compute, including objects, mental computation, estimation, paper and pencil, and calculators

Representation
- Creating and using representations to organize, record, and communicate mathematical ideas
- Selecting, applying, and translating among mathematical representations to solve problems

MATERIALS
- Overhead transparency of the three-column Paper Explorer on *Practice* page 123
- *Number Cubes
- *Counters or pawns

TECHNOLOGY
📀 Presentation Lesson 5.12

TEST PREP
Cumulative Review
Mental Math reviews addition shortcuts (Lessons 5.9 and 5.10).

The Paper Explorer— Multidigit Addition

Context of the Lesson This is the third lesson using the Paper Explorer. As in previous lessons, place emphasis on having students move the counters so they match the already given sums, rather than have students determine the sums. Students will get frustrated if they are asked to determine sums, and they will make a wrong move and get the wrong answer. This is especially true if students already know how to calculate the correct sum. The idea is to explore the relationships rather than calculate sums.

See page 159B for Math Background for teachers for this lesson.

Planning for Learning ● DIFFERENTIATE INSTRUCTION

INTERVENTION
If . . . students lack the prerequisite skill of interpreting addition word problems,

Then . . . teach *Intervention* Lesson 5.C.

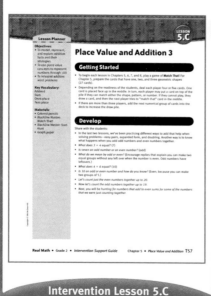

Intervention Lesson 5.C

ENGLISH LEARNER
Preview

If . . . students need language support,

Then . . . use Lesson 5.12 in *English Learner Support Guide* to preview lesson concepts and vocabulary.

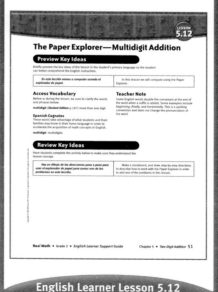

English Learner Lesson 5.12

ENRICH
If . . . students are proficient in the lesson concepts,

Then . . . emphasize chapter projects.

PRACTICE
If . . . students would benefit from additional practice,

Then . . . extend Guided Discussion before assigning the student pages.

RETEACH
If . . . students are having difficulty understanding place value,

Then . . . extend Guided Discussion before assigning the student pages.

Access Vocabulary	**Spanish Cognates**
multidigit more than one digit	**multidigit** multidígito

Mental Math 5

Write addition exercises on the board as students find, hide, and show the sums. Possible examples include the following:

a. 46 + 39 = 85   **b.** 38 + 46 = 84
c. 23 + 19 = 42   **d.** 7 + 3 + 1 + 9 = 20
e. 6 + 7 + 4 + 2 = 19   **f.** 1 + 3 + 5 + 7 + 9 = 25

1 Develop 20

Tell Students In Today's Lesson They Will

use the Paper Explorer to add two-digit numbers.

Guided Discussion UNDERSTANDING   Whole Group

Using the Paper Explorer on the overhead projector, explain that this Paper Explorer works the same as the simpler ones used in previous lessons, but now the ones and tens Explorers are connected with a hundreds column and turned so that there are columns instead of rows.

Demonstrate how to add 7 + 8. Do this by placing counters on the 7 and 8 boxes and moving them simultaneously in the opposite directions. When one of the counters gets to the top of the units column, it should be moved to the bottom of the tens column. Explain that this is permissible because ten ones is the same quantity as one ten.

Allow individual students to demonstrate several one-digit exercises.

Next, have individual students demonstrate several exercises in which the addends are multiples of ten.

Write this number sentence on the board, and demonstrate how to find the sum on the Paper Explorer: 35 + 49 = 84. Place two counters on 30 and 5 and two more counters on 40 and 9. Have students notice that by looking at the Explorer they no longer know the original number sentence. It could have been 39 and 45, or it could have been 30 and 40 and 5 and 9. Then, move the counters in opposite directions in each column. When the counter in the units column reaches ten it may be moved to the bottom of the adjacent column, because ten ones is the same quantity as one ten. Finally, finish moving the markers in opposite directions in the tens column. You will be left with counters on 80 and 4, showing that 35 + 49 = 84.

Briefly discuss what you have done. Most students will notice that the procedure you used is essentially the same as those used on the ones and tens Paper Explorers. One new rule was added: A counter may be moved between the top of one column and the box at the bottom of the adjacent column because one ten and ten ones are the same quantity. Also one hundred and ten tens are the same quantity.

2 Assign Student Pages 25

Pages 187–188 APPLYING

Have students complete pages 187 and 188 independently. (Students may need to copy the problems on page 188 onto another sheet of paper because the Paper Explorer is on the front.) Circulate and help. Make sure students see this exercise as an exploration rather than a calculation device that they use to get a correct answer.

Emphasize the following rules:

- To keep the sum the same, move counters in opposite directions.
- A counter in the zero box may be removed because it does not affect the sum.
- A counter at the top of one column may be moved to the bottom (not the zero box) of the adjacent column on the left. Similarly, a counter at the bottom of a column may be moved to the top of the adjacent column on the right.

Monitoring Student Progress

If . . . students enjoy the challenge of using the Paper Explorer,	**Then . . .** they should be encouraged to do so over the next few days as enrichment. One more lesson in which students learn to subtract on the Paper Explorer is in Chapter 6.
If . . . students become frustrated because they do not end up with correct sums,	**Then . . .** they may be tutored individually to be sure they are moving the counters simultaneously (and whispering the number sentences as they do so). Afterwards they may do the exercises on the *Practice* page, but extensive extra teaching and practice is not necessary.

As Students Finish

 Give a choice of games from among those previously introduced, or assign games based on individual needs.

Name _____   Date _____

LESSON **5.12**   **The Paper Explorer—Multidigit Addition**

Key Ideas

A counter on one 10 box may be moved to the other without changing the sum. The same is true of the 100 boxes.

1,000	100	10
900	90	9
800	80	8
700	70	7
600	60	6
500	50	5
400	40	4
300	30	3
200	20	2
100	10	1
0	0	0

Textbook This lesson is available in the *eTextbook*.

187

LESSON 5.12 · The Paper Explorer—Multidigit Addition

Add with the Paper Explorer.
Try to get sums to match those on the page.

1. $3 + 5 = 8$

2. $4 + 8 = 12$

3. $7 + 6 = 13$

4. $8 + 5 = 13$

5. $9 + 3 = 12$

6. $4 + 7 = 11$

7. $30 + 50 = 80$

8. $40 + 80 = 120$

9. $70 + 60 = 130$

10. $80 + 50 = 130$

11. $90 + 30 = 120$

12. $39 + 47 = 86$

13. $92 + 26 = 118$

14. $28 + 31 = 59$

188   **Real Math** • Chapter 5 • Lesson 12

 Reflect   10

Guided Discussion   UNDERSTANDING   Whole Group

Allow individual students to demonstrate how they found their sums on the Explorer. Emphasize that although different students may have used different procedures (starting in different columns, for example), if they followed the three rules and moved their counters simultaneously, they will arrive at the same sums for the same number sentence.

 Cumulative Review: For cumulative review of previously learned skills, see page 191–192.

 Family Involvement: Assign the **Practice, Reteach,** or **Enrichment** activities depending on the needs of your students.

 Concept/Question Board: Have students attempt to answer any unanswered questions on the Concept/Question Board.

 Math Puzzler: Kendra has 5 coins. They equal 40¢. What coins does she have? 3 dimes and 2 nickels

Assess and Differentiate

ⓔ Assess Use **eAssess** to record and analyze evidence of student understanding.

A Gather Evidence

Use the Daily Class Assessment Records in **Assessment** or **eAssess** to record daily observations.

Informal Assessment
✔ **Mental Math**

Did the student **COMPUTING**
- ❏ respond accurately?
- ❏ respond quickly?
- ❏ respond with confidence?
- ❏ self-correct?

Informal Assessment
✔ **Guided Discussion**

Did the student **UNDERSTANDING**
- ❏ make important observations?
- ❏ extend or generalize learning?
- ❏ provide insightful answers?
- ❏ pose insightful questions?

B Summarize Findings

Analyze and summarize assessment data for each student. Determine which Assessment Follow-Up is appropriate for each student. Use the Student Assessment Record in **Assessment** or **eAssess** to update assessment records.

Assessment page T41

C Assessment Follow-Up • DIFFERENTIATE INSTRUCTION

Based on your observations, use these teaching strategies for assessment follow-up.

INTERVENTION	ENRICH	PRACTICE	RETEACH
Review student performance on **Intervention** Lesson 5.C to see if students have mastered prerequisite skills for this lesson.	**If . . .** students are proficient in the lesson concepts, **Then . . .** encourage them to work on the chapter projects or **Enrichment** Lesson 5.12.	**If . . .** students would benefit from additional practice, **Then . . .** assign **Practice** Lesson 5.12.	**If . . .** students are having difficulty using the Paper Explorer, **Then . . .** have them review groups of addends that make the same sum. For example, 30 + 20 = 50, and so does 40 + 10.

ENGLISH LEARNER

Review

Use Lesson 5.12 in **English Learner Support Guide** to review lesson concepts and vocabulary.

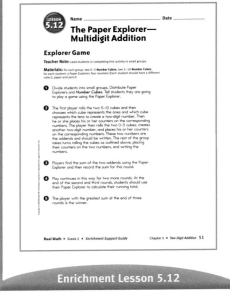

Enrichment Lesson 5.12

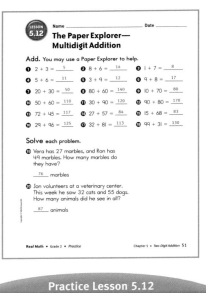

Practice Lesson 5.12

CHAPTER 5

Exploring Problem Solving

Objectives

- To solve a nonroutine problem involving the formation of equal groups
- To provide practice solving and presenting solutions to nonroutine problems
- To provide practice interpreting results to see if an answer is reasonable

Materials

None

Context of the Lesson While continuing the theme of picnics and parks introduced in the Chapter Introduction, this lesson gives students an opportunity to apply the skills they have been learning to a real-world, nonroutine problem.

1 Develop 5

Tell Students In Today's Lesson They Will

make tug-of-war teams that have the same number of children.

Guided Discussion

Remind students about previous activities in this chapter relating to parks and picnics. Have them look at the pictures on the top of page 189 while you read the following problem to them:

Three second-grade classes planned a play day in the park across the street from the school. They will have relay races, bag races, and target games in which the classes compete against each other. The students also want to have a tug-of-war, but they realize it wouldn't be fair for each class to be a team. Mr. García's class has 26 students, Ms. Taylor's class has 21 students, and Ms. Wilson's class has 25 students.

Pause here to ask students why it would not be fair for each class to be a team and what students could do to make the tug-of-war fair. Allow students to offer ideas, then continue with the story:

The students felt they had to do something to make the tug-of-war fair because some classes have more students than others. They came up with many good ideas. In the end, they decided to make four teams for the tug-of-war with the same number of students on each team. Now they need to organize the three classes into four teams. How many will be on each team?

Make sure students understand the problem by asking questions such as the following:

■ **What are you being asked to do?** to find out how many students will be on each team if there are four teams with the same number on each team

■ **Why don't they just let the classes tug against each other?** It would not be fair because some classes have more students than others.

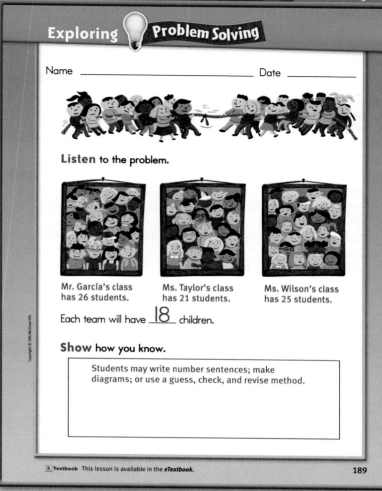

Exploring Problem Solving

Name _____ Date _____

Listen to the problem.

Mr. García's class has 26 students. Ms. Taylor's class has 21 students. Ms. Wilson's class has 25 students.

Each team will have __18__ children.

Show how you know.

Students may write number sentences; make diagrams; or use a guess, check, and revise method.

Textbook This lesson is available in the *eTextbook*. 189

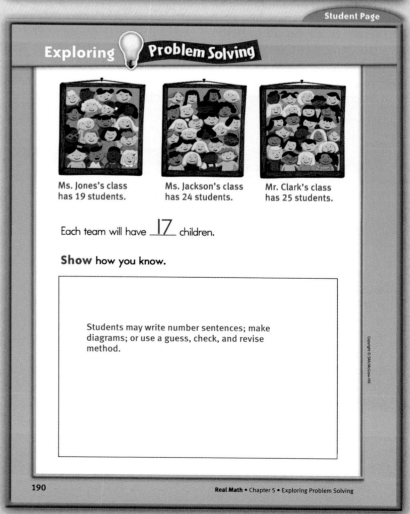

Exploring Problem Solving

Ms. Jones's class has 19 students. Ms. Jackson's class has 24 students. Mr. Clark's class has 25 students.

Each team will have __17__ children.

Show how you know.

Students may write number sentences; make diagrams; or use a guess, check, and revise method.

190 **Real Math** • Chapter 5 • Exploring Problem Solving

- **Without actually solving the problem, can you tell right away if the answer could be greater than 26?** Allow students to explain this in different ways. Possible answers: It cannot be, because you will have to take some students from each class to make the fourth team. There cannot be 26 on each team because 26 + 26 + 26 + 26 is greater than 26 + 25 + 21.
- **Might there be as few as 10 on a team?** no; Even if you organized just two of the classes into four teams, there would be more than 10 on a team because each class has more than 20 students.
- **What are some ways you might solve this problem?** Allow students to suggest and explain methods without going through entire solutions.

See Sample Solutions Strategies under Reflect.

Using Student Pages

Have students work in pairs or small groups to solve the problem. Provide support as needed. If students seem to be having difficulty, encourage them to struggle with the problem for a while. When needed, ask guiding questions such as the following:

- **How might you use base-ten materials to help solve this problem?**
- **What could you do to begin?**
- **What are some ways you have seen people use to form teams?**

Students who finish early may solve the problem on page 190, or you may assign page 190 as homework. The two problems are the same except for the numbers of students in the three classes.

 Reflect 10

Effective Communication Ask each group to share their solution and their strategies for solving the problem. Help students understand the following points:

- People sometimes use different strategies to find the same answer.
- Before you start to work on a problem, it is a good idea to think about what might be reasonable and then to check your answer to see if it is reasonable.

Sample Solutions Strategies

Students might use one or more of the following strategies to help solve the problem.

Make a Diagram

Students might make a diagram with Xs, Os, or other symbols in ten frames to represent the students in each class. Then they might cross out and redraw to show students switching from an existing class to the new team.

Use Number Sense

Students might find the total number of students in the three classes by thinking of 26 as 20 + 6, 25 as 20 + 5, and 21 as 20 + 1. They might add the tens and then the ones:

$$\underbrace{20 + 20 + 20}_{60} + \underbrace{6 + 5 + 1}_{12} = 72$$

To break 72 into four equal parts, they might break it in half and then in half again.

Guess, Check, and Revise/Write a Number Sentence

Students might first find the total number of students in the three classes and then try different numbers until they come upon one that when added four times equals the total. For example,

26	
21	12 + 12 + 12 + 12 = 48 (too low)
+ 25	20 + 20 + 20 + 20 = 80 (too high)
72	and so on

Act It Out

Students might use base-ten materials to represent the students in each class and then redistribute the materials into four equal groups.

 **Assess** 15

When evaluating student work, focus on whether students thought rationally about the problem. Questions to consider include the following:

- Did the student understand the problem?
- Was the student able to regroup when appropriate?
- Was the student able to explain his or her thinking?

Cumulative Review

Assign Pages 191–192

Use the Cumulative Review as a review of concepts and skills that students have previously learned.

Here are different ways that you can assign these problems to your students as they work through the chapter:

- With some of the lessons in the chapter, assign a set of cumulative review problems to be completed as practice or for homework.
  Lesson 5.6—Problems 1–8
  Lesson 5.7—Problems 9–10
  Lesson 5.8—Problems 11–18
  Lesson 5.9—Problems 19–24
  Lesson 5.10—Problems 25–28
  Lesson 5.11—Problems 29–31
  Lesson 5.12—Problems 32–35
- At any point during the chapter, assign part or all of the cumulative review problems to be completed as practice or for homework.

Cumulative Review

Problems 1–8 review using multiple addends, Lesson 2.7.

Problems 9–10 review measuring length in centimeters, Lesson 4.2.

Problems 11–18 review relating addition and subtraction, Lesson 1.10.

Problems 19–24 review missing addends and subtraction, Lesson 3.2.

Problems 25–28 review two-digit addition, Lesson 5.6.

Problems 29–31 review adding tens, Lesson 5.2.

Problems 32–35 review addition shortcuts, Lesson 5.10.

Monitoring Student Progress

If . . . students miss more than one problem in a section, **Then . . .** refer to the indicated lesson for remediation suggestions.

Cumulative Review

Name _____ Date _____

Using Multiple Addends Lesson 2.7
Add.

1. $5 + 5 + 4 = \underline{14}$
2. $4 + 8 + 2 = \underline{14}$
3. $10 + 8 + 0 = \underline{18}$
4. $4 + 5 + 9 = \underline{18}$
5. $5 + 6 + 7 = \underline{18}$
6. $1 + 10 + 9 = \underline{20}$
7. $4 + 4 + 4 = \underline{12}$
8. $3 + 4 + 7 = \underline{14}$

Measuring Length—Centimeters Lesson 4.2
Measure the length of each line in centimeters.

9. $\underline{3}$ centimeters
10. $\underline{6}$ centimeters

Relating Addition and Subtraction Lesson 1.10
Add or subtract.

11. $4 + 6 = \underline{10}$
12. $10 - 6 = \underline{4}$
13. $6 + 4 = \underline{10}$
14. $10 - 4 = \underline{6}$
15. $8 + 5 = \underline{13}$
16. $13 - 5 = \underline{8}$
17. $5 + 8 = \underline{13}$
18. $13 - 8 = \underline{5}$

Textbook This lesson is available in the *eTextbook*.

191

Cumulative Review

Missing Addends and Subtraction Lesson 3.2
Fill in the blanks.

19. $7 + \underline{11} = 18$
20. $14 - \underline{8} = 6$
21. $9 + \underline{5} = 14$
22. $7 + \underline{8} = 15$
23. $14 - \underline{7} = 7$
24. $17 - 4 = \underline{13}$

Practice with Two-Digit Addition Lesson 5.6
Add.

25. $79 + 8 = \underline{87}$
26. $64 + 25 = \underline{89}$
27. $52 + 32 = \underline{84}$
28. $33 + 33 = \underline{66}$

Adding Tens Lesson 5.2
Add.

29. $6 + 8 = \underline{14}$
30. $50 + 40 = \underline{90}$
31. $60 + 80 = \underline{140}$

Addition Shortcuts Lesson 5.10
Add. Use shortcuts if you can.

32. $20 + 40 + 60 + 80 + 100 = \underline{300}$
33. $6 + 7 + 4 + 3 = \underline{20}$
34. $1 + 3 + 7 + 9 = \underline{20}$
35. $1 + 2 + 3 + 4 + 5 + 6 + 7 + 8 + 9 = \underline{45}$

192

Real Math • Chapter 5

Wrap-Up

 Discuss 5

Concept/Question Board

Review the Concept/Question Board with students.

- Discuss students' contributions to the Concept side of the Board.
- Have students repose their questions, and lead a discussion to find satisfactory answers.

Chapter Projects APPLYING

Provide an opportunity for students who have worked on one or more of the projects outlined on page 160C to share their work with the class. Allow each student or student group five minutes to present or discuss their projects. For formal assessment, use the rubrics found in *Across the Curriculum Math Connections;* the rubric for **Take an Online Field Trip** is on page 57, and the rubric for **Track Bird Sightings** is on page 61. For informal assessment, use the following rubric and questions.

	Exceeds Expectations	Meets Expectations	Minimally Meets Expectations
Applies mathematics in real-world situations:	❏	❏	❏
Demonstrates strong engagement in the activity:	❏	❏	❏

Take an Online Field Trip

- What is the most important thing for you to consider when choosing a park to visit?
- What parks did you pick? Why did you pick them?
- What features do the parks have?
- What was the total number of animals and plants in each park?
- How did finding information about parks help you pick one to visit?
- If you were able to, would you like to visit this park? Why or why not?

Track Bird Sightings

- What types of birds did you observe?
- How many birds in total did you observe?
- What information did you put in your spreadsheet?
- Was it useful to create a bar graph from your data? Why or why not?
- What other information could you have included in your observations?
- What other ways could you graph the information you found?

Key Ideas Review UNDERSTANDING

Have students complete the Review questions independently or in small groups. Then discuss each question as a class.

Possible Answers

Problem ❶ Problems 1–3 review using bundles of craft sticks to represent two-digit numbers. Students should remember that in a two-digit number, the first number represents the number of tens and the second number represents the number of ones. The number 43 means 4 tens and 3 ones.

Problem ❷ Students should remember that they can regroup tens. Three tens and 17 is the same as 47.

Problem ❸ Students should remember that there are 10 craft sticks in each bundle.

Problem ❹ Problems 4–5 review the beginning steps of learning the algorithm for two-digit addition. Students should remember that they set up the addition problem similarly to how they would set up a single-digit vertical addition problem, but they should label the tens. The answer is b.

Problem ❺ Students should remember that they add tens and add ones separately and keep the labels, so the answer is 5 tens and 13.

Problem ❻ Students should be able to determine who will have the greater sum (and, therefore, win the game) without actually doing the addition. Because both problems have 45 as the first addend, the problem with the greater second addend will have the greater sum. Therefore, Kwame's problem (45 + 95) will beat Amy's problem (45 + 59).

Problem ❼ Students should remember that a shortcut for adding problems with multiple addends is to look for addends that make sums of 10. In the problem 5 + 5 + 4 + 6, the first and second addends make 10, and the third and fourth addends make 10, so the answer is 20.

Problem ❽ Students should remember that a shortcut for adding when one of the addends ends in 9 is to borrow 1 from the other addend to make one addend a multiple of 10. Therefore, 17 + 19 would be the same as 16 + 20.

Problem ❾ Problems 9–10 review groupings of craft sticks. The picture shows 3 bundles of 10 and 2 single sticks, or 32 sticks.

Problem ❿ Students should recognize that 2 bundles of 10 sticks and 12 single sticks is equivalent to 3 bundles of 10 and 2 single sticks. The answer is b.

 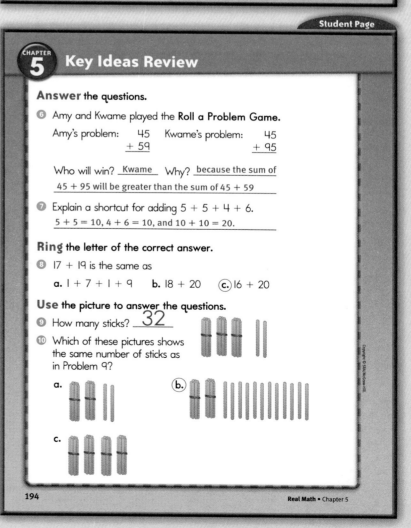

Chapter Review

Use the Chapter 5 Review to indicate areas in which each student is having difficulty or in which the class may need help. If students do well on the Chapter 5 Review, you may wish to skip directly to the Chapter Test; if not, you may want to spend a day or so helping students overcome their individual difficulties before taking the Practice Test.

Next to each set of problems is a list of the lessons in the chapter that covered those concepts. If they need help, students can refer to a specific lesson for additional instruction. You can also use this information to make additional assignments based on the previous lesson concepts.

Have students complete pages 195–196 on their own.

Monitoring Student Progress

Problems 1–2 Lesson 5.8

If . . . students have difficulty with these problems,

Then . . . have them rewrite the word problems as multiple-number sentences.

Problems 3–8 Lesson 5.2

If . . . students have difficulty with these problems,

Then . . . review the Guided Discussion from this lesson and include additional practice problems.

Problems 9–10 Lessons 5.1, 5.4

If . . . students miss more than two of these problems,

Then . . . have them play the **Get to 100 by Tens or Ones Game.**

Problems 11–21 Lessons 5.9–5.10

If . . . students have difficulty with these problems,

Then . . . have them make a table of all the addition number sentences that have 10 as the result. Then have them use the table to apply shortcuts.

Problems 22–23 Lesson 5.6

If . . . students have difficulty with these problems,

Then . . . review the Guided Discussion and Key Ideas from this lesson with additional examples.

Name _____ Date _____

Lesson 5.8 **Solve.**

A yo-yo costs 39¢, and a whistle costs 14¢.

❶ How much does it cost for both? $\underline{53¢}$

❷ How much do two whistles cost? $\underline{28¢}$

Lesson 5.2 **Add.**

❸ $10 + 10 = \underline{20}$ ❻ $30 + 10 = \underline{40}$

❹ $20 + 10 = \underline{30}$ ❼ $40 + 20 = \underline{60}$

❺ $10 + 10 + 10 = \underline{30}$ ❽ $70 + 90 = \underline{160}$

Lessons 5.1 and 5.4 **How many cents? Write your answers.**

❾ $\underline{51}$ ¢

❿ $71 + 25 = \underline{96}$. There are $\underline{96}$ ¢.

Student Page

Lessons 5.9–5.10 **Add. Use shortcuts if you can.**

⑪ $12 + 39 = \underline{51}$ ⑮ $29 + 27 = \underline{56}$

⑫ $41 + 29 = \underline{70}$ ⑯ $35 + 45 = \underline{80}$

⑬ $23 + 46 = \underline{69}$ ⑰ $52 + 16 = \underline{68}$

⑭ $16 + 14 = \underline{30}$ ⑱ $36 + 39 = \underline{75}$

⑲ $1 + 3 + 5 + 7 + 9 = \underline{25}$

⑳ $9 + 1 + 10 + 19 + 1 + 30 = \underline{70}$

㉑ The pool in the park is shaped like a rectangle. One side is 50 meters long, and another side is 25 meters long. What is the perimeter of the pool?

$\underline{150}$ meters

Lesson 5.6 **Add. Write what you did.**

㉒ 3 tens and 7
+ 5 tens and 2
_____
8 tens and 9
or $\underline{89}$

㉓ 5 tens and 1
+ 3 tens and 9
_____
8 tens and 10
or $\underline{90}$

3 Chapter Tests 40

Practice Test

Student Pages 197–200

- The Chapter 5 Practice Test on **Student Edition** pages 197–200 provides an opportunity to formally evaluate students' proficiency with concepts developed in this chapter.
- The content is similar to the Chapter 5 Review, in standardized format.

Problems ㉕ and ㉖   **Extended Response**

Students practice their map visualization skills when they answer problem 25. They look for different routes and determine the shortest path from one location to another. For Problem 26, students practice addition of multiple addends. They are also encouraged to explain their thinking, thereby helping to strengthen their problem-solving strategies and skills.

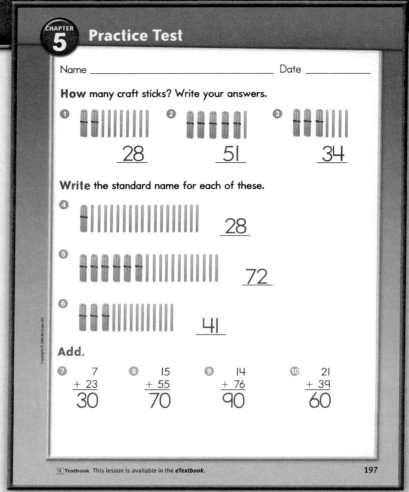

CHAPTER 5 **Practice Test**

Name _____ Date _____

How many craft sticks? Write your answers.

① 28   ② 51   ③ 34

Write the standard name for each of these.

④ 28

⑤ 72

⑥ 41

Add.

⑦ 7
  + 23
  30

⑧ 15
  + 55
  70

⑨ 14
  + 76
  90

⑩ 21
  + 39
  60

Textbook This lesson is available in the *eTextbook*.   197

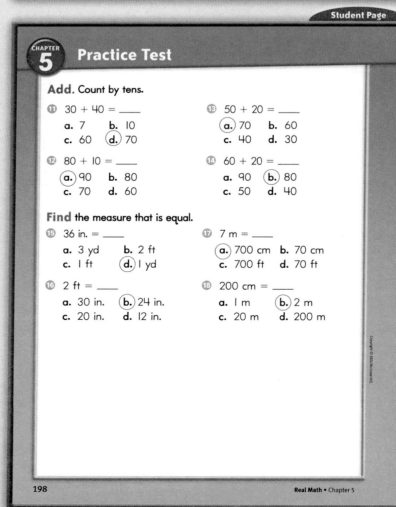

Student Page

CHAPTER 5 **Practice Test**

Add. Count by tens.

⑪ 30 + 40 = ____
  a. 7   **b.** 10
  c. 60   **(d.)** 70

⑬ 50 + 20 = ____
  (a.) 70   **b.** 60
  c. 40   **d.** 30

⑫ 80 + 10 = ____
  (a.) 90   **b.** 80
  c. 70   **d.** 60

⑭ 60 + 20 = ____
  a. 90   **(b.)** 80
  c. 50   **d.** 40

Find the measure that is equal.

⑮ 36 in. = ____
  a. 3 yd   **b.** 2 ft
  c. 1 ft   **(d.)** 1 yd

⑰ 7 m = ____
  (a.) 700 cm   **b.** 70 cm
  c. 700 ft   **d.** 70 ft

⑯ 2 ft = ____
  a. 30 in.   **(b.)** 24 in.
  c. 20 in.   **d.** 12 in.

⑱ 200 cm = ____
  a. 1 m   **(b.)** 2 m
  c. 20 m   **d.** 200 m

198   Real Math • Chapter 5

Practice Test

Name _____ Date _____

Add.

19. 33 + 37 = ____
    a. 60   **b.** 64   **c.** 70   **d.** 74

20. 72 + 28 = ____
    a. 100   **b.** 80   **c.** 56   **d.** 46

21. 16 + 15 = ____
    a. 20   **b.** 21   **c.** 30   **d.** 31

Solve.

22. Yoshi drove 30 miles to visit her aunt. Then she drove 20 miles to visit her grandfather. The next day, she drove 40 miles to get home. How many miles in all did she drive?
    a. 90   **b.** 70   **c.** 60   **d.** 50

23. Helen bought 2 shirts for $20 each and 1 dress for $30. How much did Helen spend?
    a. $40   **b.** $50   **c.** $70   **d.** $80

24. Nick spent 34¢ on a pad of paper and 27¢ on a pen. How much did he spend in all?
    a. 51¢   **b.** 61¢   **c.** 63¢   **d.** 67¢

Textbook This lesson is available in the *eTextbook.*

199

CHAPTER 5 Practice Test

Use the map to solve.

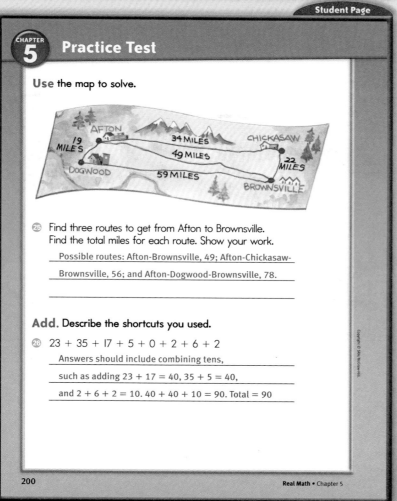

25. Find three routes to get from Afton to Brownsville. Find the total miles for each route. Show your work.

    Possible routes: Afton-Brownsville, 49; Afton-Chickasaw-

    Brownsville, 56; and Afton-Dogwood-Brownsville, 78.

Add. Describe the shortcuts you used.

26. 23 + 35 + 17 + 5 + 0 + 2 + 6 + 2

    Answers should include combining tens,

    such as adding 23 + 17 = 40, 35 + 5 = 40,

    and 2 + 6 + 2 = 10. 40 + 40 + 10 = 90. Total = 90

200   **Real Math • Chapter 5**

Chapter Test ✓ COMPUTING

For further evaluation instead of or in addition to this test, you may wish to have students take the Chapter 5 Test provided in *Assessment*.

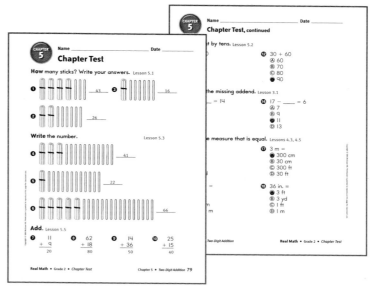

Assessment, pages 79–80

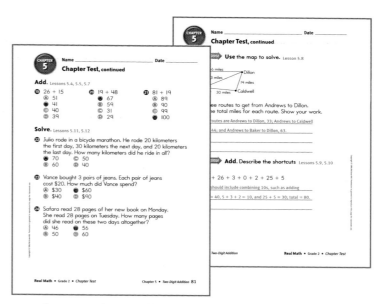

Assessment, pages 81–82

4 Assess and Differentiate

 Assess Use *eAssess* to record and analyze evidence of student understanding.

A Gather Evidence

Use the Daily Class Assessment Records in **Assessment** or **eAssess** to record Informal and Formal Assessments.

Informal Assessment

☑ **Key Ideas Review**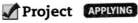

Did the student
- ❏ make important observations?
- ❏ extend or generalize learning?
- ❏ provide insightful answers?
- ❏ pose insightful questions?

Informal Assessment

☑ **Project** APPLYING

Did the student
- ❏ meet the project objectives?
- ❏ communicate clearly?
- ❏ complete the project accurately?
- ❏ connect mathematics to real-world situations?

Formal Assessment

☑ **Chapter Test**

Score the test, and record the results.

B Summarize Findings

Analyze and summarize assessment data for each student. Determine which Chapter Follow-Up is appropriate for each student. Use the Student Assessment Record in **Assessment** or **eAssess** to update assessment records.

C Chapter Follow-Up ● DIFFERENTIATE INSTRUCTION

Based on your observations, use these teaching strategies for chapter follow-up.

ENRICH	PRACTICE	RETEACH	INTERVENTION
If . . . students demonstrate a **secure understanding** of chapter concepts,	**If . . .** students demonstrate **competent understanding** of chapter concepts,	**If . . .** students demonstrate **emerging understanding** of chapter concepts,	**If . . .** students demonstrate **minimal understanding** of chapter concepts,
Then . . . move on to the next chapter.	**Then . . .** move on to the next chapter.	**Then . . .** move on to the next chapter, but continue to provide cumulative review.	**Then . . .** intensive intervention is still needed before they start the next chapter.

Sharing with Cousin Trixie

Context of the Thinking Story While spending the day at the park, Trixie, Ferdie, and Portia share grapes. They also share a bicycle for an hour.

Lesson Planner

OBJECTIVES
To develop logical thinking while integrating reading skills with mathematics

NCTM STANDARDS

Number and Operations
- Counting with understanding
- Understanding situations that entail multiplication and division
- Developing and using strategies for whole-number computations

Connections
Recognizing connections among mathematical ideas

READING STANDARDS
- Listening for details
- Drawing conclusions
- Evaluating information
- Making inferences

Using the Thinking Story
The Thinking Story may be used at any time throughout the chapter. Read the Thinking Story "Sharing with Cousin Trixie" to your class. As you read the story, give students time to think about each question, but not so much that they forget the point being made.

Sharing with Cousin Trixie

One day when Ferdie and Portia were in the park, Cousin Trixie appeared with a small bag of grapes. "Today I have something we can share," she said. "And I'll let you do the dividing, Ferdie."

Ferdie poured the grapes onto a napkin on a park table. He wanted to divide them, but he wasn't quite sure how to do it.

How would you do it? by having each person take one grape in turn, for example

"There might be enough to give everyone six grapes," Ferdie said. "Here are six for you, Trixie, and six for you, Portia, and, oops…" He looked at the rest of the grapes. "That leaves only three for me."

How many grapes were there? fifteen

"It's nice of you to give more to the girls," said Trixie. "But that means the grapes are not being shared evenly."

How could they make things right? They could start again and pass out the grapes one at a time.

"Why don't we give you the grapes and you can start over," said Portia.

Is there another way?   **They could give each other some of their grapes.**

"If each of us gives you some of our grapes, it might work out that we all have the same number," said Trixie.

How many grapes do Portia and Trixie each have?   **six**

How many grapes does Ferdie have?   **three**

How many grapes would each girl have to give Ferdie for all of them to have the same number?   **one**

How many grapes would each child have then?   **five**

Portia and Trixie each gave Ferdie one grape. "Now we each have five," said Portia. "That's sharing evenly."

On the way home, they found Manolita riding a bicycle. "What a great bike!" said Ferdie. "May I borrow it?"

"All right," said Manolita. "But only for an hour. I'll come back and get it then."

Ferdie forgot about the girls and began riding the bicycle.

"Of all the nerve!" said Trixie.

What's wrong?   **Ferdie didn't offer to share.**

"You're not sharing," said Portia.

"How can I share a bicycle?" Ferdie asked. "Only one person can ride it at a time."

How could they share the bicycle? **by taking turns**

"We'll take turns," Portia suggested. "Trixie can ride it for one minute, then I'll ride it for one minute, then Ferdie can ride it for one minute. Then we'll keep on taking turns for the whole hour."

Can you think of another way? **Take longer turns.**

Trixie looked at her watch. "One minute at a time isn't long enough for riding a bike," she said. "I have a better way. Ferdie can ride the bike for 15 minutes, then Portia can ride it for 15 minutes, and then I'll ride it for the rest of the hour."

Is that a fair way to share the bicycle? **no**

How much time will Trixie have to ride the bicycle? **30 minutes**

"That's not fair," Portia said. "If Ferdie and I each have it for 15 minutes, that's half an hour—and you'll have half an hour for yourself."

"Then you figure out a better way," Cousin Trixie said huffily.

"Let's each ride it for 30 minutes," Ferdie suggested. "That will be even."

What's wrong with Ferdie's idea? **It adds up to an hour and a half.**

"That adds up to an hour and a half," Cousin Trixie said. "And we have the bike for only an hour. You'll have to do better than that."

"Then let's try 20 minutes," said Ferdie.

"Twenty and 20 and 20—that should add up to about an hour."

How many minutes does that add up to? **60**

Is that an hour? **yes**

"That's right," said Cousin Trixie. "If we take the bike for 20 minutes apiece, that will use up the hour exactly. You're learning fast about sharing, Ferdie. Only it's too bad that we had to use up 10 of your 20 minutes deciding what we are going to do."

The End

Guided Discussion

As students answer the questions in the story, ask them to communicate how they chose their answers. Allow students to debate the answers if necessary.

Using Student Pages 201–202

Have students follow the instructions and complete the **Student Edition** activities. Read the instructions aloud if students are having difficulty. If students have difficulty figuring out the number of grapes needed on each napkin, provide students with real objects to manipulate to solve the problem.

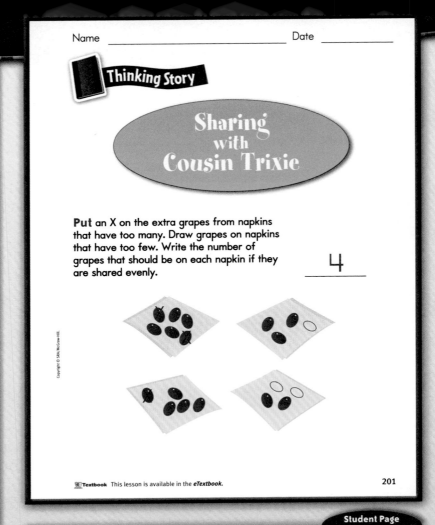

Name _____ Date _____

Thinking Story

Sharing with Cousin Trixie

Put an X on the extra grapes from napkins that have too many. Draw grapes on napkins that have too few. Write the number of grapes that should be on each napkin if they are shared evenly.

4

eTextbook This lesson is available in the *eTextbook*. 201

Student Page

You and three friends have an hour to share a bicycle. Color the amount of time each person would have to ride.

202   **Real Math** • Chapter 5

Lesson Study

Reflect on each of the lessons you taught in this chapter. Rate each one on the following scale, and then consider ways to maintain or improve positive teaching experiences in the future.

Lessons	Very Effective	Effective	Less Effective	What Worked	Ways to Improve
5.1 Place Value					
5.2 Adding Tens					
5.3 Regrouping for Addition					
5.4 Adding Two-Digit Numbers					
5.5 More Adding Two-Digit Numbers					
5.6 Practice with Two-Digit Addition					
5.7 More Practice Adding Two-Digit Numbers					
5.8 Applications of Two-Digit Addition					
5.9 Grouping by Tens					
5.10 Addition Shortcuts					
5.11 The Paper Explorer—Adding Tens					
5.12 The Paper Explorer—Multidigit Addition					

Two-Digit Subtraction

Teaching for Understanding

In this chapter students are introduced to regrouping tens as ones in preparation for two-digit subtraction. Students will write two-digit numbers in expanded form (2 tens) as well as traditional form (20) and exchange tens for ones using a variety of base-ten materials.

Prerequisite Skills and Concepts

● Subtraction Facts ● Adding Two-Digit Numbers ● Place Value to 100

Two-Digit Subtraction Skills Trace

Before Grade 2	Grade 2	After Grade 2
Grades K–1 Informally and formally introduced subtracting from 10	**Chapter 3** developed understanding of the relationship between single-digit addition and subtraction by providing related exercises and problems. **This chapter** develops fluency with computational strategies for two-digit subtraction.	Review and mastery of the meaning of two-digit subtraction Formal introduction of larger numbers and more complex patterns

Problem Solving

Problem solving is in every lesson. This chapter includes the following:

CHAPTER INTRODUCTION Students use two-digit subtraction while designing a habitat for polar bears. (pp. 203I–204C)

EXPLORING PROBLEM SOLVING The first lesson continues the zoo theme while providing addition and subtraction skill practice (pp. 217–218, 218A). The second lesson provides nonroutine problems based on planning a visit to the zoo (pp. 229–230, 230A).

THINKING STORY In "Ferdie Borrows and Borrows and Borrows," students help a character keep track of earning by adding and subtracting amounts of money (pp. 241A–241E, 241–242).

Games

Develop reasoning skills, and provide extensive practice.

• **Yard Sale Game**—Subtraction version (Lesson 6.1)
• **Roll a Problem (Subtraction) Game** (Lesson 6.6)

Math Background

Two-Digit Subtraction

The Subtraction Algorithm and Manipulatives

- Base-ten materials (craft sticks bundled in groups of ten) are used to help students develop a standard algorithm for multidigit subtraction. The use of base-ten manipulatives is important because it leads to an understanding of place value and to why the subtraction algorithm works.

- Students who simply memorize an algorithm can produce correct answers but have little understanding of why the procedures work. In order for students to understand more difficult algorithms in future mathematics, a firm understanding of the simpler algorithms is necessary.

- Once students have developed a firm understanding of why the regrouping process for subtraction works, and how to use it to find answers, allow them to solve problems without using craft sticks or other concrete materials. Students may reach this stage at different times throughout the chapter, so continue to make manipulatives available for those who need them.

- Play money is a more abstract manipulative, because one $10 bill does not "look" equivalent to ten $1 bills. Using play money may be useful for students as a transitional stage between modeling a problem with base-ten materials such as bundled craft sticks and working entirely with pencil and paper. Play money may also be useful for modeling word problem situations, because many real-life applications of addition and subtraction involve money.

Alternate Algorithms

Some students (or their parents) may be familiar with other subtraction algorithms. *Real Math* does not teach alternate algorithms so that students focus on using a single algorithm that they understand well. However, if students have learned an alternate algorithm that they understand and can use efficiently (consistently finding correct answers in a reasonable amount of time), do not insist that they use the algorithm taught in this chapter.

Common Errors

The most common error students make with multidigit subtraction is attempting to determine answers simply by subtracting digits in columns without regard to which digit is which or considering that the digits are part of greater numbers. Thus, they often make mistakes like this:

$$
\begin{array}{r}
42 \\
- 16 \\
\hline
34
\end{array}
$$

The focus in this chapter on first regrouping numbers to facilitate subtraction, using concrete materials in groups of ten, is designed to force students to think about the numbers involved before they begin making calculations.

What Research Says
About Subtraction with Regrouping

How Children Learn Multidigit Subtraction

"Subtraction follows a progression that generally parallels that for addition. Some U.S. children also invent counting-down methods that model the taking away of numbers by counting back from the total. But counting down and counting backward are difficult for many children. . . . When counting up is not introduced, many children may not invent it until the second or third grade, if at all. Intervention studies with U.S. first graders that helped them see subtraction situations as taking away the first *x* objects enabled them to learn and understand counting-up-to procedures for subtraction. Their subtraction accuracy became as high as that for addition."

Kilpatrick, J., J. Swafford, and B. Findell, eds. *Adding It Up: Helping Children Learn Mathematics.* Washington, D.C.: National Research Council/National Academy Press, 2001, pp. 190–191.

Learning Trajectories for Multidigit Addition

Key steps in the learning trajectory for measurement from the second grade range are described below. For the complete trajectory, see Appendix B.

Age Range	Level Name	Level	Description
6	Numbers-in-Numbers +/−	9	Evidence of the advancement in adding is when a child recognizes that a number is part of a whole and can solve problems when the start is unknown (_ + 4 = 9) with counting strategies.
7	Deriver +/−	10	At the next level a child can use flexible strategies and derived combinations (for example, "7 + 7 is 14, so 7 + 8 is 15") to solve all types of problems.
8+	Problem Solver +/−	11	As children develop their addition and subtraction abilities, they can solve all types of problems by using flexible strategies and many known combinations.

Clements, D. H., J. Sarama, & A. -M. DiBiase, eds. *Engaging Young Children in Mathematics: Standards for Early Childhood Mathematics Education.* Mahwah, New Jersey: Lawrence Erlbaum Associates, Publishers, 2004.

Research-Based Teaching Techniques

Learning single-digit addition and subtraction is generally characterized as "learning math facts." It is assumed that children must memorize these facts, yet research has shown that addition and subtraction have their roots in counting, counting on, number sense, the ability to compose and decompose numbers, and place value. Research has shown that learning methods for adding and subtracting with understanding is much more effective than rote memorization of seemingly isolated facts. "The ideas and skills involved in multidigit computation are supported by most of the big ideas of number and operations. Unfortunately, given present-day instruction, many children think of multidigit numbers only as single-digit numbers sitting side by side, ignoring their place value, which invites different kinds of errors. To develop computational methods that they understand, children require strong experience in kindergarten (or earlier) hearing the pattern of repeating tens in the number words and relating them to quantities groups in tens and seeing teen numbers and two-digit numbers as embedded numbers (52 is 50 and 2)."

Clements, Douglas and J. Sarama, eds. *Engaging Young Children in Mathematics: Standards for Early Childhood Mathematics Education.* Mahwah, New Jersey: Lawrence Erlbaum Associates, Publishers, 2004, p. 25.

RESEARCH IN ACTION

Expanded Form In Chapter 6 the reading and interpretation of numbers written in both standard form and expanded form and the use of expanded form for representing numbers will be explored.

Inverse Operations Chapter 6 will reinforce the inverse relationship between addition and subtraction by focusing attention on the use of addition to check solutions to subtraction problems.

Renaming In Chapter 6 students will explore activities involving renaming of numbers and the use of expanded form in describing numbers. These activities will reinforce the students' understanding of place value based on their use of base-ten concepts and language associated with the base-ten number system.

Vocabulary

regroup (Lesson 6.1) to change the grouping of numbers by separating ones from tens and grouping the parts with other like values

English Learner

Cognates

For English learners a quick way to acquire new English vocabulary is to build on what is known in the primary language.

English	Spanish
regroup	reagrupar
groups	grupos
subtract	sustraer
problem	problema
bicycle	bicicleta
price	precio
dollars	dólares
correct	correcto
solution	solución
to apply	aplicar
equal	igual
distance	distancia
map	mapa

Access Vocabulary

English learners may understand words in different contexts or not understand idioms. Review chapter vocabulary for this concern. For example:

rewrite	to write again in a new way
rods	The rods used in this lesson are thin, straight pieces of plastic. Each rod represents 10 ones.
record what you did	write down or make a record of what you did
two-digit number	A two-digit number has tens and ones.
steps	the orderly process of accomplishing a task
check your solution	review your answer to make sure it is correct
clerk	a person who works in a store
equals	is the same as
back and forth	a round-trip

Chapter Planner

Lessons	Objectives	NCTM Standards	State Standards
6.1 Regrouping Tens as Ones pages 205A–206A 45–60 minutes	**To regroup tens as ones** by converting numbers in standard form into expanded form	Number and Operations, Connections, Data Analysis and Probability	
6.2 Subtracting Tens pages 207A–208A 45–60 minutes	**To introduce subtracting multiples of ten from two-digit numbers,** presenting the numbers in standard form as well as expanded form	Number and Operations, Problem Solving	
6.3 Subtracting from Tens pages 209A–210A 45–60 minutes	**To introduce subtracting two-digit numbers from multiples of ten,** focusing on why regrouping is necessary	Number and Operations, Algebra, Problem Solving	
6.4 Subtracting Two-Digit Numbers pages 211A–212A 45–60 minutes	**To introduce a general procedure for subtracting any two-digit numbers** with a focus on using a more conventional notation for borrowing	Number and Operations, Algebra	
6.5 Using a Paper Explorer to Understand Subtraction pages 213A–214A 45–60 minutes	**To explore base-ten subtraction,** using a Paper Explorer	Number and Operations, Communication, Problem Solving, Connections	
6.6 Practicing Two-Digit Subtraction pages 215A–216A 45–60 minutes	**To provide reinforcement and review of two-digit subtraction,** using a different base-ten material, money	Number and Operations	
6.7 Checking Subtraction pages 221A–222A 45–60 minutes	**To use addition to check two-digit subtraction answers** with a focus on solving word problems	Number and Operations, Problem Solving	
6.8 Applying Subtraction pages 223A–224A 45–60 minutes	**To apply strategies for subtracting two-digit numbers** with a focus on solving realistic problems involving money	Number and Operations, Problem Solving, Connections	
6.9 Comparing Two-Digit Subtraction Expressions pages 225A–226A 45–60 minutes	**To extend the use of addition and subtraction** with a focus on solving for equalities and inequalities	Number and Operations, Algebra, Representation	
6.10 Problem Solving with Two-Digit Subtraction pages 227A–228A 45–60 minutes	**To apply problem-solving strategies** with a focus on writing number sentences, solving for missing terms, and creating word problems	Number and Operations, Algebra	

Vocabulary	Manipulatives and Materials	Games *to reinforce skills and concepts*
regroup	• *Number Cubes* • Play money • Overhead bills and coins • **Yard Sale Game Mat** • Craft sticks and rubber bands	**Yard Sale Game**
	• *Number Cubes* • **Yard Sale Game Mat** • Play money • Base-ten blocks	**Yard Sale Game**
	• *Number Cubes* • Craft sticks and rubber bands	
	• *Number Cubes* • Base-ten blocks • Overhead bills and coins • Craft sticks and rubber bands • Play money	
	• *Number Cubes* • Blank transparency to write on • Overhead transparency of *Practice* page 124 • Counters or pawns of two different colors	
	• *Number Cubes* • Craft sticks and rubber bands • Play money	**Roll a Problem Game**
	• *Number Cubes* • Craft sticks and rubber bands	
	• *Number Cubes* • Play money • Overhead bills and coins	
	Number Cubes	
	Number Cubes	

Additional Resources

Differentiated Instruction

Intervention Support Guide Provides instruction for the following prerequisite skills:

- Lesson 6.A Place Value and Subtraction–1
- Lesson 6.B Place Value and Subtraction–2
- Lesson 6.C Place Value and Subtraction–3

Enrichment Support Guide Extends lesson concepts

Practice Reinforces lesson skills and concepts

Reteach Support Guide Provides alternate instruction for lesson concepts

English Learner Support Guide Previews and reviews lesson concepts and vocabulary for English learners

Technology

The following electronic resources are available:

- **ⓔPlanner** Lessons 6.1–6.10
- **ⓔPresentation** Lessons 6.1–6.10
- **ⓔTextbook** Lessons 6.1–6.10
- **ⓔAssess** Lessons 6.1–6.10
- **ⓔMathTools** *Base Ten* Lessons 6.2, 6.3
  Coins and Money Lessons 6.7, 6.8
  Sets Former Lesson 6.9
- **Building Blocks** *School Supply Shop* Lesson 6.2
  Math-O-Scope Lesson 6.3
  Word Problems with Tools 4 Lesson 6.8
  Number Compare 4 Lesson 6.9

Assessment
Informal Assessment rubrics at the end of each lesson provide daily evaluation of student math proficiency.

Chapter Planner, continued

Problem Solving	When to Use	Objectives	NCTM Standards	Skills Covered
Chapter Introduction (pp. 203I–204C) 15–30 minutes	Use following the Chapter 6 Pretest	To introduce chapter concepts in a problem-solving setting	Problem Solving, Communication	Two-digit subtraction
Exploring Problem Solving (pp. 217–218, 218A) 30–45 minutes	Use anytime during the chapter	To explore methods of solving nonroutine problems	Problem Solving, Communication	Two-digit subtraction
Exploring Problem Solving (pp. 229–230, 230A) 45–60 minutes	Use anytime during the chapter	To explore methods of solving nonroutine problems	Problem Solving, Communication	Two-digit subtraction
Thinking Story—Ferdie Borrows and Borrows and Borrows (pp. 241A–241E, 241–242) 20–30 minutes	Use anytime during the chapter	To develop logical reasoning while integrating reading skills with mathematics	Number and Operations, Problem Solving	Addition and subtraction applications involving money

Review	When to Use	Objectives	NCTM Standards	Skills Covered
Cumulative Review (p. 219–220) 15–30 minutes	Use anytime after Lesson 6.6	To review concepts and skills taught earlier in the year	Number and Operations	Subtraction strategies
Cumulative Review (p. 231–232) 15–30 minutes	Use anytime after Lesson 6.10	To review concepts and skills taught earlier in the year	Number and Operations	Subtraction strategies
Chapter 6 Review (pp. 235A, 235–236) 30–45 minutes	Use after Lesson 6.10	To review concepts and skills taught in the chapter	Number and Operations	Subtraction strategies

Assessment	When to Use	Objectives	NCTM Standards	Skills Covered
Informal Assessment Rubrics (pp. 206A–228A) 5 minutes per student	Use at the end of each lesson	To provide daily evaluation of math proficiency	Number and Operations, Communication	Computing, Understanding, Reasoning, Applying, Engaging
Pretest (Assessment pp. 84–85) 15–30 minutes	Use prior to Chapter 6	To provide assessment of prerequisite and chapter topics	Number and Operations, Problem solving	Computing, Understanding, Reasoning, Applying, Engaging
Individual Oral Assessment (p. 220A) 5 minutes per student	Use after Lesson 6.6	To provide alternate means of assessing students' progress	Number and Operations	Two-digit subtraction
Mastery Checkpoint (Assessment pp. T59–T61) 5 minutes per student	Use after Lessons 6.7, 6.8, 6.10	To provide assessment of mastery of key skills	Number and Operations	Two-digit subtraction
Chapter 6 Practice Test (pp. 237–238, 239–240) 30–45 minutes	Use after or in place of the Chapter 6 Review	To provide assessment or additional practice of the chapter concepts	Number and Operations, Problem Solving	Two-digit subtraction
Chapter 6 Test (Assessment pp. 91–94) 30–45 minutes	Use after or in place of the Chapter 6 Review	To provide assessment on the chapter concepts	Number and Operations, Problem Solving	Two-digit subtraction

Technology Resources and Support

Visit SRAonline.com for online versions of the *Real Math* eSuite.

Technology for Teachers

e Presentation	Lessons 6.1–6.10 Use the *ePresentation* to interactively present chapter content.
e Planner	Use the Chapter and Lesson Planners to outline activities and time frames for Chapter 6.
e Assess	Students can take the following assessments in *eAssess:* • Chapter Pretest • Mastery Checkpoint **Lessons 6.7, 6.8, and 6.10** • Chapter Test Teachers can record results and print reports for all assessments in this chapter.
e MathTools	**Base Ten** Lessons 6.2, 6.3 **Coins and Money** Lessons 6.7, 6.8 **Sets Former** Lesson 6.9

Technology for Students

e Textbook	An electronic, interactive version of the **Student Edition** is available for all lessons in Chapter 6.
e MathTools	**Base Ten** Lessons 6.2, 6.3 **Coins and Money** Lessons 6.7, 6.8 **Sets Former** Lesson 6.9
TECH KNOWLEDGE	*TechKnowledge* Level 2 provides lessons that specifically teach the Unit 10 Internet applications that students can use while working on this chapter's project.
Building Blocks	**School Supply Shop** Lesson 6.2 **Math-O-Scope** Lesson 6.3 **Word Problems with Tools 4** Lesson 6.8 **Number Compare 4** Lesson 6.9

Two-Digit Subtraction

 1 Introduce Chapter 6 `10`

Chapter Objectives

This opener helps students prepare for the work with two-digit subtraction in this chapter by providing an activity in which they count and take away tens. Explain to students that in this chapter they will build on what they already know about subtraction. They will learn

- regrouping.
- subtracting from tens.
- two-digit subtraction.

Pretest ✓ COMPUTING

Administer the Pretest in *Assessment* pages 84–85.

The Pretest covers the following prerequisite skills:

- Relating addition and subtraction (Problems 1–4)
- Function tables (Problems 5 and 6)
- Adding one-digit and two-digit numbers (Problems 7–10)
- Tally chart (Problems 11–14)

The Pretest also covers the following topics from this chapter:

- Subtracting one-digit and two-digit numbers (Problems 15–18)
- Comparing numbers using equalities and inequalities (Problems 19–22)

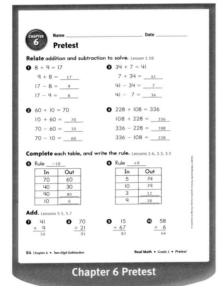

Chapter 6 Pretest

Access Prior Knowledge ✓ UNDERSTANDING

Guided Discussion

Use the photograph on page 203 to initiate a discussion about zoos. Ask questions such as the following:

- **Who has been to the zoo?** Encourage students who have been to the zoo to raise their hands.
- **What are some of the animals you've seen at a zoo?** Possible answers: bears, giraffes, tigers
- **What are some of the things the animals need?** food, water, a place to live
- **How do the animals get the things they need?** The people who work at the zoo provide them.

 2 Exploring Problem Solving `15`

Tell Students In Today's Lesson They Will

- design a habitat for polar bears so it has space for the bears to swim, walk around, play, and sleep and a place for the zoo workers to work.
- determine how much space is allotted for each of the activities above.
- explain how they solved the problem.

Materials

- Graph paper
- Scissors

Using Student Pages APPLYING

Discuss how the zoo habitat shown in the photograph on page 203 is like the animal's natural home in the wild. Introduce the term *habitat* as a way to refer to the place where an animal lives.

Have students look at page 204 as you read the following problem to them:

Imagine you are working at a zoo. You are in charge of designing a habitat for two polar bears that will arrive soon. The habitat will be square, just like the grid on your page. You need to include a pond in the shape of a rectangle and an area for animal workers, also in the shape of a rectangle. You may put the pond and the work space anywhere you want them. The pond must be 6 squares long and 5 squares wide. The worker area must be 5 squares long and 4 squares wide. I will give you some graph paper so you can make cutouts and try them in different places before you draw your final design.

When you are finished drawing, you need to find out three things:

■ *How many squares of space does the pond take up?*

■ *How many squares does the worker area take up?*

■ *How much space is left for the bears to walk around in?*

Make sure students understand the problem by asking questions such as the following:

- **What are you supposed to do in this problem?** Design a polar-bear habitat in a zoo. Determine how much space is used for the pond, for the workers, and for the bears to walk around in.
- **After you have decided where you want the pond and the work space, what should you do?** Draw the design on the grid.
- **What do the squares on the grid stand for?** space in the habitat
- **How might you find out how many squares are in each space?** Count them. Commend students who suggest shortcuts such as counting by 5s and/or by 10s.

Give each group a sheet of 1-centimeter graph paper and a pair of scissors. Circulate and provide support as needed, but allow students to struggle with the problem by trying different approaches.

CHAPTER 6 · Two-Digit Subtraction

In This Chapter You Will Learn
- regrouping.
- subtracting from tens.
- two-digit subtraction.

203

Problem Solving

Name _____ Date _____

Listen to the problem. Draw your design.

How much space will the pond take? __30__ squares

How big will the area for the workers be? __20__ squares

How much space will be left for the polar bears to walk? __50__ squares

How do you know? _____

_____

_____

204   **Real Math** • Chapter 6

Concept/Question Board APPLYING

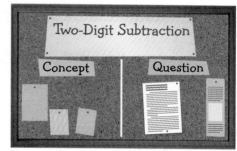

Questions
Have students think of and write three questions they have about two-digit subtraction and how it can be used. Then have them select one question to post on the Question side of the Board.

Concepts
As students work through the chapter, have them collect examples of how two-digit subtraction is used in everyday situations. For each example, have them write a problem that relates to the item(s). Have them display their examples on the Concept side of the Board. Suggest the following:
- lunch money
- sport scores

Answers
Throughout the chapter, have students post answers to the questions and solutions to the problems on the Board.

3 Reflect

20

 **Knowledge Age Skills**

Effective Communication Have each group present its design, its answers, and the strategies used for determining numbers of squares. Also have groups explain why they placed the pond and work space where they did. Encourage students to question placements that are not practical, such as a work space with no access except by walking through the habitat.

In discussion, bring out the following points:

- People may use different strategies to find the same answer.
- Sometimes a strategy may be appropriate even if the answer is wrong.
- Different people may use different ways to show the same answer. Whatever way you use should be clear enough for others to understand it easily.

If no one has placed the pond or work area diagonally, draw a sketch of such placement. Then ask students how they could determine how many squares would be left for the bears, because counting squares would be difficult.

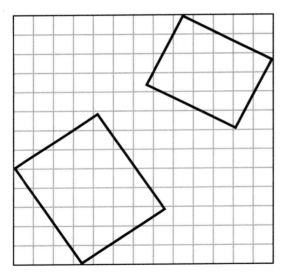

Sample Solutions Strategies

To figure out how much room there is for the bears to walk around in, students might use one or more of the following strategies.

Use Operation Sense

Students might use what they have learned about adding two-digit numbers. For instance, they might add to see that the total space used by the pond and work area is 20 + 30, or 50. Then they could ask themselves: *What plus 50 is 100?*

Write a Number Sentence

Students might write a missing-addend sentence like this one:
20 + 30 + ____ = 100

Using Number Sense/Subtraction

Students might use their knowledge of subtraction facts. For example, if they know that 10 − 3 = 7, they might realize that 10 tens − 3 tens is 7 tens, so 100 − 30 = 70. Similarly, because 7 − 2 = 5, then 70 − 20 = 50.

Use a Systematic Approach

Students might count by 5s, by 10s, or by both to simplify their counting.

Draw a Picture

Students might draw and use a number line to subtract by starting at 100 and moving back 30 and then back 20.

Use a Physical Model

Students might place their cutouts on the grid and move them next to each other to form a 5 × 10 grid. Then they might use one of a variety of methods to count the uncovered squares.

 Home Connection

At this time, you may want to send home the letter on pages 22–25 of *Home Connection.* This letter describes what students will be learning and what activities they can do at home to support their work in school.

Home Connection Page 22

Assess and Differentiate

 Assess Use *eAssess* to record and analyze evidence of student understanding.

A Gather Evidence

Use the Daily Class Assessment Records in **Assessment** or **eAssess** to record Informal and Formal Assessments.

Informal Assessment
☑ **Access Prior Knowledge**
Did the student **UNDERSTANDING**
- ❑ make important observations?
- ❑ extend or generalize learning?
- ❑ provide insightful answers?
- ❑ pose insightful questions?

Informal Assessment
☑ **Concept/Question Board**
Did the student **APPLYING**
- ❑ apply learning in new situations?
- ❑ contribute concepts?
- ❑ contribute answers?
- ❑ connect mathematics to real-world situations?

Formal Assessment
☑ **Pretest**
Review student answers in each problem set.
- ❑ Relating addition and subtraction (Problems 1–4)
- ❑ Function tables (Problems 5 and 6)
- ❑ Adding one-digit and two-digit numbers (Problems 7–10)
- ❑ Tally chart (Problems 11–14)
- ❑ Subtracting one-digit and two-digit numbers (Problems 15–18)
- ❑ Comparing numbers using equalities and inequalities (Problems 19–22)

B Summarize Findings

Analyze and summarize assessment data for each student. Determine which Assessment Follow-Up is appropriate for each student. Use the Student Assessment Record in **Assessment** or **eAssess** to update assessment records.

C Assessment Follow-Up • DIFFERENTIATE INSTRUCTION

Based on your observations of each student, use these teaching strategies for a general approach to the chapter. Look for specific Differentiate Instruction and Monitoring Student Progress strategies in each lesson that relate specifically to the lesson content.

ENRICH	PRACTICE	RETEACH	INTERVENTION	ENGLISH LEARNER
If . . . students demonstrate a **secure understanding** of chapter concepts, **Then . . .** move quickly through the chapter or use **Enrichment** Lessons 6.1–6.10 as assessment follow-up to extend and apply understanding.	**If . . .** students grasp chapter concepts with **competent understanding**, **Then . . .** use **Practice** Lessons 6.1–6.10 as lesson follow-up to develop fluency.	**If . . .** students have prerequisite understanding but demonstrate **emerging understanding** of chapter concepts, **Then . . .** use **Reteach** Lessons 6.3, 6.6, and 6.9 to reteach lesson concepts.	**If . . .** students are not competent with prerequisite skills, **Then . . .** use **Intervention** Lessons 6.A–6.C before each lesson to develop fluency with prerequisite skills.	Use **English Learner Support Guide** Lessons 6.1–6.10 for strategies to preteach lesson vocabulary and concepts.

Chapter Projects

Math Across the Curriculum

Preview the chapter projects with students. Assign projects or have students choose from the projects to extend and enrich concepts in this chapter.

Create a Presentation

1–2 weeks

MATH OBJECTIVE
To reinforce studies of applying subtraction by calculating information about an animal

LANGUAGE ARTS OBJECTIVE
To reinforce studies of visual aids by creating a presentation about a zoo animal

TECHNOLOGY OBJECTIVE
To use a presentation program to make a slide show

• •

Have students use mathematics to calculate information to use in a presentation about a zoo animal. To broaden the language arts concept, have students choose animals from works you are currently studying.

As part of the project, students should consider the following issues:

- important facts about a zoo animal
- physical characteristics of an animal
- how to apply subtraction to numerical data about an animal
- how to create a slide show about an animal
- how to use a slide show as a visual aid in giving a presentation

For specific step-by-step instructions for this project, see *Across the Curriculum Math Connections* pages 62–65.

Creative Work with Ideas Students create slide shows to use as a visual aid in their presentations.

Effective Communication Students communicate ideas clearly and convincingly while giving presentations.

Create a Field Guide

3–4 weeks

MATH OBJECTIVE
To reinforce studies of addition and subtraction by adding and subtracting zoo admission prices

FINE ARTS OBJECTIVE
To reinforce studies of emphasis by using emphasis in a zoo map

TECHNOLOGY OBJECTIVE
To use electronic reference sources to research zoo animals

• •

Have students use technology to

- gather information about two different zoos.
- research three zoo animals.
- draw and label a zoo map by using emphasis.
- calculate family admission prices.

For this project, students use the Internet to investigate the following information:

- the Nashville Zoo
- the San Diego Zoo

For specific step-by-step instructions for this project, see *Across the Curriculum Math Connections* pages 66–71.

High-Level Responsibility Students budget their time while creating field guides.

Creative Work with Ideas Students gather information to use in original designs.

TechKnowledge Level 2 provides lessons that specifically teach the Unit 10 Internet and Unit 9 Electronic Reference applications that students can use in this project.

Lesson Planner

OBJECTIVES
To provide practice in converting numbers in standard form into expanded form

NCTM STANDARDS

NUMBER AND OPERATIONS
- Connecting number words and numerals to the quantities they represent using various models
- Using multiple models to develop an understanding of place value
- Developing a sense of whole numbers and representing them in flexible ways, including relating, composing, and decomposing numbers

Data Analysis and Probability
Representing data using concrete objects, pictures, and graphs

Connections
Recognizing and using connections among mathematical ideas

MATERIALS
- *Number Cubes
- *Play money
- *Yard Sale Game Mat
- *Craft sticks and rubber bands

TECHNOLOGY
ⓔPresentation Lesson 6.1

TEST PREP
Cumulative Review (Review)
Mental Math reviews adding multiples of tens (Lesson 5.2).

Regrouping Tens as Ones

Context of the Lesson This is the first lesson leading to mastery of the two-digit subtraction algorithm. In this lesson students will write two-digit numbers in expanded form and exchange tens for ones. This is to prepare them to subtract two-digit numbers.

See page 203B for Math Background for teachers for this lesson.

Planning for Learning ● DIFFERENTIATE INSTRUCTION

INTERVENTION

If . . . students lack the prerequisite skill of place value to 100,

Then . . . teach **Intervention** Lesson 6.A.

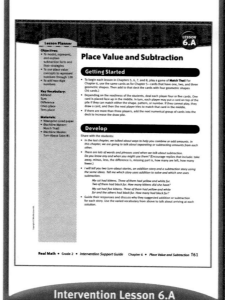

Intervention Lesson 6.A

ENGLISH LEARNER

Preview

If . . . students need language support,

Then . . . use Lesson 6.1 in **English Learner Support Guide** to preview lesson concepts and vocabulary.

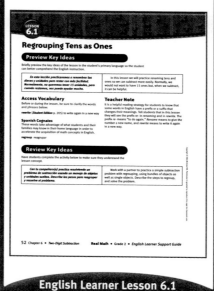

English Learner Lesson 6.1

ENRICH

If . . . students are proficient in the lesson concepts,

Then . . . have them play the variation of the **Yard Sale Game.**

PRACTICE

If . . . students would benefit from additional practice,

Then . . . extend Skill Practice before assigning the student pages.

RETEACH

If . . . students are having difficulty understanding exchanging tens for ones,

Then . . . extend Guided Discussion before assigning the student pages.

Vocabulary
regroup \rē´grŭp\ **v.** to change the grouping of numbers by separating ones from tens and grouping the parts with other like values

Access Vocabulary
rewrite to write again in a new way

Spanish Cognates
regroup reagrupar

---

*Manipulative Kit Item

Mental Math 5

  Present exercises in which students add tens. Possible exercises include the following:

a. 50 + 40 = 90

b. 60 + 20 = 80

c. 30 + 40 = 70

d. 10 + 20 = 30

e. 70 + 30 = 100

f. 80 + 10 = 90

1 Develop 20

Tell Students In Today's Lesson They Will

exchange tens for ones.

Guided Discussion `UNDERSTANDING` Small Group

Have students imagine they are buying a ticket to the guided tour at the zoo. The student gives the clerk $30 (three $10 bills), and the ticket costs $23. How much change should the student get?

- Have students work individually or in small groups to explore and try to solve this problem. Give each group three bundles of ten craft sticks.
- As students solve the problem, it should become clear to them that in order to find the answer, they need to break apart, or regroup, one of the bundles of ten craft sticks.

Strategy Building `UNDERSTANDING` Small Group

Exchanging Tens for Ones

Distribute craft sticks to pairs of students. Then present several two-digit numbers, and have students regroup craft sticks to show one fewer ten and ten more ones. Possible examples include the following:

38 = 2 tens and 18 ones

51 = 4 tens and 11 ones

60 = 5 tens and 10 ones

Allow students to work together to exchange tens for ones. Encourage them to keep written lists of how the numbers are changing as they make their exchanges.

- **What do you do with the ones after exchanging tens for ones?** The exchanged ones should be added to the original ones in the ones column.

Skill Practice `COMPUTING` Whole Group

Present students with two-digit numbers, and have students rename each number to show one fewer ten. Possible examples include the following:

a. 45 3 tens and 15

b. 73 6 tens and 13

c. 29 1 ten and 19

d. 58 4 tens and 18

Strategy Building `ENGAGING`

Game Yard Sale Game Mat

Demonstrate a subtraction variation of the **Yard Sale Game Mat** by playing the game with a student. Materials and rules for how to play can be found on a copy of the game mat in the back of this *Teacher's Edition*. The game is played the same way as the addition version with the following exceptions:

- Each player is given three $100 bills. Fifteen $1 and fifteen $10 bills are placed in the bank for each player.
- When landing on an item, the player must pay the bank the price of the object pictured.
- The first player to run out of money wins.

Variation

Change the denominations of money given to each player. Each player should receive two $50 bills; three $100, $20, $10, and $5 bills; and six $1 bills. As in the other version, each player is given only the three $100 bills at the start of play.

Monitoring Student Progress

If . . . students are having difficulty regrouping a two-digit number to show one fewer ten,	Then . . . model the exchange process with counters.

2 Assign Student Pages 20

Pages 205–206 `ENGAGING`

Have students complete pages 205 and 206 independently.

Monitoring Student Progress

If . . . students are having difficulty recognizing the process of trading tens for ones,	Then . . . provide individual help by asking questions such as the following:
	■ **What will you do to the tens?** Trade 1 ten for 10 ones.
	■ **What will you do to the ones set?** Add 10 ones to the ones set.

As Students Finish

 Game Allow enough time for students to play the subtraction version of the **Yard Sale Game.**

Name _____ Date _____

LESSON 6.1 Regrouping Tens as Ones

Key Ideas

You can **regroup** craft sticks to show one fewer ten and ten more ones.

$55 = 4$ tens and 15

Rewrite each number to show one fewer ten.

1. $63 = \underline{5}$ tens and $\underline{13}$
2. $49 = \underline{3}$ tens and $\underline{19}$
3. $38 = \underline{2}$ tens and $\underline{18}$
4. $43 = \underline{3}$ tens and $\underline{13}$
5. $60 = \underline{5}$ tens and $\underline{10}$

6. $22 = \underline{1}$ ten and $\underline{12}$
7. $36 = \underline{2}$ tens and $\underline{16}$
8. $15 = \underline{0}$ tens and $\underline{15}$
9. $78 = \underline{6}$ tens and $\underline{18}$
10. $46 = \underline{3}$ tens and $\underline{16}$

Textbook This lesson is available in the *eTextbook*.

205

LESSON 6.1 • Regrouping Tens as Ones

Rewrite each number to show one fewer ten.

11. $50 = \underline{4}$ tens and $\underline{10}$
12. $48 = \underline{3}$ tens and $\underline{18}$
13. $100 = \underline{9}$ tens and $\underline{10}$
14. $89 = \underline{7}$ tens and $\underline{19}$
15. $56 = \underline{4}$ tens and $\underline{16}$

16. $97 = \underline{8}$ tens and $\underline{17}$
17. $61 = \underline{5}$ tens and $\underline{11}$
18. $14 = \underline{0}$ tens and $\underline{14}$
19. $37 = \underline{2}$ tens and $\underline{17}$
20. $28 = \underline{1}$ ten and $\underline{18}$

Writing + Math Journal

Explain how to rewrite the number 73 to show one fewer ten.

206 Real Math • Chapter 6 • Lesson 1

---

3 Reflect

5

Guided Discussion REASONING

Whole Group

Review the answers to the student pages. Then, write a two-digit subtraction problem on the board or overhead projector such as the following: 36 – 17.

■ **How can we rewrite the number 36 to show more ones?** Students should recognize the pattern of taking away 1 ten from the 3 tens and adding it to the ones. The new number will be 2 tens and 16. **Have students discuss this with each other before responding. Then have students do the subtraction.** 36 – 17 = 19, or 2 tens and 16 minus 1 ten and 7 ones = 1 ten and 9 ones

Writing + Math Journal

Discuss students' answers. Students should regroup so they have 6 tens and 13.

Cumulative Review: For cumulative review of previously learned skills, see page 219–220.

Family Involvement: Assign the *Practice, Reteach,* or *Enrichment* activities depending on the needs of your students. Have students play the subtraction version of the **Yard Sale Game** with a family member.

Concept/Question Board: Have students look for additional examples using two-digit subtraction and post them on the Concept/Question Board.

Math Puzzler: I have 5 coins. They equal 40¢. What coins do I have? 3 dimes and 2 nickels

Assess and Differentiate

 Assess Use *eAssess* to record and analyze evidence of student understanding.

A Gather Evidence

Use the Daily Class Assessment Records in *Assessment* or *eAssess* to record daily observations.

Informal Assessment
 Strategy Building

Did the student `UNDERSTANDING`
- ❏ make important observations?
- ❏ extend or generalize learning?
- ❏ provide insightful answers?
- ❏ pose insightful questions?

Informal Assessment
✓ **Skill Practice**

Did the student `COMPUTING`
- ❏ respond accurately?
- ❏ respond quickly?
- ❏ respond with confidence?
- ❏ self-correct?

B Summarize Findings

Analyze and summarize assessment data for each student. Determine which Assessment Follow-Up is appropriate for each student. Use the Student Assessment Record in *Assessment* or *eAssess* to update assessment records.

Assessment page T41

C Assessment Follow-Up • DIFFERENTIATE INSTRUCTION

Based on your observations, use these teaching strategies for assessment follow-up.

INTERVENTION

Review student performance on *Intervention* Lesson 6.A to see if students have mastered prerequisite skills for this lesson.

ENGLISH LEARNER

Review

Use Lesson 6.1 in *English Learner Support Guide* to review lesson concepts and vocabulary.

ENRICH

If . . . students are proficient in the lesson concepts,

Then . . . encourage them to work on the chapter projects or *Enrichment* Lesson 6.1.

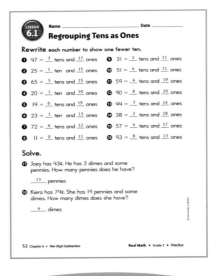

Enrichment Lesson 6.1

PRACTICE

If . . . students would benefit from additional practice,

Then . . . assign *Practice* Lesson 6.1.

Practice Lesson 6.1

RETEACH

If . . . students are having difficulty understanding exchanging tens for ones,

Then . . . have them practice regrouping craft sticks. For example, have students show four bundles of ten and five single sticks. Then have students remove the rubber band from one bundle to regroup the sticks as three bundles and fifteen singles.

To introduce subtracting multiples of ten from two-digit numbers

NCTM STANDARDS

Number and Operations
- Using multiple models to develop an understanding of place value
- Connecting number words and numerals to the quantities they represent using various physical models
- Understanding the effects of adding and subtracting whole numbers
- Developing and using strategies for whole-number computation
- Using a variety of methods and tools to compute

Problem Solving
- Building new mathematical knowledge through problem solving
- Solving problems that arise in mathematics and in other concepts

MATERIALS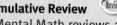
- *Number Cubes
- *Play money
- *Base-ten blocks
- *Yard Sale Game Mat

TECHNOLOGY
- Ⓔ **Presentation** Lesson 6.2
- Ⓔ **MathTools** Base-Ten Blocks
- **Building Blocks** School Supply Shop

TEST PREP

Cumulative Review
- Mental Math reviews adding tens (Lesson 5.2).
- Problems 1–2 review using money (Lesson 1.5).

Multistep Problems
Problem 18

Subtracting Tens

Context of the Lesson Lesson 6.1 introduced students to regrouping tens as ones in preparation for two-digit subtraction. This lesson focuses on subtracting multiples of tens. As you are saying and writing numbers in this lesson, present them in both the expanded (2 tens and 0 ones) form and traditional (twenty) form.

See page 203B for Math Background for teachers for this lesson.

Planning for Learning ● DIFFERENTIATE INSTRUCTION

INTERVENTION

If . . . students lack the prerequisite skill of subtraction facts,

Then . . . teach **Intervention** Lesson 6.B.

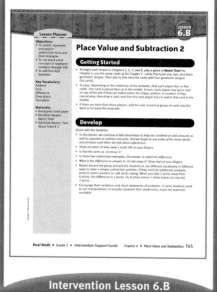

Intervention Lesson 6.B

ENGLISH LEARNER

Preview

If . . . students need language support,

Then . . . use Lesson 6.2 in **English Learner Support Guide** to preview lesson concepts and vocabulary.

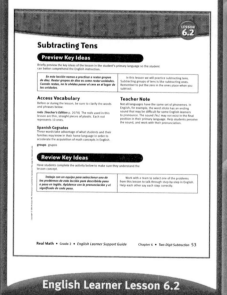

English Learner Lesson 6.2

ENRICH

If . . . students are proficient in the lesson concepts,

Then . . . allot additional game time.

PRACTICE

If . . . students would benefit from additional practice,

Then . . . extend Skill Practice before assigning the student pages.

RETEACH

If . . . students are having difficulty understanding subtracting tens,

Then . . . extend Guided Discussion before assigning the student pages.

Access Vocabulary
rods The rods used in this lesson are thin, straight pieces of plastic. Each rod represents 10 ones.

Spanish Cognates
groups grupos

Mental Math 5

   Present addition exercises using tens, and have students show the answers using their **Number Cubes.** None of the sums should be greater than 100. Possible exercises include the following:

a. 80 + 20 = 100   **b.** 90 + 10 = 100
c. 50 + 30 = 80   **d.** 20 + 60 = 80
e. 10 + 70 = 80   **f.** 30 + 70 = 100
g. 40 + 30 = 70   **h.** 50 + 40 = 90

1 Develop 20

Tell Students In Today's Lesson They Will
subtract tens.

Whole Group

Guided Discussion MathTools UNDERSTANDING

Demonstrate how to subtract multiples of ten.

Have students imagine they are planning a field trip to the zoo for four classes. There are 70 students altogether. Twenty students did not turn in their permission slips and can't go.

■ **How would you figure out how many students are going on the field trip to the zoo?** subtract 20 from 70

Write   70   on the board. Model the solution using base-ten
$-\ 20$

blocks or **eMathTools: Base-Ten Blocks.** Show 7 rods.

■ **How many rods are there?** 7
■ **How many ones?** 70

Take away 2 rods.

■ **How many rods are left?** 5
■ **How many ones are left?** 50

Show that there are 5 rods of 10 cubes, or 50 units, left.

Work through more exercises subtracting multiples of ten. Possible exercises include the following:

a. 60 − 40 = 20   **b.** 70 − 30 = 40   **c.** 90 − 60 = 30

As you work through each problem, say the numbers in expanded form as you write them in standard form. For example: 6 tens or 60, minus 4 tens or 40, equals 2 tens or 20.

Skill Practice   COMPUTING

Small Group

Demonstrate the following subtraction activity, and then have students work in pairs.

● One student writes a subtraction expression in units. For example: 7 − 5 =
● The other student solves the exercise, and then writes a similar exercise using tens. For example, 7 − 5 = 2, 70 − 50 =

● The first student then solves the new expression. 70 − 50 = 20
● Partners switch roles and repeat. Possible exercises include the following:

a. 8 − 4 = 4; 80 − 40 = 40   **b.** 5 − 1 = 4; 50 − 10 = 40
c. 6 − 2 = 4; 60 − 20 = 40   **d.** 9− 2 = 7; 90 − 20 = 70

2 Assign Student Pages 15

Pages 207–208 APPLYING

Have students complete pages 207 and 208 independently or in small groups.

Monitoring Student Progress

If . . . students are having difficulty seeing the relationship between ones and tens,

Then . . . have students form a two-digit number with their **Number Cubes.** Then ask questions such as the following:

■ **If you add 10 to this number, which cube must be changed?** the tens cube

■ **If you add 1 to this number, which cube must be changed?** the ones cube

As Students Finish

Game Have students play the version of the **Yard Sale Game** introduced in the previous lesson.

Building Blocks Have students use **School Supply Shop** to practice counting by tens.

Name _____   Date _____

LESSON
6.2   **Subtracting Tens**

Key Ideas

Subtracting groups of tens is like subtracting ones.

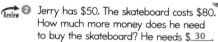

$60 - 20 = 40$ $6 - 2 = 4$

Solve these problems.

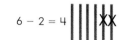

→ **1** Mika had $30. She spent $20 at the zoo.
Now she has $ 10 .

→ **2** Jerry has $50. The skateboard costs $80.
How much more money does he need
to buy the skateboard? He needs $ 30 .

3 $30 - 10 = \underline{20}$ **4** $80 - 20 = \underline{60}$

   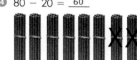

Subtract or add.

| **5** $\begin{array}{r}60\\+\,30\\\hline 90\end{array}$ | **6** $\begin{array}{r}90\\-\,40\\\hline 50\end{array}$ | **7** $\begin{array}{r}90\\-\,50\\\hline 40\end{array}$ | **8** $\begin{array}{r}80\\-\,50\\\hline 30\end{array}$ | **9** $\begin{array}{r}80\\-\,60\\\hline 20\end{array}$ | **10** $\begin{array}{r}70\\-\,60\\\hline 10\end{array}$ |

Textbook This lesson is available in the *eTextbook*.

207

LESSON 6.2 · Subtracting Tens

Subtract or add.

11 $30 + 40 = 70$ **13** $70 - 20 = 50$

12 $70 - 30 = 40$ **14** $50 + 20 = 70$

Solve these problems.

15 Chandra planted about 70 radish seeds. About
50 of the seeds sprouted. About how many did
not sprout? 20

16 Sara's goal is to collect 100 different baseball cards.
So far she has collected 40 of them. How
many more cards must she collect to reach
her goal? 60

17 Andrea needed $40 to buy a bicycle. She
earned $10 babysitting. Then she earned
some more money weeding gardens.
Does she have enough money now?
can't tell—insufficient information

18 Heide bought a basketball for $30. She
gave the clerk 2 $20 bills. How much change
should she get? $10

19 A pine tree was about 80 feet tall. A storm
came, and the top 10 feet broke off. About how
tall is the tree now? 70 feet

20 Mr. Joseph planned to drive about 100 miles
from San Diego to Long Beach. So far,
he has driven about 50 miles. About
how much farther must he drive?
50 miles

208

---

3 Reflect   10

Guided Discussion    MathTools   REASONING   Whole Group

Write two related subtraction exercises on the board. Possible
examples include the following:

$\begin{array}{r}70\\-\,20\end{array}$ $\begin{array}{r}71\\-\,20\end{array}$

Ask for volunteers to find the differences.

■ **How are you finding the answers?** If $70 - 20 = 50$, then $71 - 20$
must be one more than 50.

Students may demonstrate by using base-ten blocks or *eMathTools:*
Base-Ten Blocks. Repeat the exercise with several other problems. If
students are comfortable with the exercise, try varying the altered
number by more than one, or by changing the number so that it is
less than the multiple of ten.

Cumulative Review: For cumulative review of previously
learned skills, see page 219–220.

Family Involvement: Assign the **Practice, Reteach,** or
Enrichment activities depending on the needs of your students.
Have students play the subtraction version of the **Yard Sale Game**
with a family member.

Concept/Question Board: Have students look for additional
examples using two-digit subtraction and post them on the
Concept/Question Board.

Math Puzzler: There are 17 bottles of juice left on the
store shelf. Eight are grape. The rest are orange. How many are
orange? 9

Assess and Differentiate

 Assess Use **eAssess** to record and analyze evidence of student understanding.

A Gather Evidence

Use the Daily Class Assessment Records in **Assessment** or **eAssess** to record daily observations.

Informal Assessment
✓ Skill Practice

Did the student **COMPUTING**
- ❑ respond accurately?
- ❑ respond quickly?
- ❑ respond with confidence?
- ❑ self-correct?

Informal Assessment
✓ Student Pages

Did the student **APPLYING**
- ❑ apply learning in new situations?
- ❑ contribute concepts?
- ❑ contribute answers?
- ❑ connect mathematics to real-world situations?

B Summarize Findings

Analyze and summarize assessment data for each student. Determine which Assessment Follow-Up is appropriate for each student. Use the Student Assessment Record in **Assessment** or **eAssess** to update assessment records.

Assessment page T41

C Assessment Follow-Up • DIFFERENTIATE INSTRUCTION

Based on your observations, use these teaching strategies for assessment follow-up.

INTERVENTION

Review student performance on **Intervention** Lesson 6.B to see if students have mastered prerequisite skills for this lesson.

ENGLISH LEARNER

Review

Use Lesson 6.2 in **English Learner Support Guide** to review lesson concepts and vocabulary.

ENRICH

If . . . students are proficient in the lesson concepts,

Then . . . encourage them to work on the chapter projects or **Enrichment** Lesson 6.2.

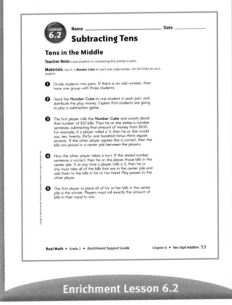

Enrichment Lesson 6.2

PRACTICE

If . . . students would benefit from additional practice,

Then . . . assign **Practice** Lesson 6.2.

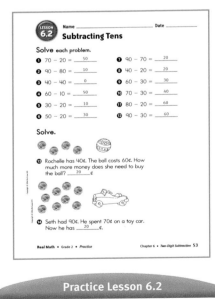

Practice Lesson 6.2

RETEACH

If . . . students are having difficulty understanding subtracting tens,

Then . . . review the relationship between subtracting multiples of ten and subtracting ones.

OBJECTIVES
- To teach how to subtract two-digit numbers from multiples of ten
- To teach when regrouping for subtraction is needed

NCTM STANDARDS
Number and Operations
- Using multiple models to develop an understanding of place value
- Connecting number words and numerals to the quantities they represent using physical models and representations
- Understanding the effects of adding and subtracting whole numbers
- Developing and using strategies for whole-number computations

Algebra
Modeling situations that involve the addition and subtraction of whole numbers using objects

Problem Solving
Applying and adapting a variety of appropriate strategies to solve problems

MATERIALS
- *Number Cubes
- *Craft sticks
- *Rubber bands

TECHNOLOGY
- ⓔ Presentation Lesson 6.3
- ⓔ MathTools Base-Ten Blocks
- Building Blocks Math-O-Scope

TEST PREP
Cumulative Review
- Mental Math reviews subtracting multiples of ten (Lesson 6.2).
- Problems 2, 6, 9, 10, and 12 review subtracting multiples of ten (Lesson 6.2).

Extended Response
Problems 16 and 18

Writing + Math
Journal

*Manipulative Kit Item

Subtracting from Tens

Context of the Lesson In the previous lesson students subtracted multiples of ten. In this lesson students will subtract two-digit numbers from multiples of ten. Students learn why regrouping is necessary by solving a subtraction problem using craft sticks. Exercises that require regrouping are deliberately mixed with those that do not. While it is true that students find it easier to subtract numbers that do not require regrouping, those exercises tend to reinforce the belief many students have that they can simply subtract in columns without worrying about the next column. Students are likely to simply subtract the smaller number in the ones column from the large one and treat the tens column the same way.

See page 203B for Math Background for teachers for this lesson.

Planning for Learning ● DIFFERENTIATE INSTRUCTION

INTERVENTION
If . . . students lack the prerequisite skill of adding two-digit numbers,

Then . . . teach *Intervention* Lesson 6.C.

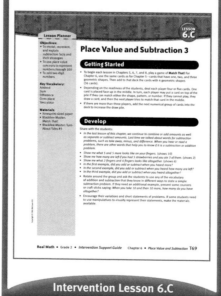

Intervention Lesson 6.C

ENGLISH LEARNER
Preview

If . . . students need language support,

Then . . . use Lesson 6.3 in *English Learner Support Guide* to preview lesson concepts and vocabulary.

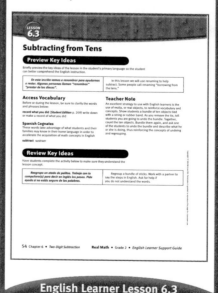

English Learner Lesson 6.3

ENRICH
If . . . students are proficient in the lesson concepts,

Then . . . allot time to allow students to explore subtracting two-digit numbers using the *eMathTools: Base-Ten Blocks*.

PRACTICE
If . . . students would benefit from additional practice,

Then . . . extend Skill Practice before assigning the student pages.

RETEACH
If . . . students are having difficulty understanding subtracting tens,

Then . . . extend Guided Discussion before assigning the student pages.

Access Vocabulary
record what you did write down or make a record of what you did

Spanish Cognates
subtract sustraer

Mental Math 5

  Present exercises in which students subtract two multiples of tens. Possible exercises include the following:

a. $80 - 30 = 50$

b. $70 - 30 = 40$

c. $60 - 60 = 0$

d. $50 - 10 = 40$

e. $20 - 10 = 10$

f. $90 - 60 = 30$

g. $40 - 20 = 20$

h. $10 - 10 = 0$

1 Develop 20

Tell Students In Today's Lesson They Will

subtract two-digit numbers from tens.

Guided Discussion REASONING   Whole Group

Divide students into groups of four or five, and lead a class discussion. Give each group eight bundles of ten craft sticks. Keep eight bundles of sticks for yourself so you can model the problem with students.

Have students imagine the school has 80 tickets in booklets of 10 for the walrus exhibit at the zoo. They want 32 tickets for their class. How would they subtract 32 tickets from 80?

Have groups experiment by using craft sticks to figure out how they would take away 32 from 80. Allow students to try to solve the problem on their own. If they are having difficulty, perform the following demonstration as students work along.

- Since the sticks are in bundles of 10, it is easy to take away 30 sticks by removing 3 bundles of 10. Remove those, and place them to the side.
- However, in order to subtract the 2 single sticks, students will have to break up a bundle. As you break up a bundle of sticks, stop and show students that what they are really doing is regrouping tens as ones. Say,

■ **Now instead of having 5 tens and 0, I have 4 tens and 10.**

Have students subtract the 2 single sticks.

■ **How many sticks do you have now?** 4 tens and 8 or 48

Write 80 on the board.

$$\begin{array}{r} 80 \\ -\ 32 \\ \hline 48 \end{array}$$

Skill Practice COMPUTING   Small Group

Have students repeat the previous procedure by doing similar exercises and recording their work as you go around the room. Eventually, students should realize that it is easier to check the ones place first to see if they are going to need to regroup before beginning the problem. Exercises may include the following:

a. $60 - 37 = 23$

b. $80 - 54 = 26$

c. $50 - 15 = 35$

d. $90 - 48 = 42$

Monitoring Student Progress

If . . . students have difficulty regrouping before subtracting,

Then . . . have them work independently or in small groups while they practice exchanging tens for ones using base-ten materials.

2 Assign Student Pages 20

Pages 209–210 APPLYING   Small Group

Have students work in groups to complete page 209. Have students use craft sticks, if needed, to complete page 210 independently. Make sure students understand the regrouping process before encouraging them to stop using manipulatives.

As Students Finish

Game Allow students to play any of the games previously introduced, or assign a game based on students' needs.

e MathTools Have students use **Base-Ten Blocks** to practice subtracting two-digit numbers from multiples of ten.

Building Blocks Have students use **Math-O-Scope** to practice subtracting tens and review the 100 Table.

RESEARCH IN ACTION

"The written place-value system is an efficient system that lets us write large numbers, but it is also abstract and misleading. The numbers in every position look the same. To understand the meaning of the numbers in the various positions, first- and second-grade children need experience with some kind of size visual quantity supports: manipulatives or drawings that show tens to be collections of 10 ones and show hundreds to be simultaneously 10 tens and 100 ones, and so on."

Fuson, Karen. "Pre-K to Grade 2 Goals and Standards: Achieving 21st Century Mastery for All" in Clements, Douglas and J. Sarama, eds. *Engaging Young Children in Mathematics: Standards for Early Childhood Mathematics Education.* Mahwah, New Jersey: Lawrence Erlbaum Associates, Publishers, 2004, p. 125.

Key Ideas

You can use regrouping to help you subtract. $60 - 37 = ?$

$$\begin{array}{ccc} 60 & 6 \text{ tens and } 0 & 5 \text{ tens and } 10 \\ -37 & = -3 \text{ tens and } 7 & = -3 \text{ tens and } 7 \\ \hline & & 2 \text{ tens and } 3, \text{ or } 23 \end{array}$$

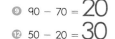   =

Subtract. Use craft sticks if you need help. Record what you did.

1. $\begin{array}{r} 90 \\ -48 \\ \hline 42 \end{array}$ 2. $\begin{array}{r} 80 \\ -30 \\ \hline 50 \end{array}$ 3. $\begin{array}{r} 70 \\ -48 \\ \hline 22 \end{array}$

4. $\begin{array}{r} 60 \\ -17 \\ \hline 43 \end{array}$ 5. $\begin{array}{r} 50 \\ -25 \\ \hline 25 \end{array}$ 6. $\begin{array}{r} 40 \\ -10 \\ \hline 30 \end{array}$

Textbook This lesson is available in the *eTextbook*.

209

LESSON 6.3 • Subtracting from Tens

7. $70 - 29 = 41$ 8. $50 - 38 = 12$ 9. $90 - 70 = 20$

10. $80 - 40 = 40$ 11. $60 - 44 = 16$ 12. $50 - 20 = 30$

13. $\begin{array}{r} 40 \\ -12 \\ \hline 28 \end{array}$ 14. $\begin{array}{r} 80 \\ -52 \\ \hline 28 \end{array}$ 15. $\begin{array}{r} 100 \\ -75 \\ \hline 25 \end{array}$

16. **Extended Response** How did you find the answer to Exercise 15? by renaming ten tens and zero as nine tens and ten

17. Ravi bought a DVD player that had a regular price of $60. It was on sale for $42. How much did Ravi save? $18

18. **Extended Response** The Kelly twins bought two of the DVD players. How much did they save together? $36
How did you find the answer? by adding the price saved twice

Writing + Math Journal

Why do you sometimes need to regroup when subtracting a two-digit number from a group of tens?

210   **Real Math** • Chapter 6 • Lesson 3

Subtracting from Tens LESSON 6.3

3 Reflect   10

Guided Discussion REASONING   Whole Group

Present an exercise such as 73 – 27. Have students discuss how they would find the difference.

Use craft sticks or *eMathTools: Base-Ten Blocks* to illustrate students' suggestions.

Extended Response

Problem 16 Discuss students' answers. Although 100 is a three-digit number, students should see that the principle for borrowing is the same.

Problem 18 Discuss students' solutions. Since they know two DVD players were sold, the savings must be 18 + 18.

Writing + Math Journal

Discuss students' answers. When regrouping in subtraction is needed, it is because you need to have more units in the ones place from which to subtract.

 Cumulative Review: For cumulative review of previously learned skills, see page 219–220.

 Family Involvement: Assign the *Practice, Reteach,* or *Enrichment* activities depending on the needs of your students.

 Concept/Question Board: Have students look for additional examples using two-digit subtraction and post them on the Concept/Question Board.

 Math Puzzler: Megan wants a key chain that costs 90¢. So far she has saved 60¢. How much more money must she save? 30¢

Assess and Differentiate

 Assess Use **eAssess** to record and analyze evidence of student understanding.

A Gather Evidence

Use the Daily Class Assessment Records in **Assessment** or **eAssess** to record daily observations.

Informal Assessment
☑ Guided Discussion

Did the student **REASONING**
- ❏ provide a clear explanation?
- ❏ communicate reasons and strategies?
- ❏ choose appropriate strategies?
- ❏ argue logically?

Informal Assessment
☑ Skill Practice

Did the student **COMPUTING**
- ❏ respond accurately?
- ❏ respond quickly?
- ❏ respond with confidence?
- ❏ self-correct?

B Summarize Findings

Analyze and summarize assessment data for each student. Determine which Assessment Follow-Up is appropriate for each student. Use the Student Assessment Record in **Assessment** or **eAssess** to update assessment records.

Assessment page T41

C Assessment Follow-Up ● DIFFERENTIATE INSTRUCTION

Based on your observations, use these teaching strategies for assessment follow-up.

INTERVENTION

Review student performance on **Intervention** Lesson 6.C to see if students have mastered prerequisite skills for this lesson.

ENGLISH LEARNER

Review

Use Lesson 6.3 in **English Learner Support Guide** to review lesson concepts and vocabulary.

ENRICH

If . . . students are proficient in the lesson concepts,

Then . . . encourage them to work on the chapter projects or **Enrichment** Lesson 6.3.

PRACTICE

If . . . students would benefit from additional practice,

Then . . . assign **Practice** Lesson 6.3.

RETEACH

If . . . students are having difficulty understanding regrouping,

Then . . . reteach the concept using **Reteach** Lesson 6.3.

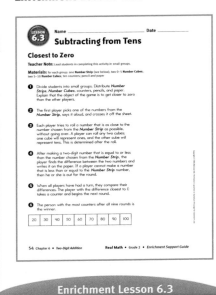

Enrichment Lesson 6.3

Practice Lesson 6.3

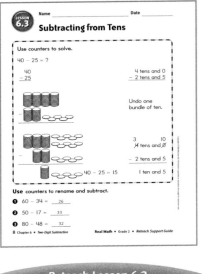

Reteach Lesson 6.3

OBJECTIVES
- To introduce a general procedure for subtracting two-digit numbers
- To introduce strategies for mental subtraction

NCTM STANDARDS
Number and Operations
- Connecting number words and numerals to the quantities they represent using various models
- Developing and using strategies for whole-number computations
- Using various methods and tools to compute

Algebra
- Illustrating general principles and properties of operations using specific numbers
- Using concrete, pictorial, and verbal representations to develop an understanding of symbolic notations
- Modeling situations that involve the addition and subtraction of whole numbers

MATERIALS
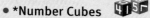
- *Number Cubes
- *Base-ten blocks
- *Overhead bills and coins
- *Craft sticks and rubber bands
- *Play money

TECHNOLOGY
ⓔ **Presentation** Lesson 6.4

TEST PREP
Cumulative Review
- Mental Math reviews identifying monetary values (Lesson 1.5).
- Problems 1–4, 6, and 8–11 review exchanging tens for ones (Lessons 6.1–6.3).

Subtracting Two-Digit Numbers

Context of the Lesson In the previous lessons students practiced exchanging tens for ones and subtracting from multiples of ten. In this lesson students will learn a general procedure for subtracting any two-digit numbers. Previously, students wrote numbers in expanded form to regroup for subtraction. Allow students who are having difficulty to continue writing numbers this way, but encourage students to begin using the more conventional notation for borrowing (crossing out and writing 1) and just thinking or saying the expanded numbers.

See page 203B for Math Background for teachers for this lesson.

Planning for Learning ● DIFFERENTIATE INSTRUCTION

INTERVENTION

If . . . students are having difficulty understanding place value to 100,

Then . . . teach *Intervention* Lesson 6.A.

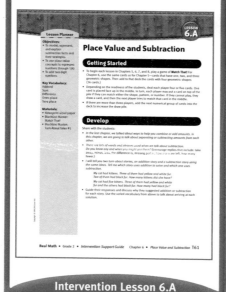

Intervention Lesson 6.A

ENGLISH LEARNER

Preview

If . . . students need language support,

Then . . . use Lesson 6.4 in *English Learner Support Guide* to preview lesson concepts and vocabulary.

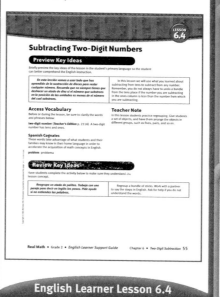

English Learner Lesson 6.4

ENRICH

If . . . students are proficient in the lesson concepts,

Then . . . emphasize Guided Discussion in Reflect.

PRACTICE

If . . . students would benefit from additional practice,

Then . . . extend Skill Practice before assigning the student pages.

RETEACH

If . . . students are having difficulty understanding subtracting two-digit numbers,

Then . . . extend Guided Discussion before assigning the student pages.

Access Vocabulary
two-digit number A two-digit number has tens and ones.

Spanish Cognates
problem problema

---

*Manipulative Kit Item

Mental Math 5

Review Present a counting drill using either overhead money or play money. Show amounts to students, and have them use **Number Cubes** to show the numerical equivalents. Possible examples include the following:

a. $73 = 7 tens cube; 3 unit cube   **b.** $36 = 3 tens cube; 6 unit cube

c. $68 = 6 tens cube; 8 unit cube   **d.** $42 = 4 tens cube; 2 unit cube

e. $59 = 5 tens cube; 9 unit cube   **f.** $85 = 8 tens cube; 5 unit cube

1 Develop 20

Tell Students In Today's Lesson They Will
learn how to subtract any 2 two-digit numbers.

Guided Discussion REASONING   Whole Group

Present a two-digit subtraction problem that requires renaming tens as ones.

Have students pretend that the City Zoo has 53 lizards in its reptile house. They want to send 25 of the lizards to a zoo in a neighboring city. How many lizards will be left at the City Zoo?

Write the subtraction problem on the board.
$$\begin{array}{r} 53 \\ -25 \end{array}$$

Say the problem in expanded form and in standard form.

■ **53, or five tens and three, minus 25, or two tens and five, equals what?**
■ **How can we solve this problem?** After students suggest renaming tens as ones and then subtracting, work through the problem together.

Have students work as a class, and have them use fingers to complete the computation. Select five students, and have them hold up 10 fingers. Select another student to hold up 3 fingers.

■ **How many fingers are they showing?** 53

Take 25 fingers away. Allow students to lead this process. Most likely, they will have two students take down all their fingers, and then have to figure out how to remove the 5 fingers.

■ **How would you remove 5 more fingers?** by having one of the students holding up 10 fingers regroup or combine fingers with the person holding up 3 single fingers

Have the two regrouped students subtract 5 fingers.

■ **How many fingers are left?** 28
■ **Can you think of a way that would have made this problem easier?** Allow students to discuss. Lead them to see through their own discussion and through more finger examples that it is easier to start on the right and regroup first, rather than waiting until the end.

Present one more two-digit subtraction problem in standard form. Walk through the process with students as you work the problem on the board.

Skill Practice COMPUTING   Small Group

Divide students into small groups and present a series of two-digit subtraction exercises on the board. Have students work together to solve them. Include some two-digit exercises that do not require regrouping. Possible exercises include the following:

a. $27 - 13 = 14$
b. $54 - 28 = 26$
c. $63 - 37 = 26$
d. $50 - 25 = 25$

2 Assign Student Pages 20

Pages 211–212 UNDERSTANDING

Have students complete pages 211–212 independently.

Monitoring Student Progress

| **If . . .** students have difficulty regrouping without using expanded numbers, | **Then . . .** work with students individually or in small groups while using manipulatives and showing how expanded notation and conventional borrowing notation are the same. |

As Students Finish

 Allow students to play any of the games previously introduced, or assign a game based on students' needs.

LESSON 6.4 Subtracting Two-Digit Numbers

Key Ideas

Use what you learned about subtracting from tens to subtract from any two-digit number.

$$53 - 25 = ?$$

53
− 25 → 5 tens and 3
        − 2 tens and 5

4
5̶13
− 25 → 4 tens and 13
        − 2 tens and 5
        2 tens and 8, or 28

Subtract.

1. $62 - 14 = 48$
2. $62 - 15 = 47$
3. $62 - 16 = 46$
4. $62 - 17 = 45$

Textbook This lesson is available in the *eTextbook*.   211

LESSON 6.4 • Subtracting Two-Digit Numbers

5. 83
   − 73
   ―――
   10

9. 33
   − 17
   ―――
   16

6. 100
   − 25
   ―――
   75

10. 63
    − 37
    ―――
    26

7. 17
   − 17
   ―――
   0

11. 18
    − 9
    ―――
    9

8. 92
   − 49
   ―――
   43

12. 26
    − 13
    ―――
    13

212   Real Math • Chapter 6 • Lesson 4

 **3 Reflect**   10

Guided Discussion ✓ REASONING   Whole Group

Write the following exercises on the board:

$62 - 25 =$

$62 - 26 =$

$62 - 27 =$

$62 - 28 =$

Ask the class to find the differences. After most students have calculated the first difference, stop and ask if they can figure out the differences without doing any more paper-and-pencil calculations. Discuss, and help students see that if they know $62 - 25 = 37$, then $62 - 26$ must be 1 less than 37, or 36, and so on. Conclude by helping students see that sometimes they can avoid calculating by looking for patterns.

Cumulative Review: For cumulative review of previously learned skills, see page 219–220.

Family Involvement: Assign the *Practice, Reteach,* or *Enrichment* activities depending on the needs of your students. Have students create two-digit subtraction exercises with a family member.

Concept/Question Board: Encourage students to continue to post questions, answers, and examples on the Concept/Question Board.

Math Puzzler: There are 40 children waiting in line at the movies. If 23 are girls, how many are boys? 17

4 Assess and Differentiate

 Assess Use *eAssess* to record and analyze evidence of student understanding.

A Gather Evidence

Use the Daily Class Assessment Records in *Assessment* or *eAssess* to record daily observations.

Informal Assessment
☑ **Skill Practice**

Did the student **COMPUTING**
- ❑ respond accurately?
- ❑ respond quickly?
- ❑ respond with confidence?
- ❑ self-correct?

Informal Assessment
☑ **Guided Discussion**

Did the student **REASONING**
- ❑ provide a clear explanation?
- ❑ communicate reasons and strategies?
- ❑ choose appropriate strategies?
- ❑ argue logically?

B Summarize Findings

Analyze and summarize assessment data for each student. Determine which Assessment Follow-Up is appropriate for each student. Use the Student Assessment Record in *Assessment* or *eAssess* to update assessment records.

Assessment page T41

C Assessment Follow-Up ● DIFFERENTIATE INSTRUCTION

Based on your observations, use these teaching strategies for assessment follow-up.

INTERVENTION

Review student performance on *Intervention* Lesson 6.A to see if students have mastered prerequisite skills for this lesson.

ENGLISH LEARNER

Review

Use Lesson 6.4 in *English Learner Support Guide* to review lesson concepts and vocabulary.

ENRICH

If . . . students are proficient in the lesson concepts,

Then . . . encourage them to work on the chapter projects or *Enrichment* Lesson 6.4.

Enrichment Lesson 6.4

PRACTICE

If . . . students would benefit from additional practice,

Then . . . assign *Practice* Lesson 6.4.

Practice Lesson 6.4

RETEACH

If . . . students are having difficulty understanding subtracting two-digit numbers,

Then . . . have students use manipulatives to model each problem.

Lesson Planner

OBJECTIVES
To explore base-ten subtraction using a Paper Explorer

NCTM STANDARDS
Number and Operations
Demonstrating an understanding of place-value concepts

Problem Solving
Applying and adapting a variety of appropriate strategies to solve problems

Connections
Recognizing and using connections among mathematical ideas

Communication
Organizing and consolidating mathematical thinking through communication

MATERIALS
- *Number Cubes
- Blank transparency to write on
- *Counters or pawns of two different colors
- A copy of the Paper Explorer on **Practice** page 124 for each student

TECHNOLOGY
e Presentation Lesson 6.5

TEST PREP
Cumulative Review
Mental Math reviews subtracting multiples of ten (Lesson 6.2).

Extended Response
Problems 11, 12, and 15

Using a Paper Explorer to Understand Subtraction

Context of the Lesson The Paper Explorer is used to show that in the base-ten system, subtracting in the tens place and in the ones place is essentially the same process. The Paper Explorer was introduced in Chapter 2 to explore single-digit addition. It was also used in Chapter 5 to explore two-digit addition.

See page 203B for Math Background for teachers for this lesson.

Planning for Learning ● DIFFERENTIATE INSTRUCTION

INTERVENTION

If . . . students lack the prerequisite skill of subtraction facts,

Then . . . teach *Intervention* Lesson 6.C.

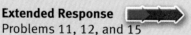
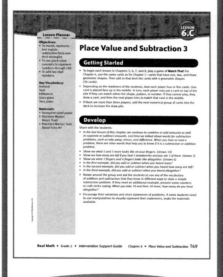

Intervention Lesson 6.C

ENGLISH LEARNER

Preview

If . . . students need language support,

Then . . . use Lesson 6.5 in *English Learner Support Guide* to preview lesson concepts and vocabulary.

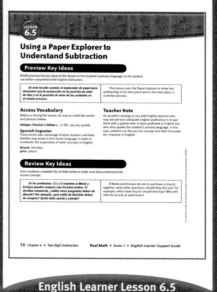

English Learner Lesson 6.5

ENRICH

If . . . students are proficient in the lesson concepts,

Then . . . allow more time to use the Paper Explorer.

PRACTICE

If . . . students would benefit from additional practice,

Then . . . extend Strategy Building before assigning the student pages.

RETEACH

If . . . students are having difficulty understanding the Paper Explorer,

Then . . . extend Guided Discussion before assigning the student pages.

Spanish Cognates
bicycle bicicleta

price precio

*Manipulative Kit Item

Mental Math 5

Present subtraction exercises using multiples of ten, and have students show their answers using **Number Cubes.** Possible exercises include the following:

a. $80 - 50 = 30$

b. $60 - 40 = 20$

c. $50 - 10 = 40$

d. $70 - 20 = 50$

e. $40 - 30 = 10$

f. $90 - 50 = 40$

1 Develop 20

Tell Students In Today's Lesson They Will

use a Paper Explorer to subtract.

Guided Discussion UNDERSTANDING Whole Group

Use a Paper Explorer overhead transparency (see **Practice** page 124).

Unlike addition, the order of a subtraction operation makes a difference in the exercise's outcome. To perform subtraction using a Paper Explorer, students will need counters of two different colors, one to represent the minuend (number being subtracted from) and one to represent the subtrahend (number being subtracted). Then to subtract, markers of different colors are moved in the same direction. In these examples, red and yellow counters are used. The following examples and strategies are given to aid in teaching but should not be given to students. The Paper Explorer should be used to allow students to develop their own strategies for solving the problems and the two-digit subtraction algorithm. That is why answers are given in the **Student Edition.** Correct answers are not being assessed, but rather students' abilities to explore and understand the algorithm.

Subtracting Multiples of Ten

$70 - 40 =$

Start with a red counter on 70 and a yellow counter on 40. Then move the counters down simultaneously.

$70 - 40$; $60 - 30$; $50 - 20$; $40 - 10$; $30 - 0$

Remove the counter from zero.

So, $70 - 40 = 30$.

Subtracting from a Multiple of Ten

$70 - 34 =$

Start with a red counter on 70, a yellow counter on 30, and a yellow counter on 4.

Regroup 70 so it is 60 and 10. To do this, move the red counter to 60, and place a second red counter in the upper 10 box.

Starting with the ones or tens column, move the red and yellow counters down together, until yellow reaches the 0 box. Remove the counters from 0. The red counters will be on the correct answer.

So, $70 - 34 = 36$.

Subtracting Two-Digit Numbers and Regrouping

$73 - 39 =$

Place one red counter on the 70 and one red counter on the 3. Place one yellow counter on the 30 and one yellow counter on the 9. Notice that in the tens column, the red counter is above the yellow counter; and in the ones column, the red counter is below the yellow counter. Keep in mind that you want to make the subtrahend in both columns equal 0 in order to find the answer to the problem. This means you must clear all yellow counters from the Explorer. In other words, when you are done with a problem, only one color of counter should still be on the Paper Explorer.

Start with the ones column. Move both counters down at the same time. When the red counter lands on 0, stop, and move the red counter off the Explorer.

Your Paper Explorer should now show $70 - 36 =$

Now, move the counters in the tens column. When the yellow counter lands on 0, stop. Now you can regroup tens in order to remove the last yellow counter. Move the red counter in the tens column to 30, and place another red counter in the 10 box of the ones column.

Now move the counters in the ones column down together until the yellow counter reaches 0 and can be removed.

So, $73 - 39 = 34$.

Strategy Building   UNDERSTANDING Whole Group

Give each student a copy of the Paper Explorer. Present problems where students subtract multiples of ten. Students will need to use two different colored counters for this problem. Remind students to move the counters at the same time as they whisper the facts. Write the corresponding facts on the board as students progress through these problems.

2 Assign Student Pages 20

Pages 213–214 ENGAGING

Have students complete page 213 in pairs as you circulate and help. Students should then complete page 214 independently.

Monitoring Student Progress

If . . . students are having difficulty getting the correct differences on the Paper Explorer,

Then . . . they are likely having difficulty moving the counters simultaneously. These students should be helped by reassuring them that they can do it by going more slowly and by whispering as they make their moves. Because the Paper Explorer is not a regular part of the curriculum, extensive extra teaching and practice is not essential.

As Students Finish

Allow students to play a game of their choice, or assign a game based on their needs.

Name _____ Date _____

LESSON
6.5 Using a Paper Explorer to
Understand Subtraction

Key Ideas

The Paper Explorer can be used to solve subtraction problems.

Use the Paper Explorer your teacher gives you. Work together to solve these problems.

1,000	100	10
900	90	9
800	80	8
700	70	7
600	60	6
500	50	5
400	40	4
300	30	3
200	20	2
100	10	1
0	0	0

① 50 − 27 = 23

② 80 − 60 = 20

③ 99 − 44 = 55

④ 57 − 23 = 34

⑤ 48 − 39 = 9

⑥ 40 − 27 = 13

⑦ 74 − 13 = 61

⑧ 100 − 93 = 7

⑨ 55 − 10 = 45

⑩ 60 − 15 = 45

Textbook This lesson is available in the *eTextbook*.

213

LESSON 6.5 • Using a Paper Explorer to Understand Subtraction

Solve these problems. Explain your answers.

Marta has $50. Enrique has $32.

⑪ **Extended Response** Can Enrique buy the bicycle? Explain. ___no; The bicycle costs more money than Enrique has.

⑫ **Extended Response** Could Marta and Enrique buy the bicycle together? Explain. __yes; 50 + 32 = $82, which is more than the cost of the bicycle.

⑬ If Marta and Enrique buy the bicycle together, how much money will they have left? __82 − 69 = $13

⑭ If Marta buys the kite, how much money will she have left? __50 − 9 = $41

⑮ **Extended Response** If Enrique buys a baseball and bat, how much money will he have left? __He cannot buy them. He needs $3 more, because 23 + 12 = 35, and Enrique has only $32.

214   **Real Math • Chapter 6 • Lesson 5**

---

3 Reflect

5

Guided Discussion REASONING

Whole Group

Review students' answers to the word problems on student page 214, and allow students to explain their solutions. Then ask students a question such as the following:

■ **Which of these problems can be solved using the Paper Explorer?**
All of the problems can be solved using the Paper Explorer.

Choose one of the problems, and guide students as you demonstrate the procedure.

Extended Response

Problem 11 Students should have discovered that the bicycle costs more money than Enrique has.

Problem 12 Students should have discovered that Marta and Enrique have enough money together to buy the bicycle.

Problem 15 Students should have discovered that Enrique cannot buy the baseball and the bat.

 Cumulative Review: For cumulative review of previously learned skills, see page 219–220.

 Family Involvement: Assign the *Practice, Reteach,* or *Enrichment* activities depending on the needs of your students.

 Concept/Question Board: Encourage students to continue to post questions, answers, and examples on the Concept/Question Board.

 Math Puzzler: Jenna studies for one hour for each subject. At 4:20 P.M. she starts studying for math and science. Will she be finished in time to watch her favorite television program at 7:30 P.M. if she takes an hour for dinner? How can you tell? yes; because she will eat and study for 3 hours until 7:20 P.M.

4 Assess and Differentiate

 Assess Use *eAssess* to record and analyze evidence of student understanding.

A Gather Evidence

Use the Daily Class Assessment Records in *Assessment* or *eAssess* to record daily observations.

Informal Assessment
☑ **Strategy Building**

Did the student **UNDERSTANDING**

- ❑ make important observations?
- ❑ extend or generalize learning?
- ❑ provide insightful answers?
- ❑ pose insightful questions?

Informal Assessment
☑ **Concept/Question Board**

Did the student **APPLYING**

- ❑ apply learning in new situations?
- ❑ contribute concepts?
- ❑ contribute answers?
- ❑ connect mathematics to real-world situations?

B Summarize Findings

Analyze and summarize assessment data for each student. Determine which Assessment Follow-Up is appropriate for each student. Use the Student Assessment Record in *Assessment* or *eAssess* to update assessment records.

Assessment page T41

C Assessment Follow-Up ● DIFFERENTIATE INSTRUCTION

Based on your observations, use these teaching strategies for assessment follow-up.

INTERVENTION

Review student performance on *Intervention* Lesson 6.C to see if students have mastered prerequisite skills for this lesson.

ENGLISH LEARNER

Review

Use Lesson 6.5 in *English Learner Support Guide* to review lesson concepts and vocabulary.

ENRICH

If . . . students are proficient in the lesson concepts,

Then . . . encourage them to work on the chapter projects or *Enrichment* Lesson 6.5.

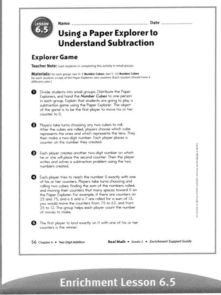

Enrichment Lesson 6.5

PRACTICE

If . . . students would benefit from additional practice,

Then . . . assign *Practice* Lesson 6.5.

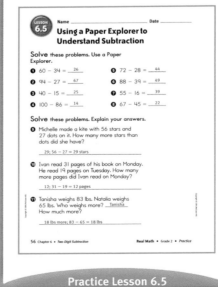

Practice Lesson 6.5

RETEACH

If . . . students are having difficulty using the Paper Explorer,

Then . . . have them make a list of equivalent subtraction exercises to refer to as they move on the Paper Explorer.

OBJECTIVES
To provide reinforcement and review of two-digit subtraction

NCTM STANDARDS
Number and Operations
- Developing a sense of whole numbers and representing and using them in flexible ways
- Demonstrating an understanding of place value concepts

MATERIALS
- *Number Cubes
- *Craft sticks and rubber bands
- *Play money
- blank overhead transparency

TECHNOLOGY
Presentation Lesson 6.6

TEST PREP
Cumulative Review
Mental Math reviews related addition and subtraction exercises (Lesson 1.10).

Extended Response
Problem 8

Practicing Two-Digit Subtraction

Context of the Lesson In this lesson students practice with a different base-ten material, play money. Students should not become dependent on any one material; therefore, it is important to vary base-ten materials.

See page 203B for Math Background for teachers for this lesson.

Planning for Learning • DIFFERENTIATE INSTRUCTION

INTERVENTION

If . . . students lack the prerequisite skill of subtraction facts,

Then . . . teach *Intervention* Lesson 6.B.

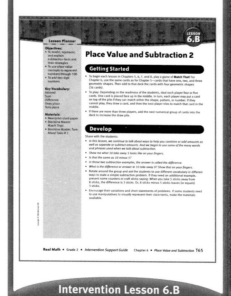

Intervention Lesson 6.B

ENGLISH LEARNER

Preview

If . . . students need language support,

Then . . . use Lesson 6.6 in *English Learner Support Guide* to preview lesson concepts and vocabulary.

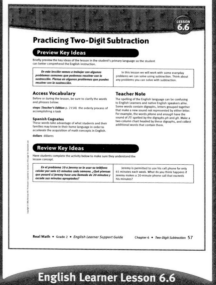

English Learner Lesson 6.6

ENRICH

If . . . students are proficient in the lesson concepts,

Then . . . emphasize additional game time.

PRACTICE

If . . . students would benefit from additional practice,

Then . . . extend Guided Discussion before assigning the student pages.

RETEACH

If . . . students are having difficulty understanding subtracting two-digit numbers,

Then . . . extend Guided Discussion before assigning the student pages.

Access Vocabulary	**Spanish Cognates**
steps the orderly process of accomplishing a task	**dollars** dólares

*Manipulative Kit Item

Mental Math 5

 Present addition and subtraction exercises in pairs. Use multiples of ten, and have students show their answers using **Number Cubes.** Possible exercises include the following:

a. 60 + 30 = 90
b. 90 − 60 = 30
c. 20 + 50 = 70
d. 70 − 20 = 50
e. 10 + 70 = 80
f. 80 − 10 = 70

1 Develop 20

Tell Students In Today's Lesson They Will

subtract two-digit numbers.

Guided Discussion   UNDERSTANDING   Whole Group

Have students review solving subtraction exercises.

Mr. Ellis, the zookeeper, is moving penguins to the City Zoo's new penguin habitat. The zoo has 35 penguins. Mr. Ellis wants to move 17 of the penguins today. How many will be left when he moves those penguins to their new habitat?

■ **How would you write a number sentence to answer the question?** 35 − 17 =
■ **How would you solve the statement? What is the answer?** by regrouping; The answer is 18.

Strategy Building   ENGAGING   Whole Group

 Roll a Problem (Subtraction) Game

Demonstrate, and then play this game as a group, as in previous chapters, to reinforce place value and probability as well as to provide practice in subtracting two-digit numbers.

See the instructions for game play on page 216 of the **Student Edition.**

- When playing the game with the entire class, use an overhead transparency, but do not turn on the light of the overhead projector, so students cannot see where you are placing numbers.
- When the round is over, reveal your problem to students.
- Without calculating with paper and pencil, ask students to raise their hands if they think they have a difference that is less than yours.
- Select a student whose hand is raised, and ask him or her to write the problem on the board. After establishing that the bottom number is not greater than the top number, have him or her explain why the difference is less than yours.
- Ask other students if they have a lesser difference. If so, have them write their problem on the board and explain why it is lesser. Continue until you have the least difference and can declare a winner or winners.

- In about 15 minutes, you should have time to do several rounds of this game.
- As the game proceeds, walk around noting students who place their numbers without regard to place value, or who routinely place the higher numbers on the bottom (in the subtrahend). If the placement of numbers does not improve through game repetition, these students will need remedial work.

A copy of this game can also be found on page 61 of **Home Connection.**

Monitoring Student Progress

If . . . students are not placing numbers correctly,

Then . . . do not introduce a strategy, but watch students and pair them with a student who is using the strategy.

2 Assign Student Pages 20

Pages 215–216   UNDERSTANDING

Have students complete page 215 independently. Allow students to use craft sticks or play money if they are having difficulty with the exercises.

Monitoring Student Progress

If . . . students have difficulty recognizing when to regroup to solve the problem,

Then . . . work through several problems (some that do and some that do not require regrouping) while using craft sticks to act out the situation.

As Students Finish

  Have students play the **Roll a Problem (Subtraction) Game** in pairs or small groups.

Practicing Two-Digit Subtraction

Name _____ Date _____

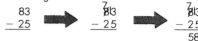

LESSON 6.6 Practicing Two-Digit Subtraction

Key Ideas

The same steps work for subtracting any numbers.

Remember to look at the ones place before subtracting.

$$\begin{array}{r} 83 \\ -25 \\ \hline \end{array} \Longrightarrow \begin{array}{r} 7\,\cancel{8}3 \\ -25 \\ \hline \end{array} \Longrightarrow \begin{array}{r} 7\,\cancel{8}3 \\ -25 \\ \hline 58 \end{array}$$

Subtract. Write your answers.

① $\begin{array}{r} 70 \\ -43 \\ \hline 27 \end{array}$ ② $\begin{array}{r} 73 \\ -43 \\ \hline 30 \end{array}$ ③ $\begin{array}{r} 74 \\ -43 \\ \hline 31 \end{array}$ ④ $\begin{array}{r} 68 \\ -39 \\ \hline 29 \end{array}$ ⑤ $\begin{array}{r} 81 \\ -26 \\ \hline 55 \end{array}$

Solve these problems.
Use play money if you need to.

⑥ David had $63. He spent $28. Now he has __$35__.

⑦ Yori has $43. She needs $62. She needs __$19__ more.

⑧ **Extended Response** Jacob has $43. Emily has $39. Do they have enough money to buy five sports tickets? __cannot tell; There is not enough information.__

⑨ Lani has $78. Tina has $92. Who has more? __Tina__ How much more? __$14__

⑩ Li had $27. She earned $18. Now she has __$45__.

Textbook This lesson is available in the *eTextbook*.

215

Game

Place Value, Subtraction, and Strategies Practice

Roll a Problem (Subtraction) Game

Players: Two or more

Materials: Paper and pencil for each player, *Number Cube* (0–5)

HOW TO PLAY

❶ Begin by drawing lines to represent a two-digit subtraction problem on a piece of paper, like this:

❷ Player One rolls the *Number Cube.*

❸ Player One announces the digit rolled, and all players write that digit in one of the spaces before the next number is rolled.

❹ After players have a completed problem, they subtract to find the difference.

❺ In each round, the player who has the number closest to, but not less than, zero is the winner. There may be ties.

216   **Real Math** • Chapter 6 • Lesson 6

---

③ Reflect

10

Guided Discussion ☑ REASONING

Whole Group

Give students a few minutes to discuss how they decide whether or not to regroup when subtracting two-digit numbers. Have students share their answers. Regrouping is necessary when the ones digit in the number they are subtracting from is less than the ones digit of the number being subtracted.

Extended Response ▶

Problem 8 Discuss students' answers. Students should notice that there was not enough information to know if Jacob and Emily have enough money to buy five sports cards.

 Cumulative Review: For cumulative review of previously learned skills, see page 219–220.

Family Involvement: Assign the *Practice, Reteach,* or *Enrichment* activities depending on the needs of your students.

Concept/Question Board: Encourage students to continue to post questions, answers, and examples on the Concept/Question Board.

Math Puzzler: Keith is 3 years older than Kendra. He is 3 years younger than James. James is twice as old as Marc, who is 9. How old are Keith, Kendra, and James? 15; 12; 18

Assess and Differentiate

 Assess Use *eAssess* to record and analyze evidence of student understanding.

A Gather Evidence

Use the Daily Class Assessment Records in *Assessment* or *eAssess* to record daily observations.

Performance Assessment
☑ **Game**

Did the student [ENGAGING]
- ❑ pay attention to others' contributions?
- ❑ contribute information and ideas?
- ❑ improve on a strategy?
- ❑ reflect on and check the accuracy of his or her work?

Informal Assessment
☑ **Guided Discussion**

Did the student [REASONING]
- ❑ provide a clear explanation?
- ❑ communicate reasons and strategies?
- ❑ choose appropriate strategies?
- ❑ argue logically?

B Summarize Findings

Analyze and summarize assessment data for each student. Determine which Assessment Follow-Up is appropriate for each student. Use the Student Assessment Record in *Assessment* or *eAssess* to update assessment records.

Assessment page T41

C Assessment Follow-Up • DIFFERENTIATE INSTRUCTION

Based on your observations, use these teaching strategies for assessment follow-up.

INTERVENTION

Review student performance on *Intervention* Lesson 6.B to see if students have mastered prerequisite skills for this lesson.

ENGLISH LEARNER

Review

Use Lesson 6.6 in *English Learner Support Guide* to review lesson concepts and vocabulary.

ENRICH

If . . . students are proficient in the lesson concepts,

Then . . . encourage them to work on the chapter projects or *Enrichment* Lesson 6.6.

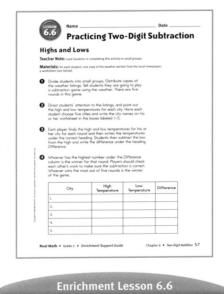

Enrichment Lesson 6.6

PRACTICE

If . . . students would benefit from additional practice,

Then . . . assign *Practice* Lesson 6.6.

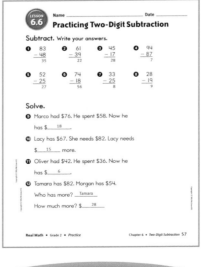

Practice Lesson 6.6

RETEACH

If . . . students are having difficulty understanding subtracting two-digit numbers,

Then . . . reteach the concept using *Reteach* Lesson 6.6.

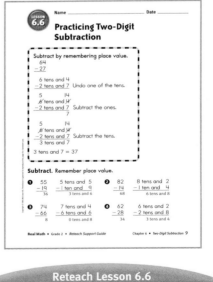

Reteach Lesson 6.6

Exploring Problem Solving

Objectives
- To explore the Make a Plan and Draw a Picture strategies
- To practice adding and subtracting two-digit numbers
- To interpret numerical results so that an answer is reasonable
- To explore solving and presenting solutions to multistep problems

Materials
Counters

Context of the Lesson Reasoning and problem solving are prevalent in every *Real Math* lesson. This lesson and other special problem-solving lessons allow more time for students to share and compare their strategies. While continuing the zoo theme from the chapter opener, this lesson also provides additional opportunity for students to use the addition and subtraction skills they have been working on in this and the previous chapter.

 **Develop**

Tell Students In Today's Lesson They Will
solve a problem about feeding sea lions.

Guided Discussion

Remind students about the polar bear habitat they designed on page 204. Tell them they are going to help the zoo again—this time by helping one of the workers feed the sea lions.

Have students look at the illustration at the top of page 217. Read this problem to them:

Ms. Smith works at the zoo in the afternoon. One of her favorite jobs is feeding fish to the sea lions. When she got ready to feed them today, she saw three buckets of fish. The worker who fed the sea lions this morning had left some buckets of fish and wrote numbers to tell how many fish were in each bucket. Ms. Smith is supposed to feed the sea lions sixty fish. She wants to know if there are enough fish in the buckets. If not, how many more fish will she need?

Make sure students understand the problem by asking questions such as the following:

- **What job is Ms. Smith about to do?** feed the sea lions
- **How many fish does she feed them?** sixty
- **How many fish are in the first bucket?** seventeen
- **How many are in the other buckets?** twelve and sixteen
- **What is the problem asking you to find?** if there are enough fish in the buckets; if there aren't enough, how many more fish Ms. Smith will need in order to have sixty fish
- **How would you figure out if Ms. Smith has enough fish?** Allow students to offer approaches to this part of the problem.

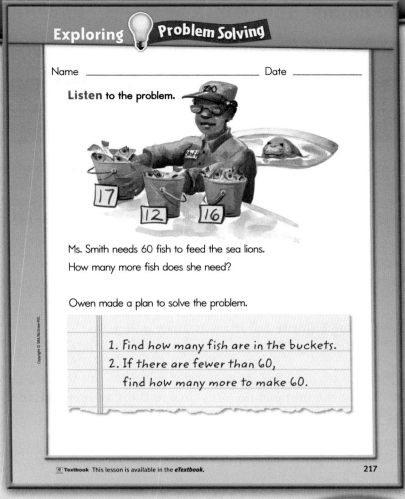

Exploring Problem Solving

Name _____ Date _____

Listen to the problem.

Ms. Smith needs 60 fish to feed the sea lions.

How many more fish does she need?

Owen made a plan to solve the problem.

1. Find how many fish are in the buckets.
2. If there are fewer than 60, find how many more to make 60.

Textbook This lesson is available in the *eTextbook*.   217

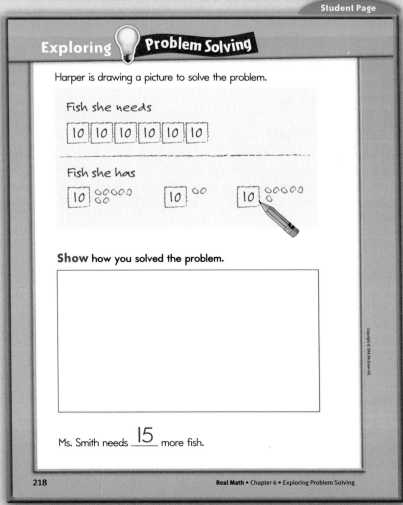

Exploring Problem Solving

Harper is drawing a picture to solve the problem.

Fish she needs
| 10 | 10 | 10 | 10 | 10 | 10 |

Fish she has
10 ooooo oo   10 oo   10 ooooo o

Show how you solved the problem.

Ms. Smith needs __15__ more fish.

218   **Real Math • Chapter 6 • Exploring Problem Solving**

Exploring Problem Solving 25

Using Student Pages

Analyzing Sample Solution 1: Make a Plan/Use Operations

Have students look at page 217 to see how Owen solved the problem. Ask questions about his strategy, such as the following:

- **What is the first step in Owen's plan?** Find how many fish there are altogether in the three buckets.
- **How will this help Owen solve the problem?** It will tell him if Ms. Smith has enough fish to feed the sea lions.
- **What is the second step in Owen's plan?** If there aren't enough fish, figure out how many more are needed to make 60 altogether.

Analyzing Sample Solution 2: Draw a Picture

Tell students that Harper is using a different strategy to try to solve the problem. Have students look at the picture of Harper's approach on page 218. Ask questions such as the following:

- **Look at the first picture. Why do you think Harper started by drawing 6 boxes with the number 10 on each box?** to show the 60 fish that Ms. Smith needs; 6 tens is 60
- **Why didn't Harper draw 60 fish instead?** It's easier to draw 6 boxes than 60 fish. It's easier to keep track of the total by making groups of 10.
- **Look at the second picture. What has Harper done in this picture?** She has drawn the fish that Ms. Smith already has in the three buckets.
- **What do you think she will do next?** Allow students to offer ideas. Harper will probably compare the number in the bottom drawing to the number in the top drawing. She might compare by combining the Os (individual fish), or she might compare by matching the 10s.

Skill Building

Have students work on the problem individually or in pairs. They may use Harper's strategy, Owen's strategy, or one of their own. Provide support as needed, remembering to suggest approaches rather than show students the answer. Remind students to check their answers.

Sample Solutions Strategies

Students might use one or more of the following strategies.

Act It Out

Students might use counters to act out the problem by combining groups of 17, 12, and 16 and then counting on until they reach 60. Conversely, they might begin with 60 counters, remove 17, 12, and then 16, and finally count those that are left.

Draw a Picture (Number Line)

Students might draw a number line, start from 0, count on 17, 12, and 16 spaces, and then count how many spaces they would need to move to reach 60.

Make a Plan/Use Operations

Students might start with 60 and successively subtract 17, 12, and 16. Or they might add 17, 12, and 16 to get 45, and then subtract 45 from 60.

Break the Problem into Parts/Use Number Sense

Students might look at each bucket separately, seeing that 20 fish in each bucket would be enough for a total of 60. Then they could figure out how many fish would need to be added to each bucket to make 20.

Write a Number Sentence

Students might use symbols, words, or a combination to model the problem; for example:

 17 + 12 + 16 = number of fish in buckets

 number of fish in buckets + ____ = 60

 Reflect 10

 Knowledge Age Skills

Problem Formulation, Planning, and Strategizing Ask students to share their solutions and their strategies. In discussion, bring out the following points:

- Often problems in real life require many steps to solve them.
- Different strategies can be used to solve the same problem.
- Different people may prefer different strategies for solving problems.
- A useful way of checking your answer is to solve the problem using two different strategies.
- When using the Draw a Picture strategy, remember that the picture does not need to look like art; it needs to help the student solve the problem.
- A simple mark, such as an X or O, takes much less time to draw than a fish. Simple marks are as useful as fancy pictures and may be more useful because they help the student focus on what is important in the problem. In this case, the number of fish matters for solving the problem, but what the fish look like does not.

Assess 15

When evaluating student work, focus on the correctness of the answer and on whether students thought rationally about the problem. Questions to consider include the following:

- Did the student understand the problem?
- Did the student understand the sample solutions strategies?
- Was the student able to explain his or her strategy?
- Did the student use addition and subtraction sensibly?

Also note which students use particularly sophisticated or creative strategies.

6
Cumulative Review

Assign Pages 219–220

Use the Cumulative Review as a review of concepts and skills that students have previously learned.

Here are different ways that you can assign these problems to your students as they work through the chapter:

- With some of the lessons in the chapter, assign a set of cumulative review problems to be completed as practice or for homework.
  Lesson 6.1—Problems 1–8
  Lesson 6.2—Problems 9–14
  Lesson 6.3—Problems 15–20
  Lesson 6.4—Problems 21–28
  Lesson 6.5—Problems 29–31
  Lesson 6.6—Problems 32–37
- At any point during the chapter, assign part or all of the cumulative review problems to be completed as practice or for homework.

Cumulative Review

Problems 1–8 review identifying odd numbers and splitting even numbers, Lesson 1.2

Problems 9–14 review adding two-digit numbers, Lesson 5.4

Problems 15–20 review regrouping tens as ones, Lesson 6.1

Problems 21–28 review subtracting two-digit numbers, Lesson 6.4

Problems 29–31 review addition and subtraction function machines, Lesson 3.3

Problems 32–37 review grouping by tens to add, Lesson 5.9

Monitoring Student Progress

If . . . students miss more than one problem in a section, **Then . . .** refer to the indicated lesson for remediation suggestions.

Cumulative Review

Name _____ Date _____

Odds and Evens Lesson 1.2

Ring the odd numbers. Write how many would be in each half if you split the even numbers.

① 64 **32** ② ⑬ ③ ㉕ ④ 46 **23**
⑤ ㊼ ⑥ 36 **18** ⑦ 16 **8** ⑧ 24 **12**

Adding Two-Digit Numbers Lesson 5.4

Add.

⑨ 34
  + 17
  51

⑩ 14
  + 28
  42

⑪ 16
  + 34
  50

⑫ 65
  + 15
  80

⑬ 52
  + 35
  87

⑭
  35
+ 23
58

There are **58** penguins.

Regrouping Tens as Ones Lesson 6.1

Rewrite each number to show one fewer ten and ten more ones.

⑮ 40 = **3** tens and **10**   ⑱ 50 = **4** tens and **10**
⑯ 20 = **1** ten and **10**   ⑲ 48 = **3** tens and **18**
⑰ 37 = **2** tens and **17**   ⑳ 56 = **4** tens and **16**

Textbook This lesson is available in the **eTextbook**.   219

Cumulative Review

Subtracting Two-Digit Numbers Lesson 6.4

Solve these problems.

㉑ 40
  − 30
  10

㉒ 30
  − 20
  10

㉓ 80
  − 30
  50

㉔ 40
  − 28
  12

㉕ 70
  − 28
  42

㉖ 90
  − 71
  19

㉗ 80
  − 20
  60

㉘ 51
  − 15
  36

Addition and Subtraction Functions Lesson 3.3

Fill in the missing numbers.

㉙ in −11 out

19	8
43	32
29	18
58	47

㉚ in −25 out

36	11
45	20
54	29
34	9

㉛ in ○ out

49	57
27	35
16	24
15	23

The rule is **+8**

Grouping by Tens Lesson 5.9

Add. Use shortcuts if you can.

㉜ 10 + 4 + 4 = **18**
㉝ 6 + 4 + 8 + 1 = **19**
㉞ 6 + 7 + 4 + 3 = **20**

㉟ 1 + 3 + 7 + 9 = **20**
㊱ 21 + 19 + 32 + 18 = **90**
㊲ 6 + 7 + 4 = **17**

220   **Real Math** • Chapter 6

Individual Oral Assessment

Purpose of the Test

The Individual Oral Assessment is designed to measure students' growing knowledge of chapter concepts. It is administered individually to each student, and it requires oral responses from each student. The test takes about five minutes to complete. See **Assessment** for detailed instructions for administering and interpreting the test, and record students' answers on the Student Assessment Recording Sheet.

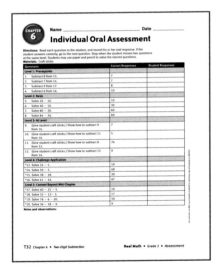

Assessment page T32

Directions

Read each question to the student, and record his or her oral response. If the student answers correctly, go to the next question. Stop when the student misses two questions at the same level. Students may use craft sticks or paper and pencil to solve the questions as indicated.

Materials

Craft sticks, paper and pencil

Questions

Level 1: Prerequisite

1. Subtract 8 from 15. 7
2. Subtract 7 from 14. 7
3. Subtract 9 from 17. 8
4. Subtract 6 from 16. 10

Level 2: Basic

5. Solve 20 − 10. 10
6. Solve 40 − 10. 30
7. Solve 80 − 20. 60
8. Solve 84 − 24. 60

Level 3: At Level

9. Use craft sticks. Show how to subtract 9 from 16. 7
10. Use craft sticks. Show how to subtract 11 from 16. 5
11. Use craft sticks. Show how to subtract 8 from 32. 24
12. Use craft sticks. Show how to subtract 15 from 24. 9

Level 4: Challenge Application

13. Use paper and pencil. Solve 24 − 5. 19
14. Use paper and pencil. Solve 50 − 2. 48
15. Use paper and pencil. Solve 38 − 18. 20
16. Use paper and pencil. Solve 61 − 14. 47

Level 5: Content Beyond Mid-Chapter

17. Use paper and pencil. Solve 40 − 25 − 5. 10
18. Use paper and pencil. Solve 32 − 12 − 3. 17
19. Use paper and pencil. Solve 76 − 6 − 20. 50
20. Use paper and pencil. Solve 36 − 18 − 9. 9

Lesson Planner

OBJECTIVES
- To use addition to check two-digit subtraction
- To provide experience in solving word problems

NCTM STANDARDS

Number and Operations
- Understanding various meanings of addition and subtraction of whole numbers and the relationship between the operations
- Understanding the effects of adding and subtracting whole numbers
- Developing and using strategies for whole-number computations
- Developing fluency with basic number combinations for addition and subtraction

Problem Solving
- Solving problems that arise in mathematics and in other contexts
- Applying and adapting a variety of appropriate strategies to solve problems

MATERIALS
- *Number Cubes
- *Craft sticks and rubber bands

TECHNOLOGY
- e Presentation Lesson 6.7
- e MathTools Coins and Money

TEST PREP
Cumulative Review
Mental Math reviews related two-digit subtraction exercises (Lessons 6.3–6.4).

Writing + Math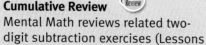
Journal

Checking Subtraction

Context of the Lesson In this lesson students will use addition to check their answers to subtraction problems. Up to this point, students have focused on working through two-digit subtraction exercises. In this lesson students also use two-digit addition to check their subtraction answers.

See page 203B for Math Background for teachers for this lesson.

Planning for Learning • DIFFERENTIATE INSTRUCTION

INTERVENTION
If . . . students lack the prerequisite skill of adding two-digit numbers,

Then . . . teach *Intervention* Lesson 6.C.

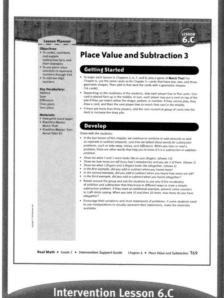

Intervention Lesson 6.C

ENGLISH LEARNER
Preview

If . . . students need language support,

Then . . . use Lesson 6.7 in *English Learner Support Guide* to preview lesson concepts and vocabulary.

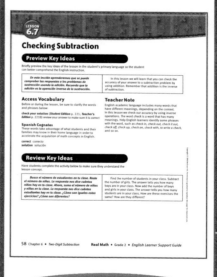

English Learner Lesson 6.7

ENRICH
If . . . students are proficient in the lesson concepts,

Then . . . emphasize the Journal activity.

PRACTICE
If . . . students would benefit from additional practice,

Then . . . extend Skill Building before assigning the student pages.

RETEACH
If . . . students are having difficulty understanding using addition to check subtraction,

Then . . . extend Guided Discussion before assigning the student pages.

Access Vocabulary
check your solution review your answer to make sure it is correct

Spanish Cognates
correct correcto

solution solución

---

*Manipulative Kit Item

Mental Math

5

  Present two-digit subtraction exercises in which one number is a multiple of ten, and have students show their answers using **Number Cubes.** Possible exercises include the following:

a. 47 − 20 = 27

b. 37 − 20 = 17

c. 40 − 11 = 29

d. 40 − 21 = 19

e. 84 − 50 = 34

f. 23 − 10 = 13

1 Develop

20

Tell Students In Today's Lesson They Will

use addition to check subtraction.

Guided Discussion MathTools UNDERSTANDING

Whole Group

Discuss how to check subtraction answers by using addition.

Tell students, *You buy a piece of fruit and a carton of skim milk in the cafeteria. Your total is 56¢. You give the cashier 75¢. He gives you 29¢ back as change. Did he give you the right amount? How could you check?*

Write the subtraction exercise on the board with the incorrect answer.

```
  75
− 56
  29
```

Discuss whether the difference is correct. Students should conclude that this answer is not correct.

■ **How can we show that the answer is wrong without subtracting?** Remind students that addition and subtraction are inverse operations and they undo each other. If the answer were correct, 29 + 56 should equal 75.

Have students find the correct answer and then show how they can use addition to check that they are correct. 75 − 56 = 19 and 19 + 56 = 75

Use **eMathTools: Coins and Money** to model the problem if students are having difficulty visualizing the procedure. Repeat this demonstration with another example.

Skill Building REASONING

Small Group

Have students work in pairs to solve several more exercises in which they must use addition to check subtraction. Include some problems in which the answers are correct.

Also include some in which the answers are greater than the minuends (top numbers) such as 43 − 28 = 75. Possible problems include the following (circled answers are incorrect):

a.	b.	c.	d.	e.
47	51	83	26	43
− 23	− 26	− 47	− 19	− 28
⑭	㉗	36	㊺	㊀

Skill Practice COMPUTING

Whole Group

 THUMBS UP

On the board or overhead projector write more problems like those in the Skill-Building activity above, but have students respond by showing thumbs-up if the answer is correct and thumbs-down if the answer is incorrect. Allow students time to work the problems on paper before responding, but encourage them to use mental math strategies. Possible problems include the following (circled answers are incorrect):

a.	b.	c.	d.	e.
58	47	83	43	51
− 27	− 28	− 29	− 35	− 24
31	㉙	㊅	㉘	27

Monitoring Student Progress

If . . . students have difficulty relating addition to subtraction as described in Guided Discussion,

Then . . . use single-digit subtraction and addition to explain the concept.

2 Assign Student Pages

20

Pages 221–222 UNDERSTANDING

Have students complete pages 221 and 222 independently. Read the word problems on page 222 aloud if students are having difficulty.

As Students Finish

 Game

Allow students to play a game of their choice, or assign a game based on their needs.

Name _____ Date _____

LESSON **6.7** **Checking Subtraction**

Key Ideas

You can check a subtraction answer by using addition.

$16 - 4 = 12$

Check your solution by adding 12 to 4.
The correct answer is 12.

$12 + 4 = 16$

Check using addition. Ring each wrong answer. Write the correct answers.

❶	❷	❸	❹
17 − 8 9	84 − 27 57	61 − 34 ㉖ 27	70 − 43 27

❺	❻	❼	❽
29 − 23 ㊿⃝52 6	40 − 32 ⑱ 8	100 − 70 30	45 − 25 ⑱ 20

❾	❿	⓫	⓬
64 − 35 ㊳ 29	75 − 25 50	75 − 26 49	75 − 27 ㊳ 48

⓭	⓮	⓯	⓰
87 − 38 49	76 − 35 ㉟ 41	92 − 13 79	70 − 43 27

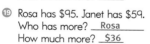 **Textbook** This lesson is available in the *eTextbook*.

221

LESSON 6.7 · Checking Subtraction

Solve these problems.

⓱ Arnold's digital camera can hold 85 pictures. He has already taken 46 pictures. How many more can he take on his trip to the zoo? __39__

⓲ Toothpaste costs 84¢. The toothbrush costs 79¢. Which costs more? __toothpaste__ How much more? __5¢__

⓳ Rosa has $95. Janet has $59. Who has more? __Rosa__ How much more? __$36__

⓴ Antonio had 73 football cards. He gave some away. Now he has 45 cards. How many did he give away? __28__

Writing + Math Journal

Write your own word problem that uses two-digit subtraction.

---

3 Reflect

10

Guided Discussion REASONING

Whole Group

Introduce an alternate strategy for solving two-digit subtraction problems. Demonstrate the following exercises by using craft sticks.

- Write
$$\begin{array}{r} 90 \\ - 39 \end{array}$$
on the board.

- Add 1 unit to each number to make
$$\begin{array}{r} 91 \\ - 40 \end{array}$$.

Write that problem on the board also. Demonstrate to students that the difference is the same for both problems.

■ **How does changing the problem make it easier to solve?** You do not have to rename tens as ones before solving.

- Write
$$\begin{array}{r} 90 \\ - 23 \end{array}$$
on the board.

- Subtract 1 from each number to make
$$\begin{array}{r} 89 \\ - 22 \end{array}$$.

Again, demonstrate to students that the difference is the same for both problems, but that changing the problem to 89 − 22 makes the problem easier to solve.

✓ Use Mastery Checkpoint 8 found in **Assessment** to evaluate student mastery of two-digit subtraction. By this time, students should be able to correctly answer eighty percent of the Mastery Checkpoint items.

Writing + Math Journal

Have students trade word problems and solve each other's problems. Then have students trade back, and use addition to check their partners' answers.

Curriculum Connection: Students may be interested in researching how digital cameras work.

Cumulative Review: For cumulative review of previously learned skills, see page 231–232.

Family Involvement: Assign the *Practice, Reteach,* or *Enrichment* activities depending on the needs of your students. Have students play a previously introduced game with a family member.

Concept/Question Board: Encourage students to continue to post questions, answers, and examples on the Concept/Question Board.

Math Puzzler: Mr. Martínez is 63 years old. His brother is 17 years younger. How old is his brother? 46 years old

Assess and Differentiate

 Assess Use *eAssess* to record and analyze evidence of student understanding.

A Gather Evidence

Use the Daily Class Assessment Records in *Assessment* or *eAssess* to record daily observations.

Formal Assessment

☑ **Mastery Checkpoint**

Did the student
- ☐ use correct procedures?
- ☐ respond with at least 80% accuracy?

8 Mastery Checkpoint 8
Two-Digit Subtraction

The student demonstrates mastery by correctly answering thirteen of the sixteen problems.

How well can you subtract?

```
❶   23        ❾   75
   - 17          - 25
   ____6         ____50

❷   42        ❿   65
   - 25          -  9
   ___17         ___56

❸   22        ⓫   92
   - 12          - 13
   ___10         ___79

❹   50        ⓬   73
   - 34          - 28
   ___16         ___45
```

Assessment page T59

B Summarize Findings

Analyze and summarize assessment data for each student. Determine which Assessment Follow-Up is appropriate for each student. Use the Student Assessment Record in *Assessment* or *eAssess* to update assessment records.

Assessment page T41

C Assessment Follow-Up • DIFFERENTIATE INSTRUCTION

Based on your observations, use these teaching strategies for assessment follow-up.

INTERVENTION

Review student performance on *Intervention* Lesson 6.C to see if students have mastered prerequisite skills for this lesson.

ENGLISH LEARNER

Review

Use Lesson 6.7 in *English Learner Support Guide* to review lesson concepts and vocabulary.

ENRICH

If . . . students are proficient in the lesson concepts,

Then . . . encourage them to work on the chapter projects or *Enrichment* Lesson 6.7.

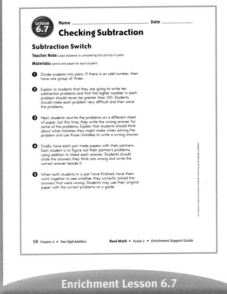

Enrichment Lesson 6.7

PRACTICE

If . . . students would benefit from additional practice,

Then . . . assign *Practice* Lesson 6.7.

Practice Lesson 6.7

RETEACH

If . . . students are having difficulty checking subtraction,

Then . . . remind them that addition and subtraction are opposites. Review fact families.

OBJECTIVES
- To apply strategies for subtracting two-digit numbers
- To demonstrate how to use subtraction to solve realistic problems involving money

NCTM STANDARDS
Number and Operations
- Developing and using strategies for whole-number computations
- Using a variety of methods and tools to compute

Problem Solving
- Building new mathematical knowledge through problem solving
- Solving problems that arise in mathematics and other contexts
- Monitoring and reflecting on the process of problem solving

Connections
Recognizing and applying mathematics in contexts outside of mathematics

MATERIALS
- *Number Cubes
- *Play money
- *Overhead bills and coins

TECHNOLOGY
- Presentation Lesson 6.8
- MathTools Coins and Money
- Building Blocks Word Problems with Tools 4

TEST PREP
Cumulative Review
- Mental Math reviews subtracting multiples of ten from multiples of ten (Lesson 6.2).
- Problems 1–8 review two-digit subtraction (Lessons 6.3–6.4).

Multistep Problems
Problems 10 and 11

Extended Response
Problem 9

Writing + Math
Journal

Applying Subtraction

Context of the Lesson This lesson extends the use of subtraction in solving realistic problems involving money. Problem 5 is an addition problem that introduces concepts that lead to an understanding of multiplication. Multiplication and division will be introduced in Chapter 11.

See page 203B for Math Background for teachers for this lesson.

Planning for Learning ● DIFFERENTIATE INSTRUCTION

INTERVENTION
If . . . students lack the prerequisite skill of place value to 100,

Then . . . teach *Intervention* Lesson 6.A.

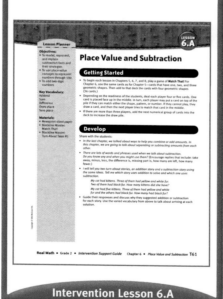

Intervention Lesson 6.A

ENGLISH LEARNER
Preview

If . . . students need language support,

Then . . . use Lesson 6.8 in *English Learner Support Guide* to preview lesson concepts and vocabulary.

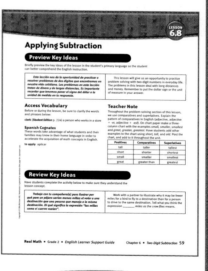

English Learner Lesson 6.8

ENRICH
If . . . students are proficient in the lesson concepts,

Then . . . emphasize Skill Building.

PRACTICE
If . . . students would benefit from additional practice,

Then . . . extend Skill Practice before assigning the student pages.

RETEACH
If . . . students are having difficulty understanding solving word problems,

Then . . . extend Guided Discussion before assigning the student pages.

Access Vocabulary
clerk a person who works in a store

Spanish Cognates
to apply aplicar

Mental Math **5**

Present a series of subtraction exercises involving multiples of ten, and have students show their answers using **Number Cubes.** Possible exercises include the following:

a. $90 - 50 = 40$ **b.** $90 - 40 = 50$ **c.** $90 - 30 = 60$
d. $90 - 20 = 70$ **e.** $80 - 40 = 40$ **f.** $80 - 50 = 30$

1 Develop **20**

Tell Students In Today's Lesson They Will

create and solve word problems using two-digit subtraction.

Guided Discussion MathTools UNDERSTANDING

Whole Group

Lead a discussion about how mathematics and money are used every day. Encourage students to briefly share their experiences with spending, earning, and saving money.

■ **How do you use money during the day? How do you use math when you are using money?** Students may talk about buying lunch, riding a bus or subway, going to the store with family members, earning an allowance, saving money for a large purchase, and so on.

Write a two-digit subtraction problem similar to the following on the board:

$$\begin{array}{r} 43 \\ -28 \\ \hline 15 \end{array}$$

Use play money ($1 and $10 bills) or **eMathTools: Coins and Money** to demonstrate solving this problem. Remind students about the process of renaming by trading one $10 bill for ten $1 bills and then subtracting.

Skill Building APPLYING

Small Group

List items with price tags labeled by dollar amounts on the board. Possible examples include the following: a DVD for $27, a CD player for $36, a CD for $18, and an MP3 player for $64.

Distribute $1 and $10 bills to the class. Allow students to work in pairs to create word problems and solve them based on the information given. Allow students to choose which operation to use (addition or subtraction). Examples of problems may include the following:

■ **I have $50. I want to buy a CD. How much money will I have left after buying a CD?** $50 - 18 = 32$; I will have $32 left.
■ **How much money would I need to buy a CD player and a CD?** $36 + 18 = 54$; I will need $54.

Allow groups to share their problems with the class when everyone has finished.

Skill Practice COMPUTING

Whole Group

Present several two-digit subtraction exercises to students. Be sure to include some that do not require regrouping so students realize that the first question they should ask themselves is whether regrouping is needed. Allow students to use play money if necessary. Problems may include the following:

a. $\begin{array}{r} 83 \\ -46 \\ \hline 37 \end{array}$ **b.** $\begin{array}{r} 34 \\ -22 \\ \hline 12 \end{array}$ **c.** $\begin{array}{r} 56 \\ -27 \\ \hline 29 \end{array}$ **d.** $\begin{array}{r} 48 \\ -28 \\ \hline 20 \end{array}$

Monitoring Student Progress

If . . . students have difficulty creating word problems,

Then . . . have them think of an everyday situation they encounter and make word problems based on that.

2 Assign Student Pages **20**

Pages 223–224 ENGAGING

Have students complete page 223 independently and then work in pairs to complete page 224.

Monitoring Student Progress

If . . . students have difficulty choosing the correct operation with the word problems,

Then . . . provide students with concrete materials to act out the situation.

As Students Finish

Building Blocks Have students use **Word Problems with Tools 4** to practice two-digit addition and subtraction word problems.

RESEARCH IN ACTION

"Although in school students are often presented with clearly specified problems to solve, outside of school they encounter situations in which part of the difficulty is to figure out exactly what the problem is. Then they need to formulate the problem so that they can use mathematics to solve it. Consequently, they are likely to need experience and practice in problem formulating as well as in problem solving. They should know a variety of solution strategies as well as which strategies might be useful for solving a specific problem."

Kilpatrick, J., J. Swafford, and B. Findell, eds. *Adding It Up: Helping Children Learn Mathematics.* Washington, D.C.: National Research Council/National Academy Press, 2001, p. 124.

Name _____ Date _____

LESSON 6.8 Applying Subtraction

Key Ideas

Subtraction can help you solve problems every day. How much money will she have left if she buys the shirt?

$40 - 27 = 13$

Find the answers.

1 $\begin{array}{r} 50 \\ -25 \\ \hline 25 \end{array}$ **2** $\begin{array}{r} 50 \\ -26 \\ \hline 24 \end{array}$ **3** $\begin{array}{r} 50 \\ -27 \\ \hline 23 \end{array}$ **4** $\begin{array}{r} 50 \\ -28 \\ \hline 22 \end{array}$

5 CDs are on sale at three for $2. How much will 9 CDs cost? __$6__ Explain. _____

First, find out how many times you add 3 to get 9, $3 + 3 + 3 = 9$; Because three CDs cost $2, you would need to add 2 three times, $2 + 2 + 2 = 6$.

6 Jeremy is allowed to use his cell phone for 65 minutes each week. He has already used 49 minutes. Does Jeremy have enough time to make a 15-minute phone call? ____yes____

Textbook This lesson is available in the *eTextbook*.

223

LESSON 6.8 • Applying Subtraction

Solve these problems using the picture. Explain your answers.

7 Nathan had $76. He bought a pair of shoes. He now has __$19__. Explain. Subtract $57 from $76.

8 Rishi bought a shirt. He gave the clerk two $20 bills. How much change did he get? __$13__

9 Extended Response Simon has $90. He wants to buy a jacket and pants. Can he? __no__ Explain. A jacket for $78 and pants for $22 cost $100. Simon has $90, so he cannot buy both.

10 Multistep Stan has a $50 bill. He buys pants and a belt. How much change should he get? __$16__; Pants at $22 and a belt at $12 equal $34; $50 - $34 = $16.

11 Multistep Tyrone bought a shirt, pants, and a belt. He gave the clerk four $20 bills. How much change should he get? __$19__; The shirt ($27) + the pants ($22) + the belt ($12) = $61. He gave the clerk $80; $80 - $61 = $19 back.

12 Look at the storefront picture. Make up your own problem. Solve it.

Students should create a word problem based on the storefront picture and use addition or subtraction to solve it.

Writing + Math **Journal**

Can you list some ways that you or your family uses subtraction?

224   **Real Math • Chapter 6 • Lesson 8**

---

3 Reflect   5

Guided Discussion REASONING   Whole Group

Select one word problem that a student created from page 224 (Problem 12), and write it on the board. Then, one at a time, have students change one thing in the problem and give the new solution. Continue having students change one thing in each newly created problem. This allows students to revisit previously solved problems in a slightly different form.

Extended Response

Problem 9 Students should have added the cost of the jacket and pants, realizing that Simon does not have enough money to buy both.

Writing + Math **Journal** REASONING

Discuss students' answers. Can they think of ways that do not involve money?

✓ Use Mastery Checkpoint 9 found in **Assessment** to evaluate students mastery of inequalities and equalities. By this time, students should be able to correctly answer eighty percent of the Mastery Checkpoint items.

Curriculum Connection: Students may be interested in looking at the prices of items in online stores or in catalogs to create their own word problems.

Cumulative Review: For cumulative review of previously learned skills, see page 231–232.

Family Involvement: Assign the **Practice, Reteach,** or **Enrichment** activities depending on the needs of your students. Have students work with a family member to create a word problem.

Concept/Question Board: Have students attempt to answer any unanswered questions on the Concept/Question Board.

Math Puzzler: You spend 42¢ on an apple and a quarter for a sticker. You pay with 75¢. How much change do you get back? 8¢

4 Assess and Differentiate

 Assess Use *eAssess* to record and analyze evidence of student understanding.

A Gather Evidence

Use the Daily Class Assessment Records in *Assessment* or *eAssess* to record daily observations.

Formal Assessment

☑ **Mastery Checkpoint**

Did the student
- ❑ use correct procedures?
- ❑ respond with at least 80% accuracy?

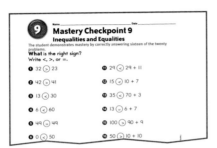

Assessment page T60

B Summarize Findings

Analyze and summarize assessment data for each student. Determine which Assessment Follow-Up is appropriate for each student. Use the Student Assessment Record in *Assessment* or *eAssess* to update assessment records.

Assessment page T41

C Assessment Follow-Up ● DIFFERENTIATE INSTRUCTION

Based on your observations, use these teaching strategies for assessment follow-up.

INTERVENTION

Review student performance on *Intervention* Lesson 6.A to see if students have mastered prerequisite skills for this lesson.

ENGLISH LEARNER

Review

Use Lesson 6.8 in *English Learner Support Guide* to review lesson concepts and vocabulary.

ENRICH

If . . . students are proficient in the lesson concepts,

Then . . . encourage them to work on the chapter projects or *Enrichment* Lesson 6.8.

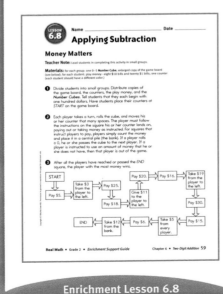

Enrichment Lesson 6.8

PRACTICE

If . . . students would benefit from additional practice,

Then . . . assign *Practice* Lesson 6.8.

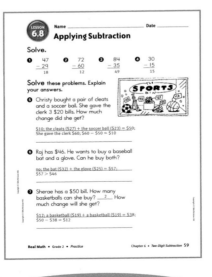

Practice Lesson 6.8

RETEACH

If . . . students are having difficulty with their subtraction skills,

Then . . . divide students into groups based on which of the following skills they need to review:
- review subtraction facts
- review regrouping
- review checking subtraction

Lesson Planner

OBJECTIVES
- To compare relationships between two sets of two-digit numbers using symbolic notation
- To gain experience solving a variety of computational exercises that involve two-digit addition and subtraction

NCTM STANDARDS

Number and Operations
Understanding the effects of adding and subtracting whole numbers

Algebra
- Using concrete, pictorial, and verbal representations to develop an understanding of invented and conventional symbolic notation
- Modeling situations that involve the addition and subtraction of whole numbers
- Describing quantitative change

Representation
Using representations to model and interpret physical, social, and mathematical phenomena

MATERIALS
*Number Cubes

TECHNOLOGY
- **e Presentation** Lesson 6.9
- **e MathTools** Sets Former
- **Building Blocks** Number Compare 4: Numerals to 100

TEST PREP

Cumulative Review
Mental Math reviews subtracting multiples of ten from multiples of ten (Lesson 6.2).

Extended Response
Problem 17

Writing + Math
Journal

*Manipulative Kit Item

Comparing Two-Digit Subtraction Expressions

Context of the Lesson This lesson extends the use of addition and subtraction in solving for equalities and inequalities. The relation signs were introduced in Lesson 1.9.

See page 203B for Math Background for teachers for this lesson.

Planning for Learning ● DIFFERENTIATE INSTRUCTION

INTERVENTION

If . . . students lack the prerequisite skill of adding two-digit numbers,

Then . . . teach **Intervention** Lesson 6.C.

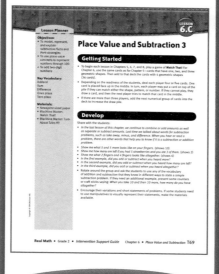

Intervention Lesson 6.C

ENGLISH LEARNER

Preview

If . . . students need language support,

Then . . . use Lesson 6.9 in **English Learner Support Guide** to preview lesson concepts and vocabulary.

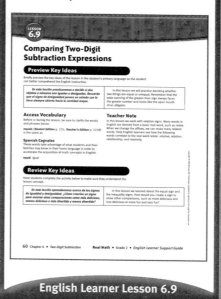

English Learner Lesson 6.9

ENRICH

If . . . students are proficient in the lesson concepts,

Then . . . emphasize Guided Discussion in Reflect.

PRACTICE

If . . . students would benefit from additional practice,

Then . . . extend Skill Practice before assigning the student pages.

RETEACH

If . . . students are having difficulty understanding equalities and inequalities,

Then . . . extend Guided Discussion before assigning the student pages.

Access Vocabulary	Spanish Cognates
equals is the same as	**equal** igual

Mental Math 5

  Present a series of related subtraction exercises involving multiples of ten, and have students show their answers using **Number Cubes.** Possible exercises include the following:

a. 90 − 50 = 40
b. 90 − 40 = 50
c. 90 − 30 = 60
d. 90 − 20 = 70
e. 80 − 40 = 40
f. 80 − 50 = 30
g. 80 − 60 = 20
h. 80 − 70 = 10

1 Develop 20

Tell Students In Today's Lesson They Will

use greater than, less than, and equal signs to compare two-digit subtraction sentences.

Whole Group

Guided Discussion MathTools REASONING

Review the relation signs <, >, and = with the class. Have students tell what they remember about the relation signs. Remind students that the smaller ends of < and > always point to the smaller number. Point out that the = sign has no smaller end because it means both numbers are the same or equal. Demonstrate using the **eMathTools: Set Tool** by creating two sets.

■ **Which set is greater than, less than, or equal to the other set?**
Have students count the objects in each set aloud to reinforce the relation between both sets.

Repeat several times as you discuss the relationship between the different sets.

Skill Practice COMPUTING

Whole Group

 Write several problems on the board. Have students give thumbs-up if the number on the left is greater, thumbs-down if it is less, and an open hand if the two sides are equal. For example, 11 ___ 13 Students should show thumbs-down because 11 is less than 13. Provide several examples of sums and differences. Possible examples include the following:

a. 23 $<$ 50
b. 65 $=$ 60 + 5
c. 12 + 8 $>$ 10 + 9
d. 26 − 5 $<$ 38 − 5

2 Assign Student Pages 20

Pages 225–226 UNDERSTANDING

Have students complete the problems on pages 225 and 226 independently.

Monitoring Student Progress

If . . . students have difficulty identifying equalities and inequalities,

Then . . . provide additional assessment to see if they are making errors because they cannot remember the signs' meanings or are making computational errors.

As Students Finish

Building Blocks Have students use **Number Compare 4: Numerals to 100** to review equalities and inequalities.

 MathTools Have students use **Set Tool** to make sets that show greater, lesser, and equal amounts.

Name _____ Date _____

LESSON 6.9 Comparing Two-Digit Subtraction Expressions

Key Ideas

\> is greater than, < is less than, = is equal to

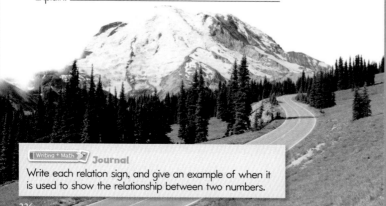

What is the correct sign? Draw >, <, or =.

① 27 $>$ 14 ③ 97 $=$ 97

② 35 $<$ 62 ④ 18 $<$ 46

Write a number to make the following sentences correct.

⑤ 35 > _____ – 42
a number between 76 and 42

⑦ 17 > 29 – _____
a number greater than 12

⑥ 32 + _____ > 57
a number greater than 25

⑧ 98 – _____ < 49
a number between 50 and 98

What is the correct sign? Draw >, <, or =.

⑨ 42 – 14 $=$ 28 ⑬ 36 – 8 $=$ 28

⑩ 56 $=$ 70 – 14 ⑭ 64 $>$ 68 – 7

⑪ 15 + 15 $>$ 28 ⑮ 4 + 12 $<$ 28

⑫ 54 $<$ 54 + 30 ⑯ 54 $=$ 17 + 37

Textbook This lesson is available in the *eTextbook*.

225

LESSON 6.9 · Comparing Two-Digit Subtraction Expressions

The Peláez family drove 37 miles from home to the national park. Then they drove 25 miles to the museum.

⑰ **Extended Response** How far is it from their home to the museum?
There is not enough information to solve.

Explain. The museum could be between the national park and their home.

⑱ How far is it from the national park to the museum? 25 miles

Explain. They drove 25 miles from the national park to get to the museum.

⑲ How far did the Peláez family drive before they got to the museum? 62 miles

Explain. To find out how far they drove, add all the distances.

Writing + Math **Journal**
Write each relation sign, and give an example of when it is used to show the relationship between two numbers.

226 Real Math • Chapter 6 • Lesson 9

---

3 Reflect 10

Guided Discussion ✓ APPLYING
Whole Group

Discuss Problems 17–19 on student page 226.

Begin by drawing a possible map showing the Peláez family's home, the museum, and the state park. Have students create drawings of their own maps that fit the number of miles given. Draw several student maps on the board.

■ **What is the farthest distance the museum can be from home?**
62 miles

■ **What is the least distance the museum could be from home?**
12 miles

Discuss the solutions to these problems, and allow students to explain why their answers are correct.

Extended Response

Problem 17 Students should realize that there is not enough information to solve this problem.

Writing + Math **Journal** ✓ ENGAGING

Have students share their answers. Pair them with another student, and have them change each other's inequalities so they are no longer true.

SOCIAL STUDIES **Curriculum Connection:** Students may be interested in learning about national parks.

Review **Cumulative Review:** For cumulative review of previously learned skills, see page 231–232.

Family Involvement: Assign the *Practice, Reteach,* or *Enrichment* activities depending on the needs of your students. Have students draw a map from home to school, or other common trip with a family member.

Math **Concept/Question Board:** Have students attempt to answer any unanswered questions on the Concept/Question Board.

Math Puzzler: A house has 6 windows in front and the same number in back. There are half as many windows on each side as there are in back. How many windows does the house have? 18

4 Assess and Differentiate

 Assess Use **eAssess** to record and analyze evidence of student understanding.

A Gather Evidence

Use the Daily Class Assessment Records in **Assessment** or **eAssess** to record daily observations.

Performance Assessment
☑ **Guided Discussion**

Did the student **APPLYING**
- ❑ apply learning in new situations?
- ❑ contribute concepts?
- ❑ contribute answers?
- ❑ connect mathematics to real-world situations?

Portfolio Assessment
☑ **Journal**

Did the student **ENGAGING**
- ❑ pay attention to others' contributions?
- ❑ contribute information and ideas?
- ❑ improve on a strategy?
- ❑ reflect on and check the accuracy of his or her work?

B Summarize Findings

Analyze and summarize assessment data for each student. Determine which Assessment Follow-Up is appropriate for each student. Use the Student Assessment Record in **Assessment** or **eAssess** to update assessment records.

Assessment page T41

C Assessment Follow-Up • DIFFERENTIATE INSTRUCTION

Based on your observations, use these teaching strategies for assessment follow-up.

INTERVENTION
Review student performance on **Intervention** Lesson 6.C to see if students have mastered prerequisite skills for this lesson.

ENGLISH LEARNER
Review
Use Lesson 6.9 in **English Learner Support Guide** to review lesson concepts and vocabulary.

ENRICH

If . . . students are proficient in the lesson concepts,

Then . . . encourage them to work on the chapter projects or **Enrichment** Lesson 6.9.

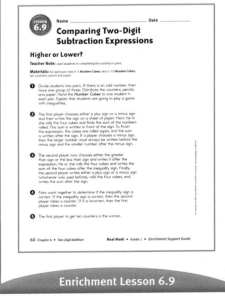

Enrichment Lesson 6.9

PRACTICE

If . . . students would benefit from additional practice,

Then . . . assign **Practice** Lesson 6.9.

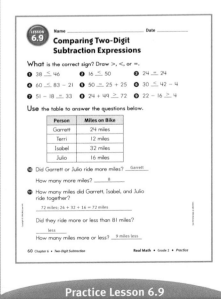

Practice Lesson 6.9

RETEACH

If . . . students are having difficulty comparing two-digit subtraction expressions,

Then . . . reteach the concept using **Reteach** Lesson 6.9.

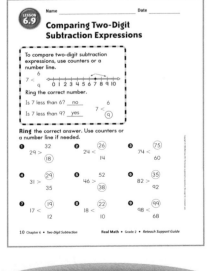

Reteach Lesson 6.9

Lesson Planner

OBJECTIVES
To provide applications involving adding and subtracting two-digit numbers

NCTM STANDARDS
Number and Operations
Using a variety of methods and tools to compute

Algebra
- Modeling situations that involve the addition and subtraction of whole numbers using objects, pictures, and symbols
- Describing quantitative change

MATERIALS
*Number Cubes

TECHNOLOGY
Presentation Lesson 6.10

TEST PREP
Cumulative Review
Mental Math reviews subtracting tens (Lesson 6.2).

Multistep Problems
Problem 8

Extended Response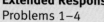
Problems 1–4

Looking Ahead
Lesson 7.1 will require six clear, cylindrical, equal-sized jars and colored water.

Problem Solving with Two-Digit Subtraction

Context of the Lesson In this lesson students will pay special attention to problem-solving strategies, including writing number sentences, solving for missing terms, and creating word problems.

See page 203B for Math Background for teachers for this lesson.

Planning for Learning ● DIFFERENTIATE INSTRUCTION

INTERVENTION

If . . . students lack the prerequisite skill of subtraction facts,

Then . . . teach **Intervention** Lesson 6.B.

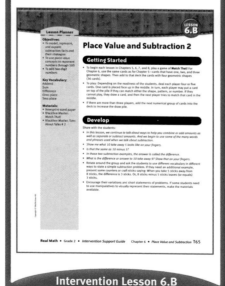

Intervention Lesson 6.B

ENGLISH LEARNER

Preview

If . . . students need language support,

Then . . . use Lesson 6.10 in **English Learner Support Guide** to preview lesson concepts and vocabulary.

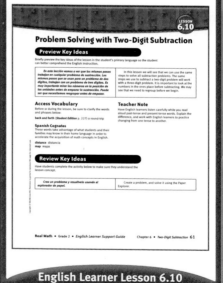

English Learner Lesson 6.10

ENRICH

If . . . students are proficient in the lesson concepts,

Then . . . emphasize Skill Building.

PRACTICE

If . . . students would benefit from additional practice,

Then . . . extend Skill Practice before assigning the student pages.

RETEACH

If . . . students are having difficulty understanding creating word problems,

Then . . . extend Guided Discussion before assigning the student pages.

Access Vocabulary
back and forth a round-trip

Spanish Cognates
distance distancia

map mapa

Teaching Lesson 6.10

Mental Math `5`

Present a series of subtraction exercises involving two-digit numbers, and have students show their answers using **Number Cubes.** Possible exercises include the following:

a. 70 − 30 = 40
b. 70 − 40 = 30
c. 70 − 50 = 20
d. 70 − 60 = 10
e. 60 − 50 = 10
f. 60 − 40 = 20

1 Develop `20`

Tell Students In Today's Lesson They Will

- write number sentences.
- create and solve word problems.
- solve for missing terms.

Guided Discussion REASONING
Whole Group

Number Sentences

Present students with oral word problems that require subtraction and addition to solve.

- **Namia went to the zoo with her uncle. She wanted to see the elephants, and her uncle wanted to see the bears. If the elephants are 65 yards away, and the bears are 27 yards beyond that, how many yards will Namia and her uncle have to walk?** 65 + 27 = 92; add
- **Brandi had $38. She spent $35 on books. How much money does she have left?** 38 − 35 = 3; $3; subtract
- **Steven is 90 centimeters tall. Debbie is 78 centimeters tall. Who is taller?** Steven **How much taller?** 90 − 78 = 12; subtract; Steven is 12 centimeters taller.
- **Jeremy is 48 inches tall. Vincent is 12 inches taller than Jeremy. How tall is Vincent?** 48 + 12 = 60; Vincent is 60 inches tall.
- **Aaron weighs 76 pounds. Paige weighs 54 pounds. Who weighs more?** Aaron **How much more does Aaron weigh?** 76 − 54 = 22; Aaron weighs 22 pounds more.
- **Mr. Han is 73 years old. Ms. Clay is 48 years old. Who is older?** Mr. Han **How much older?** 73 − 48 = 25; Mr. Han is 25 years older.

Have students work in pairs to write a number sentence and to solve the problems as they are presented. Encourage students to discuss with each other how to solve each problem. Then lead a class discussion of the methods and solutions for each problem, focusing on how students knew whether to add or subtract, before proceeding to the next problem.

Skill Building APPLYING
Small Group

Word Problems

Have each student create one word problem while working in pairs. Students may need to be prompted with physical situations such as heights and/or weights to compare. After students have finished, have them solve their partner's problem. Then share several student examples with the class.

Skill Practice COMPUTING
Whole Group

Missing Terms

 Present several missing-term number sentences on the board. Have students solve them. These could include the following:

a. 45 + <u>15</u> = 60
b. <u>60</u> − 15 = 45
c. 16 + <u>14</u> = 30
d. <u>30</u> − 14 = 16

Monitoring Student Progress

If . . . students have difficulty solving for missing terms,

Then . . . review the inverse relation between addition and subtraction sentences.

2 Assign Student Pages `20`

Pages 227–228 UNDERSTANDING

Have students complete pages 227 and 228 independently.

As Students Finish

Allow students to play a game of their choice, or assign a game based on their needs.

Name _____ Date _____

LESSON 6.10 Problem Solving with Two-Digit Subtraction

Key Ideas
Mathematics can be used to explain situations in our world. The boy can use the map to tell how far it is from the reptile house to the aviary.

Extended Response **Look** at the map. **Answer** these questions.

1. Mr. Jones wants to drive from Cheraw to Middledorf. What is the shortest driving distance? __60 miles__ Explain. __Driving the other routes would be 85 or 125 miles.__

2. Mr. Patel wants to drive from East City to End City. What is the shortest driving distance? __90 miles__ Explain. __Driving the other route would be 95 miles.__

3. Ms. Li lives in Patrick and works in Middledorf. She drives back and forth once each day. How many miles is that? __120 miles__ Explain. __The shortest route is 60 miles one way.__

4. If a bird were to fly from East City to End City, about how many miles would it fly? About __Accept all reasonable answers.__

Use information from the map above. **Create** your own word problem.

Students should create a problem that uses subtraction or addition in relation to the distances on the map.

5. _____

Textbook This lesson is available in the *eTextbook*.

227

LESSON 6.10 • Problem Solving with Two-Digit Subtraction

Mr. Meier has $90.

Write a number sentence for each question. Solve.

6. Can he buy the jacket and pants? Explain. __no; 69 + 24 = 93; 93 is greater than 90, so he cannot buy both.__

7. Can he buy the jacket and hat? __yes; 69 + 15 = 84; 84 is less than 90, so he can buy the jacket and the hat.__

8. Can he buy the pants and hat? How much money will he have left after buying the pants and the hat? __90 − 39 = $51__ __yes; 24 + 15 = 39; 39 is less than 90, so he can buy the pants and the hat.__

Fill in the missing term.

9. $25 + 63 = 88$

10. $81 - 39 = 42$

11. $64 + 27 = 91$

12. $87 - 43 = 44$

13. $41 - 23 = 18$

14. $30 + 17 = 47$

228   **Real Math** • Chapter 6 • Lesson 10

---

3 Reflect   10

Guided Discussion **REASONING**

Use the student pages to discuss strategies for problem solving.

Extended Response **REASONING**

Problems 1 and 2 Students should notice that the other routes would take longer.

Problem 3 Students should notice that the shortest route is 60 miles one way.

Problem 4 Students should notice that a bird could fly a number of different routes.

☑ Use Mastery Checkpoint 10 found in **Assessment** to evaluate student mastery of two-digit subtraction. By this time, students should be able to correctly answer eighty percent of the Mastery Checkpoint items.

Cumulative Review: For cumulative review of previously learned skills, see page 231–232.

Family Involvement: Assign the *Practice, Reteach,* or *Enrichment* activities depending on the needs of your students.

Concept/Question Board: Have students attempt to answer any unanswered questions on the Concept/Question Board.

Math Puzzler: Molly saved five $10 bills and three $1 bills. She bought a $46 video game. How many $10 bills does she have left? How many $1 bills? She has no $10 bills and seven $1 bills left.

4 Assess and Differentiate

 Assess Use *eAssess* to record and analyze evidence of student understanding.

A Gather Evidence

Use the Daily Class Assessment Records in *Assessment* or *eAssess* to record daily observations.

Formal Assessment

☑ **Mastery Checkpoint**

Did the student
- ❏ use correct procedures?
- ❏ respond with at least 80% accuracy?

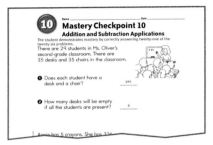

Assessment page T61

B Summarize Findings

Analyze and summarize assessment data for each student. Determine which Assessment Follow-Up is appropriate for each student. Use the Student Assessment Record in *Assessment* or *eAssess* to update assessment records.

Assessment page T41

C Assessment Follow-Up ● DIFFERENTIATE INSTRUCTION

Based on your observations, use these teaching strategies for assessment follow-up.

INTERVENTION

Review student performance on *Intervention* Lesson 6.B to see if students have mastered prerequisite skills for this lesson.

ENGLISH LEARNER

Review

Use Lesson 6.10 in *English Learner Support Guide* to review lesson concepts and vocabulary.

ENRICH

If . . . students are proficient in the lesson concepts,

Then . . . encourage them to work on the chapter projects or *Enrichment* Lesson 6.10.

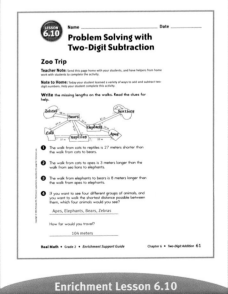

Enrichment Lesson 6.10

PRACTICE

If . . . students would benefit from additional practice,

Then . . . assign *Practice* Lesson 6.10.

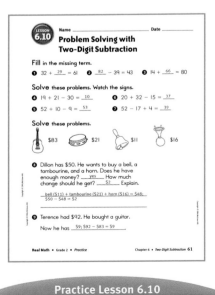

Practice Lesson 6.10

RETEACH

If . . . students are having difficulty understanding missing-term problems,

Then . . . practice using fact families until students see the patterns involved. For example, write the following equation on the board: $32 + \underline{\quad} = 67$

Have students say aloud, "32 plus what number is 67?" Ask students to use fact families to find the missing term.

CHAPTER 6 Problem Solving

Exploring Problem Solving

Objectives

- To use a table to organize steps in a multistep problem
- To solve and present solutions to nonroutine problems
- To apply addition and subtraction to real-world problems
- To develop an understanding that problems can have more than one answer
- To provide practice using maps and elapsed time

Context of the Lesson In this lesson students work for a large block of time on a single problem. This lesson builds on what the students have been learning about addition and subtraction.

1 Develop 5

Tell Students In Today's Lesson They Will
plan a visit to the zoo.

Guided Discussion

Remind students about previous activities in this chapter relating to zoos on pages 203, 204, 217, and 218. Have students look at the map on page 229. Help them understand the map by asking questions such as the following:

- **Where do people first come into the zoo?** the entrance
- **What do you see below the entrance?** a picnic ground
- **What are some other things you see on this map?** animal habitats, a theater
- **How do visitors to the zoo get from one habitat to another?** They walk along the paths.
- **What do you think the numbers along the paths mean?** how long it will take someone to get from one habitat to another
- **How long will it take to walk from the birds' habitat to the elephants' habitat?** 10 minutes
- **Do you think everyone will take exactly 10 minutes to walk that path?** Help students understand that labels such as these are general guidelines, representing an average of typical times. Not all people walk at the same speed. Also, if you stop for a drink of water or to rest, that will add to your time.
- **How long does the elephant show last?** 30 minutes; half an hour

Read this problem to students as they follow along on the student page:

Your class is going on a field trip to the zoo to continue learning about animals and their habitats. You will arrive at the zoo entrance at 10:00 in the morning. Your group may tour the zoo for 90 minutes in any way you like, but you must be back at the picnic grounds by 11:30 for lunch. You don't have to see everything, because you will have another 90 minutes after lunch to see more. Each group needs to have a plan for visiting

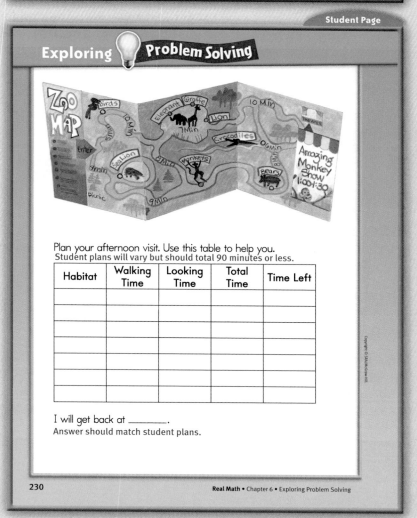

Exploring Problem Solving

Name _____ Date _____

Listen to the problem.

Plan your morning visit. Use the table to help you.
Student plans will vary but should total 90 minutes or less.

Habitat	Walking Time	Looking Time	Total Time	Time Left

I will get back at _____.
Answer should match student plans.

Textbook This lesson is available in the *eTextbook*.   229

Exploring Problem Solving

Plan your afternoon visit. Use this table to help you.
Student plans will vary but should total 90 minutes or less.

Habitat	Walking Time	Looking Time	Total Time	Time Left

I will get back at _____.
Answer should match student plans.

230   **Real Math** • Chapter 6 • Exploring Problem Solving

different parts of the zoo. If you plan and make good use of your time, then you'll be back at the picnic grounds on time. Use the table to help keep track of where you're going, how long it will take you to get there, how long you want to stay there, and how much time you have left.

Make sure students understand the problem by asking questions such as the following:

- **What are you being asked to do?** Plan a morning at the zoo so we get back to the picnic grounds in 90 minutes.
- **How can you use the map to help you?** to help us decide the order in which we want to visit the different animal habitats and to determine how long it will take to walk from one to another
- **What do you need to include beside the walking time?** how long we want to look at the animals in each habitat
- **How will you keep track of how much time you have left?** Possible answer: by recording the time we have used so far on the table and figuring out the time that is left

Using Student Pages

Have students work in pairs or small groups to plan their morning visit. Provide support as needed. If students seem to be having difficulty, encourage them to struggle with the problem for a while. When needed, ask guiding questions such as the following:

- What is the first habitat you would like to visit?
- How long will it take you to walk there from the entrance?
- How long do you want to stay at that habitat?
- After you have visited that habitat, how can you figure out how much time you have left?

Students who finish early may use the map on page 230 to plan their afternoon tour, or you may assign page 230 as homework. The two problems are the same except for the details of the animal show.

Sample Solutions Strategies

Students might use one or more of the following strategies to keep track of time in the problem.

Draw a Picture (Number Line or 100 Table)

Students might move backward on a number line or 100 Table to keep track of how many minutes are left.

Use Operations

Students might count backward or use what they know about subtraction facts to keep track of how much time is left.

Use a Physical Model

Students might move the hands or change the numbers on a watch or clock to keep track of time in their plan.

Add to a Picture

Students might write on the map what time they expect to arrive and/or leave each place in the zoo.

Problem Formulation, Planning, and Strategizing Ask each group to share their plan and their strategies for determining how much time they have left. In discussion, bring out the following points:

- There are many different plans that people can make and still be back in time.
- In a situation like this, it is not necessary to use all the time allowed. It may be preferable to leave a little extra time in case something unexpected occurs.
- When solving a problem like this, it is important to organize your work so you can keep track of your steps. A table is one way to organize steps.
- People sometimes use different strategies to find the same answer.

When evaluating student work, focus on whether students thought rationally about the problem. Questions to consider include the following:

- Did the student understand the problem?
- Did the student organize his or her tour logically?
- Was the student able to use the table effectively?
- Was the student able to explain his or her thinking?
- Was the student able to use addition and subtraction in sensible ways?

Cumulative Review

Assign Pages 231–232

Use the Cumulative Review as a review of concepts and skills that students have previously learned.

Here are different ways that you can assign these problems to your students as they work through the chapter:

- With some of the lessons in the chapter, assign a set of cumulative review problems to be completed as practice or for homework.
  Lesson 6.7—Problems 1–6
  Lesson 6.8—Problems 7–10
  Lesson 6.9—Problems 11–16
  Lesson 6.10—Problems 17–18
- At any point during the chapter, assign part or all of the cumulative review problems to be completed as practice or for homework.

Cumulative Review

Problems 1–6 review checking subtraction, Lesson 6.7

Problems 7–10 review the calendar, Lesson 1.6

Problems 11–16 review regrouping tens as ones, Lesson 6.1

Problems 17–18 review chain calculations, Lesson 3.7

Monitoring Student Progress

If . . . students miss more than one problem in a section,

Then . . . refer to the indicated lesson for remediation suggestions.

Cumulative Review

Name _____ Date _____

Checking Subtraction Lesson 6.7

Check using addition. **Ring** each wrong answer.
Write the correct answers alongside the problem.

❶ 50 − 20 = 30   ❹ 35 − 13 = ⑭⑧ 22

❷ 90 − 25 = ⑤⓪ 65   ❺ 55 − 31 = ⑧⑥ 24

❸ 47 − 21 = 26   ❻ 33 + 25 = 58

The Calendar Lesson 1.6

Fill in the missing numbers. Then answer the questions.
October has 31 days.

		October				
SUN	MON	TUE	WED	THU	FRI	SAT
1	2	3	4	5	6	7
8	9	10	11	12	13	14
15	16	17	18	19	20	21
22	23	24	25	26	27	28
29	30	31				

❼ What day is October 15? __Sunday__

❽ What date is the fourth Monday? __23rd__

❾ What day is October 31? __Tuesday__

❿ What day is the second Saturday? __14th__

Textbook This lesson is available in the *eTextbook*.   231

Cumulative Review

Regrouping Tens as Ones Lesson 6.1

Rewrite each number to show one fewer ten and ten more ones.

⑪ 68 = __5__ tens and __18__   ⑭ 14 = __0__ tens and __14__

⑫ 76 = __6__ tens and __16__   ⑮ 37 = __2__ tens and __17__

⑬ 61 = __5__ tens and __11__   ⑯ 28 = __1__ ten and __18__

Chain Calculations Lesson 3.7

Write the answers.

It takes Adam about 6 minutes to feed 2 elephants.

⑰ About how long would it take Adam to feed 6 elephants? About __18__ minutes

⑱ About how long would it take Adam to feed 9 elephants? About __27__ minutes
Explain. __It would take 24 minutes to feed 8 elephants and another 3 minutes to feed 1 more elephant. 24 + 3 = 27.__

232   **Real Math** • Chapter 6

Review

Wrap-Up

1 Discuss 5

Concept/Question Board

Review the Concept/Question Board with students.

- Discuss students' contributions to the Concept side of the Board.
- Have students repose their questions, and lead a discussion to find satisfactory answers.

Chapter Projects APPLYING

Provide an opportunity for students who have worked on one or more of the projects outlined on page 204C to share their work with the class. Allow each student or student group five minutes to present or discuss their projects. For formal assessment, use the rubrics found in *Across the Curriculum Math Connections;* the rubric for **Create a Presentation** is on page 65, and the rubric for **Create a Field Guide** is on page 71. For informal assessment, use the following rubric and questions.

	Exceeds Expectations	Meets Expectations	Minimally Meets Expectations
Applies mathematics in real-world situations:	❏	❏	❏
Demonstrates strong engagement in the activity:	❏	❏	❏

Create a Presentation

- What animal did you select for your presentation?
- What information did you include in your presentation?
- How did you use subtraction in your presentation?
- Was a slide show a good visual aid for your presentation? Why or why not?
- What other visual aids could you have used for your presentation?
- If you had to choose another animal, which one would you pick? Why?

Create a Field Guide

- What zoo did your group select? Why?
- What three animals did you research?
- What was the total cost of admission to the zoo for the family? How much for one adult and two children?
- How did you add emphasis to areas of your zoo map?
- What other information did you add to your field guide?
- What else could you add to your field guide?
- How are field guides useful when selecting a zoo?

2 Assign Student Pages 25

Key Ideas Review ☑ UNDERSTANDING

Have students complete the Review questions independently or in small groups. Then discuss each question as a class.

Possible Answers

Problem ❶ Students should remember that a number can be rewritten to show 1 fewer ten and 10 more ones. Therefore, 55 is the same as 4 tens and 15. The answer is B.

Problem ❷ The answer is C.

Problem ❸ Problems 3–5 review solving a two-digit subtraction problem with craft sticks and writing the steps. Students should remember that when writing a two-digit subtraction problem, they should first separate and label the tens and ones. The answer is 6 tens and 0 − 3 tens and 7.

Problem ❹ Students should remember that the next step is to borrow 10 ones from the tens place and rewrite the number. The answer is 5 tens and 10 − 3 tens and 7.

Problem ❺ Students should remember that the next step is to subtract. The answer should be 2 tens and 3, or 23.

Problem ❻ Problems 6–7 review using two-digit subtraction to solve everyday problems. The answer is A.

Problem ❼ The answer is B.

Problem ❽ a. The answers are 51 − 24 = 27 and 45 − 21 = 24. **b.** Students should recognize that 24 is closer to 0 than 27 is, so the answer is Erin.

Problem ❾ Students should remember that they can check their answer to a subtraction problem by adding the reverse. If 37 − 14 = 23, then 23 + 14 = 37.

Problem ❿ The answer is 28.

CHAPTER 6 Key Ideas Review

Name _____ Date _____

In this chapter you learned about two-digit subtraction. You used subtraction to solve everyday problems. You learned how to use addition to check your solution to a subtraction problem.

Ring the letter of the correct answer.

❶ How can you rewrite 55?

  a. 4 tens and 5   **(b.)** 4 tens and 15

  c. 6 tens and 15

❷ Which picture below does not show 36 sticks?

a.   **b.**   **ⓒ**

Write your answers.

Shane is going to use craft sticks to solve 60 − 37. He will write what he did.

❸ What should he write first?

   $\frac{6}{-\ 3}$ tens and $\frac{0}{7}$

❹ What should he write now?

   $\frac{5}{-\ 3}$ tens and $\frac{10}{7}$

❺ What answer will Shane get? **23**

eTextbook This lesson is available in the *eTextbook*.   233

CHAPTER 6 Key Ideas Review

Ring the letter of the number sentence you would use to solve each problem.

❻ David had $63. He spent $28. How much money does he have now?

  (a.) 63 − 28 =

  b. 28 − 63 =

  c. 63 + 28 =

❼ Cruz has 2 dimes and 7 pennies. A pencil costs 35¢. How much more money does Cruz need to buy a pencil?

  a. 27 − 35 =

  (b.) 35 − 27 =

  c. 27 + 35 =

Write your answers.

❽ Janet and Erin played the **Roll a Problem Game.**

Janet's problem looked like this: $\begin{array}{r} 51 \\ -\ 24 \\ \hline 27 \end{array}$ Erin's problem looked like this: $\begin{array}{r} 45 \\ -\ 21 \\ \hline 24 \end{array}$

  a. Solve each problem.

  b. Who had the difference closer to 0? **Erin**

❾ Andre subtracted 14 from 37 and got 23. How can he check his answer? _____

  by adding; 23 + 14 = 37

❿ Myra picked 47 apples. She gave some away. Now she has 19 apples. How many did she give away? **28**

234   **Real Math** • Chapter 6

Chapter 6 • Two-Digit Subtraction 233–234

Chapter Review

Use the Chapter 6 Review to indicate areas in which each student is having difficulty or in which the class may need help. If students do well on the Chapter 6 Review, you may wish to skip directly to the Chapter Test; if not, you may spend a day or so helping students overcome their individual difficulties before taking the Practice Test.

Next to each set of problems is a list of the lessons in the chapter that covered those concepts. If they need help, students can refer to a specific lesson for additional instruction. You can also use this information to make additional assignments based on the previous lesson concepts.

Have students complete pages 235–236 on their own. For review purposes, you may want to do some of the word problems on page 236 as a class.

Monitoring Student Progress

Problems 1–7 Lessons 6.6–6.7

If . . . students have difficulty with these problems,

Then . . . have them practice writing simple subtraction number sentences and their inverse addition number sentences.

Problems 8–13 Lesson 6.1

If . . . students have difficulty with these problems,

Then . . . have them use craft sticks to illustrate the problems.

Problems 14–15 Lesson 6.9

If . . . students have difficulty with these problems,

Then . . . determine whether the issue stems from the concept of inequality sentences or from subtraction, and then review accordingly.

Problems 16–23 Lessons 6.2–6.4

If . . . students have difficulty with these problems,

Then . . . have them play the **Add or Subtract Tens Game** for practice with adding and subtracting tens or the **Roll a Problem Game** for practice with place value and adding and subtracting two-digit numbers.

Problems 24–25 Lessons 6.8 and 6.10

If . . . students have difficulty with these problems,

Then . . . have them use play money to work through the problems.

Name _____ Date _____

Lessons 6.6–6.7 **Check** using addition. Ring each wrong answer. Then write the correct answers alongside the problem.

1. $48 - 2 = 46$
2. $71 - 24 = \circledast{95}$ **47**
3. $31 - 24 = \circledast{6}$ **7**
4. $51 - 43 = \circledast{18}$ **8**
5. $80 - 22 = 58$
6. $39 - 33 = \circledast{62}$ **6**

Solve this problem.

7. Adam has \$87. Matt has \$59.

Who has more? **Adam** How much more? **\$28**

Lesson 6.1 **Rewrite** each number to show one fewer ten and ten more ones.

8. $54 = \underline{4}$ tens and $\underline{14}$
9. $33 = \underline{2}$ tens and $\underline{13}$
10. $100 = \underline{9}$ tens and $\underline{10}$
11. $49 = \underline{3}$ tens and $\underline{19}$
12. $27 = \underline{1}$ ten and $\underline{17}$
13. $89 = \underline{7}$ tens and $\underline{19}$

Lesson 6.9 **What** is the correct sign? Draw >, <, or =.

14. $42 - 14 \; \boxed{=} \; 28$
15. $64 \; \boxed{>} \; 68 - 9$

Student Page

Lessons 6.2–6.4 **Subtract.** Use craft sticks or play money to help solve these problems. Record what you did.

16. Sophie had \$70. She spent \$20 at the fair. Now she has \$ __50__ .

17. Tim has \$68. Sheila has \$96. Who has more? __Sheila__ How much more? __\$28__

18.
$$\begin{array}{r} 50 \\ -\ 30 \\ \hline 20 \end{array}$$

19.
$$\begin{array}{r} 80 \\ -\ 20 \\ \hline 60 \end{array}$$

20.
$$\begin{array}{r} 90 \\ -\ 50 \\ \hline 40 \end{array}$$

21.
$$\begin{array}{r} 80 \\ -\ 68 \\ \hline 12 \end{array}$$

22.
$$\begin{array}{r} 40 \\ -\ 17 \\ \hline 23 \end{array}$$

23.
$$\begin{array}{r} 42 \\ -\ 12 \\ \hline 30 \end{array}$$

Lessons 6.8 and 6.10 **Write** a number sentence for each question.

Mr. Franklin has \$85.

24. Can Mr. Franklin buy the hose and the nozzle? Explain.
Yes, because $54 + 26 = 80$; 80 is less than 85, so he can buy both.

25. Multistep Can he buy all three items? No, because $8 + 26 + 54 = 88$; 88 is greater than 85, so he can't buy all three items.

3 Chapter Tests 40

Practice Test

Student Pages 237–240
- The Chapter 6 Practice Test on **Student Edition** pages 237–240 provides an opportunity to formally evaluate students' proficiency with concepts developed in this chapter.
- The content is similar to the Chapter 6 Review, in standardized format.

Problems 24 and 25 | Extended Response

Students practice addition and subtraction skills as well as problem-solving strategies as they solve these problems. Students will have to explore the cost of different combinations of objects and determine which combination matches the limit set. Students should be encouraged to see if there is more than one combination of objects that match the criterion.

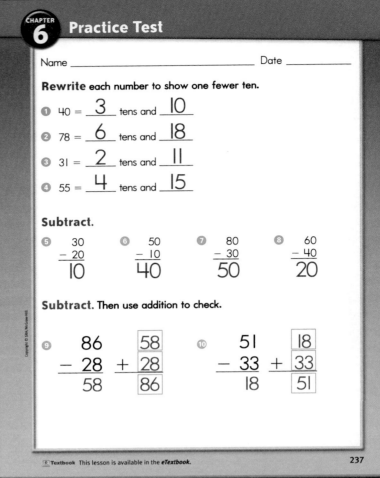

CHAPTER 6 Practice Test

Name _____ Date _____

Rewrite each number to show one fewer ten.

1. $40 = \underline{3}$ tens and $\underline{10}$
2. $78 = \underline{6}$ tens and $\underline{18}$
3. $31 = \underline{2}$ tens and $\underline{11}$
4. $55 = \underline{4}$ tens and $\underline{15}$

Subtract.

5. $\begin{array}{r} 30 \\ -\ 20 \\ \hline 10 \end{array}$
6. $\begin{array}{r} 50 \\ -\ 10 \\ \hline 40 \end{array}$
7. $\begin{array}{r} 80 \\ -\ 30 \\ \hline 50 \end{array}$
8. $\begin{array}{r} 60 \\ -\ 40 \\ \hline 20 \end{array}$

Subtract. Then use addition to check.

9. $\begin{array}{r} 86 \\ -\ 28 \\ \hline 58 \end{array}$ $\begin{array}{r} 58 \\ +\ 28 \\ \hline 86 \end{array}$
10. $\begin{array}{r} 51 \\ -\ 33 \\ \hline 18 \end{array}$ $\begin{array}{r} 18 \\ +\ 33 \\ \hline 51 \end{array}$

eTextbook This lesson is available in the **eTextbook**. 237

Student Page

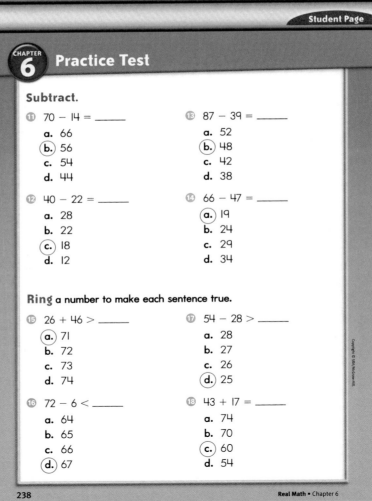

CHAPTER 6 Practice Test

Subtract.

11. $70 - 14 = $ _____
 a. 66
 b. 56
 c. 54
 d. 44

12. $40 - 22 = $ _____
 a. 28
 b. 22
 c. 18
 d. 12

13. $87 - 39 = $ _____
 a. 52
 b. 48
 c. 42
 d. 38

14. $66 - 47 = $ _____
 a. 19
 b. 24
 c. 29
 d. 34

Ring a number to make each sentence true.

15. $26 + 46 > $ _____
 a. 71
 b. 72
 c. 73
 d. 74

16. $72 - 6 < $ _____
 a. 64
 b. 65
 c. 66
 d. 67

17. $54 - 28 > $ _____
 a. 28
 b. 27
 c. 26
 d. 25

18. $43 + 17 = $ _____
 a. 74
 b. 70
 c. 60
 d. 54

238 **Real Math** • Chapter 6

Name _____ Date _____

Add or subtract.

⑲ 92 − 45 = _____

   a. 53

   (b.) 47

   c. 43

   d. 37

⑳ 42 + 18 = _____

   a. 50

   b. 56

   (c.) 60

   d. 76

Solve.

㉑ Gino earned $29 on Friday and $43 on Saturday. How much more money did he need to buy a jacket that cost $91?

   a. $72   b. $48   c. $21   (d.) $19

㉒ Lisa is making a necklace that will have 67 beads on it. She strung 18 beads before lunch and 25 beads between lunch and her piano lesson. How many beads does she have left to string?

   (a.) 24   b. 42   c. 43   d. 49

㉓ John rode a bicycle 24 kilometers on Monday and 29 kilometers on Tuesday. After his ride on Wednesday, his total was 80 kilometers in the three days. How far did he ride on Wednesday?

   a. 21 kilometers

   (b.) 27 kilometers

   c. 53 kilometers

   d. 56 kilometers

eTextbook This lesson is available in the *eTextbook*.

239

Extended Response ▶ **Solve.** Explain your answers.

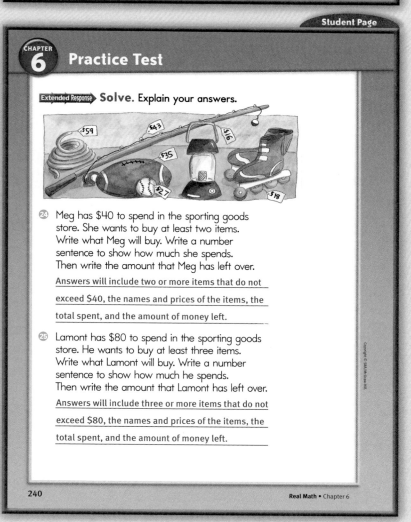

㉔ Meg has $40 to spend in the sporting goods store. She wants to buy at least two items. Write what Meg will buy. Write a number sentence to show how much she spends. Then write the amount that Meg has left over.

<u>Answers will include two or more items that do not</u>

<u>exceed $40, the names and prices of the items, the</u>

<u>total spent, and the amount of money left.</u>

㉕ Lamont has $80 to spend in the sporting goods store. He wants to buy at least three items. Write what Lamont will buy. Write a number sentence to show how much he spends. Then write the amount that Lamont has left over.

<u>Answers will include three or more items that do not</u>

<u>exceed $80, the names and prices of the items, the</u>

<u>total spent, and the amount of money left.</u>

Chapter Test ☑ COMPUTING

For further evaluation instead of or in addition to this test, you may wish to have students take the Chapter 6 Test provided in **Assessment**.

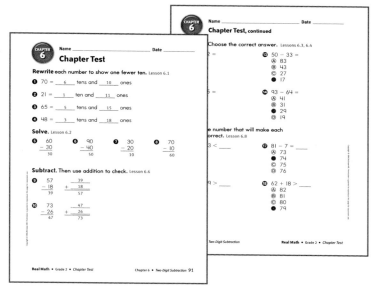

Assessment, pages 91–92

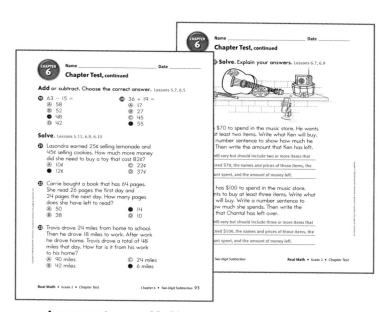

Assessment, pages 93–94

4 Assess and Differentiate

 Assess Use *eAssess* to record and analyze evidence of student understanding.

A Gather Evidence

Use the Daily Class Assessment Records in **Assessment** or **eAssess** to record Informal and Formal Assessments.

Informal Assessment
☑ **Key Ideas Review** 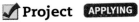 UNDERSTANDING

Did the student
- ❏ make important observations?
- ❏ extend or generalize learning?
- ❏ provide insightful answers?
- ❏ pose insightful questions?

Informal Assessment
☑ **Project** APPLYING

Did the student
- ❏ meet the project objectives?
- ❏ communicate clearly?
- ❏ complete the project accurately?
- ❏ connect mathematics to real-world situations?

Formal Assessment
☑ **Chapter Test** 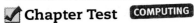 COMPUTING

Score the test, and record the results.

B Summarize Findings

Analyze and summarize assessment data for each student. Determine which Chapter Follow-Up is appropriate for each student. Use the Student Assessment Record in **Assessment** or **eAssess** to update assessment records.

C Chapter Follow-Up • DIFFERENTIATE INSTRUCTION

Based on your observations, use these teaching strategies for chapter follow-up.

ENRICH	PRACTICE	RETEACH	INTERVENTION
If . . . students demonstrate a **secure understanding** of chapter concepts, **Then . . .** move on to the next chapter.	**If . . .** students demonstrate **competent understanding** of chapter concepts, **Then . . .** move on to the next chapter.	**If . . .** students demonstrate **emerging understanding** of chapter concepts, **Then . . .** move on to the next chapter, but continue to provide cumulative review.	**If . . .** students demonstrate **minimal understanding** of chapter concepts, **Then . . .** intensive intervention is still needed before they start the next chapter.

Ferdie Borrows and Borrows and Borrows

Context of the Thinking Story Ferdie borrows money to buy animal collector cards and keeps going into debt by borrowing to pay back his debt. He finally figures out that earning money is better than borrowing money.

Lesson Planner

OBJECTIVES
To develop logical thinking while integrating reading skills with mathematics

NCTM STANDARDS

Number and Operations
Understanding the effects of adding and subtracting whole numbers

Communication
- Organizing and consolidating mathematical thinking through communication
- Communicating mathematical thinking coherently and clearly
- Analyzing and evaluating the mathematical thinking and strategies of others

READING STANDARDS
- Listening for details
- Drawing conclusions
- Evaluating information
- Recognizing cause-and-effect relationships

Using the Thinking Story

The Thinking Story may be used at any time throughout the chapter. Read the Thinking Story "Ferdie Borrows and Borrows and Borrows" to your class. As you read the story, give students time to think about each question, but not so much that they forget the point being made.

Ferdie Borrows and Borrows and Borrows

Every Saturday morning Ferdie gets an allowance of $1. By the middle of the week, and sometimes sooner, he has usually spent it. Then he has no money left.

One Tuesday after school Ferdie saw a package of animal collector cards in a store window. He reached into his pocket and counted his money. "Forty cents. And the price tag says 50¢." Then he had an idea. Maybe he could borrow enough money to buy the cards.

How much money does Ferdie need to borrow? **10¢**

His friend Marcus came by. "Hi, Marcus!" said Ferdie. "Can you lend me 50¢? I need enough money to buy a package of animal cards."

"Here you are," said Marcus, handing Ferdie 50¢. "But I need it back tomorrow."

Did Ferdie borrow the right amount of money? **no**

How much money does he have now? **90¢**

Ferdie thanked Marcus, hurried to the toy store, and bought the cards.

How much money does Ferdie have left? **40¢**

"Borrowing is great!" Ferdie told himself. "A little while ago I didn't have enough money to buy a package of animal cards, and now I have the cards and 40¢ besides. I only have one little problem."

What problem does Ferdie still have? **He has to pay Marcus back.**

The next day at school Marcus asked for his 50¢. Ferdie didn't have that much, of course. All he had was the 40¢ from the day before. But he had an idea. "If borrowing worked so well yesterday," he thought, "it should work again today."

He said to Marcus, "I'll be glad to pay you back 50¢ if you can lend me a dime."

"Sure," said Marcus, giving Ferdie 10¢.

How much money does Ferdie have now? **50¢**

"Here's your 50¢," Ferdie said cheerfully, giving Marcus the 40¢ from the day before and the 10¢ he had just borrowed. "I guess that settles my debt, right?"

"But I just lent you 10¢ more," Marcus complained.

"And I gave it back to you," Ferdie said. "So we're even."

Is that right? no

How much money did Ferdie borrow altogether? 60¢

How much did Ferdie pay back altogether? 50¢

How much money does Ferdie still owe Marcus? 10¢

Marcus was getting confused. "I think I'm losing money on this deal," he said, "but I'm not sure how. Yesterday I lent you 50¢ and you just paid that back to me. Today I lent you a dime and you gave that back to me too."

"That's right," Ferdie said. "It's all fair and square."

"But I know I had 60¢ yesterday," Marcus said. "And now I have 50¢, and I know I didn't spend any. So I know I've lost a dime."

"That's too bad," Ferdie said. "If I had a dime, I'd lend it to you."

"Wait a minute!" Marcus said, looking at the coins in his hand. "I know what happened. You used the same dime to pay back the 50¢ you owed me and the 10¢ you owed me. You can't use the same money to pay two debts. You borrowed 60¢ from me altogether, and you only paid me back 50¢. You still owe me 10¢!"

"Don't get so excited," Ferdie said. "If you think I still owe you 10¢, I'll pay you 10¢. Just wait here awhile. I know how to take care of these things."

Ferdie rushed over to his friend Willy. He was about to borrow 10¢ from him to pay Marcus back. But then he stopped and thought, "If I borrow 10¢ from Willy to pay Marcus back, I won't be any better off than I was before."

Why won't Ferdie be any better off? He will still owe someone 10¢.

"Then I'll owe Willy 10¢," Ferdie thought. So he tried a different plan. He borrowed 20¢ from Willy. Then he found Marcus and paid him back the money he owed him.

How much did Ferdie pay Marcus? 10¢

How much money does Ferdie have left? 10¢

Ferdie looked at the 10¢ he had left. "I was hoping I would have enough left to pay Willy back, but I don't," he thought.

Why doesn't Ferdie have enough left to pay Willy back? He used some money to pay Marcus.

"Borrowing isn't working out as well as I thought," Ferdie said to himself. "I always end up owing people more money than I have. There must be a better way."

While Ferdie was thinking of what to do, he used the 10¢ to buy himself a gumball from a candy machine so he would have something to do while he was thinking.

How much money does Ferdie have left now? **none**

How much does he owe? **20¢ to Willy**

"Now I owe 20¢, and I don't have any money at all. I'm worse off than I was before. Maybe if I borrowed a lot of money that would help."

After school he went to Ms. Eng's house. "Ms. Eng, could you lend me $10?" he asked.

"What do you need it for?" asked Ms. Eng.

"I need it to pay Willy 20¢ that I owe him."

"And what will you do with the rest of the money?"

"I'll pay it back to you."

"You'll never get out of debt by borrowing," said Ms. Eng. "I have a better idea how you can get the 20¢ you need."

What other ways are there for Ferdie to get money besides borrowing? **Answers will vary. Possible answers include getting paid to do a chore.**

"Our sidewalk is badly in need of sweeping," said Ms. Eng. "If you would sweep it for me, I'd gladly pay you 20¢."

"But then how would I pay it back?" Ferdie asked.

Would Ferdie have to pay back the 20¢ to Ms. Eng? **no**

Why not? **He would be earning the money, not borrowing it.**

"You don't have to pay it back if you earn it," said Ms. Eng.

Ferdie's eyes popped when he heard that. "Why, earning's even better than borrowing!" he said. "When you borrow money, people keep wanting it back."

The End

Guided Discussion

As students answer the questions in the story, ask them to communicate how they chose their answers. Allow students to debate the answers if necessary.

Using Student Pages 241–242

Have students follow the instructions and complete the **Student Edition** activities. Read the instructions aloud if students are having difficulty.

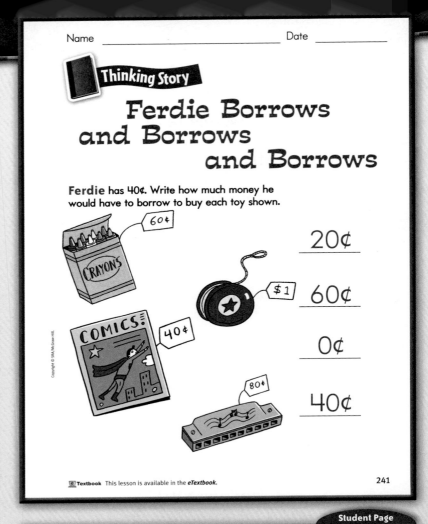

Thinking Story

Ferdie Borrows and Borrows and Borrows

Ferdie has 40¢. Write how much money he would have to borrow to buy each toy shown.

20¢

60¢

0¢

40¢

Textbook This lesson is available in the *eTextbook*.

241

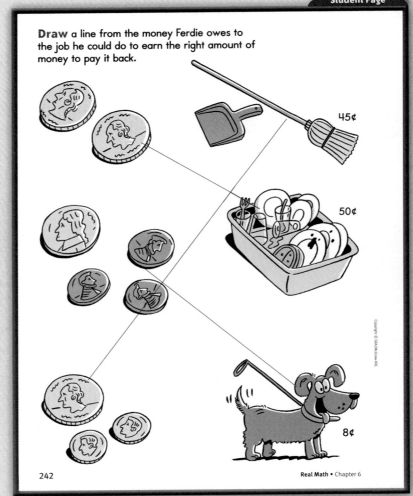

Draw a line from the money Ferdie owes to the job he could do to earn the right amount of money to pay it back.

45¢

50¢

8¢

242

Real Math • Chapter 6

Lesson Study

Reflect on each of the lessons you taught in this chapter. Rate each one on the following scale, and then consider ways to maintain or improve positive teaching experiences in the future.

Lessons	Very Effective	Effective	Less Effective	What Worked	Ways to Improve
6.1 Regrouping Tens as Ones					
6.2 Subtracting Tens					
6.3 Subtracting from Tens					
6.4 Subtracting Two-Digit Numbers					
6.5 Using a Paper Explorer to Understand Subtraction					
6.6 Practicing Two-Digit Subtraction					
6.7 Checking Subtraction					
6.8 Applying Subtraction					
6.9 Comparing Two-Digit Subtraction Expressions					
6.10 Problem Solving with Two-Digit Subtraction					

Picture Glossary

A

acute angle

angles

C

cylinder

E

eighth

F

fifth

flip

Picture Glossary

M

mode

the number that appears most often in a set of data

O

obtuse angle

P

parallel

perpendicular

polygon

a closed plane figure with three or more sides

prism

pyramid

Picture Glossary

Q

quadrilateral

R

range

the lowest and highest numbers in a set of data

rhombus

right angle

S

sixth

slide

Picture Glossary

T

thermometer

trapezoid

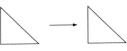

turn

V

variables

$$3 \times n = y$$

Appendix

This appendix provides additional information about key issues in mathematics education and how they are addressed in *Real Math.*

About Mathematics

"Genuine mathematics...constitutes one of the finest expressions of the human spirit. The great areas of mathematics—algebra, real analysis, complex analysis, number theory, combinatorics, probability theory, statistics, topology, geometry, and so on—have undoubtedly arisen from our experience of the world around us, in order to systematize that experience, to give it order and coherence, and thereby to enable us to predict and perhaps control future events."

Hilton, Peter. "Mathematics in Our Culture" in Gullberg, Jan. Mathematics: From the Birth of Numbers. New York: W.W. Norton & Company, 1997.

Mathematics is a way of describing relationships between numbers and other measurable quantities. As the language of science, mathematics communicates ideas in universally accepted terminology. It can express simple equations or explain relationships among the farthest objects in the known universe. Mathematics has helped make advances in medicine, technology, astronomy, meteorology, biology, physics, economics, and political science.

Mathematics has two main branches: pure mathematics, the study of abstract relationships, and applied mathematics, which applies mathematical analysis to real-world problems. The relationship between pure and applied mathematics is a complex one, and is constantly shifting.

Mathematics continues to grow at a phenomenal rate. There is no end in sight, and the application of mathematics to science becomes greater all the time.

Key Events in the Time Line of Mathematics

- Counting was the earliest mathematical activity. Early humans needed counting to keep track of herds and for trade. Early counting systems used the fingers of one or both hands, as evidenced by the predominance of the numbers 5 and 10 as the bases for most number systems today. Advances were in the concept of numbers, the invention of addition, subtraction, multiplication, and division, and concepts such as the line and the circle in geometry.

  - **2000 B.C.** The Babylonians of ancient Mesopotamia and the ancient Egyptians developed principles of arithmetic, measurement, and calculation.

    - **1400 B.C.** The first true evidence of mathematical activity in China can be found in numeration symbols on tortoise shells and oracle bones from the Shang dynasty. These inscriptions contain both tally and code symbols based on a decimal system. Early Chinese mathematics had a great influence on later civilizations.

      - **1000 B.C.** The Maya used a base-20 number system, which probably descended from early times when people counted on both fingers and toes and may have been the first to have a special symbol for zero. The Maya also developed two types of calendars, calculating the length of the lunar month and the solar year with remarkable precision.

- **6th Century B.C.** The Greeks adopted elements of mathematics from the Babylonians and the Egyptians and invented abstract mathematics founded on a logical structure of definitions, axioms (propositions accepted as self-evident), and proofs. Thales and Pythagoras were famous mathematicians.

  - **300 B.C.** Euclid, a Greek mathematician, deduced some 500 theorems comprising all the important results of Greek mathematics to that time. Euclid began by defining terms, such as line, angle, and circle. He stated ten self-evident truths, such as "The whole is greater than any of its parts."

    - **1st Century A.D.** After the decline of Greece and Rome, mathematics flourished for hundreds of years in India and the Islamic world. Their mathematical masterpieces and those of the Greeks were translated into Arabic in the centers of Islamic learning, where mathematical discoveries continued during the Middle Ages. Our present numeration system, with each digit having a value and a place value (ones, tens, hundreds, and so forth), is known as the Hindu-Arabic system.

      - **8th Century A.D.** Translators in Baghdad produced Arabic versions of Greek and Indian mathematical works. Many of the ancient Greek works on mathematics were preserved during the Middle Ages through Arabic translations and commentaries. Europe acquired much of this learning during the 12th century, when Greek and Arabic works were translated into Latin, the written language of the educated Europeans.

"Number rules the universe."

—Pythagoras, Greek philosopher and mathematician, 580–520 B.C.

"Mathematics is one of humanity's great achievements. By enhancing the capabilities of the human mind, mathematics has facilitated the development of science, technology, engineering, business, and government. Mathematics is also an intellectual achievement of great sophistication and beauty that epitomizes the power of deductive reasoning. For people to participate fully in society, they must know basic mathematics."

Kilpatrick, J., Swafford, J., and Findell, B. eds. *Adding It Up: Helping Children Learn Mathematics.* Washington, D.C.: National Research Council/National Academy Press, 2001, p. 1.

Real Math and Mathematics

Real Math has been developed with a keen respect for the history and the beauty of mathematics. Careful attention has been paid to developing children's understanding of mathematics in a coherent and logical fashion to demonstrate the connections among the different strands and branches of mathematics. *Real Math* aims for children to develop a positive attitude toward mathematics. Specific abilities and understandings will be of little value to children unless accompanied by two convictions: (a) that mathematics does what it was invented to do —solve real, interesting problems; and (b) that it is a tool that can be used confidently and well. Also, we hope that students will find mathematics enjoyable to do and that they will appreciate it aesthetically.

- **9th Century A.D.** Arab mathematician al-Khwārizmī wrote a systematic introduction to algebra. The English word *algebra* comes from *al-jabr* in the title. A 12th-century Latin translation of al-Khwārizmī's treatise was crucial for the later development of algebra in Europe. Al-Khwārizmī's name is the source of the word *algorithm*.

  - **16th Century** Mathematicians began to use symbols to make algebraic thinking and writing more concise. These symbols included $+$, $-$, $\times$, $=$, $>$ (greater than), and $<$ (less than). The most significant innovation, by French mathematician François Viète, was the systematic use of letters for variables in equations.

    - **17th Century** The founders of modern science—Nicolaus Copernicus, Johannes Kepler, Galileo, and Isaac Newton—studied the natural world as mathematicians, and they looked for its mathematical laws. Over time, mathematics grew more and more abstract as mathematicians sought to establish the foundations of their fields logically. The most important development in geometry during the 17th century was the discovery of analytic geometry by René Descartes and Pierre de Fermat, which makes it possible to study geometric figures using algebraic equations. The discovery of differential and integral calculus by Sir Isaac Newton and Gottfried Wilhelm Leibniz ranks as the crowning achievement of 17th-century mathematics. Calculus allowed the solution of many problems that had been previously insoluble, including the determination of the laws of motion and the theory of electromagnetism.

- **18th Century** During the 18th century, calculus became the cornerstone of mathematical analysis on the European continent. Mathematicians applied the discovery to a variety of problems in physics, astronomy, and engineering. In the course of doing so, they also created new areas of mathematics. The greatest mathematician of the 18th century, Leonhard Euler of Switzerland, was also the most prolific writer on mathematical subjects of all time. His treatises covered essentially the entire fields of pure and applied mathematics.

  - **The 19th Century** was a period of intense mathematical activity. It began with German mathematician Carl Friedrich Gauss, considered to be the last complete mathematician because of his contributions to all branches of the field. The century saw a great effort to place all areas of mathematics on firm theoretical foundations. The support for these foundations was logic—the deduction of basic propositions from a limited set of assumptions and definitions. Mathematicians also discovered the existence of additional geometries and algebras, and more than one kind of infinity.

    - **During the 20th Century** mathematics made rapid advances on all fronts. The foundations of mathematics became more clearly defined, while at the same time mathematics advanced the development of symbolic logic. Philosophy and physics, too, benefited from the contributions of mathematicians to the Relativity Theory and Quantum Theory. Indeed, mathematics achieved broader applications than ever before as new fields developed within mathematics (computational mathematics, game theory, and chaos theory), and other branches of knowledge, including economics and physics, achieved firmer grounding through the application of mathematics. Even the most abstract mathematics seemed to find application, and the boundaries between pure mathematics and applied mathematics grew ever fuzzier.

Content Strands of Mathematics

"One reason why mathematics enjoys special esteem, above all other sciences, is that its laws are absolutely certain and indisputable, while those of other sciences are to some extent debatable and in constant danger of being overthrown by newly discovered facts."

—Albert Einstein, physicist, 1879–1955

Algebra

Algebra is the branch of mathematics that uses symbols to represent arithmetic operations. Algebra extends arithmetic through the use of symbols and other notations, such as exponents and variables. Algebraic thinking involves understanding patterns, equations, and relationships, and includes concepts of functions and inverse operations. Because algebra uses symbols as well as numbers, it can produce general rules that apply to all numbers. What most people commonly think of as algebra involves the manipulation of equations and the solving of equations. Exposure to algebraic ideas can and should occur well before students first study algebra in middle school or high school. Even primary-grade students are capable of understanding many algebraic concepts. Developing algebraic thinking in the early grades smoothes the transition to algebra in middle school and high school and ensures success in future math and science courses, as well as in the workplace.

"Algebra begins with a search for patterns. Identifying patterns helps bring order, cohesion, and predictability to seemingly unorganized situations and allows one to make generalizations beyond the information directly available. The recognition and analysis of patterns are important components of the young child's intellectual development because they provide a foundation for the development of algebraic thinking."

Clements, Douglas and Sarama, J. eds. *Engaging Young Children in Mathematics: Standards for Early Childhood Mathematics Education.* Mahwah, New Jersey: Lawrence Erlbaum Associates, Publishers, 2004, p. 52.

Real Math and Algebra

Goal: Understanding of functional relationships between variables that represents real-world phenomena in a constant state of change

Children should be able to draw the graphs of functions and to derive information about functions from their graphs. They should understand the special importance of linear functions and the connection between the study of functions and the solution of equations and inequalities.

The algebra readiness strand that begins in the PreK level is designed to prepare students for future work in algebra by exposing them to algebraic thinking, including looking for patterns, using variables, working with functions, using integers and exponents, and being aware that mathematics is far more than just arithmetic.

Arithmetic

Arithmetic, one of the oldest branches of mathematics, arises from the most fundamental of mathematical operations: counting. The arithmetic operations—addition, subtraction, multiplication, and division—form the basis of the mathematics that we use regularly.

"Although some educators once believed that children memorize their 'basic facts' as conditioned responses, research now shows that children do not move from knowing nothing about sums and differences of numbers to having the basic number combinations memorized. Instead, they move through a series of progressively more advanced and abstract methods for working out the answers to simple arithmetic problems. Furthermore, as children get older, they use the procedures more and more efficiently."

Kilpatrick, J., Swafford, J. and Findell, B. eds. Adding It Up: Helping Children Learn Mathematics. Washington, D.C.: National Research Council/National Academy Press, 2001, p. 182–183.

Real Math and Arithmetic

Goal: Mastery of the basic operations with whole numbers (addition, subtraction, multiplication, and division)

Whatever other skills and understandings children acquire, they must have the ability to calculate a precise answer when necessary. This fundamental skill includes not only knowledge of the appropriate arithmetic algorithms, but also mastery of the basic addition, subtraction, multiplication, and division facts and understanding of the positional notation (base ten) of the whole numbers.

Mastery Checkpoints occur throughout the program to indicate when mastery of concepts and skills is expected. Skills are often introduced at least one grade level before mastery is expected and then reviewed in Mental Math and subsequent grade levels. Once taught, arithmetic skills are also integrated into other topics, such as functions and geometry.

Data Collection and Organization

Goal: Ability to organize information to make it easier to use and the ability to interpret data and graphs

> "Describing data involves reading displays of data (e.g., tables, lists, graphs); that is, finding information explicitly stated in the display, recognizing graphical conventions, and making direct connections between the original data and the display. The process is essentially what has been called reading the data.... The process of organizing and reducing data incorporates mental actions, such as ordering, grouping, and summarizing. Data reduction also includes the use of representative measures of center (often termed *measures of central tendency*), such as mean, mode, or median, and measures of spread, such as range or standard deviation."
>
> Kilpatrick, J., Swafford, J. and Findell, B. eds. *Adding It Up: Helping Children Learn Mathematics.* Washington, D.C.: National Research Council/National Academy Press, 2001, p. 289.

Real Math and Data Organization

Goal: Ability to organize and arrange data for greater intelligibility

Children should develop not only the routine skills of tabulating and graphing results, but also, at a higher level, the ability to detect patterns and trends in poorly organized data, either before or after reorganization. Children need to develop the ability to extrapolate and interpolate from data and from graphic representations. Children should also know when extrapolation or interpolation is justified and when it is not.

In *Real Math,* students work with graphs beginning in PreK. In each grade, the program emphasizes understanding what data shows.

Geometry

Geometry is the branch of mathematics that deals with the properties of space. Plane geometry is the geometry of flat surfaces, and solid geometry is the geometry of three-dimensional space figures. Geometry has many more fields, including the study of spaces with four or more dimensions.

> "Geometry can be used to understand and to represent the objects, directions, and locations in our world, and the relationships between them. Geometric shapes can be described, analyzed, transformed, and composed and decomposed into other shapes."
>
> Clements, Douglas and Sarama, J. eds. *Engaging Young Children in Mathematics: Standards for Early Childhood Mathematics Education.* Mahwah, New Jersey: Lawrence Erlbaum Associates, Publishers, 2004, p. 39.

Real Math and Geometry

Goals: Understanding of and ability to use geometric concepts in a variety of contexts

Appreciating how geometry can help to explain algebraic concepts

Measurement

Goal: Understanding of what a measurement is and how units relate to measurement

"Measurement is one of the main real-world applications of mathematics...counting is a type of measurement—it measures how many items in a collection. Measurement of continuous quantities involves assigning a number to attributes, such as length, area, and weight. Together, number and measurement are components of quantitative reasoning. In this vein, measurement helps connect the two realms of number and geometry, each providing conceptual support to the other."

Clements, Douglas and Sarama, J. eds. *Engaging Young Children in Mathematics: Standards for Early Childhood Mathematics Education.* Mahwah, New Jersey: Lawrence Erlbaum Associates, Publishers, 2004, p. 43–50.

Real Math and Measurement

Goal: Firm understanding of magnitude with respect to measurements and of the role of units in assigning numerical magnitudes to physical quantities

Children should, for example, understand the need for standard units of measurement and know how to use appropriate measurement tools (rulers, balances, liquid volume measures, and thermometers).

In *Real Math,* students work extensively with estimating measures and making actual measurements. They work with both the customary system (inches, pounds, cups) and the metric system (meters, grams, liters) separately so that they develop an intuitive feel for measurements in both systems.

Number Sense and Place Value

Goal: Understanding of the significance and use of numbers in counting, measuring, comparing, and ordering

"It is very important for teachers to provide children with opportunities to recognize the meaning of mathematical symbols, mathematical operations, and the patterns or relationships represented in the child's work with numbers. For example, the number sense that a child acquires should be based upon an understanding that inverse operations, such as addition and subtraction, undo the operations of the other. Instructionally, teachers must encourage their students to think beyond simply finding the answer and to actually have them think about the numerical relationships that are being represented or modeled by the symbols, words, or materials being used in the lesson."

Kilpatrick, J., Swafford, J. and Findell, B. eds. *Adding It Up: Helping Children Learn Mathematics.* Washington, D.C.: National Research Council/National Academy Press, 2001, p. 270–271.

Real Math and Number Sense

Goals: Firm understanding of the significance and use of numbers in counting, measuring, comparing, and ordering

The ability to think intelligently, using numbers

This basic requirement of numeracy includes the ability to recognize given answers as absurd, without doing a precise calculation, by observing that they violate experience, common sense, elementary logic, or familiar arithmetic patterns. It also includes the use of imagination and insight in using numbers to solve problems. Children should be able to recognize when, for example, a trial-and-error method is likely to be easier to use and more manageable than a standard algorithm.

Developing number sense is a primary goal of *Real Math* in every grade. Numbers are presented in a variety of representations and integrated in many contexts so that students develop thorough understanding of numbers.

Probability and Statistics

Probability and statistics deal with events where outcomes are uncertain, and they assess the likelihood of possible outcomes. Statistics is the organization and analysis of data for the purpose of simplification, comparison, and prediction.

 **and Probability and Statistics**

Goal: The ability to use probabilistic ideas in ordinary, elementary applications

Children should understand the reasons for (and something of the dangers of) using sampling techniques; they should have the ability to describe a population in terms of some simple statistic (mean, median, range); and they should understand the difference between intelligent risk taking, based on reasonable estimates of probabilities, and foolish risks, based on unsupported guesswork or wishful thinking.

Rational Numbers—Fractions, Decimals, and Percents

Goal: Understanding fractions, decimals, and percents and their relationships to each other, including the ability to perform calculations and to use rational numbers in measurement

> "Children need to learn that rational numbers are numbers in the same way that whole numbers are numbers. For children to use rational numbers to solve problems, they need to learn that the same rational number may be represented in different ways, as a fraction, a decimal, or a percent. Fraction concepts and representations need to be related to those of division, measurement, and ratio. Decimal and fractional representations need to be connected and understood. Building these connections take extensive experience with rational numbers over a substantial period of time. Researchers have documented that difficulties in working with rational numbers can often be traced to weak conceptual understanding....Instructional sequences in which more time is spent at the outset on developing

meaning for the various representations of rational numbers and the concept of unit have been shown to promote mathematical proficiency."

—Kilpatrick, J., Swafford, J. and Findell, B. eds. *Adding It Up: Helping Children Learn Mathematics.* Washington, D.C.: National Research Council/National Academy Press, 2001, p. 415–416.

Real Math **and Rational Numbers**

Goal: Understanding of rational numbers and of the relationship of fractions to decimals

Included here are the ability to do appropriate calculations with fractions or decimals (or both, as in fractions of decimals); the use of decimals in (metric unit) measurements; and the multiplication of fractions as a model for the "of" relation and as a model for areas of rectangles.

Goal: Understanding of the meaning of rates and of their relationship to the arithmetic concept of ratio

Children should be able to calculate ratios, proportions, and percentages; understand how to use them intelligently in real-life situations; understand the common units in which rates occur (such as kilometers per hour, cents per gram); understand the meaning of *per*; and be able to express ratios as fractions.

In *Real Math,* understanding of rational numbers begins in the earliest grades with sharing activities and develops understanding of rational numbers with increasing sophistication at each grade.

Mathematics Research Overview

For decades, people have been studying mathematics instruction to figure out what is and what is not effective. In the last few years, two compendiums of reliable research have been published; this research is relevant, sound, and generalizable.

Kilpatrick, J., Swafford, J. and Findell, B. eds. *Adding It Up: Helping Children Learn Mathematics.* Washington, D.C.: National Research Council/National Academy Press, 2001.

Kilpatrick, Jeremy, Martin, W. Gary, and Schifter, Deborah, eds. *A Research Companion to Principles and Standards for School Mathematics.* Reston, VA: National Council of Teachers of Mathematics, Inc., 2003.

The purpose of these books has been to synthesize the research on elementary math education to provide recommendations and advice to educators. Research can help to guide decisions about what mathematics to teach and how to teach it to improve the quality of math education and promote interest and achievement in mathematics.

Research has helped to identify

- what mathematics should be learned in elementary school to develop a solid foundation in understanding.
- effective teaching strategies for different strands of mathematics.
- classification of the learning trajectories that describe how children learn mathematics.

"The science of pure mathematics...may claim to be the most original creation of the human spirit."

Alfred North Whitehead, English mathematician and philosopher, 1861–1947

Real Math and Research

Real Math is based on several types of research. Building on mathematics education research findings over the last fifty years, *Real Math* brings the most effective curriculum and strategies to the classroom.

1. *Field Tests Real Math* is constantly being tested and improved. It was originally developed one grade level at a time over a ten-year period and was rigorously field-tested to ensure its effectiveness. Used in classrooms for over thirty years, the program has been revised to address current standards and the latest research in mathematics education, and continues its reliance on scientific field-testing and feedback from teachers.

2. *Research on Teaching Strategies Real Math* seriously attends to the latest research in mathematics education. Doug Clements's and Julie Sarama's work in early childhood mathematics forms the prekindergarten level of the program, and Joan Moss's work in fractions, decimals, and percents inspired revision of the rational number strand throughout the program. A review of relevant research precedes each chapter, and research-based strategies throughout the program are identified in the **Research in Action** feature.

3. *Research on Learning Trajectories* Much research has been conducted in identifying children's learning trajectories in mathematics. Developmental levels for early mathematics are outlined in Appendix C, and relevant information for teachers about the learning trajectories precedes each chapter. *Real Math* activities, teaching strategies, and lesson progression support the development of children through the developmental levels of the learning trajectories.

Math Proficiencies

Mathematical proficiency has five strands. These strands are not independent; they represent different aspects of a complex whole.... they are interwoven and interdependent in the development of proficiency in mathematics.

Kilpatrick, J., Swafford, J. and Findell, B. eds. Adding It Up: Helping Children Learn Mathematics. Washington, D.C.: National Research Council/National Academy Press, 2001, p. 115–133.

Each problem that I solved became a rule which served afterwards to solve other problems.

René Descartes, French philosopher and mathematician, 1596–1650

1. **Understanding** (Conceptual Understanding): Comprehending mathematical concepts, operations, and relations—knowing what mathematical symbols, diagrams, and procedures mean

    Conceptual Understanding refers to an integrated and functional grasp of mathematical ideas. Students with conceptual understanding know more than isolated facts and methods. They understand why a mathematical idea is important and the kinds of contexts in which it is useful. They have organized their knowledge into a coherent whole, which enables them to learn new ideas by connecting those ideas to what they already know. Conceptual understanding also supports retention. Because facts and methods learned with understanding are connected, they are easier to remember and use, and they can be reconstructed when forgotten. If students understand a method, they are unlikely to remember it incorrectly.

    A significant indicator of conceptual understanding is being able to represent mathematical situations in different ways and knowing how different representations can be useful for different purposes.

    Knowledge that has been learned with understanding provides the basis for generating new knowledge and for solving new and unfamiliar problems. When students have acquired conceptual understanding in an area of mathematics, they see the connections among concepts and procedures and can give arguments to explain why some facts are consequences of others. They gain confidence, which then provides a base from which they can move to another level of understanding.

2. **Computing** (Procedural Fluency): Carrying out mathematical procedures, such as adding, subtracting, multiplying, and dividing numbers flexibly, accurately, efficiently, and appropriately

    Procedural Fluency refers to knowledge of procedures, knowledge of when and how to use them appropriately, and skill in performing them flexibly, accurately, and efficiently. In the domain of numbers, procedural fluency is especially needed to support conceptual understanding of place value and the meanings of rational numbers. It also supports the analysis of similarities and differences between methods of calculating. These methods include, in addition to written procedures, mental methods for finding certain sums, differences, products, or quotients, as well as methods that use calculators, computers, or manipulative materials such as blocks, counters, or beads.

    Students need to be efficient and accurate in performing basic computations with whole numbers without always having to refer to tables or other aids. They also need to know reasonably efficient and accurate ways to add, subtract, multiply, and divide multidigit numbers, both mentally and with pencil and paper. A good conceptual understanding of place value in the base-ten system supports the development of fluency in multidigit computation. Such understanding also supports simplified but accurate mental arithmetic and more flexible ways of dealing with numbers than many students ultimately achieve.

3. **Applying** (Strategic Competence): Being able to formulate problems mathematically and to devise strategies for solving them using concepts and procedures appropriately

    Strategic Competence refers to the ability to formulate mathematical problems, represent them, and solve them. This strand is similar to what has been called *problem solving* and *problem formulation*. Although students are often presented with clearly specified problems to solve in the school setting, outside of school they encounter situations in which part of the difficulty is to figure out exactly what the problem is. Then they need to formulate the problem so that they can use mathematics to solve it. Consequently, they are likely to need experience and practice in problem formulating, as well as in problem solving. They should know a variety of solution strategies, as well as which strategies might be useful for solving a specific problem.

    To represent a problem accurately, students must first understand the situation, including its key features. They then need to generate a mathematical representation of the problem that captures the core mathematical elements and ignores the irrelevant features.

Students develop procedural fluency as they use their strategic competence to choose among effective procedures. They also learn that solving challenging mathematics problems depends on the ability to carry out procedures readily, and that problem-solving experience helps them acquire new concepts and skills.

4. **Reasoning** (Adaptive Reasoning): Using logic to explain and justify a solution to a problem or to extend from something known to something not yet known

Adaptive Reasoning refers to the capacity to think logically about the relationships among concepts and situations. Such reasoning is correct and valid, stems from careful consideration of alternatives, and includes knowledge of how to justify the conclusions. In mathematics, adaptive reasoning is the glue that holds everything together and guides learning. One uses it to navigate through the many facts, procedures, concepts, and solution methods, and to see that they all fit together in some way, that they make sense. In mathematics, deductive reasoning is used to settle disputes and disagreements. Answers are right because they follow some agreed-upon assumptions through a series of logical steps. Students who disagree about a mathematical answer need not rely on checking with the teacher, collecting opinions from their classmates, or gathering data from outside the classroom. In principle, they need only check that their reasoning is valid.

Research suggests that students are able to display reasoning ability when three conditions are met: they have a sufficient knowledge base, the task is understandable and motivating, and the context is familiar and comfortable.

5. **Engaging** (Productive Disposition): Seeing mathematics as sensible, useful, and doable—if you work at it—and being willing to do the work

Productive Disposition refers to the tendency to see sense in mathematics, to perceive it as both useful and worthwhile, to believe that steady effort in learning mathematics pays off, and to see oneself as an effective learner and doer of mathematics. If students are to develop conceptual understanding, procedural fluency, strategic competence, and adaptive reasoning abilities, they must believe mathematics is understandable, not arbitrary; that with diligent effort, it can be learned and used; and that they are capable of figuring it out. Developing a productive disposition requires frequent opportunities to make sense of mathematics, to recognize the benefits of perseverance, and to experience the rewards of sense making in mathematics.

Students' dispositions toward mathematics are a major factor in determining their educational success. Students who have developed a productive disposition are confident in their knowledge and ability. They see that mathematics is both reasonable and intelligible, and believe that, with appropriate effort and experience, they can learn.

Real Math and Math Proficiency

The goals of *Real Math* are to develop the five interwoven proficiencies. In every lesson, activities are designed to address understanding, computing, reasoning, applying, and engaging in an integrated fashion. Most games, for example, can be thought of as one or more mathematical problems. Students must first identify that a problem or problems exist, then provide a structure of the problem and use reasoning to arrive at a solution. At the same time, students are developing fluency in arithmetic. There is little question that students demonstrate engagement with mathematics as well when they are playing a *Real Math* game. Similarly, many activities in *Real Math* are engaging because the situations are those that are real to students. The students are well motivated to learn the mathematics involved in each situation.

Real Math Computational Expectations

At every grade level, **Real Math** develops each strand of mathematics with understanding, teaching children to appreciate and think mathematically. Problem solving, communicating mathematically, algebra, measurement, geometry, probability, and statistics, for example, are explored in every grade. Below are the computational expectations that are developed with understanding at each grade level that build fluency with number.

PreK

There are two key ideas emphasized in number.

1. Numbers can be used to tell us how many, describe order, and measure; they involve numerous relations and can be represented in various ways.

2. Operations with numbers can be used to model a variety of real-world situations and to solve problems; they can be carried out in various ways.

Grade K

- Numbers (cardinal and ordinal) through 100
- Counting; writing numerals
- Measurement with nonstandard units
- One-to-one matching
- Adding and subtracting whole numbers in the 0–100 range

Grade 1

- Numbers 0 through 100
- Addition and subtraction concepts
- Basic addition facts (through 10 + 10)
- Measurement with nonstandard units
- Introductory work with multiplication, fractions, recording data, maps, and inequalities

Grade 2

- Numbers through 10,000
- Basic addition and subtraction facts
- Multidigit addition and subtraction algorithms
- Introduction to multiplication and division
- Measurement with standard units
- Fractions of area and fractions of numbers
- Reading maps

Grade 3

- Numbers through 1,000,000 and beyond
- Fractions and decimals
- Multiplication and division
- Multiplication facts through 10 × 10
- Multidigit multiplication algorithms
- Measurement
- Graphing and functions
- Adding and subtracting decimals

Grade 4

- General multidigit multiplication algorithm
- Division by a one-digit divisor
- Addition and subtraction of common fractions
- Rounding and approximation
- Linear functions and composite and inverse functions
- Graphing such functions
- Multiplying decimals and whole numbers
- Introduction to mixed numbers

Grade 5

- Multidigit division algorithm
- Rounding
- Linear functions and composite and inverse functions
- Graphing such functions
- Introduction of negative numbers
- Rates, ratios, and percentages
- Relation of fractions and decimals
- Addition, subtraction, and multiplication of fractions, mixed numbers, and decimals
- Division with decimal dividends and quotients

Grade 6

- All operations with whole numbers, fractions, and decimals
- Some operations with negative numbers
- Computational shortcuts
- Compass and ruler constructions
- Nonlinear functions
- Graphing such functions
- Exponents

Basic Facts

The "basic" computation facts involve addition expressions in which the addends are whole numbers from 0 through 10, and the corresponding subtraction expressions; multiplication expressions in which the factors are whole numbers from 0 through 10, and the corresponding division expressions. Fluency with basic facts is the ability to use facts quickly, accurately, and appropriately. Fluency is necessary before students can use multidigit algorithms efficiently. *Real Math* uses a variety of methods to ensure that students become fluent with basic facts by developing an understanding of how facts are related rather than by encouraging rote memorization.

If students have difficulty with some basic facts, you can help them by providing (or helping them discover) specific strategies for the facts they have not mastered. If students use their thinking skills and understand our base-ten number system and relationships between numbers, they can use strategies, such as the following, to help with quick and accurate recall.

Note that *Real Math* teaches the addition and multiplication facts systematically to emphasize the relationships between the facts, but the subtraction and division facts are taught as inverses of addition and multiplication. When simple organizing relationships are available, those are also taught.

Addition Fact Helpers

These strategies can help with many of the addition facts.

To add:	Think of:
0	No change
1	Counting up 1
2	Counting up 2
4	One less than adding 5
5	Finger sets
6	One more than adding 5
9	One less than adding 10
10	Write 1 in the tens place

Other strategies which may be helpful include the following:

- **Commutative Law** (for example, $6 + 9$ and $9 + 6$)
  Students should recognize that if they can add two numbers in one order, they also know the sum in the opposite order. You can demonstrate this using concrete objects that are arranged in two different ways or a picture of two sets that is turned 180°. This realization cuts roughly in half the number of facts students need to learn.

- **Doubles** (for example, $4 + 4$ and $7 + 7$)
  Most students find the doubles facts easy to learn, since only one distinct addend is involved in each fact. The **Roll a Double Game** provides targeted practice with doubles facts.

- **Near doubles** (for example, $4 + 5$, $8 + 7$, and $7 + 9$)
  When the two addends in a fact differ by 1 or 2, students can relate the fact to a doubles fact. For example, $8 + 7$ must be 1 more than $7 + 7$, so it is $14 + 1$, or 15. One way to find $7 + 9$ is to recognize that since 7 is 1 less than 8 and 9 is 1 more than 8, we know $7 + 9 = 8 + 8$, or 16.

- **Sums of 10** (for example, $3 + 7$ and $2 + 8$)
  Students can become familiar with pairs of numbers that add to 10 by thinking of their fingers—raising 3 fingers then 7 fingers results in all 10 fingers being raised. The **Roll a Ten Game** provides targeted practice with the skill of recognizing sums of 10, which is useful for mental computation.

- **Remaining facts** The strategies above will help with all facts except $8 + 3$, $7 + 4$, and $8 + 4$. If students have trouble with these, you can demonstrate that $8 + 3$ and $7 + 4$ are both 1 more than $7 + 3$, and that $8 + 4 = 8 + 2 + 2 = 10 + 2$.

Subtraction Fact Helpers

Strategies that may help with subtraction facts include the following:

- **Subtracting 0** Subtracting 0 leaves a number unchanged.

- **Subtracting 5** Think of taking away one hand worth of fingers (a finger set of 5).

- **Subtracting 9** To subtract 9, you can first subtract 10, then add 1. For example, $16 - 9 = 6 + 1$, or 7.

- **Subtracting 10** To subtract 10 from a number between 10 and 20, simply remove the tens digit. For example, $13 - 10 = 3$.

- **Differences of 10** (for example, $17 - 7$)
  When two numbers from 0 through 19 have the same ones digit, their difference is always 10.

To find other subtraction facts, think of the corresponding addition fact.

Multiplication Fact Helpers

To multiply by:	Think:
0	The product is 0.
1	The product is the other number.
2	Add the number to itself.
3	Add the number to its double.
4	Double the double.
5	Multiply the number by 10 and take half.
6	Add the number to 5 times the number, or double 3 times the number.
8	Double 4 times the number.
9	Subtract the number from 10 times the number.
10	Write a 0 after the number to indicate that number of tens.

Other strategies which may be helpful include the following:

- **Commutative Law** (for example, 6×9 and 9×6) Students should recognize that if they can multiply two numbers in one order, they also know the product of the numbers in the opposite order. You can demonstrate this using an array that is turned sideways so that rows become columns and columns become rows. This realization cuts roughly in half the number of facts students need to learn.

- **Square facts** (for example, 3×3 and 7×7) Most students find the square facts relatively easy to learn, since only one distinct factor is involved in each fact.

- **Near squares** (for example, 8×7 and 6×8) When the two factors in a fact differ by 1 or 2, students can relate the product to a square fact. When the difference is 1, the product can be found by adding the smaller factor to its square. For example, 8×7 is 7 more than 7×7 — that is, $49 + 7 = 56$. When the difference is 2, students can use the pattern $(n - 1)(n + 1) = n^2 - 1$. They can discover this pattern in the multiplication table even though they cannot prove it algebraically. For example, $6 \times 8 = (7 - 1)(7 + 1) = 49 - 1 = 48$.

- **Multiples of 9** Once students are familiar with most of the multiplication facts, you may want to point out that the sum of the digits in multiples of 9 is always a multiple of 9. They can use this to check their work or to recall a product if they can find the first digit. For example, 7×9 is a little less than 7×10, or 70, so the first digit is 6. Since $6 + 3 = 9$, the product is 63. It is best not to introduce this pattern when students are first learning multiplication facts because they may inappropriately apply it to other factors. It is not true, for instance, that the sum of the digits of a multiple of 8 is a multiple of 8 (although the "rule" does also work for 3).

Another quick way to multiply a whole number (0 through 10) by 9 is to spread out fingers and turn down the finger corresponding to the other factor (for example, the third finger to find 3 times 9). The product is "read" by counting the fingers to the left of the folded finger as tens, and the fingers to the right as ones. Two fingers and seven fingers represents 27. The fact that the sum of the digits of multiples of 9 through 90 is always 9, and the fact that these multiples can be found by subtracting the other number from 10 times, it can be used to show why the finger trick works.

- **Division** Since the division facts do not fall neatly into patterns, the most efficient way to find division facts is to think of the corresponding multiplication fact. For example, $56 \div 7 = 8$ because $8 \times 7 = 56$.

Ways to Practice Facts

Even after students have learned all the basic facts with understanding, they need practice to retain their fluency. There are several useful ways for students to practice facts at school or at home.

- **Games** Playing appropriate games is an excellent way to provide practice with many facts in a brief period of time, while engaging even those students who are already fluent with basic facts.

  Good games for addition practice include **Roll a 15, Addition Table,** and **Addition Crossing.**

  Good games for multiplication practice include **Multiplication Table, Multiple Crossing,** and **Multigo.**

- **Flash Cards** When used appropriately, flash cards are a good way to provide either targeted practice with certain facts or general practice with all facts. Incorrect answers should simply receive no reaction—negative reinforcement is counterproductive since it often leads to frustration.

- **Frequent "quizzing"** If a student or class is struggling with just a few facts, ask about those facts frequently throughout the day. Encourage parents to do the same before and after school.

- **Other Applications through Word Problems, Projects, and Activities** Applications offer opportunities for meaningful fact practice.

- **Mental Math** Frequent mental math exercises encourage cumulative review and abstract thinking practice.

- **Speed Tests** Administer speed tests to encourage automatic recall periodically after most students have learned the basic facts to ensure that students are maintaining and improving their skills. Students should work to improve their own performance, rather than comparing their results to those of others.

Algorithms

An algorithm is a set of steps for carrying out a procedure. There are many commonly used algorithms for addition, subtraction, multiplication, and division of multidigit numbers. The beauty and power of our base numeration system is that having learned a procedure for two-digit numbers, we can use the same steps in any place without reference to place value. **Real Math** guides students to discover one standard algorithm for each operation. However, if students have previously learned a different algorithm, or have figured out efficient procedures for some computations on their own, they should not be restricted to the procedures taught in class. In fact, **Real Math** encourages students to avoid using standard algorithms whenever they can find a more efficient procedure.

When developing algorithms, **Real Math** places students in an environment in which they are almost forced to discover an efficient standard algorithm. But when finished, ideally students should believe they would have discovered it with help from the teacher or textbook and would be able to rediscover it if necessary.

Addition

A standard algorithm for addition is introduced using two sets of sticks bundled in groups of ten.

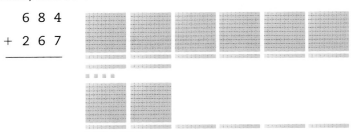

There are 7 tens and 15 ones. Regroup 10 ones as 1 ten.

Now there are 8 tens and 5 ones, so 37 + 48 = 85.

To avoid regrouping at the end, we can start adding with the ones place. We can record each step.

Beginning on the rightmost (ones) column, find the sum of the digits in the column. Write the ones digit of the sum below the addition line, and carry the tens digit to the top of the tens column. Then repeat this process for the tens, hundreds, and so on.

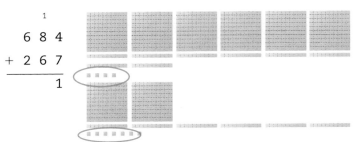

Add the ones: 4 + 7 = 11. Think, 11 ones = 1 ten and 1 one. Write the 1 one below the addition line. Write the 1 ten on top of the tens column.

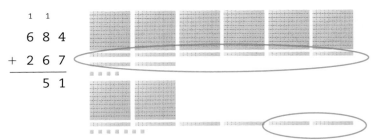

Add the tens: 1 + 8 + 6 = 15. Think, 15 tens = 1 hundred and 5 tens. Write the 5 tens below the addition line. Write the 1 hundred on top of the hundreds column.

Add the hundreds: 1 + 6 + 2 = 9. Write the 9 hundreds below the hundreds column.

```
  1 1
  6 8 4
+ 2 6 7
───────
  9 5 1
```

Note: You may wish to discourage students from writing the "carried" digit if they can get along without it. Extra digits can lead to confusion, especially when students later learn the multiplication algorithm.

Subtraction

As with the addition algorithm, a standard algorithm for subtraction is introduced using a set of sticks bundled in groups of ten.

$$
\begin{array}{r}
8\ 5 \\
-\ 3\ 7 \\
\hline
\end{array}
$$

There are not enough ones to take away 7.

Regroup 1 ten as 10 ones.

$$
\begin{array}{r}
8\ 5 \\
-\ 3\ 7 \\
\hline
\end{array}
$$

There are 4 tens and 8 ones.

$85 - 37 = 48$

It is easiest if we start subtracting with the ones place. We can record each step.

Beginning at the rightmost (ones) column, find the difference of that column. If the difference cannot be found, then rename the number in the next column to the left. Rewrite the tens and ones to reflect renaming. Then repeat this process for the tens, hundreds, and so on.

$$
\begin{array}{r}
1\ 1\ 6\ 5 \\
-\ \ \ \ 4\ 2\ 8 \\
\hline
\end{array}
$$

Since 8 ones cannot be taken from 5 ones, rename 6 tens as 5 tens and 10 ones.

$$
\begin{array}{r}
{\scriptstyle 5\ \ 15} \\
1\ 1\ \cancel{6}\ \cancel{5} \\
-\ \ \ \ 4\ 2\ 8 \\
\hline
\end{array}
$$

Subtract the ones.

$$
\begin{array}{r}
{\scriptstyle 5\ \ 15} \\
1\ 1\ \cancel{6}\ \cancel{5} \\
-\ \ \ \ 4\ 2\ 8 \\
\hline
7
\end{array}
$$

Subtract the tens.

$$
\begin{array}{r}
{\scriptstyle 5\ \ 15} \\
1\ 1\ \cancel{6}\ \cancel{5} \\
-\ \ \ \ 4\ 2\ 8 \\
\hline
3\ 7
\end{array}
$$

Since 4 hundreds cannot be taken from 1 hundred, rename 1 thousand as 10 hundreds.

$$
\begin{array}{r}
{\scriptstyle 5\ \ 15} \\
1\ 1\ \cancel{6}\ \cancel{5} \\
-\ \ \ \ 4\ 2\ 8 \\
\hline
3\ 7
\end{array}
$$

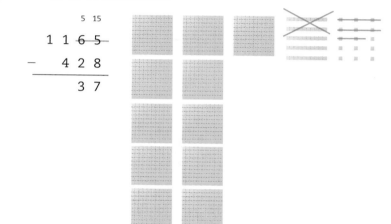

Subtract the hundreds.

$$
\begin{array}{r}
{\scriptstyle 5\ \ 15} \\
1\ 1\ \cancel{6}\ \cancel{5} \\
-\ \ \ \ 4\ 2\ 8 \\
\hline
7\ 3\ 7
\end{array}
$$

Multiplication

Efficient multiplication of multidigit numbers uses the Distributive Law. To multiply by a multidigit number, you can rewrite the product as a series of partial products. For example, $43 \times 8 = (40 + 3) \times 8 = (40 \times 8) + (3 \times 8) = 320 + 24 = 344$.

Products of two multidigit numbers can be found by writing each factor in expanded form and finding the products of each pair of terms. For example, $46 \times 73 = (40 + 6) \times (70 + 3) = (40 \times 70) + (40 \times 3) + (6 \times 70) + (6 \times 3)$.

Real Math introduces these ideas using area models in which each partial product is shown as a separate area. The product of the numbers (the sum of the areas of each rectangle) is the sum of the partial products.

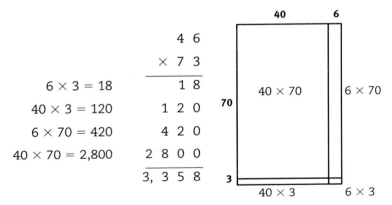

```
    4 3
  ×   8
  ─────
    2 4
  3 2 0
  ─────
  3 4 4
```

$6 \times 3 = 18$

$40 \times 3 = 120$

$6 \times 70 = 420$

$40 \times 70 = 2,800$

```
      4 6
    × 7 3
    ─────
      1 8
    1 2 0
    4 2 0
  2 8 0 0
  ───────
  3, 3 5 8
```

A similar area model can be (and is) used to demonstrate the distributive law.

Standard algorithm

Once students understand the idea of partial products, they are introduced to a more efficient way of recording their work.

Beginning at the rightmost column, find the product. Write the ones digit of the product below the line, and carry the tens digit to the top of the tens column. Then repeat this process for each digit of the second factor.

```
    4 6
  × 7 3
  ─────
```

Multiply 3 times the ones: $6 \times 3 = 18$.

18 ones = 1 ten and 8 ones

```
    1
    4 6
  × 7 3
  ─────
      8
```

Multiply 3 times the tens and add the carried ten: $(4 \times 3) + 1 = 13$. Record 13 tens.

```
    1
    4 6
  × 7 3
  ─────
  1 3 8
```

Multiply 7 tens times the ones: $7 \times 6 = 42$.

42 tens = 4 hundreds and 2 tens

```
    4
    4 6
  × 7 3
  ─────
  1 3 8
      2
```

Multiply 7 tens times 4 tens and add the 4 carried tens: $(7 \times 4) + 4 = 32$

```
    4
    4 6
  × 7 3
  ─────
  1 3 8
  3 2 2
```

Add the partial products.

```
      4
    4 6
  × 7 3
  ─────
  1 3 8
  3 2 2
  ─────
  3, 3 5 8
```

To avoid confusion, students should write the "carried" digits only if necessary. If they do write these digits, they should cross out the digits for the first multiplier before writing the digits for the second multiplier.

Division

Division with a multidigit dividend is introduced using an example in which an amount of money (expressed in $100, $10, and $1 bills) is shared as equally as possible by a number of students. As students share the money, they exchange $100 bills for $10 bills and $10 bills for $1 bills as needed.

Share $836 (8 $100 bills, 3 $10 bills, and 6 $1 bills) among 7 students.

Each student gets 1 $100 bill, so write 100 above the dividend. Now $700 has been distributed, so subtract 700 from the total.

$$
\begin{array}{r}
100 \\
7\,)\overline{836} \\
-700 \\
\hline
136
\end{array}
$$

Now there is 1 $100 bill, 3 $10 bills, and 6 $1 bills. Exchange the 1 $100 bill for 10 $10 bills, to leave 13 $1 bills.

Each student gets 1 $10 bill, so write 10 above the dividend and subtract 70.

$$
\begin{array}{r}
10 \\
100 \\
7\,)\overline{836} \\
-700 \\
\hline
136 \\
-70 \\
\hline
66
\end{array}
$$

Now there are 6 $10 bills and 6 $1 bills left. Exchange the 6 $10 bills for 60 $1 bills, to leave 66 $1 bills.

Each student gets 9 $1 bills, so write 9 above the dividend and subtract 63 (7 × 9).

$$
\begin{array}{r}
9 \\
10 \\
100 \\
7\,)\overline{836} \\
-700 \\
\hline
136 \\
-70 \\
\hline
66 \\
-63 \\
\hline
3
\end{array}
$$

Since 100 + 10 + 9 = 119, each student gets $119. There will be $3 left over.

This naturally leads to a standard algorithm which involves asking how many times the divisor divides into the thousands, hundreds, tens, and ones of the dividend.

Standard algorithm

Once students understand the steps in division, they are introduced to progressively more efficient ways of writing them. Three different versions of the algorithm are taught. Each uses the same steps, but they differ in the amount of writing they require.

Long Form	Shorter Form	Shorter Form
1,276 Remainder 4	With Zeros	Without Zeros
	Be careful to put the answers in the correct column.	Subtract and "bring down" only the next digit. Be careful to put the answers in the correct columns.

$$
\begin{array}{r}
6 \\
70 \\
200 \\
1000 \\
7\,)\overline{8936} \\
-7000 \\
\hline
1936 \\
-1400 \\
\hline
536 \\
-490 \\
\hline
46 \\
-42 \\
\hline
4
\end{array}
\qquad
\begin{array}{r}
1276 \;\text{R4} \\
7\,)\overline{8936} \\
-7000 \\
\hline
1936 \\
-1400 \\
\hline
536 \\
-490 \\
\hline
46 \\
-42 \\
\hline
4
\end{array}
\qquad
\begin{array}{r}
1276 \;\text{R4} \\
7\,)\overline{8936} \\
-7 \\
\hline
19 \\
-14 \\
\hline
53 \\
-49 \\
\hline
46 \\
-42 \\
\hline
4
\end{array}
$$

Shortest Form

Write "remainders" in front of the next digit.

$$
\begin{array}{r}
1\ 2\ 7\ 6 \;\text{R4} \\
7\,)\overline{8^{1}9^{5}3^{4}6}
\end{array}
$$

Technology

Technology has changed the world of mathematics. Technological tools have reduced the need for tedious calculations and have enabled significant advances in applications of mathematics. Technology can also help to make teaching more effective and efficient. Well-designed math software activities have proven effective in advancing children's math achievements. Technology can also help teachers organize planning and instruction and manage record keeping.

Real Math Technology for Teachers

ePlanner provides a tool to help teachers plan and organize daily lessons and plot out year-long goals.

- Daily lesson plan with lesson and homework detail
- Weekly lesson plan
- Monthly plan
- Yearly plan with lesson detail
- Lesson summaries and electronic lessons from the *ePresentation* that can be accessed at home
- Program resources (blacklines, technology, manipulatives lists)
- Correlation to state guidelines
- Assign Homework

ePresentation is an electronic presentation of all of the *Real Math* lessons, *eGames,* and *eMathTools.* Teachers can use this daily or periodically to vary instructional presentations.

eAssess enables teachers to record, track, and report on all aspects of students' math performances and progress toward achieving state and national standards.

Professional Development

A series of five courses that teach different aspects of instruction for math proficiency

- Teaching for Understanding
- Teaching Computational Fluency
- Teaching Mathematical Reasoning and Problem Solving
- Teaching Applications of Mathematics
- Teaching Mathematics

Each course covers a definition of the proficiency, what teachers need to know about it, how children learn, effective strategies, differentiating instruction, and assessment.

Real Math Technology for Students

Calculators: Basic arithmetic skills are essential in mathematics. It is important for students to learn how to use calculators wisely and when appropriate. It is also important that students understand arithmetic procedures and are able to do computations by hand when calculators are impractical or unavailable. To this end, *Real Math* teaches students how to use a calculator effectively. Children should be able to recognize when a calculator is useful and when other methods, such as mental approximation or precise calculation, are more appropriate. Students should also be expected to approximate answers and use numbers intelligently so that they can detect absurd answers that might result, for example, from pushing the wrong keys or using an inappropriate calculation.

> **"A large number of empirical studies of calculator use, including long-term studies, have generally shown that the use of calculators does not threaten the development of basic skills and that it can enhance conceptual understanding, strategic competence, and disposition toward mathematics....The question...is not whether, but how, calculators should be used."**
>
> Kilpatrick, J., Swafford, J. and Findell, B. eds. *Adding It Up: Helping Children Learn Mathematics.* Washington, D.C.: National Research Council/National Academy Press, 2001, p. 354–355.

In *Real Math,* students first learn arithmetic skills and only then use calculators to help them solve more complex problems using those skills. Specific instruction addresses when it is and is not appropriate to use a calculator.

Computer Math Technology for Students

Real Math develops familiarity with the nature and purpose of computers. We believe that children should have the opportunity to use computers. Whether or not children have the advantage of access to a computer, it is essential that they understand the principles on which computers function and the role they are capable of playing in our daily domestic, social, and professional lives. Children should appreciate that computers enable us to obtain numerical answers to large-scale mathematical problems easily and quickly.

eGames, can be accessed apart from or are available within the eTextbook and ePresentation, provide electronic versions of several of the cube games and game mats. eGames are referenced in relevant lessons in the Teacher's Edition.

Building Blocks software provides computer math activities that address specific developmental levels of the math learning trajectories. Building Blocks software is critical to the prekindergarten level of Real Math and provides support activities for specific concepts in Grades K–6.

Some Building Blocks activities have different levels of difficulty, indicated by ranges in the Activity Names below. The list provides an overview of all of the Building Blocks activities, along with the domains, descriptions, and appropriate age ranges.

Domain: Trajectory	Activity Name	Description	Age Range
Geometry: Composition/Decomposition	Create a Scene	Students explore shapes by moving and manipulating them to make pictures.	4–12
Geometry: Composition/Decomposition	Piece Puzzler 1–5, Piece Puzzler Free Explore, and Super Shape 1–7	Students complete puzzles using pattern or tangram shapes.	4–12
Geometry: Imagery	Geometry Snapshots 1–8	Students match configurations of a variety of shapes (e.g., line segments in different arrangements, 3–6 tiled shapes, embedded shapes) to corresponding configurations, given only a brief view of the goal shapes.	5–12
Geometry: Shapes (Identifying)	Memory Geometry 1–5	Students match familiar geometric shapes (shapes in same or similar sizes, same orientation) within the framework of a Concentration card game.	3–5
Geometry: Shapes (Matching)	Mystery Pictures 1–4 and Mystery Pictures Free Explore	Students construct predefined pictures by selecting shapes that match a series of target shapes.	3–8
Geometry: Shapes (Parts)	Shape Parts 1–7	Students build or fix some real-world object, exploring shape and properties of shapes.	5–12
Geometry: Shapes (Properties)	Legends of the Lost Shape	Students identify target shapes using textual clues provided.	8–12
Geometry: Shapes (Properties)	Shape Shop 1–3	Students identify a wide range of shapes given their names, with more difficult distractors.	8–12
Measurement: Length	Comparisons	Students are shown pictures of two objects and are asked to click on the one that fits the prompt (longer, shorter, heavier, and so on).	4–8
Measurement: Length	Deep Sea Compare	Students compare the length of two objects by representing them with a third object.	5–7
Measurement: Length	Reptile Ruler	Students learn about linear measurement by using a ruler to determine the length of various reptiles.	7–10
Measurement: Length	Workin' on the Railroad	Students identify the length (in nonstandard units) of railroad trestles they built to span a gully.	6–9
Multiplication/Division	Arrays in Area	Students build arrays and then determine the area of those arrays.	8–11
Multiplication/Division	Comic Book Shop	Students use skip counting to produce products that are multiples of 10s, 5s, 2s, and 3s. The task is to identify the product, given a number and bundles.	7–9
Multiplication/Division	Egg-stremely Equal	Students divide large sets of eggs into several equal parts.	4–8
Multiplication/Division	Field Trip	Students solve multidigit multiplication problems in a field-trip environment (e.g., equal number of students on each bus; number of tickets needed for all students).	8–11
Multiplication/Division	Snack Time	Students use direct modeling to solve multiplication problems.	6–8
Multiplication/Division	Word Problems with Tools 5–6, 10	Students use number tools to solve single and multidigit multiplication and division problems.	8–11
Multiplication/Division	Clean the Plates	Students use skip counting to produce products that are multiples of 10s, 5s, 2s, and 3s.	7–9
Numbers: Adding and Subtracting	Barkley's Bones 1–10 and 1–20	Students determine the missing addend in $X + \_\_ = Z$ problems to feed bone treats to a dog ($Z = 10$ or less).	5–8

Professional Development

Domain: Trajectory	Activity Name	Description	Age Range
Number: Adding and Subtracting	Double Compare 1–10 and 1–20	Students compare sums of cards (to 10 or 20) to determine which sum is greater.	5–8
Number: Adding and Subtracting	Word Problems with Tools 1–4, 7–9, 11–12	Students use number tools to solve single and multidigit addition and subtraction problems.	8–12
Number: Adding and Subtracting and Counting	Counting Activities (Road Race Counting Game, Numeral Train Game, et. al.)	Students identify numerals or dot amounts (totals to 20) and move forward a corresponding number of spaces on a game board.	3–9
Number: Adding and Subtracting and Multiplying and Dividing	Function Machine 1–4	Students provide inputs to a function and examine the resulting outputs to determine the definition of that function. Functions include either addition, subtraction, multiplication, or division.	6–12
Number: Comparing	Ordinal Construction Company	Students learn ordinal positions (1st through 10th) by moving objects between floors of a building.	5–7
Number: Comparing	Rocket Blast 1–3	Given a number line with only initial and final endpoints labeled and a location on that line, students determine the number label for that location.	6–12
Number: Comparing and Counting	Party Time 1–3 and Party Time Free Explore	Students use party utensils to practice one-to-one correspondence, identify numerals that represent target amounts, and match object amounts to target numerals.	4–6
Number: Comparing and Multiplication and Division	Number Compare 1–5	Students compare two cards and choose the one with the greater value.	4–11
Number: Comparing, Counting, Adding, and Subtracting	Pizza Pizzazz 1–5 and Pizza Pizzazz Free Explore	Students count items, match target amounts, and explore missing addends related to toppings on pizzas.	3–8
Number: Counting (Object)	Countdown Crazy	Students click digits in sequence to count down from 10 to 0.	5–7
Number: Counting (Object)	Memory Number 1–3	Students match displays containing both numerals and collections to matching displays within the framework of a Concentration card game.	4–6
Number: Counting (Object) and Adding and Subtracting	Dinosaur Shop 1–4 and Dinosaur Shop Free Explore	Students use toy dinosaurs to identify numerals representing target amounts, match object amounts to target numerals, add groups of objects, and find missing addends.	4–7
Number: Counting (Objects)	Book Stacks	Students fill an order by counting up from a two-digit number through the next decade. Students count on (through at least one decade) from a given number as they load books onto a cart.	6–8
Number: Counting (Objects)	School Supply Shop	Students count school supplies bundled in groups of ten to reach a target number up to 100.	
Number: Counting (Objects)	Tire Recycling	Students use skip counting by 2s and 5s to count tires as the tires are moved.	6–8
Number: Counting (Strategies)	Build Stairs 1–3, and Build Stairs Free Explore	Students practice counting, sequencing, and ordering by building staircases.	4–7
Number: Counting (Strategies)	Math-O-Scope	Students identify the numbers that surround a given number in the context of a 100s Table.	7–9
Number: Counting (Strategies)	Tidal Tally	Students identify missing addends (hidden objects) by counting on from given addends (visible objects) to reach a numerical total.	6–9
Number: Counting (Verbal)	Count and Race	Students count up to 50 by adding cars to a racetrack one at a time.	3–6
Number: Counting (Verbal)	Before and After Math	Students identify and select numbers that come either just before or right after a target number.	4–7
Number: Counting (Verbal)	Kitchen Counter	Students click on objects one at a time while the numbers from 1 to 10 are counted aloud.	3–6
Number: Subitizing	Number Snapshots 1–10	Students match numerals or dot collections to corresponding numerals or collections given only a brief view of the goal collections.	3–12
Patterning	Marching Patterns 1–3	Students extend a linear pattern of marchers by one full repetition of an entire unit (AB, AAB, ABB, and ABC patterns).	5–7
Patterning	Pattern Planes 1–3	Students duplicate a linear pattern of flags based on an outline that serves as a guide (AB, AAB, ABB, and ABC patterns).	4–6
Patterning	Pattern Zoo 1–3 and Free Explore	Students identify a linear pattern of fruit that matches a target pattern to feed zoo animals (AB, AAB, ABB, and ABC patterns). Students explore patterning by creating rhythmic patterns of their own.	3–6

 **MathTools**

Data Organization and Display Tools

- **Spreadsheet**—allows students to manage, display, sort, and calculate data; links to the graphing tool for further data display
- **Graphing Tool**—displays data in circle graphs, line graphs, or bar graphs
- **Venn Diagram**—allows students to sort data visually
- **Coordinate Grid Tool**—plots points and function rules

Calculation and Counting Tools

- **Calculator**—allows students to launch a calculator to perform mathematical operations
- **Function Machine**—an electronic version of a function machine that students use to solve missing variable problems
- **Multiplication and Division Table**—an interactive version of a table that highlights relationships between multiplication and division facts
- **Addition and Subtraction Table**—an interactive version of a table that highlights relationships between addition and subtraction facts
- **100 Table**—an interactive version of a table that highlights patterns and relationships among numbers
- **Number Line**—an electronic number line that allows students to skip count and see the relationships among whole numbers, fractions, decimals, and percents
- **Number Stairs**—a tool to illustrate counting in units
- **Probability Tool**—uses **Number Cubes,** spinners, or tumble drums to test scenarios of probability
- **Sets Former**—allows students to visually represent and manipulate different sets of objects for a variety of counting and computation activities
- **Base Ten**—allows students to manipulate base-ten blocks for counting and computation
- **Coins and Money**—uses visual representations of coins and money to represent counting
- **Fractions**—represents fractional units for counting and understanding relationships
- **Array Tool**—presents arrays to represent multiplication and division patterns and relationships

Measurement and Conversion Tools

- **Stopwatch**—measures real time for development of counting and time concepts
- **Calendar**—an electronic calendar to develop concepts of time
- **Metric/Customary Conversion**—converts metric and customary measurements in length, distance, mass and weight, time, temperature, and capacity
- **Estimating Proportion Tool**—allows visual representations of proportions in order to develop understanding of ratios, fractions, and decimals

Geometric Exploration Tools

- **Tessellations**—allows students to create tessellation patterns by rotating, coloring, and tiling shapes
- **Net Tool**—allows students to manipulate 2-D shapes and then print them to create 3-D shapes
- **Shape Tool**—explores and manipulates shapes to create designs
- **Geometry Sketch Tool**—allows drawing, manipulating, and measuring a wide variety of shapes
- **Pythagorean Theorem Tool**—launches right triangles to explore the Pythagorean Theorem
- **Shape Creator**—allows students to input specifications and see which shapes result

Using Games

The Role of Games

Games provide enjoyable practice. They give students a way of becoming proficient in the mathematical skills to which they have been introduced. Many **Real Math** games do more. They offer students a chance to recognize situations, real to the student, that can be understood through mathematical thinking, which leads to the identification and solution of strategy problems. This usually leads to in-depth mathematical communication between students regarding the problem and solution.

A benefit of this development through games is that there is no need to teach students the best solution. The process of trying to find a better strategy is the useful activity.

Games also afford teachers the opportunity to monitor progress. By observing game-playing sessions, teachers can assess students' computational fluency, understanding, reasoning, and engagement.

Games allow students of all levels of ability to compete fairly. Winning games requires a mix of chance, skills, and thinking strategies.

Games and Skills

Each of the games in **Real Math** involves the use of specific math skills. When a lesson plan prescribes a game, it does so because the principal skills involved in that game need attention at that time. Most games provide practice in many skills. For example, nearly all the games help students develop and apply intuitive concepts of probability. Many games afford students the opportunity to apply problem-solving strategies, such as recognizing a problem, working backward, or making an approximation.

Types of Games

Cube Games

These games are included in appropriate lessons in the **Student** and **Teacher's Editions**. The games' rules usually appear on the student pages. Many of the cube games have variations that extend the mathematics or provide applications for new strategies. Variations can be learned quickly, making the cube games even more practical. Directions for all cube games are also reproduced in **Home Connection,** as well as in the **Home Connection Game Kit**.

Mat Games

Mat games can be found in the **Game Mat Kit** and are reproduced in Appendix D of this **Teacher's Edition**. The mat games are referenced in appropriate lessons.

e Games

These games are electronic versions of some of the cube and mat games. They are referenced in appropriate lessons throughout the program. The **eGames** can be accessed online, on the **eGames** CD-ROM, or through the **eTextbook, ePresentation,** or **ePlanner.**

Multiple Crossing

4	5	6	7	8	9	10	
4	5	6	7	8	9	10	
8	10	12	14	16	18	20	
12	15	18	21	24	27	30	
16	20	24	28	32	36	40	
20	25	30	35	40	45	50	
24	30	36	42	48	54	60	
28	35	42	49	56	63	70	
32	40	48	56	64	72	80	
36	45	54	63	72	81	90	
40	50	60	70	80	90	100	
30	40	50	60	70	80		

Math Focus: Practicing basic facts—using factors up to 10

Object of the Game: To be the first to complete a continuous path across the board

Players: Two

MATERIALS

Two cubes   Two cubes   25 counters of the same color for each player

SET UP

- Choose a direction. One of you will move horizontally (left to right), and the other will move vertically (up and down).
- Players roll the 0-5 number cube. The person who rolls the higher number chooses his or her counters and is followed by the second player.

HOW TO PLAY

1. Take turns rolling any two cubes. Put a counter on any square that holds the product of the two numbers you rolled.

2. If you roll a 0, you cannot place a counter on a square.

3. The first player to make a continuous path from one side to the opposite side is the winner. Your path can go up, down, forward, backward, or diagonally, as long as all the squares are touching each other.

Sample Game

Building Blocks

These electronic activities are referenced in appropriate lessons throughout the lower grades of **Real Math.** The PreK level of the **Building Blocks** software, which includes the activities appropriate for prekindergarten, is a crucial part of the PreK curriculum. The **Building Blocks** activities referenced in appropriate lessons at the other grade levels reinforce key concepts.

Choosing Games

Some lesson plans suggest a particular game; some suggest that teachers select appropriate games for students based on needed skill practice; and some suggest that students be given a free choice of games. The authors recommend that teachers maintain a balance between selecting games for students and having students choose games for themselves.

To help students choose games, teachers can make a chart of the games that have been introduced to date. The chart can be a simple list or an organized collection of game mats, titles, game rules, materials lists, and illustrations. A group of students might be put in charge of making the display and updating it whenever a new game is introduced.

When you do prescribe games, check the game directory in Appendix D. This listing of the principal skills involved in each game will help you select those games that will give each student an appropriate form of practice.

Learning Game Rules

Rules for each cube game are given in the lesson in which the game is introduced. The directions for game mats are found on the game mats. Here are some tips for making sure that games are played correctly:

- Familiarize yourself with each game before showing students how to play it. Read the instructions, and then play the game by yourself or with a colleague or a friend.

- Demonstrate—do not tell—how a game is played. Even for straightforward games, oral instructions can sound complicated. Introduce a game by demonstrating it in front of the class, with you playing against the class, with you playing against one student (representing the class), or with two students (representing teams) playing against each other. The **ePresentation** allows teachers to present and demonstrate all games to the entire class at one time. Make sure that each student can see while you demonstrate a game.

- Verbalize the rules as you demonstrate games. End the demonstration when all the rules have been covered.

- Supervise to see that students get off to the right start after you have introduced a game.

- Let students teach other students. Those who have grasped the game rules can help those who have not.

Organizing Successful Game Sessions

- Pair children wisely. There are times when it will be appropriate to pair children of the same ability. However, this rule should not become invariable because most games involve some luck. Furthermore, if a student who is not attentive while playing a game plays with one who is, the first student may realize that paying attention may help.

- Change groupings from day to day. Students can learn different things by playing with different partners.

- Be sure students are challenged by a game. Most games have easier and harder variations.

- Assign a referee to each group. When students get so absorbed in their own efforts that they do not follow the rules, a referee can be useful. This is particularly appropriate for kindergarten through second grade. The referee can see that the rules are followed, remind each player when it is his or her turn, settle disputes, keep track of scores, and in some games, act as a banker.

- Make game mats accessible. Store mats so they are easy for the students to find and to return without your help.

- Encourage students to play games during free time, in school, and at home, as well as during the scheduled game sessions.

- Allow students opportunities to create and name their own variations of the games. In some cases, you may want to describe a student's variation to the entire class and ask him or her to name it. Be alert, however, to avoid student-invented variations that reduce the skill practice or thinking value of the game.

- Get help during game-playing sessions. Likely candidates are parents, grandparents, teacher's aides, or students in upper grades. Be sure the helpers know the rules of the games by having them play the chosen games ahead of time.

Game-Playing Behavior

Establishing the proper atmosphere for game playing makes the sessions more effective and easier to manage. Encourage enjoyment rather than competition. Emphasize sportsmanship, fair play, and taking turns. Beginning with the first game-playing session, teach students to control their excitement and to speak using low voices. Cubes, when rolled, should stay within a confined area. Insisting that students roll cubes on an $11'' \times 8\frac{1}{2}''$ pad, cardboard field, or on the backs of their textbooks reduces noise and inappropriate exuberance.

Problem Solving

Problem solving and reasoning are fundamental math proficiencies. Without the ability to reason mathematically, identify problems, and devise appropriate strategies to solve them, computational fluency has little relevance. There are several keys to developing students' problem-solving abilities.

1. Use Real Problems

The first and most important step in helping students become good problem solvers is to provide opportunities to identify and solve problems that are genuinely interesting and, therefore, motivating. We call these *real problems*. To help understand what we mean by *real,* we can consider three types of problems: those that are real, those that are realistic, and those that are contrived.

Contrived Problems appear largely in textbooks — never in real life. They often occur when it is difficult to find an application for a particular type of computation, so a forced, contrived situation is invented. For example, knowing how much antifreeze to add to a radiator that is $\frac{4}{7}$ full and which has a 4-gallon capacity is a contrived problem. One would never know that the radiator was $\frac{4}{7}$ full, and even if one did have that piece of useless information, nobody would calculate how much antifreeze to add. They would simply fill the tank to capacity. When students encounter such problems, they learn the wrong lesson — that mathematics is an endeavor that makes work, not one that saves work and solves useful problems. We avoid using contrived problems in **Real Math.**

Realistic Problems mirror the kind of mathematics that people do in real life. Although not as motivating as real problems, they are an important part of a mathematics program and are the main source of word problems found in our student texts. Unit pricing, comparing or combining quantities or measures, balancing a checkbook, and learning to read a telephone bill are all examples of realistic problems.

Real Problems are developed from the reality of the person being asked to solve the problem; they come from the social situation of the problem solver and his or her desire to find a solution. Thus, what is real to a first grader is not the same as what is real to a third grader or to an adult. The same problem may be real to one person and realistic to another who is engaged in a different activity, but if a problem is real to one person, then it can never be a contrived problem. Carefully selected games are a source of real problems because figuring out a strategy to win a game is of real interest to a school child. Thinking stories, too, can be real, because they have the proper balance of storyline, fantasy, humor, and reality, appropriate for the intended grade level.

Carefully developed activities are another source of real problems.

Finding real problems is one of the more difficult challenges in curriculum development, one that we take seriously and work hard at achieving. But it is here where teachers can help immensely. One of the most important prerequisites for developing real problem-solving opportunities is to know the students — know what they are interested in and know what is real to them. And so **Real Math** is rich in opportunities to individualize mathematics to the interests of the students.

2. Develop Critical-Thinking Skills

Students must have tools that are useful for solving problems. Computational skills are, of course, important, but they are not enough. Students also need an arsenal of critical-thinking skills (sometimes called *problem-solving strategies,* and sometimes called *heuristics*) that they can call upon to solve particular problems. These skills should not be taught in isolation. Rather, students should learn to use them in different contexts. By doing so, students are more likely to recognize in which situations a particular skill will be useful and when it is not likely to be useful.

We can group critical-thinking skills into two categories — those that are useful in virtually all situations and those that are useful in specific contexts.

Strategies for Every Problem-Solving Situation

Identify the problem — The first step in becoming a good problem solver is to learn how to identify when a problem does, in fact, exist. Too often in school mathematics, we give students problems to solve, even many interesting problems, but the problems are always given by the teacher or provided by the textbook—they are never identified by the student as arising from a particular context. That is not the way we encounter problems in the real world. **Real Math** lessons are rich in opportunities for students to identify problems.

Understand the problem — Without exception, students must understand each problem or physical situation and do only what makes sense to them. Applying rules in unthinking ways, using key words that avoid thinking, or using other shortcuts that subvert or eliminate understanding are all counterproductive, and although they might lead to correct answers in contrived situations, such tactics do not help students become good problem solvers, and they are not used in **Real Math.** There are no exceptions.

Reflect on the problem — Students must learn to reflect on problems both before and after solving them. Before a solution is found, students might reflect on problems that they have encountered earlier. A solution to a problem encountered earlier might offer a clue about how to structure the solution to the current problem. Good problem solvers also reflect on problems after they have been solved. What have I learned from this problem that might help with other problems? Was there an easier or a more elegant solution? Can I think of related problems that I have not yet solved? Asking such questions is likely to help students become good problem solvers. Every **Real Math** lesson concludes with an opportunity for students to reflect on what they have learned, expand on what they have learned, or ask new questions that arise from what they have learned.

Revisit the problem — Good problem solvers tend to think about a problem after they have solved it. By doing so they are likely to better understand the processes they used and see things the second and third time that they did not see the first time. One of the central roles of games in **Real Math** is to afford students the opportunity to revisit problems. Students do this by replaying games that allow them to formulate and reformulate winning strategies.

Problem-Solving Strategies

Below is a partial listing of critical-thinking skills that are likely to be useful in specific contexts.

Draw a Picture — Sometimes drawing a picture will help to visualize and hence understand a problem.

Look for a Pattern — Some problems can be solved by looking for and finding patterns.

Guess, Check, and Revise — If a direct procedure cannot be found, it is sometimes useful to make an educated guess and then check to see if that answer makes sense. This procedure often involves making several successive guesses, each based on feedback from earlier guesses. The process of guessing and checking will often lead to a better understanding of the problem and to a procedure for solving it without future guessing.

Make a Table or Graph — Organizing information in a table or graph will often reveal important trends and patterns.

Work Backward — For some problems, working backward helps to reveal a pattern or patterns.

Work an Easier Problem — If a problem appears too difficult, it sometimes helps to solve a related, but easier, problem. Solving the easier problem will often reveal strategies likely to be useful for solving the more difficult problem.

Detect Absurdities — Spotting answers that are contrary to reason, even if the correct answer is not known, is often an important part of the problem-solving process.

Ask the Right Questions — Knowing when necessary information is missing, knowing how to find the information, and knowing how to ask the right questions to find the information is often useful.

Approximate — Many problems do not require precise answers. Knowing when a precise answer is appropriate and when an approximate answer is appropriate is important, as is sufficient knowledge of the number system in order to make approximations.

3. Involve All Students in Problem Solving

Problem solving is an activity that must involve all students, not just those who are more able or who have mastered particular computational skills. **Real Math** lessons are designed to provide many such opportunities.

4. Problem Solving in Every Lesson

If students are to see the usefulness of mathematics for solving interesting problems that are relevant to their own lives, and if they are to have lots of experience solving problems, such activities must be part of every mathematics lesson — not something that is reserved for Fridays or perhaps isolated in one or two chapters of a textbook. That is why we include problem-solving opportunities in every lesson in **Real Math.** There are no exceptions.

Real Math and Problem Solving

Real Math lessons are rich in problem-solving opportunities and are adaptable to many styles of teaching. The principal sources of problem-solving opportunities come from the following:

Games

Real Math games are a principal source for practice of traditional basic skills. Most games do more: they give students an opportunity to work out important mathematical ideas and strategies. Thus, students might start a game by just getting the skill practice, but after a while they might realize that the game involves more than practice — that a winning strategy must be developed. At that point students have identified a problem. Because winning the game is often a real problem for students, there is genuine motivation to find a solution. Moreover, each time students replay the game, there is an opportunity to revisit a problem previously encountered and find alternative and more sophisticated strategies that might have been missed earlier. Although students compete with each other during game-playing sessions, they often communicate their strategies to each other and discuss them.

Thinking Stories

Thinking Stories found in kindergarten and Grades one, two, and three are an essential part of the **Real Math** approach to developing problem-solving abilities; they develop creativity and common sense in the use of mathematics. The problem-solving skills that are stressed include recognizing absurd answers, recognizing obvious answers (those that don't need calculation), recognizing when a problem can be solved using mathematics and when other, non-mathematical knowledge is needed, and so on. The stories are real stories, designed to be read to the students and discussed. The various characters in the stories have peculiarities in thinking that the students come to know. Mr. Breezy, for example, is always giving more information than what is needed, while Ms. Eng is often vague and provides too little information. Thus when Mr. Breezy appears in a story, students learn to listen and think about what information is not useful, whereas when Ms. Eng appears, students learn to ask questions to get the information that she has failed to give. Because the stories are read to the students, we can use a much richer vocabulary than what would be necessary if students read the stories themselves. Thus we do not divorce language from mathematics — rather we make use of language to build problem-solving skills.

Exploring Problem Solving

Three sets of explorations in every chapter focus specifically on introducing, comparing, and using strategies for identifying and solving problems from many curricular areas or realistic situations. Students analyze solution methods and share other possible solutions.

Activities

The many whole-class and small-group activities allow students to apply mathematics in different contexts, which are often cross-curricular. Such activities are rich in opportunities for students to communicate their ideas within their small groups and also to others from whom they are seeking information.

Mathematics is being lazy. Mathematics is letting the principles do the work for you so that you do not have to do the work for yourself.

George Pólya, mathematician, 1887–1985

Computation Pages

As in most programs, pages that provide needed computation practice are included throughout **Real Math.** But because we frequently include groups of related exercises on these pages, students learn to look for them and use the resulting patterns to avoid tedious computations. For example, an exercise such as $54 + 73 =$ might be followed by $54 + 74 =$ and $54 + 75 =$. Students who notice this pattern can compute the first sum, but then note that each successive sum is one more than the previous sum. Such patterns appear often in **Real Math.**

Word Problems

Realistic word problems appear frequently throughout **Real Math.** They illustrate situations in which mathematics is useful in the real world, and they are a source of much practice. To be certain that students understand the situations described in these problems, we never group problems of the same type together, such as giving problems, which all call for addition. To do so would allow students to simply look for the numbers and use the indicated operation. They would not have to understand the problem and would not have to think. To encourage thinking, we include problems that include too much information, too little information, problems that can be solved by mathematics, and those that cannot. We also include problems in which an approximate answer is more useful than a precise answer, and those in which a precise answer is more useful than an approximate answer. We do not allow students to rely on key words either, because doing so allows students to avoid thinking and to apply procedures that are likely to work only with problems that appear in textbooks.

Guided Discussion

"Discourse should not be confined to answers only, but should include discussion of connections to other problems, alternative representations and solution methods, the nature of justification and argumentation, and the like."

Kilpatrick, J., Swafford, J. and Findell, B. eds. *Adding It Up: Helping Children Learn Mathematics*. Washington, D.C.: National Research Council/National Academy Press. 2001, p. 425–426.

Mathematical discussions have the potential to greatly advance mathematical understanding. A good discussion provides opportunities for students to explain their thinking, to expand or challenge their understanding by listening to others' contributions, and to justify their reasoning. Good mathematical discussions enable teachers to assess and understand student thinking to inform their future instruction.

"Writing and talking enable learners to make their mathematical thinking visible. It is through writing and talking that teachers obtain a window into their students' thinking. Both writing and talking are tools for discovery, enabling learners to make new connections as they engage in the process. The fluid nature of talk allows for the quick brainstorming of many ideas, while the permanent quality of writing provides an important trail of our children's thinking."

Whitin, Phyllis and Whitin, David J. *Math Is Language Too*. Urbana, IL: National Council of Teachers of English. 2000, p. 17.

Discussion Management

These points will help produce more discussions:

1. Restate some or all of what the student has said, and then ask the student to respond and verify whether or not the teacher's restatement is correct. (However, always restating what students say may discourage students from listening to each other the first time.)

2. Ask students to restate someone else's reasoning, which gives the rest of the class another rendition of the first student's contribution and provides evidence that other students could and did hear. It is also evidence for the speaker's points.

3. Ask students to apply and explain their own reasoning to someone else's reasoning. This will involve more students in the discussion and will encourage student interactions.

4. Prompt students by asking for further commentary to support a position.

5. Use free time. This time allows students to think and consider answers to complicated questions before they speak.

Chapin, Suzanne, O'Connor, Catherine, and Anderson, Nancy Canavan. *Classroom Discussions: Using Math Talk to Help Students Learn*. Sausalito, CA: Math Solutions Publications, 2003, p. 12–16.

Real Math and Guided Discussion

Guided Discussion plays a prominent role in the Develop and Reflect parts of virtually every lesson in *Real Math*. Routines for Guided Discussion are included in the Getting Started section of each grade level to develop effective discussion strategies.

Questions that Promote Learning

Not all questions have the same effect. Questions help teachers to learn what students are thinking and to consider instructional implications of that knowledge. Below are ideas for formulating questions to promote learning during Guided Discussion.

Engaging questions to invite students to participate in a discussion

Identify terms, relationships, and methods already known that are connected to the topic.	What is _____? What does _____ mean?
Share opinions about the topic.	What do you think about _____?
Relate concrete experiences that are pertinent to the topic.	Have you ever been asked to do this before?
Verify the results.	How do you know this is true?

Exploratory questions to help students consider connections and consequences

Identify a specific difficulty, and decide how to solve it.	What was the hardest part of the problem? Is there an easier way to solve it?
Relate personal experience in solving the problem.	What did you do in the past to solve the problem?
Draw analogies to other situations.	How is this the same as or different from other problems?
Process and record results.	Write the steps you used to solve the problem.

Synthesizing questions to help students pull ideas together.

Identify patterns.	What pattern do you see in everyone's results?
Generalize.	What is a good way to solve this kind of problem?
Elaborate rules, definitions, and laws that express the generalization.	Explain or justify the steps for solving problems like this.
Argue, prove, or demonstrate assumptions.	Which way is the best way to solve a problem like this? How is it better?
Use references.	Who else solved the problem in this way?

Clarifying questions to help students explain their thinking or to help you understand their thinking

Reflect on examples and analyze results.	Which is the easiest/hardest/most fun way of approaching the problem, and why?
Provide examples.	What is an example of a problem like this?
Describe stages and observations.	What was the thinking process you used to solve the problem?
Understand and accept limitations of personal and peer knowledge, and search for other information sources.	Is there a better way? How could we find out?

Refocusing questions to help students get back on track

Refocusing questions are most useful when students are working in nonproductive ways.	How is this like _____? What does this say about _____?

Knowledge Age Skills and Talents

The twenty-first century is the dawn of the Knowledge Age. In contrast to the Industrial Age or Information Age, the Knowledge Age requires a specific set of skills and talents. These include the ability to write and speak clearly, analyze information, conduct research, and solve difficult problems. According to a February 2005 study conducted by Peter D. Hart Research Associates for Achieve, Inc., of high school graduates

❏ 51% feel that there are some gaps in their science preparation (14% large gaps)

❏ 46% say that there are gaps in their oral communication skills (15% large gaps)

❏ 45% identify some gaps in their ability to do research (13% say there are large gaps)

❏ 41% say that there are some gaps in their mathematics preparation (16% large gaps)

❏ 38% feel that there are some gaps in the quality of writing that is expected (10% large gaps)

Elementary education can help to build these knowledge age skills in the following ways.

Throughout **Real Math,** activities are included to teach, build, apply, and practice knowledge age skills in the course of learning mathematics.

The following competencies are developed in each grade level in the course of the Develop and Reflect sections of each lesson, as well as in the Concept/Question Board and Project activities.

- **High-Level Responsibility**—Helping students to take over more of the high-level parts of the learning process that are traditionally treated as part of the teacher's job; for instance, goal-setting, activating prior knowledge, monitoring, and determining next steps

- **Teamwork**—Encouraging group work and grading on the basis of contributions to the success of group efforts rather than solely on the basis of individual performance

- **Effective Communication**—Taking responsibility for communicating clearly both orally and in writing

- **Creative Work with Ideas**—Emphasizing ideas and idea improvement rather than task completion and getting the right answer

- **Problem Formulation, Planning, and Strategizing**—Recognizing difficulties and opportunities in a situation and converting these into solvable problems. Recognizing a problem as solvable implies having a strategy, a way to proceed, and so strategies become a natural subject of discussion

- **Self-Monitoring and Self- and Group Assessment**—Making students aware of and responsible for achieving mandated learning objectives

Manipulatives and How to Use Them

"The use of concrete materials, sometimes termed manipulatives, for teaching mathematics is widely accepted, particularly in elementary grades. Manipulatives should always be seen as a means and not an end in themselves. They require careful use over sufficient time to allow students to build meaning and make connections....Simply putting materials on desks is not enough to guarantee students will learn appropriate mathematics. The relationship between learning and the use of manipulatives is far more complex than many mathematics educators have thought....When students use a manipulative, they need to be helped to see its relevant aspects and to link those aspects to appropriate symbolism and mathematical concepts and operations....If students do not see the connections among object, symbol, language, and idea, using a manipulative becomes just one more thing to learn rather than a process leading to a larger mathematical learning goal....The evidence indicates...that manipulatives can provide valuable support for student learning when teachers interact over time with the students to help them build links between the object, the symbol, and the mathematical idea that both represent."

Kilpatrick, J., Swafford, J. and Findell, B. eds. *Adding It Up: Helping Children Learn Mathematics.* Washington, D.C.: National Research Council/National Academy Press. 2001, p. 353–354.

"The laws of nature are written in the language of mathematics...the symbols are triangles, circles, and other geometrical figures, without whose help it is impossible to comprehend a single word."

Galileo Galilei, Italian astronomer and physicist, 1564–1642

Real Math and Manipulatives

The purpose of using manipulatives is to help students understand mathematics, not to get answers to problems. Too often students know rules but do not know how or why the rules work. By explaining abstract concepts with manipulatives, students can develop and demonstrate understanding of mathematical concepts. Manipulatives are used whenever appropriate in **Real Math.** Each time they are used, there is also a plan to remove the need for them so that once the understanding is achieved, students focus attention on fluency and the abstract. The power of mathematics is in its abstractness.

Because the goal is to understand and use abstract mathematics, **Real Math** tries to provide several models such as craft sticks and rubber bands, fingers, or play money for base ten. Teachers should feel free to use still other models, but they should be sure to encourage abstract work without the manipulative as soon as students understand the underlying concept and are able to proceed without the physical crutch.

Below are common manipulatives and their principal purposes.

Manipulatives	Description	Purpose	Concepts to Develop
Money	Pennies, nickels, dimes, quarters, half dollars, $1, $5, $10, $20, $50, and $100 bills	Demonstrate concepts and values of money and applications of base-ten arithmetic and develop the division algorithm	• Number sense • Base-ten system • Place value
Pattern Blocks	Colorful blocks in different geometric shapes (hexagons, squares, trapezoids, triangles, and parallelograms, and rhombi) and colors	Create and demonstrate different types of color and shape patterns and to explore the mathematics of tiling and tesselations	• Number sense • Fractions • Geometry • Proportional reasoning
Attribute Blocks	Blocks in five shapes (circle, hexagon, rectangle, square, and triangle), different sizes, thicknesses, and colors	Build shape identification, logical thinking, and comparing and ordering concepts	• Number sense • Geometry
Platonic Solids	Wooden 3-D cone, cube, pyramid, and sphere	Develop geometric concepts of space figures	• Geometry
Mirror	Small nonbreakable mirror	Develop concepts of symmetry	• Geometry
Geoboard	Plastic board with pegs and rubber bands laid out in a square grid	Explore shapes, area, perimeter, symmetry, design, and fractions of shapes	• Geometry • Measurement
Protractor	Clear protractor in graduations from 0–180 degrees	Measure angles	• Geometry • Measurement
Compass	Center point and pencil	Draw and measure circles	• Geometry • Measurement
Gummed Tape	Adhesive paper tape	Create geometric figures and shapes	• Geometry
Fraction Tiles	Plastic tiles in sets of different fractional increments including $\frac{1}{8}, \frac{1}{4}, \frac{1}{3}, \frac{1}{2}$, and 1	Explore parts of wholes and adding and subtracting fractions	• Number sense • Fractions and rational numbers • Measurement
Spinners	Plastic spinners	Explore probability	• Probability • Number operations
Counters	Colored plastic disks	Explore patterns and counting	• Number sense • Counting • Probability • Number operations
Base-Ten Blocks	Plastic shapes in cubes, flats, rods, and units	Explore base-ten systems, counting, and number operations	• Number sense • Counting • Number operation
Craft Sticks and Rubber Bands	Wood sticks	Explore the base-ten system, place value, and standard multidigit addition and subtraction algorithms	• Number sense • Counting • Number operation
Counters	Plastic shapes	Explore counting and ordering numbers	• Number sense • Counting • Number operation
Math-Link Cubes	Plastic cubes that nest together	Explore counting, patterns, number operations, and composing and decomposing numbers	• Number sense • Counting • Patterns • Number operations • Rational number
Ruler and Tape Measure	Plastic customary and metric ruler and tape measure	Explore metric and customary measurements of length	• Measurement • Counting
Measuring Cups and Liter Pitcher	Plastic metric and customary measurement containers	Explore metric and customary measurements of capacity	• Measurement • Geometry • Fractions, decimals, and percents
Double Pan Balance and Platform Scales	Scale and balance and weight set	Explore metric and customary measurements of weight; help understand and solve linear equations	• Measurement
Thermometer	Celsius and Fahrenheit thermometers	Explore temperature measurements	• Measurement
Clock Face	Plastic analog clock face	Explore time measurements	• Measurement
Stopwatch	Electronic stopwatch	Explore time measurements	• Measurement • Fractions, decimals, and percents

Differentiating Instruction

> "In the context of education, we define *differentiation as* 'a teacher's reacting responsively to a learner's needs.' A teacher who is differentiating understands a student's need to express humor or work with a group, or to have additional teaching on a particular skill, or to delve more deeply into a particular topic....Differentiation is simply attending to the learning needs of a particular student or small group of students rather than the more typical pattern of teaching the class as though all individuals in it were basically alike. The goal of a differentiated classroom is maximum student growth and individual success."
>
> —Tomlinson, Carol Ann and Allan, Susan Demirsky. *Leadership for Differentiating Schools and Classrooms*. Alexandria, VA: Association for Supervision and Curriculum Development. 2000, p. 4.

All students can benefit from differentiated instruction. Differentiated instruction is dependent on ongoing, daily assessment and an interest in and understanding of how children learn and develop concepts.

How to Differentiate

Instruction can be differentiated in three key ways:

- **Content** What the teacher wants students to learn and the materials or mechanisms through which that is accomplished.

  Differentiating the content may entail teaching prerequisite concepts to students who need intervention or by asking questions that will cause students to think beyond the concepts covered in the lesson.

- **Process** How or what activities the students do to ensure that they use key skills to make sense of the content

  Differentiating the process may include grouping students in different ways, or alternating the pace of the lesson by moving more slowly or more quickly than originally planned. It might also include stressing different modalities: visual, auditory, or kinesthetic.

- **Product** How the student will demonstrate what he or she has come to know

  Differentiating the product may include assigning **Enrichment, Practice,** or **Reteach** activities to complete.

Differentiating instruction does not mean chaos or a classroom devoid of structure with everyone working on different goals. Lessons should have clearly defined purposes with students focused on one key understanding.

Analyzing Student Needs

Teachers successful at differentiating instruction are typically in tune with individual student needs. These needs vary and should be addressed in the context of the key ideas of the lesson. By preparing for differentiation and considering what you as a teacher might do when you encounter different student needs, you can have materials and strategies at the ready.

For a particular concept or lesson, different students may need

- challenge.
- social interaction.
- alternative instruction.
- independence.
- personal attention.
- serious intervention.
- language support.
- creative expression.
- cooperative grouping.
- extra practice.

 **Real Math** **and Differentiated Instruction**

Every lesson of *Real Math* begins with Planning for Learning: Differentiate Instruction ideas. These include

- *Intervention* that teach prerequisite skills for students who are not ready for the lesson concepts.
- *English Learner Preview* lesson that previews lesson concepts and vocabulary for students learning English.
- *Enrichment* ideas for expanding parts of the lesson if, as you are teaching, you realize students are already confident with the lesson concepts.
- *Practice* strategies for extending parts of the lesson, if you realize during the lesson that students would benefit from more practice.

- *Reteach* ideas for re-presenting and reinforcing the key teaching of the lesson, if you realize that students are not grasping the concepts.

During the lesson, Monitoring Student Progress presents tips for addressing specific concerns.

At the end of the lesson, Assessment Follow-Up provides activities to review, reteach, practice, or enrich lesson concepts depending on student performance.

Key Principles of a Differentiated Classroom

- The teacher is clear about what matters in subject matter.
- The teacher understands, appreciates, and builds upon student differences.

- Assessment and instruction are inseparable.
- The teacher adjusts content, process, and product in response to student readiness, interests, and learning profiles.
- All students participate in respectful work.
- Students and teachers are collaborators in learning.
- Goals of a differentiated classroom are maximum growth and individual success.
- Flexibility is the hallmark of a differentiated classroom.

Tomlinson, Carol Ann and Allan, Susan Demirsky. *Leadership for Differentiating Schools and Classrooms.* Alexandria, VA: Association for Supervision and Curriculum Development. 2000, p. 48.

Themes

Each chapter of **Real Math** involves a theme to provide application and context for the mathematics. The theme is evidenced in the Problem Solving activities in the Chapter Opener, the Exploring Problem Solving activities in the middle and end of the chapter, and the Thinking Stories in grades K–3.

Grade	K	1	2	3	4	5	6
Chapter 1	School	Animals	Library	Friendship	Risks and Consequences	Cooperation and Competition	Perserverance
Chapter 2	Animals	Animals	Pets	Friendship	Risks and Consequences	Cooperation and Competition	Perserverance
Chapter 3	Finding Friends	Neighborhood	Origami	City Wildlife	Dollars and Sense	Astronomy	Ancient Civilizations
Chapter 4	Wind	Games	Toy Factory	City Wildlife	Dollars and Sense	Astronomy	Ancient Civilizations
Chapter 5	Gardens	Neighborhood	Parks/Picnics	Imagination	From Mystery to Medicine	Heritage	Taking a Stand
Chapter 6	Flags, Parades, and Celebrations	Neighborhood	Zoo	Imagination	From Mystery to Medicine	Heritage	Taking a Stand
Chapter 7	Teamwork	Animals	Museums	Money	Survival	Making a New Nation	Beyond the Notes
Chapter 8	The Sea	Homes	Dinosaurs	Money	Survival	Making a New Nation	Beyond the Notes
Chapter 9		Neighborhood	Mail Delivery	Storytelling	Communication	Going West	Ecology
Chapter 10		Weather	Growing Plants	Storytelling	Communication	Going West	Ecology
Chapter 11		Homes	Ethnic Food	Country Life	A Changing America	Journeys and Quests	A Question of Value
Chapter 12			Frontier Homes	Country Life	A Changing America	Journeys and Quests	A Question of Value

Assessment

Much has been written about the importance of assessment. The Assessment Standards book from the National Council of Teachers of Mathematics tells us that classroom assessment should

- provide a rich variety of mathematical topics and problem situations.

- give students opportunities to investigate problems in many ways.

- question and listen to students.

- look for evidence of learning from many sources.

- expect students to use concepts and procedures effectively in solving problems.

The goals of assessment are to

- improve instruction by informing teachers of the effectiveness of their lessons.

- promote growth of students by identifying where they need additional instruction and support.

- recognize accomplishments.

Real Math and Assessment

Real Math provides opportunities for formal and informal assessments and convenient ways to record, track, and report on student achievements.

Informal Assessments

Informal assessment involves ongoing observations of student involvement in class activities. Informal assessments are tailored to evaluate students on the five areas of mathematic proficiency: computing, understanding, reasoning, applying, and engaging.

Every lesson includes two **Assessment** checkmarks in the **Teacher's Edition** next to activities tailored to reveal students' math proficiencies. These activities may include Guided Discussion, Skill Building, Strategy Building, Games, or Journals. The checkmarks alert teachers to carefully observe students during the activity. Rubric checklists in Assess and Differentiate of the lesson describe specific positive behaviors to look for as signs of development. As teachers become familiar with the rubric checklists, they can access them through memory. Teachers can record their observations in the Daily Class Assessment Records for each proficiency.

Computing	• respond accurately • respond quickly • respond with confidence • self-correct
Understanding	• make important observations • extend or generalize learning • provide insightful answers • pose insightful questions
Reasoning	• provide a clear explanation • communicate reasons and strategies • choose appropriate strategies • argue logically
Applying	• apply learning in new situations • contribute concepts • contribute answers • connect mathematics to real-world situations
Engaging	• pay attention to others' contributions • contribute information and ideas • improve on a strategy • reflect on and check the accuracy of his or her work

Daily checklist observations can be summarized in the Student Assessment Record for the chapter or in **eAssess** to provide a long-term holistic view of student proficiency. If teachers record these observations, these daily informal assessments can be powerful indicators of student proficiency, and as such help inform instruction, as well as provide feedback to students and their parents.

Formal Assessment

There are several opportunities for formal assessment in every chapter. All assessments can be recorded further in the Student Assessment Record or in **eAssess** for every chapter to provide a comprehensive view of student achievement.

- **Pretests** test prerequisite and chapter concepts to provide a diagnostic assessment of student understanding for the upcoming chapter.
- **Speed Tests** appear in lessons to test computational fluency.
- **Mastery Checkpoints** provide assessments for skills that should be mastered at particular points in the program. The Mastery Checkpoint Chart provides a class view of student progress toward mastery of particular skills.
- **Oral Assessment** in the middle of the chapter is an opportunity for teachers to interact individually with students to assess their growth in proficiency. An Individual Oral Assessment recording sheet is available in **Assessment** for each Oral Assessment for teacher convenience.
- **Daily Quizzes** are available to provide a quick review and assessment of student understanding of lesson concepts and skills.
- **Chapter Tests** offer a way to assess student understanding of chapter content and skills.

 Assess

The **eAssess** program offers a powerful way to record and track student progress. Teachers can enter data on a daily or weekly basis. The more data a teacher inputs—including records of Formal and Informal Assessments, completion of student pages, completion of projects, and additional activities—the more comprehensive and reliable the reports that can be generated will be.

Using **eAssess,** teachers can generate reports that show student performance in reference to the entire class, to the individual, and to state and/or national standards. These reports provide a comprehensive view of individual student and class performance that can provide valuable feedback for your instruction and for student and parent conferences.

More information, including masters of recording sheets and tests, can be found in **Assessment.**

Handwriting Models

Starting point, straight down

Starting point, around right, slanting left, and straight across right

Starting point, around right, in at the middle, and around right

Starting point, straight down, and straight across right. Starting point, straight down, and crossing line
(Avoid confusion with 9.)

Straight down, curve around right and up. Starting point, straight across right
(Avoid confusion with S.)

Starting point, slanting left, around the bottom curving up around left and into the curve

Starting point, straight across right, and slanting down left

Starting point, curving left, curving down and around right, slanting up right to starting point

Starting point, curving around left all the way, and straight down

Starting point, straight down. Starting point, curving left all the way around to starting point

*Students follow natural developmental progressions in learning, developing mathematical ideas in their own ways. Curriculum research has revealed sequences of activities that are effective in guiding students through these levels of thinking. These developmental paths can be described as learning trajectories. Each learning trajectory has levels of understanding, each more sophisticated than the last, and with tasks that promote growth from one level to the next. The **Building Blocks** Learning Trajectories give simple labels, descriptions, and examples of each level. Complete learning trajectories describe the goals of learning, the thinking and learning processes of students at various levels, and the learning activities in which they might engage.*

Learning Trajectories for Primary Grades Mathematics

Developmental Levels

The following provides the developmental levels from the first signs of development in different strands of mathematics through approximately age 8. Research shows that when teachers understand how students develop mathematics understanding, they are more effective in questioning, analyzing, and providing activities that further students' development than teachers who are unaware of the development process. Consequently, students have a much richer and more successful math experience in the primary grades.

Frequently Asked Questions (FAQ)

1. ***When are students "at" a level?*** Students are at a certain level when most of their behaviors reflect the thinking—ideas and skills—of that level. Often, they show a few behaviors from the next (and previous) levels as they learn.

2. ***Can students work at more than one level at the same time?*** Yes, although most students work mainly at one level or in transition between two levels (naturally, if they are tired or distracted, they may operate at a much lower level). Levels are not "absolute." They are "benchmarks" of complex growth that represent distinct ways of thinking. So, another way to think of them is as a sequence of different patterns of thinking. Students are continually learning within levels and moving between them.

3. ***Can students jump ahead?*** Yes, especially if there are separate "subtopics." For example, we have combined many counting competencies into one "Counting" sequence with subtopics, such as verbal counting skills. Some students learn to count to 100 at age six after

learning to count objects to 10 or more; some may learn that verbal skill earlier. The subtopic of verbal counting skills would still be followed.

4. ***How do these developmental levels support teaching and learning?*** The levels help teachers, as well as curriculum developers, to assess, teach, and sequence activities. *Teachers who understand learning trajectories and the developmental levels that are at their foundation are more effective and efficient.* Through planned teaching and also by encouraging informal, incidental mathematics, teachers help students learn *at an appropriate and deep level.*

5. ***Should I plan to help students develop just the levels that correspond to my students' ages?*** No! The ages in the table are typical ages when students develop these ideas. *But these are rough guides only—students differ widely.* Furthermore, the ages below are lower bounds on what students achieve without instruction. So, these are *"starting levels,"* not goals. We have found that students who are provided high-quality mathematics experiences are capable of developing to levels one or more years beyond their peers.

Each column in the table, such as "Counting," represents a main developmental progression that underlies the learning trajectory for that topic.

Clements, D. H., Sarama, J., & DiBiase, A.M. *Engaging Young Students in Mathematics: Standards for Early Childhood Mathematics Education.* Mahwah, NJ: Lawrence Erlbaum Associates.

Clements, D. H., & Sarama, J. "Early Childhood Mathematics Learning." In F. K. Lester, Jr. (Ed.), *Second Handbook of Research on Mathematics Teaching and Learning.* New York: Information Age Publishing.

Developmental Levels for Counting

The ability to count with confidence develops over the course of several years. Beginning in infancy, students show signs of understanding numbers. With instruction and number experience, most students can count fluently by age eight, with much progress in counting occurring in kindergarten and first grade. Most students follow a natural developmental progression in learning to count with recognizable stages or levels. This developmental path can be described as part of a learning trajectory.

Age Range	Level Name	Level	Description
1–2	Precounter	1	A student at the earliest level of counting may name some numbers meaninglessly. The student may skip numbers and have no sense of sequence.
1–2	Chanter	2	At this level, a student may sing-song numbers, but without meaning.
2	Reciter	3	At this level, the student may verbally count with separate words, but not necessarily in the correct order.
3	Reciter (10)	4	A student at this level may verbally count to 10 with some correspondence with objects. He or she may point to objects to count a few items, but then lose track.
3	Corresponder	5	At this level, a student may keep one-to-one correspondence between counting words and objects—at least for small groups of objects laid in a line. A corresponder may answer "how many" by recounting the objects starting over with one each time.
4	Counter (Small Numbers)	6	At around 4 years of age, students may begin to count meaningfully. They may accurately count objects to 5 and answer the "how many" question with the last number counted. These students may count verbally to 10 and may write or draw to represent 1–5.
4	Producer—Counter to (Small Numbers)	7	The next level after counting small numbers is to produce a group of four objects. When asked to show four of something, for example, this student may give four objects.
4	Counter (10)	8	This student may count structured arrangements of objects to 10. He or she may be able to write or draw to represent 10 and may accurately count a line of nine blocks and say there are 9. A student at this level may find the number just after or just before another number, but only by counting up from 1.
5	Counter and Producer—Counter to (10+)	10	Around 5 years of age, students may begin to count out objects accurately to 10 and then beyond to 30. They may keep track of objects that have and have not been counted, even in different arrangements. They may write or draw to represent 1 to 10 and then 20 and 30, and may give the next number to 20 or 30. They also begin to recognize errors in others' counting and are able to eliminate most errors in their own counting.

Age Range	Level Name	Level	Description
5	Counter Backward from 10	10	Another milestone at about age 5 is being able to count backward from 10.
6	Counter from N (N+1, N−1)	11	Around 6 years of age, students may begin to count on, counting verbally and with objects from numbers other than 1. Another noticeable accomplishment is that students may determine the number immediately before or after another number without having to start back at 1.
6	Skip Counting by 10s to 100	12	A student at this level may count by 10s to 100. They may count through decades knowing that 40 comes after 39, for example.
6	Counter to 100	13	A student at this level may count by 1s through 100, including the decade transitions from 39 to 40, 49 to 50, and so on.
6	Counter On Using Patterns	14	At this level, a student may keep track of counting acts by using numerical patterns, such as tapping as he or she counts.
6	Skip Counter	15	At this level, students can count by 5s and 2s with understanding.
6	Counter of Imagined Items	16	At this level, a student may count mental images of hidden objects.
6	Counter On Keeping Track	17	A student at this level may keep track of counting acts numerically with the ability to count up one to four more from a given number.
6	Counter of Quantitative Units	18	At this level, a student can count unusual units, such as "wholes" when shown combinations of wholes and parts. For example, when shown three whole plastic eggs and four halves, a student at this level will say there are five whole eggs.
6	Counter to 200	19	At this level, a student may count accurately to 200 and beyond, recognizing the patterns of ones, tens, and hundreds.
7	Number Conserver	20	A major milestone around age 7 is the ability to conserve number. A student who conserves number understands that a number is unchanged even if a group of objects is rearranged. For example, if there is a row of ten buttons, the student understands there are still ten without recounting, even if they are rearranged in a long row or a circle.
7	Counter Forward and Back	21	A student at this level may count in either direction and recognize that sequence of decades mirrors single-digit sequence.

Developmental Levels for Comparing and Ordering Numbers

Comparing and ordering sets is a critical skill for students as they determine whether one set is larger than another in order to make sure sets are equal and "fair." Prekindergartners can learn to use matching to compare collections or to create equivalent collections. Finding out how many more or fewer in one collection is more demanding than simply comparing two collections. The ability to compare and order sets with fluency develops over the course of several years. With instruction and number experience, most students develop foundational understanding of number relationships and place value at ages four and five. Most students follow a natural developmental progression in learning to compare and order numbers with recognizable stages or levels. This developmental path can be described as part of a learning trajectory.

Age Range	Level Name	Level	Description
2	Object Corresponder	1	At this early level, a student puts objects into one-to-one correspondence, but with only intuitive understanding of resulting equivalence. For example, a student may know that each carton has a straw, but does not necessarily know there are the same numbers of straws and cartons.
2	Perceptual Comparer	2	At this level, a student can compare collections that are quite different in size (for example, one is at least twice the other) and know that one has more than the other. If the collections are similar, the student can compare very small collections.
3	First-Second Ordinal Counter	3	At this level the student can identify the "first" and often "second" object in a sequence.
3	Nonverbal Comparer of Similar Items	4	At this level, a student can identify that different organizations of the same number of small groups are equal and different from other sets (1–4 items). For example, a student can identify ●●● and ●●● as equal and different from ●● or ●●.
3	Nonverbal Comparer of Dissimilar Items	5	At this level, a student can match small, equal collections of dissimilar items, such as shells and dots, and show that they are the same number.
6	Nonverbal Comparer of Dissimilar Items	6	A student at this level can match small, equal collections of shells and dots, thus showing they are the same number.
4	Matching Comparer	7	As students progress, they begin to compare groups of 1–6 by matching. For example, a student gives one toy bone to every dog and says there are the same number of dogs and bones.
4	Knows-to-Count Comparer	8	A significant step occurs when the student begins to count collections to compare. At the early levels, students are not always accurate when a larger collection's objects are smaller in size than the objects in the smaller collection. For example, a student at this level may accurately count two equal collections, but when asked, says the collection of larger blocks has more.
4	Counting Comparer (Same Size)	9	At this level, students make accurate comparisons via counting, but only when objects are about the same size and groups are small (about 1–5 items).
5	Counting Comparer (5)	10	As students develop their ability to compare sets, they compare accurately by counting, even when a larger collection's objects are smaller. A student at this level can figure out how many more or less.

Age Range	Level Name	Level	Description
5	Ordinal Counter	11	At this level, a student identifies and uses ordinal numbers from "first" to "tenth." For example, the student can identify who is "third in line."
6	Counting Comparer (10)	12	This level can be observed when the student compares sets by counting, even when a larger collection's objects are smaller, up to 10. A student at this level can accurately count two collections of 9 items each, and says they have the same number, even if one collection has larger blocks.
6	Mental Number Line to 10	13	As students move into this level, they begin to use mental rather than physical images and knowledge of number relationships to determine relative size and position. For example, a student at this level can answer which number is closer to 6, 4 or 9, without counting physical objects.
6	Serial Orderer to 6+	14	The student demonstrates development in comparing when they begin to order lengths marked into units (1–6, then beyond). For example, given towers of cubes, this student can put them in order, 1 to 6. Later the student begins to order collections. For example, given cards with one to six dots on them, the student can put them in order.
7	Place Value Comparer	15	Further development is made when a student begins to compare numbers with place value understanding. For example, a student at this level can explain that "63 is more than 59 because six tens is more than five tens, even if there are more than three ones."
7	Mental Number Line to 100	16	Students demonstrate the next level in comparing and ordering when they can use mental images and knowledge of number relationships, including ones embedded in tens, to determine relative size and position. For example, when asked, "Which is closer to 45, 30 or 50?" a student at this level may say "45 is right next to 50, but 30 isn't."
8+	Mental Number Line to 1,000s	17	At about age 8, students may begin to use mental images of numbers up to 1,000 and knowledge of number relationships, including place value, to determine relative size and position. For example, when asked, "Which is closer to 3,500—2,000 or 7,000?" a student at this level may say "70 is double 35, but 20 is only fifteen from 35, so twenty hundreds, 2,000, is closer."

Developmental Levels for Recognizing Number and Subitizing (Instantly Recognizing)

The ability to recognize number values develops over the course of several years and is a foundational part of number sense. Beginning at about age two, students begin to name groups of objects. The ability to instantly know how many are in a group, called *subitizing*, begins at about age three. By age eight, with instruction and number experience, most students can identify groups of items and use place values and multiplication skills to count them. Most students follow a natural developmental progression in learning to count with recognizable stages or levels. This developmental path can be described as part of a learning trajectory.

Age Range	Level Name	Level	Description
2	Small Collection Namer	1	The first sign occurs when the student can name groups of 1 to 2, sometimes 3. For example, when shown a pair of shoes, this young student says, "two shoes."
3	Nonverbal Subitizer	2	This level occurs when, shown a small collection (1 to 4), the student can put out a matching group nonverbally, but cannot necessarily give the number telling how many. For example, when 4 objects are shown, the student makes a set of 4 objects to "match."
3	Maker of Small Collections	3	At this level, a student can nonverbally make a small collection (no more than 5, usually 1 to 3) with the same number as another collection. For example, when shown a collection of 3, the student makes another collection of 3.
4	Perceptual Subitizer to 4	4	Progress is made when a student instantly recognizes collections up to 4 and verbally names the number of items. For example, when shown 4 objects briefly, the student says "4."
5	Perceptual Subitizer to 5	5	This level is the ability to instantly recognize collections up to 5 and verbally name the number of items. For example, when shown 5 objects, the student says "5."

Age Range	Level Name	Level	Description
5	Conceptual Subitizer to 5	6	At this level, the student can verbally label all arrangements to 5, using groups. For example, a student at this level might say, "I saw 2 and 2, and so I saw 4."
5	Conceptual Subitizer to 10	7	This step is when the student can verbally label most arrangements to 6, then up to 10, using groups. For example, a student at this level might say, "In my mind, I made 2 groups of 3 and 1 more, so 7."
6	Conceptual Subitizer to 20	8	Next, a student can verbally label structured arrangements up to 20, using groups. For example, the student may say, "I saw 3 fives, so 5, 10, 15."
7	Conceptual Subitizer with Place Value and Skip Counting	9	At this level, a student is able to use skip counting and place value to verbally label structured arrangements. For example, the student may say, "I saw groups of tens and twos, so 10, 20, 30, 40, 42, 44, 46...46!"
8+	Conceptual Subitizer with Place Value and Multiplication	10	As students develop their ability to subitize, they use groups, multiplication, and place value to verbally label structured arrangements. At this level, a student may say, "I saw groups of tens and threes, so I thought, 5 tens is 50 and 4 threes is 12, so 62 in all."

Developmental Levels for Composing (Knowing Combinations of Numbers)

Composing and decomposing are combining and separating operations that allow students to build concepts of "parts" and "wholes." Most prekindergartners can "see" that two items and one item make three items. Later, students learn to separate a group into parts in various ways and then to count to produce all of the number "partners" of a given number. Eventually students think of a number and know the different addition facts that make that number. Most students follow a natural developmental progression in learning to compose and decompose numbers with recognizable stages or levels. This developmental path can be described as part of a learning trajectory.

Age Range	Level Name	Level	Description
4	Pre-Part-Whole Recognizer	1	At the earliest levels of composing, a student only nonverbally recognizes parts and wholes. For example, when shown 4 red blocks and 2 blue blocks, a young student may intuitively appreciate that "all the blocks" includes the red and blue blocks, but when asked how many there are in all, the student may name a small number, such as 1.
5	Inexact Part-Whole Recognizer	2	A sign of development is that the student knows a whole is bigger than parts, but does not accurately quantify. For example, when shown 4 red blocks and 2 blue blocks and asked how many there are in all, the student may name a "large number," such as 5 or 10.
5	Composer to 4, then 5	3	At this level, a student begins to know number combinations. A student at this level quickly names parts of any whole, or the whole given the parts. For example, when shown 4, then 1 is secretly hidden, and then shown the 3 remaining, the student may quickly say "1" is hidden.

Age Range	Level Name	Level	Description
6	Composer to 7	4	The next sign of development is when a student knows number combinations to totals of 7. A student at this level quickly names parts of any whole, or the whole when given parts, and can double numbers to 10. For example, when shown 6, then 4 are secretly hidden, and then shown the 2 remaining, the student may quickly say "4" are hidden.
6	Composer to 10	5	This level is when a student knows number combinations to totals of 10. A student at this level may quickly name parts of any whole, or the whole when given parts, and can double numbers to 20. For example, this student would be able to say "9 and 9 is 18."
7	Composer with Tens and Ones	6	At this level, the student understands two-digit numbers as tens and ones, can count with dimes and pennies, and can perform two-digit addition with regrouping. For example, a student at this level may explain, "17 and 36 is like 17 and 3, which is 20, and 33, which is 53."

Developmental Levels for Adding and Subtracting

Single-digit addition and subtraction are generally characterized as "math facts." It is assumed students must memorize these facts, yet research has shown that addition and subtraction have their roots in counting, counting on, number sense, the ability to compose and decompose numbers, and place value. Research has also shown that learning methods for addition and subtraction with understanding is much more effective than rote memorization of seemingly isolated facts. Most students follow an observable developmental progression in learning to add and subtract numbers with recognizable stages or levels. This developmental path can be described as part of a learning trajectory.

Age Range	Level Name	Level	Description
1	Pre +/−	1	At the earliest level, a student shows no sign of being able to add or subtract.
3	Nonverbal +/−	2	The first sign is when a student can add and subtract very small collections nonverbally. For example, when shown 2 objects, then 1 object being hidden under a napkin, the student identifies or makes a set of 3 objects to "match."
4	Small Number +/−	3	This level is when a student can find sums for joining problems up to 3 + 2 by counting with objects. For example, when asked, "You have 2 balls and get 1 more. How many in all?" the student may count out 2, then count out 1 more, then count all 3: "1, 2, 3, 3!"
5	Find Result +/−	4	**Addition** Evidence of this level in addition is when a student can find sums for joining (you had 3 apples and get 3 more; how many do you have in all?) and part-part-whole (there are 6 girls and 5 boys on the playground; how many students were there in all?) problems by direct modeling, counting all, with objects. For example, when asked, "You have 2 red balls and 3 blue balls. How many in all?" the student may count out 2 red, then count out 3 blue, then count all 5. **Subtraction** In subtraction, a student can also solve take-away problems by separating with objects. For example, when asked, "You have 5 balls and give 2 to Tom. How many do you have left?" the student may count out 5 balls, then take away 2, and then count the remaining 3.
5	Find Change +/−	5	**Addition** At this level, a student can find the missing addend (5 + _ = 7) by adding on objects. For example, when asked, "You have 5 balls and then get some more. Now you have 7 in all. How many did you get?" The student may count out 5, then count those 5 again starting at 1, then add more, counting "6, 7," then count the balls added to find the answer, 2. **Subtraction** A student can compare by matching in simple situations. For example, when asked, "Here are 6 dogs and 4 balls. If we give a ball to each dog, how many dogs will not get a ball?" a student at this level may count out 6 dogs, match 4 balls to 4 of them, then count the 2 dogs that have no ball.
5	Make It	6	A significant advancement occurs when a student is able to count on. This student can add on objects to make one number into another without counting from 1. For example, when told, "This puppet has 4 balls, but she should have 6. Make it 6," the student may put up 4 fingers on one hand, immediately count up from 4 while putting up 2 fingers on the other hand, saying, "5, 6," and then count or recognize the 2 fingers.

Age Range	Level Name	Level	Description
6	Counting Strategies +/−	7	This level occurs when a student can find sums for joining (you had 8 apples and get 3 more...) and part-part-whole (6 girls and 5 boys...) problems with finger patterns or by adding on objects or counting on. For example, when asked "How much is 4 and 3 more?" the student may answer "4...5, 6, 7. 7!" Students at this level can also solve missing addend (3 + _ = 7) or compare problems by counting on. When asked, for example, "You have 6 balls. How many more would you need to have 8?" the student may say, "6, 7 [puts up first finger], 8 [puts up second finger]. 2!"
6	Part-Whole +/−	8	Further development has occurred when the student has part-whole understanding. This student can solve problems using flexible strategies and some derived facts (for example, "5 + 5 is 10, so 5 + 6 is 11"), can sometimes do start-unknown problems (_ + 6 = 11), but only by trial and error. When asked, "You had some balls. Then you get 6 more. Now you have 11 balls. How many did you start with?" this student may lay out 6, then 3, count, and get 9. The student may put 1 more, say 10, then put 1 more. The student may count up from 6 to 11, then recount the group added, and say, "5!"
6	Numbers-in-Numbers +/−	9	Evidence of this level is when a student recognizes that a number is part of a whole and can solve problems when the start is unknown (_ + 4 = 9) with counting strategies. For example, when asked, "You have some balls, then you get 4 more balls, now you have 9. How many did you have to start with?" this student may count, putting up fingers, "5, 6, 7, 8, 9." The student may look at his or her fingers and say, "5!"
7	Deriver +/−	10	At this level, a student can use flexible strategies and derived combinations (for example, "7 + 7 is 14, so 7 + 8 is 15") to solve all types of problems. For example, when asked, "What's 7 plus 8?" this student thinks: 7 + 8 = 7 + [7 + 1] = [7 + 7] + 1 = 14 + 1 = 15. The student can also solve multidigit problems by incrementing or combining 10s and 1s. For example, when asked "What's 28 + 35?" this student may think: 20 + 30 = 50; + 8 = 58; 2 more is 60, and 3 more is 63. Combining 10s and 1s: 20 + 30 = 50. 8 + 5 is like 8 plus 2 and 3 more, so it is 13–50 and 13 is 63.
8+	Problem Solver +/−	11	As students develop their addition and subtraction abilities, they can solve by using flexible strategies and many known combinations. For example, when asked, "If I have 13 and you have 9, how could we have the same number?" this student may say, "9 and 1 is 10, then 3 more makes 13. 1 and 3 is 4. I need 4 more!"
8+	Multidigit +/−	12	Further development is shown when students can use composition of 10s and all previous strategies to solve multidigit +/− problems. For example, when asked, "What's 37 − 18?" this student may say, "Take 1 ten off the 3 tens; that's 2 tens. Take 7 off the 7. That's 2 tens and 0...20. I have one more to take off. That's 19." Or, when asked, "What's 28 + 35?" this child may think, 30 + 35 would be 65. But it's 28, so it's 2 less...63.

Developmental Levels for Multiplying and Dividing

Multiplication and division builds on addition and subtraction understanding and is dependent upon counting and place-value concepts. As students begin to learn to multiply, they make equal groups and count them all. They then learn skip counting and derive related products from products they know. Finding and using patterns aids in learning multiplication and division facts with understanding. Students typically follow an observable developmental progression in learning to multiply and divide numbers with recognizable stages or levels. This developmental path can be described as part of a learning trajectory.

Age Range	Level Name	Level	Description
2	Non-quantitative Sharer "Dumper"	1	Multiplication and division concepts begin very early with the problem of sharing. Early evidence of these concepts can be observed when a student dumps out blocks and gives some (not an equal number) to each person.
3	Beginning Grouper and Distributive Sharer	2	Progression to this level can be observed when a student is able to make small groups (fewer than 5). This student can share by "dealing out," but often only between 2 people, although he or she may not appreciate the numerical result. For example, to share 4 blocks, this student may give each person a block, check that each person has one, and repeat this.
4	Grouper and Distributive Sharer	3	The next level occurs when a student makes small equal groups (fewer than 6). This student can deal out equally between 2 or more recipients, but may not understand that equal quantities are produced. For example, the student may share 6 blocks by dealing out blocks to herself and a friend one at a time.
5	Concrete Modeler $\times/\div$	4	As students develop, they are able to solve small-number multiplying problems by grouping—making each group and counting all. At this level, a student can solve division/sharing problems with informal strategies, using concrete objects—up to 20 objects and 2 to 5 people—although the student may not understand equivalence of groups. For example, the student may distribute 20 objects by dealing out 2 blocks to each of 5 people, then 1 to each, until the blocks are gone.
6	Parts and Wholes $\times/\div$	5	A new level is evidenced when the student understands the inverse relation between divisor and quotient. For example, this student may understand "If you share with more people, each person gets fewer."

Age Range	Level Name	Level	Description
7	Skip Counter $\times/\div$	6	As students develop understanding in multiplication and division, they begin to use skip counting for multiplication and for measurement division (finding out how many groups). For example, given 20 blocks, 4 to each person, and asked how many people, the student may skip count by 4, holding up 1 finger for each count of 4. A student at this level may also use trial and error for partitive division (finding out how many in each group). For example, given 20 blocks, 5 people, and asked how many each should get, this student may give 3 to each, then 1 more, then 1 more.
8+	Deriver $\times/\div$	7	At this level, students use strategies and derived combinations and solve multidigit problems by operating on tens and ones separately. For example, a student at this level may explain "7 × 6, five 7s is 35, so 7 more is 42."
8+	Array Quantifier	8	Further development can be observed when a student begins to work with arrays. For example, given 7 × 4 with most of 5 × 4 covered, a student at this level may say, "There are 8 in these 2 rows, and 5 rows of 4 is 20, so 28 in all."
8+	Partitive Divisor	9	This level can be observed when a student is able to figure out how many are in each group. For example, given 20 blocks, 5 people, and asked how many each should get, a student at this level may say, "4, because 5 groups of 4 is 20."
8+	Multidigit $\times/\div$	10	As students progress, they begin to use multiple strategies for multiplication and division, from compensating to paper-and-pencil procedures. For example, a student becoming fluent in multiplication might explain that "19 times 5 is 95, because 20 fives is 100, and 1 less five is 95."

Learning Trajectories

Developmental Levels for Measuring

Measurement is one of the main real-world applications of mathematics. Counting is a type of measurement which determines how many items are in a collection. Measurement also involves assigning a number to attributes of length, area, and weight. Prekindergarten students know that mass, weight, and length exist, but they do not know how to reason about these or to accurately measure them. As students develop their understanding of measurement, they begin to use tools to measure and understand the need for standard units of measure. Students typically follow an observable developmental progression in learning to measure with recognizable stages or levels. This developmental path can be described as part of a learning trajectory.

Age Range	Level Name	Level	Description
3	Length Quantity Recognizer	1	At the earliest level, students can identify length as an attribute. For example, they might say, "I'm tall, see?"
4	Length Direct Comparer	2	In this level, students can physically align 2 objects to determine which is longer or if they are the same length. For example, they can stand 2 sticks up next to each other on a table and say, "This one's bigger."
5	Indirect Length Comparer	3	A sign of further development is when a student can compare the length of 2 objects by representing them with a third object. For example, a student might compare the length of 2 objects with a piece of string. Additional evidence of this level is that when asked to measure, the student may assign a length by guessing or moving along a length while counting (without equal-length units). The student may also move a finger along a line segment, saying 10, 20, 30, 31, 32.
6	Serial Orderer to 6+	4	At this level, a student can order lengths, marked in 1 to 6 units. For example, given towers of cubes, a student at this level may put them in order, 1 to 6.
6	End-to-End Length Measurer	5	At this level, the student can lay units end-to-end, although he or she may not see the need for equal-length units. For example, a student might lay 9-inch cubes in a line beside a book to measure how long it is.

Age Range	Level Name	Level	Description
7	Length Unit Iterator	6	A significant change occurs when a student can use a ruler and see the need for identical units.
7	Length Unit Relater	7	At this level, a student can relate size and number of units. For example, the student may explain, "If you measure with centimeters instead of inches, you'll need more of them because each one is smaller."
8	Length Measurer	8	As students develop measurement ability, they begin to measure, knowing the need for identical units, the relationships between different units, partitions of unit, and the zero point on rulers. At this level, the student also begins to estimate. The student may explain, "I used a meterstick 3 times, then there was a little left over. So, I lined it up from 0 and found 14 centimeters. So, it's 3 meters, 14 centimeters in all."
8	Conceptual Ruler Measurer	9	Further development in measurement is evidenced when a student possesses an "internal" measurement tool. At this level, the student mentally moves along an object, segmenting it, and counting the segments. This student also uses arithmetic to measure and estimates with accuracy. For example, a student at this level may explain, "I imagine one meterstick after another along the edge of the room. That's how I estimated the room's length to be 9 meters."

Developmental Levels for Recognizing Geometric Shapes

Geometric shapes can be used to represent and understand objects. Analyzing, comparing, and classifying shapes helps create new knowledge of shapes and their relationships. Shapes can be decomposed or composed into other shapes. Through their everyday activities, students build both intuitive and explicit knowledge of geometric figures. Most students can recognize and name basic two-dimensional shapes at four years of age. However, young students can learn richer concepts about shape if they have varied examples and nonexamples of shape, discussions about shapes and their characteristics, a wide variety of shape classes, and interesting tasks. Students typically follow an observable developmental progression in learning about shapes with recognizable stages or levels. This developmental path can be described as part of a learning trajectory.

Age Range	Level Name	Level	Description
2	Shape Matcher—Identical	1	The earliest sign of understanding shape is when a student can match basic shapes (circle, square, typical triangle) with the same size and orientation.
2	Sizes	2	A sign of development is when a student can match basic shapes with different sizes.
2	Orientations	3	This level of development is when a student can match basic shapes with different orientations.
3	Shape Recognizer—Typical	4	A sign of development is when a student can recognize and name a prototypical circle, square, and, less often, a typical triangle. For example, the student names this a square. Some students may name different sizes, shapes, and orientations of rectangles, but also accept some shapes that look rectangular but are not rectangles. Students name these shapes "rectangles" (including the nonrectangular parallelogram).
3	Shape Matcher—More Shapes	5	As students develop understanding of shape, they can match a wider variety of shapes with the same size and orientation.
4	Shape Recognizer—Circles, Squares, and Triangles	6	This sign of development is when a student can recognize some nonprototypical squares and triangles and may recognize some rectangles, but usually not rhombi (diamonds). Often, the student does not differentiate sides/corners. The student at this level may name these as triangles.
4	Constructor of Shapes from Parts Looks Like	7	A significant sign of development is when a student represents a shape by making a shape "look like" a goal shape. For example, when asked to make a triangle with sticks, the student may create the following: .

Age Range	Level Name	Level	Description
5	Shape Recognizer—All Rectangles	8	As students develop understanding of shape, they recognize more rectangle sizes, shapes, and orientations of rectangles. For example, a student at this level may correctly name these shapes "rectangles."
5	Side Recognizer	9	A sign of development is when a student recognizes parts of shapes and identifies sides as distinct geometric objects. For example, when asked what this shape is, the student may say it is a quadrilateral (or has 4 sides) after counting and running a finger along the length of each side.
5	Angle Recognizer	10	At this level, a student can recognize angles as separate geometric objects. For example, when asked, "Why is this a triangle," the student may say, "It has three angles" and count them, pointing clearly to each vertex (point at the corner).
5	Shape Recognizer—More Shapes	11	As students develop, they are able to recognize most basic shapes and prototypical examples of other shapes, such as hexagon, rhombus (diamond), and trapezoid. For example, a student can correctly identify and name all the following shapes:
6	Shape Identifier	12	At this level, the student can name most common shapes, including rhombi, "ellipses-is-not-circle." A student at this level implicitly recognizes right angles, so distinguishes between a rectangle and a parallelogram without right angles. A student may correctly name all the following shapes:
6	Angle Matcher	13	A sign of development is when the student can match angles concretely. For example, given several triangles, the student may find two with the same angles by laying the angles on top of one another.

Learning Trajectories

Age Range	Level Name	Level	Description
7	Parts of Shapes Identifier	14	At this level, the student can identify shapes in terms of their components. For example, the student may say, "No matter how skinny it looks, that's a triangle because it has 3 sides and 3 angles."
7	Constructor of Shapes from Parts—Exact	15	A significant step is when the student can represent a shape with completely correct construction, based on knowledge of components and relationships. For example, when asked to make a triangle with sticks, the student may create the following:
8	Shape Class Identifier	16	As students develop, they begin to use class membership (for example, to sort) not explicitly based on properties. For example, a student at this level may say, "I put the triangles over here, and the quadrilaterals, including squares, rectangles, rhombi, and trapezoids, over there."
8	Shape Property Identifier	17	At this level, a student can use properties explicitly. For example, a student may say, "I put the shapes with opposite sides that are parallel over here, and those with 4 sides but not both pairs of sides parallel over there."

Age Range	Level Name	Level	Description
8	Angle Size Comparer	18	The next sign of development is when a student can separate and compare angle sizes. For example, the student may say, "I put all the shapes that have right angles here, and all the ones that have bigger or smaller angles over there."
8	Angle Measurer	19	A significant step in development is when a student can use a protractor to measure angles.
8	Property Class Identifier	20	The next sign of development is when a student can use class membership for shapes (for example, to sort or consider shapes "similar") explicitly based on properties, including angle measure. For example, the student may say, "I put the equilateral triangles over here, and the right triangles over here."
8	Angle Synthesizer	21	As students develop understanding of shape, they can combine various meanings of angle (turn, corner, slant). For example, a student at this level could explain, "This ramp is at a 45° angle to the ground."

Developmental Levels for Composing Geometric Shapes

Students move through levels in the composition and decomposition of two-dimensional figures. Very young students cannot compose shapes but then gain ability to combine shapes into pictures, synthesize combinations of shapes into new shapes, and eventually substitute and build different kinds of shapes. Students typically follow an observable developmental progression in learning to compose shapes with recognizable stages or levels. This developmental path can be described as part of a learning trajectory.

Age Range	Level Name	Level	Description
2	Pre-Composer	1	The earliest sign of development is when a student can manipulate shapes as individuals, but is unable to combine them to compose a larger shape.
3	Pre-Decomposer	2	At this level, a student can decompose shapes, but only by trial and error.
4	Piece Assembler	3	Around age 4, a student can begin to make pictures in which each shape represents a unique role (for example, one shape for each body part) and shapes touch. A student at this level can fill simple outline puzzles using trial and error.
5	Picture Maker	4	As students develop, they are able to put several shapes together to make one part of a picture (for example, 2 shapes for 1 arm). A student at this level uses trial and error and does not anticipate creation of the new geometric shape. The student can choose shapes using "general shape" or side length, and fill "easy" outline puzzles that suggest the placement of each shape (but note that the student is trying to put a square in the puzzle where its right angles will not fit).
5	Simple Decomposer	5	A significant step occurs when the student is able to decompose ("take apart" into smaller shapes) simple shapes that have obvious clues as to their decomposition.
5	Shape Composer	6	A sign of development is when a student composes shapes with anticipation ("I know what will fit!"). A student at this level chooses shapes using angles as well as side lengths. Rotation and flipping are used intentionally to select and place shapes.

Age Range	Level Name	Level	Description
6	Substitution Composer	7	A sign of development is when a student is able to make new shapes out of smaller shapes and uses trial and error to substitute groups of shapes for other shapes in order to create new shapes in different ways. For example, the student can substitute shapes to fill outline puzzles in different ways.
6	Shape Decomposer (with Help)	8	As students develop, they can decompose shapes by using imagery that is suggested and supported by the task or environment.
7	Shape Composite Repeater	9	This level is demonstrated when the student can construct and duplicate units of units (shapes made from other shapes) intentionally, and understands each as being both multiple, small shapes and one larger shape. For example, the student may continue a pattern of shapes that leads to tiling.
7	Shape Decomposer with Imagery	10	A significant sign of development is when a student is able to decompose shapes flexibly by using independently generated imagery.
8	Shape Composer— Units of Units	11	Students demonstrate further understanding when they are able to build and apply units of units (shapes made from other shapes). For example, in constructing spatial patterns, the student can extend patterning activity to create a tiling with a new unit shape—a unit of unit shapes that he or she recognizes and consciously constructs. For example, the student may build *T*s out of 4 squares, use 4 *T*s to build squares, and use squares to tile a rectangle.
8	Shape Decomposer — Units of Units	12	As students develop understanding of shape, they can decompose shapes flexibly by using independently generated imagery and planned decompositions of shapes that themselves are decompositions.

Developmental Levels for Comparing Geometric Shapes

As early as four years of age, students can create and use strategies, such as moving shapes to compare their parts or to place one on top of the other for judging whether two figures are the same shape. From PreK to Grade 2, they can develop sophisticated and accurate mathematical procedures for comparing geometric shapes. Students typically follow an observable developmental progression in learning about how shapes are the same and different with recognizable stages or levels. This developmental path can be described as part of a learning trajectory.

Age Range	Level Name	Level	Description
3	"Same Thing" Comparer	1	The first sign of understanding is when the student can compare real-world objects. For example, the student may say two pictures of houses are the same or different.
4	"Similar" Comparer	2	Thist sign of development occurs when the student judges two shapes to be the same if they are more visually similar than different. For example, the student may say, "These are the same. They are pointy at the top."
4	Part Comparer	3	At this level, a student can say that two shapes are the same after matching one side on each. For example, a student may say, "These are the same" (matching the two sides).
4	Some Attributes Comparer	4	As students develop, they look for differences in attributes, but may examine only part of a shape. For example, a student at this level may say, "These are the same" (indicating the top halves of the shapes are similar by laying them on top of each other).
5	Most Attributes Comparer	5	At this level, the student looks for differences in attributes, examining full shapes, but may ignore some spatial relationships. For example, a student may say, "These are the same."
7	Congruence Determiner	6	A sign of development is when a student determines congruence by comparing all attributes and all spatial relationships. For example, a student at this level may say that two shapes are the same shape and the same size after comparing every one of their sides and angles.
7	Congruence Superposer	7	As students develop understanding, they can move and place objects on top of each other to determine congruence. For example, a student at this level may say that two shapes are the same shape and the same size after laying them on top of each other.
8	Congruence Representer	8	Continued development is evidenced as students refer to geometric properties and explain transformations. For example, a student at this level may say, "These must be congruent because they have equal sides, all square corners, and I can move them on top of each other exactly."

Developmental Levels for Spatial Sense and Motions

Infants and toddlers spend a great deal of time learning about the properties and relations of objects in space. Very young students know and use the shape of their environment in navigation activities. With guidance they can learn to "mathematize" this knowledge. They can learn about direction, perspective, distance, symbolization, location, and coordinates. Students typically follow an observable developmental progression in developing spatial sense with recognizable stages or levels. This developmental path can be described as part of a learning trajectory.

Age Range	Level Name	Level	Description
4	Simple Turner	1	An early sign of spatial sense is when a student mentally turns an object to perform easy tasks. For example, given a shape with the top marked with color, the student may correctly identify which of three shapes it would look like if it were turned "like this" (90 degree turn demonstrated), before physically moving the shape.
5	Beginning Slider, Flipper, Turner	2	This sign of development occurs when a student can use the correct motions, but is not always accurate in direction and amount. For example, a student at this level may know a shape has to be flipped to match another shape, but flips it in the wrong direction.
6	Slider, Flipper, Turner	3	As students develop spatial sense, they can perform slides and flips, often only horizontal and vertical, by using manipulatives. For example, a student at this level may perform turns of 45, 90, and 180 degrees and know a shape must be turned 90 degrees to the right to fit into a puzzle.
7	Diagonal Mover	4	A sign of development is when a student can perform diagonal slides and flips. For example, a student at this level may know a shape must be turned or flipped over an oblique line (45 degree orientation) to fit into a puzzle.
8	Mental Mover	5	Further signs of development occur when a student can predict results of moving shapes using mental images. A student at this level may say, "If you turned this 120 degrees, it would be just like this one."

Developmental Levels for Patterning and Early Algebra

Algebra begins with a search for patterns. Identifying patterns helps bring order, cohesion, and predictability to seemingly unorganized situations and allows one to make generalizations beyond the information directly available. The recognition and analysis of patterns are important components of the young student's intellectual development because they provide a foundation for the development of algebraic thinking. Although prekindergarten students engage in pattern-related activities and recognize patterns in their everyday environment, research has revealed that an abstract understanding of patterns develops gradually during the early childhood years. Students typically follow an observable developmental progression in learning about patterns with recognizable stages or levels. This developmental path can be described as part of a learning trajectory.

Age Range	Level Name	Level	Description
2	Pre-Patterner	1	A student at the earliest level does not recognize patterns. For example, a student may name a striped shirt with no repeating unit a "pattern."
3	Pattern Recognizer	2	At this level, the student can recognize a simple pattern. For example, a student at this level may say, "I'm wearing a pattern" about a shirt with black and white stripes.
4	Pattern Fixer	3	At this level the student fills in missing elements of a pattern.
4	Pattern Duplicator AB	4	A sign of development is when the student can duplicate an ABABAB pattern, although the student may have to work alongside the model pattern. For example, given objects in a row, ABABAB, the student may make his or her own ABABAB row in a different location.
4	Pattern Duplicator	5	At this level, the student is able to duplicate simple patterns (not just alongside the model pattern). For example, given objects in a row, ABBABBABB, the student may make his or her own ABBABBABB row in a different location.

Age Range	Level Name	Level	Description
5	Pattern Extender	6	A sign of development is when the student can extend simple patterns. For example, given objects in a row, ABBABBABB, he or she may add ABBABB to the end of the row.
6	Pattern Maker from n	7	As a student develops patterning, he or she is able to fill in a missing element of a pattern. For example, given objects in a row with one missing, ABBAB_ABB, he or she may identify and fill in the missing element.
7	Pattern Unit Recognizer	8	At this level, a student can identify the smallest unit of a pattern. For example, given objects in a row with one missing, ABBAB_ABB, he or she may identify and fill in the missing element.

Glossary

A

absolute value The distance of a number from 0. For example, the absolute value of 7, written as |7|, is 7. The absolute value of −4, written as |−4|, is 4.

acute angle An angle with a measure greater than 0 degrees and less than 90 degrees.

addend One of the numbers being added in an addition sentence. In the sentence 41 + 27 = 68, the numbers 41 and 27 are addends.

addition A mathematical operation used for "putting things together." Numbers being added are called *addends*. The result of addition is called a *sum*. In the number sentence 15 + 63 = 78, the numbers 15 and 63 are addends.

additive inverses Two numbers whose sum is 0. For example, 9 + −9 = 0. The additive inverse of 9 is −9, and the additive inverse of −9 is 9.

adjacent angles Two angles with a common side that do not otherwise overlap. In the diagram, angles 1 and 2 are adjacent angles. So are angles 2 and 3, angles 3 and 4, and angles 4 and 1.

algorithm A step-by-step procedure for carrying out a computation or solving a problem.

angle Two rays with a common endpoint. The common endpoint is called the vertex of the angle.

area A measure of the surface inside a closed boundary. The formula for the area of a rectangle or parallelogram is $A = b \times h$, where A represents the area, b represents the length of the base, and h the height of the figure.

array A rectangular arrangement of objects in rows and columns in which each row has the same number of elements and each column has the same number of elements.

attribute A feature such as size, shape, or color.

average See **mean**. The **median** and **mode** are also sometimes called the average.

axis (plural **axes**) A number line used in a coordinate grid.

B

bar graph A graph in which the lengths of horizontal or vertical bars represent the magnitude of the data represented.

base See **exponential notation.**

base (of a parallelogram) One of the sides of a parallelogram; also, the length of this side. The length of a perpendicular line segment between the base and the side opposite the base is the height of the parallelogram.

base (of a polyhedron) The "bottom" face of a polyhedron; the face whose shape determines the type of prism or pyramid.

base (of a rectangle) One of the sides of a rectangle; also, the length of this side. The length of the side perpendicular to the base is the height of the rectangle.

base (of a triangle) One of the sides of a triangle; also, the length of this side. The shortest distance between the base and the vertex opposite the base is the height of the triangle.

base ten The commonly used numeration system, in which the ten digits 0, 1, 2,..., 9 have values that depend on the place in which they appear in a numeral (ones, tens, hundreds, and so on, to the left of the decimal point; tenths, hundredths, and so on, to the right of the decimal point).

benchmark A number or measure used as a standard of comparison for other numbers or measures.

bisect To divide a segment, angle, or figure into two parts of equal measure.

C

capacity A measure of how much liquid or substance a container can hold. See also **volume.**

centi- A prefix for units in the metric system meaning one hundredth.

centimeter (cm) In the metric system, a unit of length defined as $\frac{1}{100}$ of a meter; equal to 10 millimeters or $\frac{1}{10}$ of a decimeter.

circle The set of all points in a plane that are a given distance (the radius) from a given point (the center of the circle).

circle graph A graph in which a circular region is divided into sectors to represent the categories in a set of data. The circle represents the whole set of data.

circumference The distance around a circle or sphere.

clipped range In a set of numbers, the range calculated without the greatest and least value, or with the two or three greatest and least values removed.

closed figure A figure that divides the plane into two regions, inside and outside the figure. A closed space figure divides space into two regions in the same way.

common denominator Any nonzero number that is a multiple of the denominators of two or more fractions.

common factor Any number that is a factor of two or more numbers.

complementary angles Two angles whose measures total 90 degrees.

composite function A function with two or more operations. For example, this function multiplies the input number by 5 then adds 3.

composite number A whole number that has more than two whole number factors. For example, 14 is a composite number because it has more than two whole number factors.

concave (nonconvex) **polygon** A polygon in which a line segment between two of the points on the boundary lies outside the polygon.

cone A space figure having a circular base, curved surface, and one vertex.

congruent Having identical sizes and shapes. Congruent figures are said to be congruent to each other.

convex polygon A polygon in which line segments between any two points on the boundary lie inside or on the polygon.

coordinate One or more numbers used to fix the position of a point (on a line, in a plane, in space, and so on).

coordinate grid A device for locating points in a plane by means of ordered pairs or coordinates. A coordinate grid is formed by two number lines that intersect at their 0-points.

corresponding angles Two angles in the same relative position in two figures, or in similar locations in relation to a transversal intersecting two lines. In the diagram below, angles 1 and 5, 3 and 7, 2 and 6, and 4 and 8 are corresponding angles. If the lines are parallel, then the corresponding angles are congruent.

corresponding sides Two sides in the same relative position in two figures. In the diagram, AB and A'B', BC and B'C', and AC and A'C' are corresponding sides.

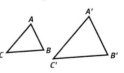

cube A space figure whose six faces are congruent squares that meet at right angles.

cubic centimeter (cm³) A metric unit of volume; the volume of a cube 1 centimeter on an edge. 1 cubic centimeter is equal to 1 milliliter.

cubic unit A unit used in a volume and capacity measurement.

customary system of measurement The measuring system used most often in the United States. Units for linear measure (length, distance) include inch, foot, yard, and mile; units for weight include ounce and pound; units for capacity (amount of liquid or other substance a container can hold) include fluid ounce, cup, pint, quart, and gallon.

cylinder A space figure having a curved surface and parallel circular or elliptical bases that are congruent.

D

decimal A number written in standard notation, usually one containing a decimal point, as in 3.78.

decimal approximation A decimal that is close to the value of a rational number. By extending the decimal approximation to additional digits, it is possible to come as close as desired to the value of the rational number. For example, decimal approximations of $\frac{1}{12}$ are 0.083, 0.0833, 0.08333, and so on.

decimal equivalent A decimal that names the same number as a fraction. For example, the decimal equivalent of $\frac{3}{4}$ is 0.75. The only rational numbers with decimal equivalents are those that can be written as fractions whose denominators have prime factors only of 2 and 5. For example, $\frac{1}{2}$, $\frac{1}{4}$, and $\frac{1}{20}$ have decimal equivalents, but $\frac{1}{6}$, $\frac{1}{7}$, and $\frac{1}{9}$ have only decimal approximations.

degree (°) A unit of measure for angles; based on dividing a circle into 360 equal parts. Also, a unit of measure for temperature.

degree Celsius (°C) In the metric system, the unit for measuring temperature. Water freezes at 0°C and boils at 100°C.

degree Fahrenheit (°F) In the U.S. customary system, the unit for measuring temperature. Water freezes at 32°F and boils at 212°F.

deltahedron A polyhedron whose faces are congruent equilateral triangles.

denominator The number of equal parts into which a whole is divided. In the fraction $\frac{a}{b}$, b is the denominator. See also **numerator.**

diameter A line segment, going through the center of a circle, that starts at one point on the circle and ends at the opposite point on the circle; also, the length of such a line segment. The diameter of a circle is twice its radius. AB is a diameter of this circle.

See also **circle.**

difference The result of subtraction. In the subtraction sentence 40 − 10 = 30, the difference is 30.

digit In the base-ten numeration system, one of the symbols 0, 1, 2, 3, 4, 5, 6, 7, 8, 9. Digits can be used to write a numeral for any whole number in the base-ten numbering system. For example, the numeral 145 is made up of the digits 1, 4, and 5.

distributive law A law that relates two operations on numbers, usually multiplication and addition, or multiplication and subtraction. Distributive law of multiplication over addition: $a \times (b + c) = (a \times b) + (a \times c)$

dividend See **division.**

divisibility rule A rule that indicates whether a whole number is divisible by another whole number. For example, to tell whether a number is divisible by 3, check whether the sum of its digits is divisible by 3. The number 48 is divisible by 3 since 4 + 8 = 12, and 12 is divisible by 3.

divisible by One whole number is divisible by another whole number if the result of the division is a whole number (with a remainder of 0). For example, 35 is divisible by 5, because 35 divided by 5 is 7 with a remainder of 0. If a number n is divisible by a number x, then x is a factor of n. See also **factor of a whole number n.**

division A mathematical operation used for "equal sharing" or "separating into equal parts." Division is the inverse operation of multiplication. The *dividend* is the total before sharing. The *divisor* is the number of equal parts or the number in each equal part. The *quotient* is the result of division. For example, in 35 ÷ 5 = 7, 35 is the dividend, 5 is the divisor, and 7 is the quotient. If 35 objects are separated into 5 equal parts, there are 7 objects in each part. If 35 objects are separated into parts with 5 in each part, there are 7 equal parts. The number left over when a set of objects is shared equally or separated into equal groups is called the *remainder.* For 35 ÷ 5, the quotient is 7 and the remainder is 0. For 36 ÷ 5, the quotient is 7 and the remainder is 1.

divisor See **division.**

dodecahedron A space figure with twelve faces. In a regular dodecahedron, each face is formed by a pentagon.

E

edge The line segment where two faces of a polyhedron meet.

endpoint The point at either end of a line segment; also, the point at the end of a ray. Line segments are named after their endpoints; a line segment between and including points A and B is usually called segment AB or segment BA.

equation A mathematical sentence that states the equality of two expressions. For example, 3 + 7 = 10, y = x + 7, and 4 + 7 = 8 + 3 are equations.

equilateral polygon A polygon in which all sides are the same length.

equivalent Equal in value, but in a different form. For example, $\frac{1}{2}$, $\frac{2}{4}$, 0.5, and 50% are equivalent forms of the same number.

equivalent fractions Fractions that have different numerators and denominators but name the same number. For example, $\frac{2}{3}$ and $\frac{6}{9}$ are equivalent fractions.

estimate A judgment of a time, measurement, number, or other quantity that may not be exactly right.

evaluate an algebraic expression To replace each variable in an algebraic expression with a particular number and then calculate the value of the expression.

evaluate a numerical expression To carry out the operations in a numerical expression to find the value of the expression.

even number A whole number such as 0, 2, 4, 6, and so on, that can be divided by 2 with no remainder. See also **odd number.**

event A happening or occurrence. The tossing of a coin is an event.

exponent See **exponential notation.**

exponential notation A shorthand way of representing repeated multiplication of the same factor. For example, 4^3 is exponential notation for $4 \times 4 \times 4$. The small raised 3, called the *exponent*, indicates how many times the number 4, called the *base*, is used as a factor.

expression A group of mathematical symbols (numbers, operation signs, variables, grouping symbols) that represents a number (or can represent a number if values are assigned to any variables it contains).

F

face A flat surface on a space figure.

fact family A group of addition or multiplication facts grouped together with the related subtraction or division facts. For example, 4 + 8 = 12, 8 + 4 = 12, 12 − 4 = 8, and 12 − 8 = 4 form an addition fact family. The facts $4 \times 3 = 12$, $3 \times 4 = 12$, 12 ÷ 3 = 4, and 12 ÷ 4 = 3 form a multiplication fact family.

Glossary

factor (noun) One of the numbers that is multiplied in a multiplication expression. For example, in $4 \times 1.5 = 6$, the factors are 4 and 1.5. See also **multiplication.**

factor (verb) To represent a quantity as a product of factors. For example, 20 factors to 4×5, 2×10, or $2 \times 2 \times 5$.

factor of a whole number n A whole number, which, when multiplied by another whole number, results in the number n. The whole number n is divisible by its factors. For example, 3 and 5 are factors of 15 because $3 \times 5 = 15$, and 15 is divisible by 3 and 5.

factor tree A method used to obtain the prime factorization of a number. The original number is represented as a product of factors, and each of those factors is represented as a product of factors, and so on, until the factor string consists of prime numbers.

fair A coin, spinner, number cube, and so on is said to be fair if, over a large number of tosses, the results are consistent with the predictions of probability. On a fair coin, heads and tails should come up about equally often; the six sides of a fair number cube should come up about equally often.

fair game A game in which each player has the same chance of winning. If any player has an advantage or disadvantage (for example, by playing first), then the game is not fair.

finger sets An organized way taught in *Real Math* of showing numbers using fingers.

formula A general rule for finding the value of something. A formula is usually written as an equation with variables representing unknown quantities. For example, a formula for distance traveled at a constant rate of speed is $d = r \times t$, where d stands for distance, r for rate, and t for time.

fraction A number in the form $\frac{a}{b}$, where a and b are integers and b is greater than 0. Fractions are used to name part of a whole object or part of a whole collection of objects, or to compare two quantities. A fraction can represent division; for example, $\frac{2}{5}$ can be thought of as 2 divided by 5.

frequency The number of times an event or value occurs in a set of data.

function machine An imaginary machine that processes numbers according to a certain rule. A number (input) is put into the machine and is transformed into a second number (output) by application of the rule.

G

greatest common factor The largest factor that two or more numbers have in common. For example, the common factors of 24 and 30 are 1, 2, 3, and 6. The greatest common factor of 24 and 30 is 6.

H

height (of a polygon) The length of the line segment perpendicular to the base of the polygon (or an extension of the base) from the opposite side or vertex.

height (of a polyhedron) The perpendicular distance between the bases of the polyhedron or between a base and the opposite vertex.

heptagon A polygon with seven sides.

hexagon A polygon with six sides.

histogram A bar graph in which the labels for the bars are numerical intervals.

hypotenuse In a right triangle, the side opposite the right angle.

I

icosahedron A space figure with twenty triangular faces.

improper fraction A fraction that names a number greater than or equal to 1; a fraction whose numerator is equal to or greater than its denominator. Examples of improper fractions are $\frac{4}{3}$, $\frac{10}{8}$, and $\frac{4}{4}$.

inch (in.) In the U. S. customary system, a unit of length equal to $\frac{1}{12}$ of a foot.

independent events Events A and B for which knowing that event A has occurred does not influence the probability that event B will occur.

indirect measurement Methods for determining heights, distances, and other quantities that cannot be measured or are not measured directly.

inequality A number sentence stating that two quantities are not equal. Relation symbols for inequalities include < (is less than), > (is greater than), and ≠ (is not equal to).

integers The set of integers is {..., -4, -3, -2, -1, 0, 1, 2, 3, 4, ...}. The set of integers consists of whole numbers and their opposites.

intersect To meet (at a point, a line, and so on), sharing a common point or points.

interior The set of all points in a plane "inside" a closed plane figure, such as a polygon or circle. Also, the set of all points in space "inside" a closed space figure, such as a polyhedron or sphere.

isosceles Having two sides of the same length; commonly used to refer to triangles and trapezoids.

K

kilo- A prefix for units in the metric system meaning one thousand.

L

least common denominator The least common multiple of the denominators of every fraction in a given set of fractions. For example, 12 is the least common denominator of $\frac{2}{3}$, $\frac{1}{4}$, and $\frac{5}{6}$. See also **least common multiple.**

least common multiple The smallest number that is a multiple of two or more numbers. For example, some common multiples of 6 and 8 are 24, 48, and 72. 24 is the least common multiple of 6 and 8.

leg of a right triangle A side of a right triangle that is not the hypotenuse.

line A straight path that extends infinitely in opposite directions.

line graph (broken-line graph) A graph in which points are connected by line segments to represent data.

line of symmetry A line that separates a figure into halves. The figure can be folded along this line into two parts which exactly fit on top of each other.

line segment A straight path joining two points, called *endpoints* of the line segment. A straight path can be described as the shortest distance between two points.

line symmetry A figure has line symmetry (also called *bilateral symmetry*) if a line of symmetry can be drawn through the figure.

liter (L) A metric unit of capacity, equal to the volume of a cube 10 centimeters on an edge. $1 L = 1,000 mL = 1,000 cm^3$. A liter is slightly larger than a quart. See also **milliliter (mL).**

M

map scale A ratio that compares the distance between two locations shown on a map with the actual distance between them.

mean A typical or central value that may be used to describe a set of numbers. It can be found by adding the numbers in the set and dividing the sum by the number of numbers. The mean is often referred to as the *average*.

median The middle value in a set of data when the data are listed in order from least to greatest (or greatest to least). If the number of values in the set is even (so that there is no "middle" value), the median is the mean of the two middle values.

meter (m) The basic unit of length in the metric system, equal to 10 decimeters, 100 centimeters, and 1,000 millimeters.

metric system of measurement A measurement system based on the base-ten numeration system and used in most countries in the world. Units for linear measure (length, distance) include millimeter, centimeter, meter, kilometer; units for mass (weight) include gram and kilogram; units for capacity (amount of liquid or other substance a container can hold) include milliliter and liter.

midpoint A point halfway between two points.

milli- A prefix for units in the metric system meaning one thousandth.

milliliter (mL) A metric unit of capacity, equal to 1/1,000 of a liter and 1 cubic centimeter.

millimeter (mm) In the metric system, a unit of length equal to 1/10 of a centimeter and 1/1,000 of a meter.

minuend See **subtraction.**

mixed number A number greater than 1, written as a whole number and a fraction less than 1. For example, $5\frac{1}{2}$ is equal to $5 + \frac{1}{2}$.

mode The value or values that occur most often in a set of data.

multiple of a number _n_ The product of a whole number and the number _n_. For example, the numbers 0, 4, 8, 12, and 16 are all multiples of 4 because $4 \times 0 = 0, 4 \times 1 = 4, 4 \times 2 = 8, 4 \times 3 = 12$, and $4 \times 4 = 16$.

multiplication A mathematical operation used to find the total number of things in several equal groups, or to find a quantity that is a certain number of times as much or as many as another number. Numbers being multiplied are called _factors_. The result of multiplication is called the _product_. In $8 \times 12 = 96$, 8 and 12 are the factors and 96 is the product.

multiplicative inverses Two numbers whose product is 1. For example, the multiplicative inverse of $\frac{2}{5}$ is $\frac{5}{2}$, and the multiplicative inverse of 8 is $\frac{1}{8}$. Multiplicative inverses are also called _reciprocals_ of each other.

N

negative number A number less than 0; a number to the left of 0 on a horizontal number line.

number line A line on which equidistant points correspond to integers in order.

number sentence A sentence that is made up of numerals and a relation symbol ($<$, $>$, or $=$). Most number sentences also contain at least one operation symbol. Number sentences may also have grouping symbols, such as parentheses.

numeral The written name of a number.

numerator In a whole divided into a number of equal parts, the number of equal parts being considered. In the fraction $\frac{a}{b}$, a is the numerator.

O

obtuse angle An angle with a measure greater than 90 degrees and less than 180 degrees.

octagon An eight-sided polygon.

octahedron A space figure with eight faces.

odd number A whole number that is not divisible by 2, such as 1, 3, 5, and so on. When an odd number is divided by 2, the remainder is 1. A whole number is either an odd number or an even number.

opposite of a number A number that is the same distance from 0 on the number line as the given number, but on the opposite side of 0. If a is a negative number, the opposite of a will be a positive number. For example, if $a = -5$, then $-a$ is 5. See also **additive inverses.**

ordered pair Two numbers or objects for which order is important. Often, two numbers in a specific order used to locate a point on a coordinate grid. They are usually written inside parentheses; for example, (2, 3). See also **coordinate.**

ordinal number A number used to express position or order in a series, such as first, third, tenth. People generally use ordinal numbers to name dates; for example, "May fifth" rather than "May five."

origin The point where the x- and y-axes intersect on a coordinate grid. The coordinates of the origin are (0, 0).

outcome The result of an event. Heads and tails are the two outcomes of the event of tossing a coin.

P

parallel lines (segments, rays) Lines (segments, rays) going in the same direction that are the same distance apart and never meet.

parallelogram A quadrilateral that has two pairs of parallel sides. Pairs of opposite sides and opposite angles of a parallelogram are congruent.

parentheses A pair of symbols, (and), used to show in which order operations should be done. For example, the expression $(3 \times 5) + 7$ says to multiply 5 by 3 then add 7. The expression $3 \times (5 + 7)$ says to add 5 and 7 and then multiply by 3.

pattern A model, plan, or rule that uses words or variables to describe a set of shapes or numbers that repeat in a predictable way.

pentagon A polygon with five sides.

percent A rational number that can be written as a fraction with a denominator of 100. The symbol % is used to represent percent. 1% means 1/100 or 0.01. For example, "53% of the students in the school are girls" means that out of every 100 students in the school, 53 are girls.

perimeter The distance along a path around a plane figure. A formula for the perimeter of a rectangle is $P = 2 \times (B + H)$, where B represents the base and H is the height of the rectangle. Perimeter may also refer to the path itself.

perpendicular Two rays, lines, line segments, or other figures that form right angles are said to be perpendicular to each other.

pi The ratio of the circumference of a circle to its diameter. Pi is the same for every circle, approximately 3.14 or $\frac{22}{7}$. Also written as the Greek letter π.

pictograph A graph constructed with pictures or icons, in which each picture stands for a certain number. Pictographs make it easier to visually compare quantities.

place value A way of determining the value of a digit in a numeral, written in standard notation, according to its position, or place, in the numeral. In base-ten numbers, each place has a value ten times that of the place to its right and one-tenth the value of the place to its left.

plane A flat surface that extends forever.

plane figure A figure that can be contained in a plane (that is, having length and width but no height).

point A basic concept of geometry; usually thought of as a location in space, without size.

polygon A closed plane figure consisting of line segments (sides) connected endpoint to endpoint. The interior of a polygon consists of all the points of the plane "inside" the polygon. An _n_-gon is a polygon with _n_ sides; for example, an 8-gon has 8 sides.

polyhedron A closed space figure, all of whose surfaces (faces) are flat. Each face consists of a polygon and the interior of the polygon.

Glossary

power A product of factors that are all the same. For example, $6 \times 6 \times 6$ (or 216) is called 6 to the third power, or the third power of 6, because 6 is a factor three times. The expression $6 \times 6 \times 6$ can also be written as 6^3.

power of 10 A whole number that can be written as a product using only 10 as a factor. For example, 100 is equal to 10×10 or 10^2, so 100 is called 10 squared, the second power of 10, or 10 to the second power. Other powers of 10 include 10^1, or 10, and 10^3, or 1,000.

precision (of a count or measurement) An indicator of how close a count or measure is believed to be to the actual count or measure. The precision of a measurement may be improved by using measuring instruments with smaller units.

prime factorization A whole number expressed as a product of prime factors. For example, the prime factorization of 18 is $2 \times 3 \times 3$. A number has only one prime factorization (except for the order in which the factors are written).

prime number A whole number greater than 1 that has exactly two whole number factors, 1 and itself. For example, 13 is a prime number because its only factors are 1 and 13. A prime number is divisible only by 1 and itself. The first five prime numbers are 2, 3, 5, 7, and 11. See also **composite number.**

prism A polyhedron with two parallel faces (bases) that are the same size and shape. Prisms are classified according to the shape of the two parallel bases. The bases of a prism are connected by parallelograms that are often rectangular.

probability A number between 0 and 1 that indicates the likelihood that something (an event) will happen. The closer a probability is to 1, the more likely it is that an event will happen.

product See **multiplication.**

protractor A tool for measuring or drawing angles. When measuring an angle, the vertex of the angle should be at the center of the protractor and one side should be aligned with the 0 mark.

pyramid A polyhedron in which one face (the base) is a polygon and the other faces are formed by triangles with a common vertex (the apex). A pyramid is classified according to the shape of its base, as a triangular pyramid, square pyramid, pentagonal pyramid, and so on.

Pythagorean Theorem A mathematical theorem, proven by the Greek mathematician Pythagoras and known to many others before and since, that states that if the legs of a right triangle have lengths a and b, and the hypotenuse has length c, then $a^2 + b^2 = c^2$.

Q

quadrilateral A polygon with four sides.

quotient See **division.**

R

radius A line segment that goes from the center of a circle to any point on the circle; also, the length of such a line segment.

random sample A sample taken from a population in a way that gives all members of the population the same chance of being selected.

range The difference between the maximum and minimum values in a set of data.

rate A ratio comparing two quantities with unlike units. For example, a measure such as 23 miles per gallon of gas compares mileage with gas usage.

ratio A comparison of two quantities using division. Ratios can be expressed with fractions, decimals, percents, or words. For example, if a team wins 4 games out of 5 games played, the ratio of wins to total games is $\frac{4}{5}$, 0.8, or 80%.

rational number Any number that can be represented in the form $a \div b$ or $\frac{a}{b}$, where a and b are integers and b is positive. Some, but not all, rational numbers have exact decimal equivalents.

ray A straight path that extends infinitely in one direction from a point, which is called its *endpoint*.

reciprocal See **multiplicative inverses.**

rectangle A parallelogram with four right angles.

reduced form A fraction in which the numerator and denominator have no common factors except 1.

reflection A transformation in which a figure "flips" so that its image is the reverse of the original.

regular polygon A convex polygon in which all the sides are the same length and all the angles have the same measure.

regular polyhedron (plural **polyhedra**) A polyhedron with faces that are all congruent regular polygons with their interiors. The same number of faces meet at each vertex. There are five regular polyhedra:

tetrahedron four faces, each formed by an equilateral triangle

cube six faces, each formed by a square

octahedron eight faces, each formed by an equilateral triangle

dodecahedron twelve faces, each formed by a regular pentagon

icosahedron twenty faces, each formed by an equilateral triangle

relation symbol A symbol used to express the relationship between two numbers or expressions. Among the symbols used in number sentences are = for "is equal to," < for "is less than," > for "is greater than," and ≠ for "is not equal to."

remainder See **division.**

rhombus A parallelogram whose sides are all the same length.

right angle An angle with a measure of 90 degrees, representing a quarter of a full turn.

right triangle A triangle that has a right angle.

rotation A transformation in which a figure "turns" around a center point or axis.

rotational symmetry Property of a figure that can be rotated around a point (less than a full, 360-degree turn) in such a way that the resulting figure exactly matches the original figure. If a figure has rotational symmetry, its order of rotational symmetry is the number of different ways it can be rotated to match itself exactly. "No rotation" is counted as one of the ways.

rounding Changing a number to another number that is easier to work with and is close enough for the purpose. For example, 12,924 rounded to the nearest thousand is 13,000 and rounded to the nearest hundred is 12,900.

S

sample A subset of a group used to represent the whole group.

scale The ratio of the distance on a map or drawing to the actual distance.

scalene triangle A triangle in which all three sides have different lengths.

scale drawing An accurate picture of an object in which all parts are drawn to the same scale. If an actual object measures 32 by 48 meters, a scale drawing of it might measure 32 by 48 millimeters.

scale model A model that represents an object or display in proportions based on a determined scale.

scientific notation A method of expressing a number as the product of two factors, one of which is a number greater than or equal to 1 but less than 10, and the other of which is a power of 10. The notation is used to describe very great (or very small) numbers. For example, 4,000,000 in scientific notation is 4×10^6.

similar figures Figures that are exactly the same shape but not necessarily the same size.

space figure A figure which cannot be contained in a plane. Common space figures include the rectangular prism, square pyramid, cylinder, cone, and sphere.

sphere The set of all points in space that are a given distance (the radius) from a given point (the center). A ball is shaped like a sphere.

square number A number that is the product of a whole number and itself. The number 36 is a square number, because $36 = 6 \times 6$.

square of a number The product of a number multiplied by itself. For example, 2.5 squared is $(2.5)^2$.

square root The square root of a number n is a number which, when multiplied by itself, results in the number n. For example, 8 is a square root of 64, because $8 \times 8 = 64$.

square unit A unit used to measure area—usually a square that is 1 inch, 1 centimeter, 1 yard, or other standard unit of length on each side.

standard notation The most familiar way of representing whole numbers, integers, and decimals by writing digits in specified places; the way numbers are usually written in everyday situations.

statistics The science of collecting, classifying, and interpreting numerical data as it is related to a particular subject.

stem-and-leaf plot A display of data in which digits with larger place values are named as stems, and digits with smaller place values are named as leaves.

straight angle An angle of 180 degrees; a line with one point identified as the vertex of the angle.

subtraction A mathematical operation used for "taking away" or comparing ("How much more?"). Subtraction is the inverse operation of addition. The number being subtracted is called the *subtrahend*; the number it is subtracted from is called the *minuend*; the result of subtraction is called the *difference*. In the number sentence $63 - 45 = 18$, 63 is the minuend, 45 is the subtrahend, and 18 is the difference.

subtrahend See **subtraction.**

supplementary angles Two angles whose measures total 180 degrees.

surface area The sum of the areas of the faces or surfaces of a space figure.

symmetrical Having the same size and shape across a dividing line or around a point.

T

tessellation An arrangement of closed shapes that covers a surface completely without overlaps or gaps.

tetrahedron A space figure with four faces, each formed by an equilateral triangle.

theorem A mathematical statement that can be proved to be true (or, sometimes, a statement that is proposed and needs to be proved). For example, the Pythagorean Theorem states that if the legs of a right triangle have lengths a and b, and the hypotenuse has length c, then $a^2 + b^2 = c^2$.

transformation An operation that moves or changes a geometric figure in a specified way. Rotations, reflections, and translations are types of transformations.

translation A transformation in which a figure "slides" along a line.

transversal A line which intersects two or more other lines.

trapezoid A quadrilateral with exactly one pair of parallel sides.

tree diagram A tool used to solve probability problems in which there is a series of events. This tree diagram represents a situation where the first event has three possible outcomes and the second event has two possible outcomes.

triangle A polygon with three sides. An *equilateral* triangle has three sides of the same length. An *isosceles* triangle has two sides of the same length. A *scalene* triangle has no sides of the same length.

U

unit (of measure) An agreed-upon standard with which measurements are compared.

unit fraction A fraction whose numerator is 1. For example, $\frac{1}{2}$, $\frac{1}{3}$, and $\frac{1}{10}$ are unit fractions.

unit cost The cost of one item or one specified amount of an item. If 20 pencils cost 60¢, then the unit cost is 3¢ per pencil.

unlike denominators Unequal denominators, as in $\frac{3}{4}$ and $\frac{5}{6}$.

V

variable A letter or other symbol that represents a number, one specific number, or many different values.

Venn diagram A picture that uses circles to show relationships between sets. Elements that belong to more than one set are placed in the overlap between the circles.

vertex The point at which the rays of an angle, two sides of a polygon, or the edges of a polyhedron meet.

vertical angles Two intersecting lines form four adjacent angles. In the diagram, angles 2 and 4 are vertical angles. They have no sides in common. Their measures are equal. Similarly, angles 1 and 3 are vertical angles.

volume A measure of the amount of space occupied by a space figure.

W

whole number Any of the numbers 0, 1, 2, 3, 4, and so on. Whole numbers are the numbers used for counting and zero.

Scope and Sequence

	PreK	K	1	2	3	4	5	6
Addition (Whole Numbers)								
Meaning of addition	•	•	•	•				
Basic facts			•	•	•	•	•	•
Missing addend problems			•	•	•	•	•	•
Three or more addends			•	•	•	•	•	•
Two-digit numbers				•	•	•	•	•
Three-digit numbers					•	•	•	•
Greater numbers						•	•	•
Adding money				•	•	•	•	•
Estimating sums				•	•	•	•	•
Algebra								
Properties of whole numbers					•	•	•	•
Integers (negative numbers)					•	•	•	•
Operations with integers						•	•	•
Missing-term problems	•			•	•	•	•	•
Making and solving number sentences and equations				•	•	•	•	•
Variables					•	•	•	•
Parentheses and order of operations						•	•	•
Inverse operations			•	•	•	•	•	•
Function machines/tables		•	•	•	•	•	•	•
Function rules		•	•	•	•	•	•	•
Inverse functions				•	•	•	•	•
Composite functions					•	•	•	•
Coordinate graphing								
One quadrant					•	•	•	•
Four quadrants						•	•	•
Graphing linear functions					•	•	•	•
Graphing nonlinear functions							•	•
Using formulas								•
Square numbers					•	•		•
Square roots						•		•
Decimals and Money								
Place value					•	•	•	•
Comparing and ordering					•	•	•	•
Rounding						•	•	•
Relating decimals and fractions				•	•	•	•	•
Relating decimals and percents						•	•	•
Adding				•	•	•	•	•
Estimating sums				•	•	•	•	•
Subtracting				•	•	•	•	•
Estimating differences					•	•	•	•
Multiplying by powers of 10						•	•	•
Multiplying by a whole number						•	•	•
Multiplying by a decimal								•
Estimating products						•	•	•
Dividing by powers of 10						•	•	•
Dividing by a whole number					•	•	•	•
Dividing by a decimal								•
Estimating quotients							•	•

	PreK	K	1	2	3	4	5	6
Identifying and counting currency		•	•	•	•			
Exchanging money		•	•	•	•			
Making change			•	•	•			
Computing with money		•	•	•	•	•	•	•

Division (Whole Numbers)

	PreK	K	1	2	3	4	5	6
Meaning of division	•	•	•	•	•	•		
Basic facts				•	•	•	•	•
Remainders					•	•	•	•
Missing-term problems				•	•	•	•	•
One-digit divisors					•	•	•	•
Two-digit divisors						•	•	•
Greater divisors							•	•
Dividing by multiples of 10							•	•
Dividing money					•	•	•	•
Estimating quotients					•	•	•	•

Fractions

	PreK	K	1	2	3	4	5	6
Fractions of a whole		•	•	•	•	•	•	•
Fractions of a set			•	•	•	•	•	•
Fractions of a number			•	•	•	•	•	•
Comparing/ordering			•	•	•	•	•	•
Equivalent fractions			•	•	•	•	•	•
Reduced form						•	•	•
Mixed numbers and improper fractions					•	•	•	•
Adding—like denominators					•	•	•	•
Adding—unlike denominators						•	•	•
Adding mixed numbers						•	•	•
Subtracting—like denominators					•	•	•	•
Subtracting—unlike denominators						•	•	•
Subtracting mixed numbers						•	•	•
Multiplying by a whole number						•	•	•
Multiplying by a fraction or mixed number						•	•	•
Reciprocals							•	•
Dividing a fraction by a whole number							•	•
Dividing by a fraction or mixed number							•	•

Geometry

	PreK	K	1	2	3	4	5	6
Identifying/drawing figures	•	•	•	•	•	•	•	•
Classifying figures	•	•	•	•	•	•	•	•
Classifying triangles				•	•	•	•	•
Classifying quadrilaterals				•	•	•	•	•
Solid figures		•	•	•	•	•	•	•
Congruence	•	•	•	•	•	•	•	•
Similarity					•	•	•	•
Line symmetry		•	•	•	•	•	•	•
Rotational symmetry						•	•	•
Translation/reflection/rotation	•			•	•	•	•	•
Measuring and classifying angles				•	•	•	•	•
Parallel and perpendicular lines				•	•	•	•	•
Relationships with parallel lines				•	•	•	•	•
Perimeter				•	•	•	•	•

	PreK	K	1	2	3	4	5	6
Radius and diameter					•	•	•	•
Circumference					•		•	•
Areas of triangles					•	•	•	•
Areas of quadrilaterals				•	•	•	•	•
Surface area					•	•	•	•
Volume				•	•	•	•	•
Pythagorean Theorem								
Points, lines, and planes (new category)						•	•	
Open and closed figures (new category)			•					
Spatial visualization	•							

Manipulatives

	PreK	K	1	2	3	4	5	6
Used in concept development	•	•	•	•	•	•	•	•
Used in reteaching and individualized instruction	•	•	•	•	•	•	•	•

Measurement

	PreK	K	1	2	3	4	5	6
Converting within customary system					•	•	•	•
Converting within metric system				•	•	•	•	•
Length								
Estimate	•	•	•	•	•	•		
Compare	•	•	•	•	•	•		
Use nonstandard units	•	•		•	•			
Use customary units				•	•	•		•
Use metric units				•	•	•	•	•
Mass/Weight								
Estimate	•	•	•	•	•			
Compare	•	•	•	•				
Use nonstandard units		•		•				
Use customary units				•	•	•	•	•
Use metric units				•	•	•	•	•
Capacity								
Estimate	•	•	•	•				
Compare	•	•	•	•				
Use nonstandard units		•	•	•				
Use customary units				•	•	•	•	•
Use metric units				•	•	•	•	•
Temperature								
Estimate		•						•
Use degrees Fahrenheit				•	•	•	•	•
Use degrees Celsius				•	•	•	•	•
Telling time								
To the hour		•	•	•	•			
To the half hour			•	•	•			
To the quarter hour				•	•			
To the minute				•	•			
Adding and subtracting time					•	•	•	
A.M. and P.M.				•	•			
Estimating time		•	•					
Calculating elapsed time			•	•	•	•	•	
Reading a calendar		•	•	•	•		•	
Reading maps		•	•	•	•	•	•	•

Mental Arithmetic

	PreK	K	1	2	3	4	5	6
Basic fact strategies—addition and subtraction								
Use patterns			•	•				
Count on			•	•				
Count on or back	•	•	•	•				
Use doubles			•	•				
Use doubles plus 1			•	•				
Multiples of 10/Base-ten		•	•	•	•	•		
Use properties			•	•	•			
Use related facts			•	•				
Basic fact strategies—multiplication and division								
Use patterns				•	•	•		
Use skip counting					•	•		
Use properties					•	•		
Use related facts					•	•		
Chain calculations					•	•		
Multidigit addition and subtraction					•	•	•	•
Multidigit multiplication and division					•	•	•	•
Multiples and powers of 10				•	•	•	•	•
Using computational patterns					•	•	•	•
Approximation					•	•	•	•
Find a fraction of a number					•	•	•	•
Find a percent of a number						•	•	•
Use divisibility rules						•	•	•
Find equivalent fractions, decimals, and percents						•	•	•

Multiplication (Whole Numbers)

	PreK	K	1	2	3	4	5	6
Meaning of multiplication			•	•	•	•	•	•
Basic facts				•	•	•	•	•
Missing-factor problems				•	•	•	•	•
One-digit multipliers				•	•	•	•	•
Two-digit multipliers					•	•	•	•
Greater multipliers						•	•	•
Multiplying by multiples of 10					•	•	•	•
Multiplying money						•	•	•
Estimating products						•	•	•

Number and Numeration

	PreK	K	1	2	3	4	5	6
Reading and writing numbers	•	•	•	•	•	•	•	•
Number lines	•	•	•	•	•	•	•	•
Counting	•	•	•	•	•	•		
Skip counting			•	•	•	•		
Ordinal numbers	•	•	•	•				
Place value						•		
Comparing and ordering numbers	•	•	•	•	•	•	•	•
Rounding				•	•	•	•	•
Estimation/Approximation			•	•	•	•	•	•
Integers (negative numbers)						•	•	•
Even/odd numbers			•	•	•	•		
Prime and composite numbers						•	•	•
Factors and prime factorization						•	•	•

	PreK	K	1	2	3	4	5	6
Common factors						•	•	•
Common multiples						•	•	•
Checking divisibility						•	•	•
Exponents						•	•	•
Exponential notation and scientific notation							•	•
Square roots						•		•

Patterns, Relations, and Functions

	PreK	K	1	2	3	4	5	6
Classifying objects	•	•	•	•				
Number patterns	•	•	•	•	•	•	•	•
Picture patterns	•	•	•	•				
Geometric patterns	•	•	•	•		•		•
Ordered pairs					•	•	•	•
Graphing ordered pairs					•	•	•	•
Inequalities				•	•	•	•	•
Function machines/tables		•	•	•	•	•	•	•
Function rules		•	•	•	•	•	•	•
Graphing functions						•	•	•

Probability

	PreK	K	1	2	3	4	5	6
Determining possible outcomes		•	•	•	•	•	•	•
Predicting outcomes		•	•	•	•	•	•	•
Conducting experiments		•	•	•	•	•	•	•
Experimental probability		•	•	•	•	•	•	•
Theoretical probability						•	•	•
Using probability to plan strategies			•	•	•	•	•	•

Problem Solving

	PreK	K	1	2	3	4	5	6
Multistep problems				•	•	•	•	•
Multiple solutions				•	•	•	•	•
No solutions				•	•	•	•	•
Interpreting data		•	•	•	•	•	•	•
Checking reasonableness		•	•	•	•	•	•	•
Solving problems with too much information			•	•	•	•	•	•
Interpreting the quotient and remainder					•	•	•	•
Choosing the appropriate operation		•	•	•	•	•	•	•
Using estimation		•	•	•	•	•	•	•
Using guess, check, and adjust		•	•	•	•	•	•	•
Solving a simpler problem				•	•	•	•	•
Eliminating possibilities				•	•	•	•	•
Acting it out	•	•	•	•	•	•	•	•
Using/finding a pattern		•	•	•	•	•	•	•
Using/making a table		•	•	•	•	•	•	•
Using/drawing a picture or diagram	•	•	•	•	•	•	•	•
Using manipulatives	•	•	•	•	•	•	•	•

Ratio and Proportion

	PreK	K	1	2	3	4	5	6
Meaning/use of ratio and proportion						•	•	•
Rates						•	•	•
Similar figures						•	•	•
Map scales							•	•
Meaning of percent						•		•
Percent of a number						•		•

	PreK	K	1	2	3	4	5	6
Percent discounts							•	•
Sales tax							•	•
Simple/compound interest							•	•

Statistics and Graphing

	PreK	K	1	2	3	4	5	6
Surveying			•	•	•	•	•	•
Tallying			•	•	•	•	•	•
Making tables with data			•	•	•	•	•	•
Real and picture graphs		•	•	•	•	•	•	•
Bar graphs		•	•	•	•	•	•	•
Line graphs				•	•	•	•	•
Circle graphs					•	•	•	•
Analyzing graphs		•	•	•	•	•	•	•
Finding the mean						•	•	•
Finding the median						•	•	•
Finding the mode						•	•	•

Subtraction (Whole Numbers)

	PreK	K	1	2	3	4	5	6
Meaning of subtraction	•	•	•	•				
Basic facts			•	•	•	•	•	•
Missing-term problems			•	•	•	•	•	•
Two-digit numbers			•	•	•	•	•	•
Three-digit numbers					•	•	•	•
Greater numbers					•	•	•	•
Subtracting money				•	•	•	•	•
Estimating differences					•	•	•	•

Technology

Calculators

	PreK	K	1	2	3	4	5	6
Computation with whole numbers						•	•	•
Computation with decimals						•	•	•
Computation with fractions								•
Computation with integers (negative numbers)								•
Using function rules						•	•	•
Order of operations						•	•	•
Function keys							•	•

Computers

	PreK	K	1	2	3	4	5	6
Spreadsheets					•	•	•	•
Functions		•	•	•	•	•	•	•
Graphs			•	•	•	•	•	•
Geometry	•	•	•	•	•	•	•	•
Charts and tables				•	•	•	•	•

Game Directory

Game	Principle Skills	Begin Using* Student Edition	Begin Using* Teacher's Edition
Tracing and Writing Numbers	Tracing, writing, ordering, and finding numbers 0–10	Page 4	Lesson 1.1
Odds-Evens Game	Identifying odd and even numbers through ten	Page 6	Lesson 1.2
Counting and Writing Numbers	Counting and writing numbers 0–100	Page 8	Lesson 1.3
Yard Sale Game**	Changing money ($1 bills for $10 bills, $10 bills for $100 bills)		Lesson 1.5
Calendar Game ⓔGames	Using a monthly calendar		Lesson 1.6
Addition Table Game	Using an addition table with two addends of 5 or less		Lesson 2.1
Harder Addition Table Game	Using an addition table with two addends of 10 or less		Lesson 2.1
Addition Crossing Game	Practicing basic facts; using addends up to 10; using mathematical reasoning		Lesson 2.3
Doubles Game	Adding doubles	Page 50	Lesson 2.4
Frog Pond Game	Adding with two addends of 10 or less		Lesson 2.5
Harder Frog Pond Game	Adding with two addends of ten or less		Lesson 2.5
Roll a 15 ⓔGames	Adding two, three, or four numbers (0–10); using intuitive notions of probability	Page 60	Lesson 2.7
Space Game	Solving addition and missing-addend problems with sums of 10 or less		Lesson 3.2
Harder Space Game	Solving addition, subtraction, missing-addend, missing-minuend, and missing-subtrahend problems with numbers 10 or less		Lesson 3.2
Roll 20 to 5 ⓔGames	Subtracting 10 or less from numbers through 20	Page 84	Lesson 3.3
Find the Distance 1 Game	Estimating straight distances to the nearest centimeter; comparing line lengths		Lesson 4.2
Find the Distance 2 Game	Estimating straight distances to the nearest centimeter; comparing line lengths		Lesson 4.2
Get to 100 by Tens or Ones ⓔGames	Adding mentally with numbers through 100	Page 162	Lesson 5.1
Roll a Problem	Adding multidigit numbers; place value; using intuitive notions of probability	Page 179	Lesson 5.8

Game	Principle Skills	Begin Using* Student Edition	Begin Using* Teacher's Edition
Roll a Problem (Subtraction)	Subtracting multidigit numbers; place value; using intuitive notions of probability	Page 216	Lesson 6.6
Fraction Game ⓔGames	Recognizing fractional areas of a circle; recognizing which fractional areas when combined are more than half the area of a circle		Lesson 7.6
Harder Counting and Writing Numbers	Counting in the 0–1,000 range; writing numbers in the 0–1,000 range	Page 334	Lesson 9.1
Rummage Sale Game	Changing money ($1, $10, and $100 bills for those of larger denominations); regrouping in preparation for multidigit addition		Lesson 9.4
Checkbook Game	Adding and subtracting two-digit and three-digit numbers; maintaining a record of money transactions		Lesson 9.7
Make 1,000 ⓔGames	Approximating answers to multidigit addition and subtraction problems; solving multidigit addition and subtraction problems	Page 354	Lesson 9.10
Map Game ⓔGames	Using numbers to represent magnitude and direction; using compass directions		Lesson 10.2
Harder Time Game	Telling time to the hour, half hour, and quarter hour		Lesson 10.9
Multiplication Table Game ⓔGames	Using a multiplication table; multiplying with two factors of 5 or less		Lesson 11.5
Harder Multiplication Table Game	Using a multiplication table; multiplying with two factors of 10 or less		Lesson 11.5
Harder What's the Problem?	Using addition, subtraction, multiplication, and division to make different number sentences with the same answers		Lesson 12.6

* These games and their variations should be used many times throughout the year. Feel free to use them again anytime after they are introduced.

** Games in red are from the Game Mat Kit.

ⓔ**Games** These games are available as *eGames*.

ADDITION CROSSING

+	0	1	2	3	4	5	6	7	8	9	10
0	0	1	2	3	4	5	6	7	8	9	10
1	1	2	3	4	5	6	7	8	9	10	11
2	2	3	4	5	6	7	8	9	10	11	12
3	3	4	5	6	7	8	9	10	11	12	13
4	4	5	6	7	8	9	10	11	12	13	14
5	5	6	7	8	9	10	11	12	13	14	15
6	6	7	8	9	10	11	12	13	14	15	16
7	7	8	9	10	11	12	13	14	15	16	17
8	8	9	10	11	12	13	14	15	16	17	18
9	9	10	11	12	13	14	15	16	17	18	19
10	10	11	12	13	14	15	16	17	18	19	20

Math Focus:
- Practicing basic facts – using addends up to 10
- Using an addition table

Object of the Game: To be the first to complete a continuous path across the board

Players: Two

MATERIALS
Two cubes

Two cubes

25 counters of the same color for each player

SET UP
▲ Choose a direction. One of you will move horizontally (left to right) and the other will move vertically (up and down).

▲ Players roll the 0–5 **Number Cube.** The person who rolls the greater number chooses his or her counters and is followed by the second player.

HOW TO PLAY
❶ Take turns rolling any two cubes. Put a counter on any square that shows the sum of the addition fact you rolled. (For example, if you roll 3 and 8, you can put a counter on 3 + 8 or 8 + 3.)

❷ The first player to make a continuous path from one side to the opposite side is the winner. Your path can go up, down, forward, backward, or diagonally, as long as all the squares are touching each other.

ADDITION CROSSING

ADDITION TABLE GAME

Addition Table Game

Math Focus:
- Practicing basic facts—using two addends of 5 or less
- Using an addition table

Object of the Game: To have more counters at the end of the game

Players: Two

MATERIALS

Two cubes

36 counters or pennies

SET UP

▲ Every circle on the mat must be covered with a counter.

▲ Players roll the 0–5 *Number Cube.* The person who rolls the higher number goes first.

HOW TO PLAY

1. Players take turns rolling both cubes and making addition sentences out of the numbers. For example, if a 4 and a 2 are rolled, the player could say either "4 plus 2 equals 6" or "2 plus 4 equals 6."

2. After giving the addition sentence, players check their answers by looking under the appropriate counter. If correct, the player keeps the counter; if incorrect, the player replaces the counter.

3. Once the counter on a circle has been won, the circle remains empty. A player who cannot make an addition sentence that applies to a covered *circle* cannot win a counter that turn.

4. The player with more counters at the end of the game wins.

+	0	1	2	3	4	5
0	0	1	2	3	4	5
1	1	2	3	4	5	6
2	2	3	4	5	6	7
3	3	4	5	6	7	8
4	4	5	6	7	8	9
5	5	6	7	8	9	10

HARDER ADDITION TABLE GAME

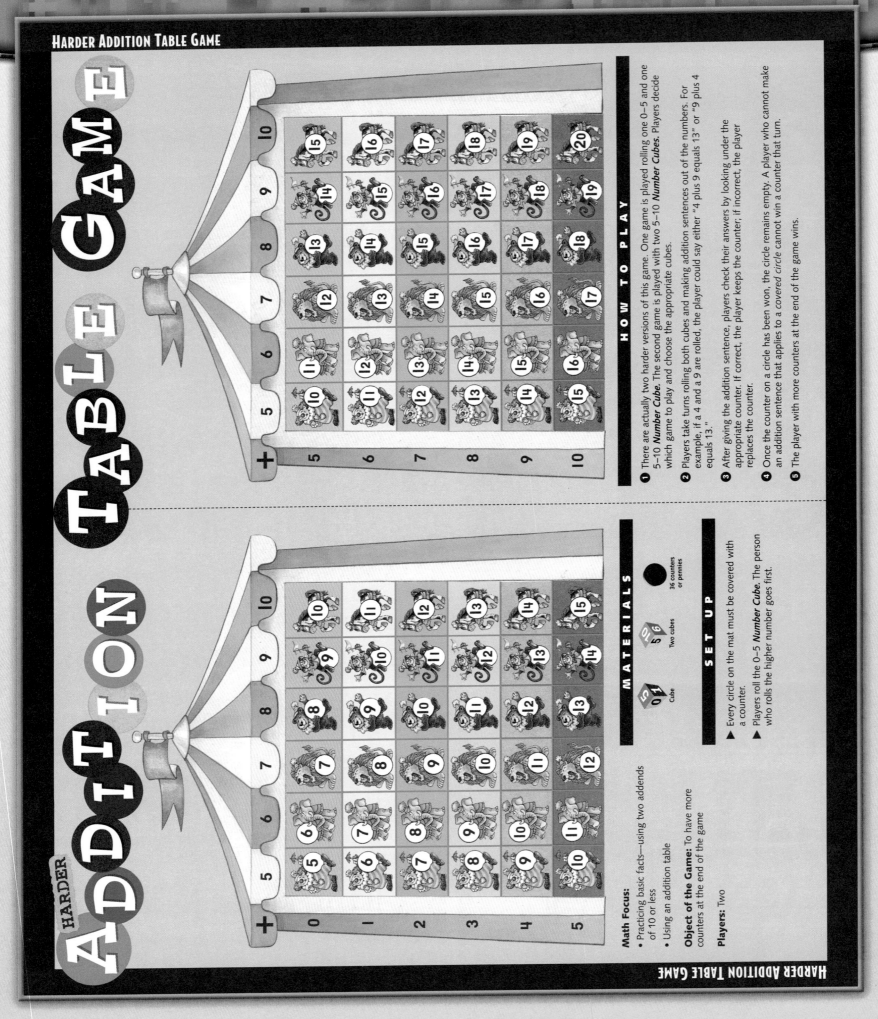

Math Focus:
- Practicing basic facts—using two addends of 10 or less
- Using an addition table

Object of the Game: To have more counters at the end of the game

Players: Two

MATERIALS

Cube

Two cubes

36 counters or pennies

SET UP

▶ Every circle on the mat must be covered with a counter.

▶ Players roll the 0–5 *Number Cube*. The person who rolls the higher number goes first.

HOW TO PLAY

1. There are actually two harder versions of this game. One game is played rolling one 0–5 and one 5–10 *Number Cube*. The second game is played with two 5–10 *Number Cubes*. Players decide which game to play and choose the appropriate cubes.

2. Players take turns rolling both cubes and making addition sentences out of the numbers. For example, if a 4 and a 9 are rolled, the player could say either "4 plus 9 equals 13" or "9 plus 4 equals 13."

3. After giving the addition sentence, players check their answers by looking under the appropriate counter. If correct, the player keeps the counter; if incorrect, the player replaces the counter.

4. Once the counter on a circle has been won, the circle remains empty. A player who cannot make an addition sentence that applies to a *covered circle* cannot win a counter that turn.

5. The player with more counters at the end of the game wins.

CALENDAR GAME

SUNDAY	MONDAY	TUESDAY	WEDNESDAY	THURSDAY	FRIDAY	SATURDAY
○	○	○	○	○	○	○

START → | **1** | **2** | **3**

4	5	6	7	8	9	10
11	12	13	14	15	16	17
18	19	20	21	22	23	24
25	26	27	28	29	30	31

FINISH

Math Focus: Using a monthly calendar

Object of the Game: To be the first to reach FINISH

Players: Two or three

MATERIALS

Cube

Place marker and counter of the same color per player

SET UP

▶ Players place their counters on one of the days of the week. Players must choose different days.

▶ The players then put their place markers on START.

▶ Players roll the 0–5 **Number Cube.** The person who rolls the highest number goes first.

HOW TO PLAY

1. Players take turns rolling the cube and advancing through the 31 days of the month. Players must say aloud the day of the week where they land.

2. A player who lands on an opponent's chosen day must either return to START if still within the first seven days of the month or go back seven days. The player remains on this space until the next roll.

3. If a player is already on an opponent's chosen day and rolls a 0, he or she must move back another seven days.

4. The first player to reach FINISH wins.

CALENDAR GAME

Sunday	Monday	Tuesday	Wednesday	Thursday	Friday	Saturday
Start Your Balance is $1000	**1** Supermarket — Pay $35	**2** Dentist Bill — Pay $50	**3** Electric Bill — Pay $26	**4** STOCK DIVIDEND — Earn $50	**5** Insurance Bill — Pay $38	**6** THEATER TICKETS — Pay $20
7 Eat in Restaurant — Pay $20	**8** WORK OVERTIME — Earn $23	**9** Supermarket — Pay $51	**10** United Fund — Pay $100	**11** Go Back 7 Spaces	**12** Income TAX — Pay $212	**13** Go to Movies — Pay $5
14 Visit Museum — FREE	**15** RENT — Pay $150	**16** Holiday! — No bills today	**17** Supermarket — Pay $47	**18** BUY BOOKS — Pay $14	**19** Telephone Bill — Pay $17	**20** Receive Rebate Check — Earn $15
21 VISIT ZOO — FREE	**22** Supermarket — Pay $35	**23** Go Back 7 Spaces	**24** Parking Ticket — Pay $5	**25** Go Ahead 2 Spaces	**26** Automobile Repairs — Pay $285	**27** WORK OVERTIME — Earn $48
28 Eat in Restaurant — Pay $22	**29** NEW SHOES — Pay $15	**30** Supermarket — Pay $51	**31** Go Back 7 Spaces	**Finish** Wait until all players finish		

CHECKBOOK GAME

Math Focus:
- Adding and subtracting two-digit and three-digit numbers
- Maintaining a record of money transactions

Object of the Game: To have the largest balance at the end of the month

Players: Two or three

MATERIALS

 Place markers

 Cube

 One balance sheet per player

SET UP

▶ Photocopies of the sample balance sheet can be handed out to students.

▶ Players prepare their balance sheets by writing "Start" on the first line under DATE and "$1000" on the first line under BALANCE.

▶ Players put their place markers on START.

▶ Players roll the 0–5 *Number Cube.* The person who rolls the highest number goes first.

HOW TO PLAY

1. Players take turns rolling the cube and moving their markers the number of spaces indicated.

2. Players follow the directions on the spaces where they land, entering the date and all payments or earnings on their balance sheets and recalculating their balances.

3. Play continues until all the players have either reached FINISH or run out of money.

4. The player with the largest balance at the end of the game is declared the winner. The other players then check the addition and subtraction in the winner's balance sheet. If the balance does not check, the player with the highest correct balance becomes the winner.

SAMPLE BALANCE SHEET

Date	Earn	Pay	Balance

CHECKBOOK GAME

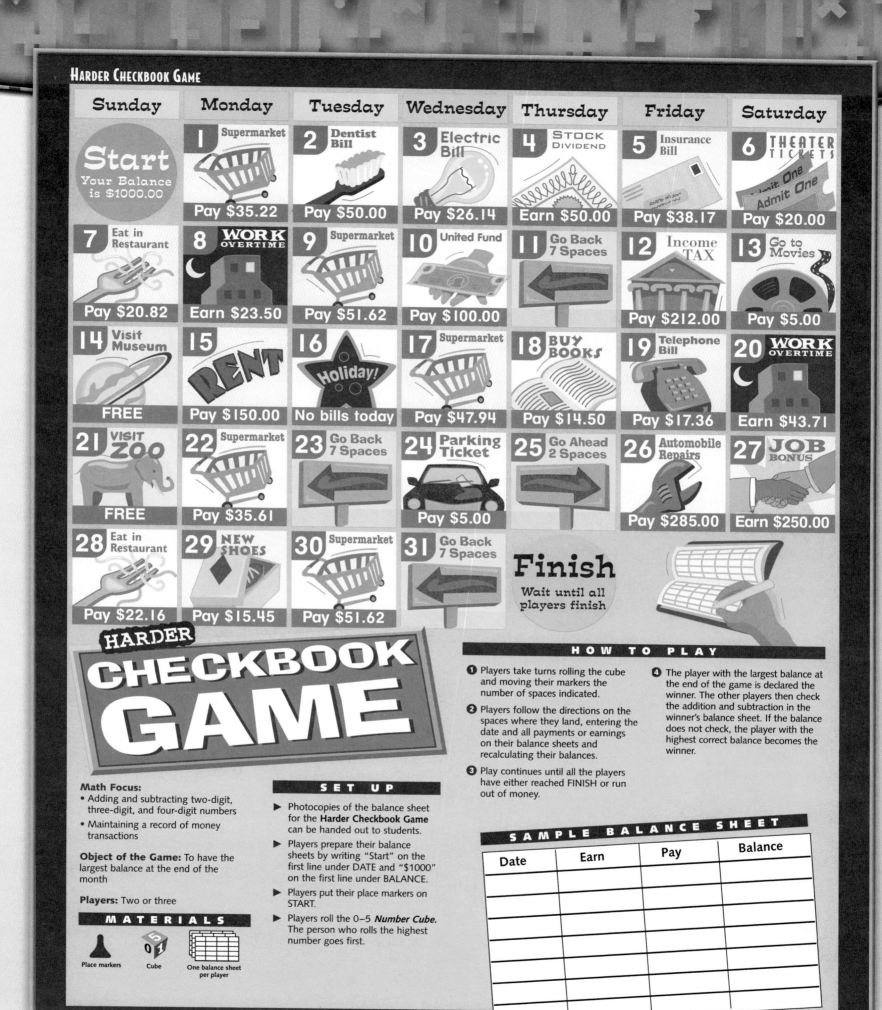

Sunday	Monday	Tuesday	Wednesday	Thursday	Friday	Saturday
Start Your Balance is $1000.00	**1** Supermarket — Pay $35.22	**2** Dentist Bill — Pay $50.00	**3** Electric Bill — Pay $26.14	**4** STOCK DIVIDEND — Earn $50.00	**5** Insurance Bill — Pay $38.17	**6** THEATER TICKETS — Pay $20.00
7 Eat in Restaurant — Pay $20.82	**8** WORK OVERTIME — Earn $23.50	**9** Supermarket — Pay $51.62	**10** United Fund — Pay $100.00	**11** Go Back 7 Spaces	**12** Income TAX — Pay $212.00	**13** Go to Movies — Pay $5.00
14 Visit Museum — FREE	**15** RENT — Pay $150.00	**16** Holiday! No bills today	**17** Supermarket — Pay $47.94	**18** BUY BOOKS — Pay $14.50	**19** Telephone Bill — Pay $17.36	**20** WORK OVERTIME — Earn $43.71
21 VISIT ZOO — FREE	**22** Supermarket — Pay $35.61	**23** Go Back 7 Spaces	**24** Parking Ticket — Pay $5.00	**25** Go Ahead 2 Spaces	**26** Automobile Repairs — Pay $285.00	**27** JOB BONUS — Earn $250.00
28 Eat in Restaurant — Pay $22.16	**29** NEW SHOES — Pay $15.45	**30** Supermarket — Pay $51.62	**31** Go Back 7 Spaces	**Finish** Wait until all players finish		

HARDER CHECKBOOK GAME

Math Focus:
- Adding and subtracting two-digit, three-digit, and four-digit numbers
- Maintaining a record of money transactions

Object of the Game: To have the largest balance at the end of the month

Players: Two or three

MATERIALS

Place markers | Cube | One balance sheet per player

SET UP

► Photocopies of the balance sheet for the **Harder Checkbook Game** can be handed out to students.

► Players prepare their balance sheets by writing "Start" on the first line under DATE and "$1000" on the first line under BALANCE.

► Players put their place markers on START.

► Players roll the 0–5 *Number Cube.* The person who rolls the highest number goes first.

HOW TO PLAY

1 Players take turns rolling the cube and moving their markers the number of spaces indicated.

2 Players follow the directions on the spaces where they land, entering the date and all payments or earnings on their balance sheets and recalculating their balances.

3 Play continues until all the players have either reached FINISH or run out of money.

4 The player with the largest balance at the end of the game is declared the winner. The other players then check the addition and subtraction in the winner's balance sheet. If the balance does not check, the player with the highest correct balance becomes the winner.

SAMPLE BALANCE SHEET

Date	Earn	Pay	Balance

HARDER CHECKBOOK GAME

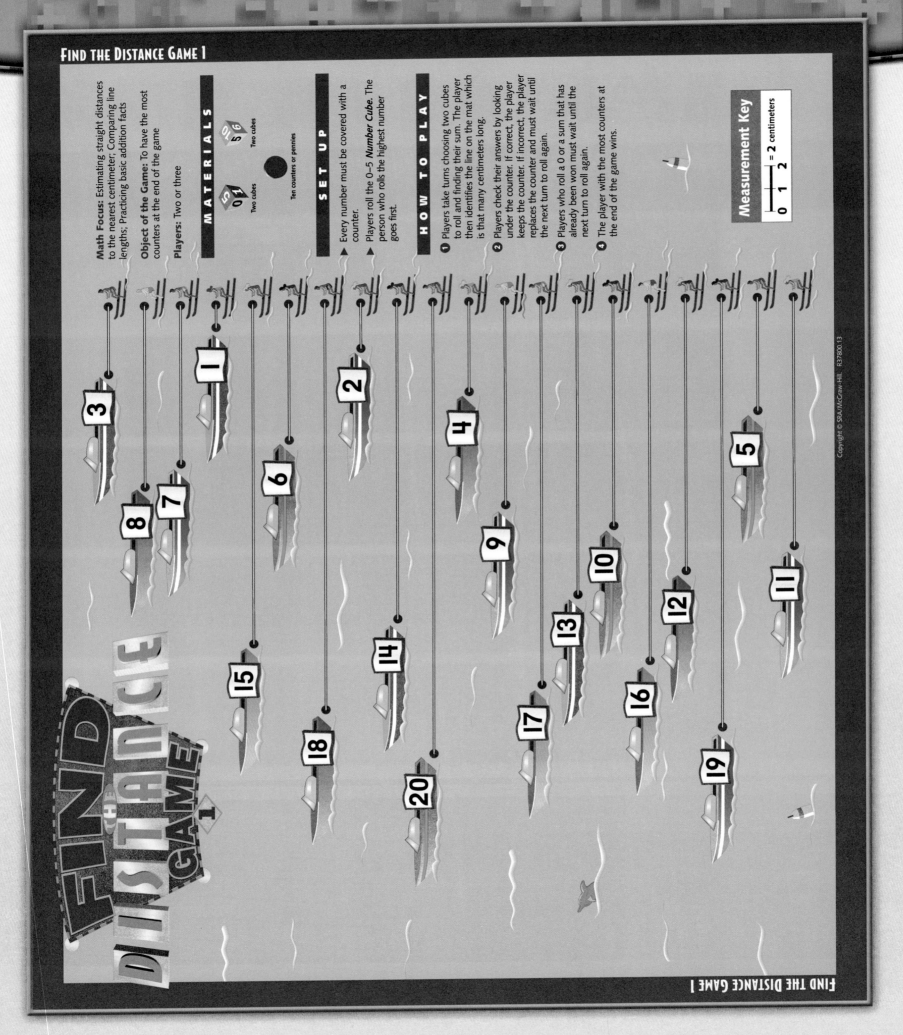

FIND the DISTANCE GAME 1

Math Focus: Estimating straight distances to the nearest centimeter; Comparing line lengths; Practicing basic addition facts

Object of the Game: To have the most counters at the end of the game

Players: Two or three

MATERIALS

Two cubes

Two cubes

Ten counters or pennies

SET UP

▲ Every number must be covered with a counter.

▲ Players roll the 0–5 *Number Cube.* The person who rolls the highest number goes first.

HOW TO PLAY

1 Players take turns choosing two cubes to roll and finding their sum. The player then identifies the line on the mat which is that many centimeters long.

2 Players check their answers by looking under the counter. If correct, the player keeps the counter. If incorrect, the player replaces the counter and must wait until the next turn to roll again.

3 Players who roll a 0 or a sum that has already been won must wait until the next turn to roll again.

4 The player with the most counters at the end of the game wins.

Measurement Key

= 2 centimeters

FIND THE DISTANCE GAME 1

FIND THE DISTANCE GAME 2

Math Focus: Estimating straight distances to the nearest centimeter; Comparing line lengths; Practicing basic addition facts

Object of the Game: To have the most counters at the end of the game

Players: Two or three

MATERIALS

Two cubes

Two cubes

Twenty counters or pennies

SET UP

▶ Every number must be covered with a counter.

▶ Players roll the 0–5 *Number Cube.* The person who rolls the highest number goes first.

HOW TO PLAY

1. Players take turns choosing two cubes to roll and finding their sum. The player then identifies the line on the mat which is that many centimeters long.

2. Players check their answers by looking under the counter. If correct, the player keeps the counter. If incorrect, the player replaces the counter and must wait until the next turn to roll again.

3. Players who roll a 0 or a sum that has already been won must wait until the next turn to roll again.

4. The player with the most counters at the end of the game wins.

BALLOONS

Measurement Key

= **6** centimeters

FIND THE DISTANCE GAME 2

FRACTION GAME

1/1

1/2 1/2

1/2 1/2

1/3 1/3
1/3

1/3 1/3
1/3

1/3 1/3
1/3

1/2
1/2

1/2

1/4 1/4
1/4 1/4

1/4 1/4
1/4 1/4

1/4 1/4
1/4 1/4

1/5 1/5
1/5
1/5 1/5

1/3 1/3
1/3

1/4 1/4
1/4
1/4 1/4

1/5 1/5
1/5
1/5 1/5

1/5 1/5
1/5
1/5 1/5

1/5 1/5
1/5
1/5 1/5

Math Focus:
- Recognizing fractional areas of a circle up to fifths
- Recognizing which common fractions sum to more than one half when added together

Object of the Game: To own more circles at the end of the game

Players: Two

MATERIALS

Two cubes

25 counters of the same color for each player, or 25 pennies and 25 nickels

SET UP

► Players roll the 0–5 *Number Cube.* The person who rolls the higher number goes first.

► The first player chooses his or her counters. The second player uses the remaining pieces.

HOW TO PLAY

❶ Players take turns rolling the cubes and making fractions equal to or less than 1.

❷ Players may divide their roll between more than one circle. For example, a player who rolls a 4 and a 5 may cover 1/5 of one circle and 3/5 of another.

❸ Players who roll one 0 cannot place a counter. Players who roll double 0s may roll both cubes again.

❹ A circle is awarded to a player who has covered more than half of it. That player puts a counter in the center of the circle and returns any of the opponent's counters. If half of a circle is covered by one player and half by the other player, neither player may own the circle.

❺ Play continues until all the circles are either owned or completely covered. The player with more circles is the winner.

FRACTION GAME

FROG POND GAME

Go

Math Focus: Practicing basic math–using two addends of 10 or less

Object of the Game: To have the most counters at the end of the game

Players: Two or three

MATERIALS

Place markers

Cube

20 counters or pennies per player

SET UP

▲ Every circle on the mat must be covered with a counter.

▲ Extra counters are placed on the space marked BANK.

▲ Players put their place markers on GO.

▲ Players roll the 0–5 *Number Cube.* The person who rolls the highest number goes first.

HOW TO PLAY

1 Players take turns rolling the cube and moving their markers the number of spaces indicated.

2 After landing on a space, a player may win the counter there by correctly completing the addition sentence.

3 Players check their answers by lifting the counters. If correct, the player keeps the counter. If incorrect, the player replaces the counter and remains on that space.

4 A player cannot win a counter if there is none in a space. A player who gives an incorrect answer and rolls a 0 on the next turn can try again to win the counter.

5 Players collect two counters from the bank each time they pass or land on GO.

6 The player with the most counters at the end of the game wins.

$0 + 9 = 9$

$4 + 4 = 8$

$9 + 3 = 12$

$10 + 10 = 20$

$5 + 6 = 11$

$8 + 8 = 16$

$3 + 2 = 5$

$1 + 8 = 9$

bank

$8 + 7 = 15$

$5 + 1 = 6$

$7 + 6 = 13$

$10 + 4 = 14$

$7 + 2 = 9$

$6 + 9 = 15$

$3 + 6 = 9$

$2 + 9 = 11$

HARDER FROG POND GAME

Go

$16 - 7 = 9$

$14 - 7 = 7$

$6 + 10 = 16$

$17 - 9 = 8$

$10 - 2 = 8$

$6 + 8 = 14$

$12 - 6 = 6$

$9 + 9 = 18$

$10 + 2 = 12$

bank

$5 + 5 = 10$

$3 + 7 = 10$

$13 - 5 = 8$

$17 - 10 = 7$

$15 - 6 = 9$

$3 + 4 = 7$

$12 - 5 = 7$

Math Focus: Solving mixed addition and subtraction fact problems

Object of the Game: To have the most counters at the end of the game

Players: Two or three

MATERIALS

Place markers

Cube

20 counters or pennies per player

SET UP

▶ Every circle on the mat must be covered with a counter.

▶ Extra counters are placed on the space marked BANK.

▶ Players roll the 0–5 *Number Cube.* The person who rolls the highest number goes first.

HOW TO PLAY

1 Players take turns rolling the cube and moving their markers the number of spaces indicated.

2 After landing on a space, a player may win the counter there by correctly completing the addition or subtraction sentence.

3 Players check their answers by lifting the counters. If correct, the player keeps the counter. If incorrect, the player replaces the counter and remains on that space.

4 A player cannot win a counter if there is none in a space. A player who gives an incorrect answer and rolls a 0 on the next turn can try again to win the counter.

5 Players collect two counters from the bank each time they pass or land on GO.

6 The player with the most counters at the end of the game wins.

MAP GAME

Math Focus: Using compass directions and mathematical reasoning

Object of the Game: To be the first to cover six pictures

Players: Two or three

MATERIALS

Place markers

Cube

Ten counters of the same color for each player, or ten pennies, nickels, and dimes

SET UP

▲ Players roll the 0–5 *Number Cube.* The person who rolls the highest number chooses which counters to use and is followed by the other players.

▲ Players put their place markers on START.

▲ The person who rolled the highest number also goes first.

HOW TO PLAY

1. Before rolling, players must announce in which direction they intend to move that turn. Players who forget to announce their direction before rolling cannot move that turn.

2. Players roll the cube and move their markers the number of spaces indicated. If they land on a picture, they cover it with a counter.

3. Players cannot move if they roll a number that would land them on a picture that is already covered. Also, players who roll a number that would take them off the board cannot move that turn.

4. During the game, players can move freely back and forth across the START square.

5. The first player to cover six pictures wins the game.

MAP GAME

EAST

NORTH

START

SOUTH

WEST

Multiplication Table Game

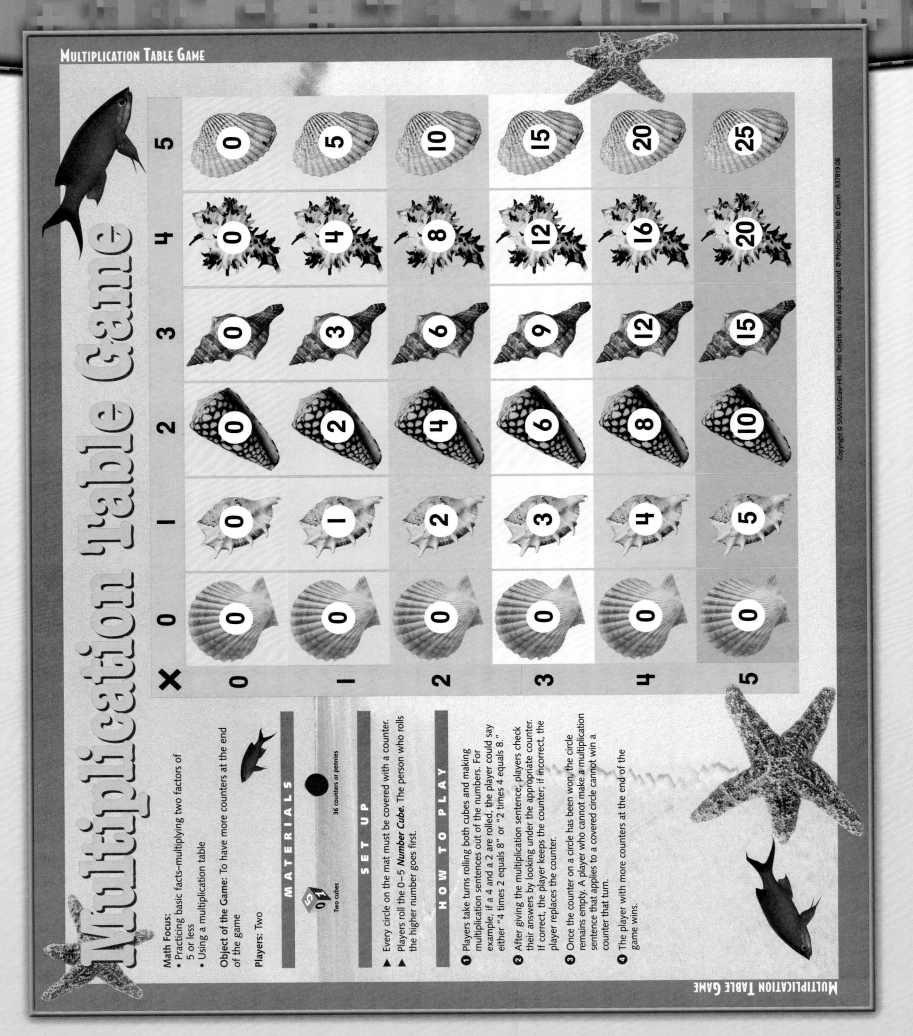

×	0	1	2	3	4	5
0	0	0	0	0	0	0
1	0	1	2	3	4	5
2	0	2	4	6	8	10
3	0	3	6	9	12	15
4	0	4	8	12	16	20
5	0	5	10	15	20	25

Math Focus:
- Practicing basic facts—multiplying two factors of 5 or less
- Using a multiplication table

Object of the Game: To have more counters at the end of the game

Players: Two

MATERIALS

Two cubes

36 counters or pennies

SET UP

▲ Every circle on the mat must be covered with a counter.

▲ Players roll the 0–5 *Number Cube.* The person who rolls the higher number goes first.

HOW TO PLAY

❶ Players take turns rolling both cubes and making multiplication sentences out of the numbers. For example, if a 4 and a 2 are rolled, the player could say either "4 times 2 equals 8" or "2 times 4 equals 8."

❷ After giving the multiplication sentence, players check their answers by looking under the appropriate counter. If correct, the player keeps the counter; if incorrect, the player replaces the counter.

❸ Once the counter on a circle has been won, the circle remains empty. A player who cannot make a multiplication sentence that applies to a covered circle cannot win a counter that turn.

❹ The player with more counters at the end of the game wins.

MULTIPLICATION TABLE GAME

HARDER Multiplication Table Game

Math Focus:
- Practicing basic facts—multiplying two factors of 10 or less
- Using a multiplication table

Object of the Game: To have more counters at the end of the game

Players: Two

MATERIALS

Cube

Two cubes

36 counters or pennies

SET UP

- Every circle on the mat must be covered with a counter.
- Players roll the 0–5 *Number Cube.* The person who rolls the higher number goes first.

HOW TO PLAY

1. There are actually two harder versions of this game. One game is played rolling one 0–5 and one 5–10 *Number Cube.* The second game is played with two 5–10 *Number Cubes.* Players take turns rolling both cubes and making multiplication sentences out of the numbers. For example, if a 4 and a 9 are rolled, the player could say either "4 times 9 equals 36" or "9 times 4 equals 36."

2. After giving the multiplication sentence, players check their answers by looking under the appropriate counter.

   If correct, the player keeps the counter; if incorrect, the player replaces the counter.

3. Once the counter on a circle has been won, the circle remains empty. A player who cannot make a multiplication sentence that applies to a covered circle cannot win a counter that turn.

4. The player with more counters at the end of the game wins.

Table (5–10)

✕	5	6	7	8	9	10
5	25	30	35	40	45	50
6	30	36	42	48	54	60
7	35	42	49	56	63	70
8	40	48	56	64	72	80
9	45	54	63	72	81	90
10	50	60	70	80	90	100

Table (0–5 and 5–10)

✕	5	6	7	8	9	10
0	0	0	0	0	0	0
1	5	6	7	8	9	10
2	10	12	14	16	18	20
3	15	18	21	24	27	30
4	20	24	28	32	36	40
5	25	30	35	40	45	50

RUMMAGE SALE GAME

GO!

$100 $22 $10

$23

$47 $201

$63 $110

$114 $101

$3

$35

$14

$81

$5

$25

Math Focus:
- Changing money ($1, $10, $100)
- Practicing regrouping in preparation for multidigit addition

Object of the Game: To be the first player to collect a $1,000 bill

Players: Two or three

SET UP

▲ Players sort the money into piles next to the game mat.
▲ Players put their place markers on GO.
▲ Players roll the 0–5 *Number Cube.* The person who rolls the highest number goes first.

HOW TO PLAY

1 Players take turns rolling the cube and moving their place markers the number of spaces indicated.

2 After landing on a space, the player says the price of the object pictured there and collects that amount from the money next to the game mat. Players must count the bills aloud.

3 Players do not collect money for passing or landing on GO.

4 Players should keep their $1, $10, and $100 bills in separate piles. They must trade up whenever possible: ones for tens, tens for hundreds, and hundreds for a thousand. The first player to collect a $1,000 bill wins the game.

MATERIALS

Place markers

Cube

Per player:
ten $1 bills
ten $10 bills
ten $100 bills
one $1,000 bill

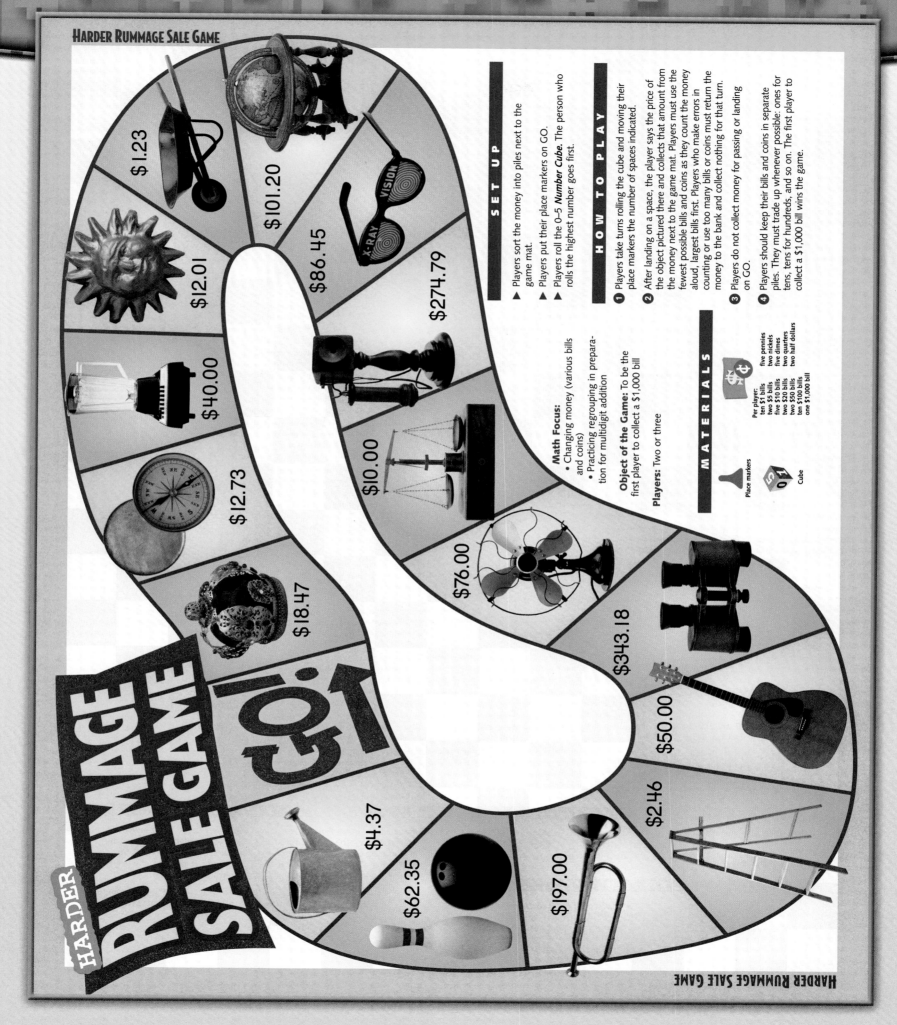

HARDER RUMMAGE SALE GAME

RUMMAGE SALE GAME
HARDER

GO

$1.23

$101.20

$86.45

$274.79

$12.01

$40.00

$12.73

$10.00

$18.47

$76.00

$343.18

$50.00

$2.46

$4.37

$62.35

$197.00

SET UP

▲ Players sort the money into piles next to the game mat.

▲ Players put their place markers on GO.

▲ Players roll the 0–5 *Number Cube*. The person who rolls the highest number goes first.

HOW TO PLAY

❶ Players take turns rolling the cube and moving their place markers the number of spaces indicated.

❷ After landing on a space, the player says the price of the object pictured there and collects that amount from the money next to the game mat. Players must use the fewest possible bills and coins as they count the money aloud, largest bills first. Players who make errors in counting or use too many bills or coins must return the money to the bank and collect nothing for that turn.

❸ Players do not collect money for passing or landing on GO.

❹ Players should keep their bills and coins in separate piles. They must trade up whenever possible: ones for tens, tens for hundreds, and so on. The first player to collect a $1,000 bill wins the game.

Math Focus:
• Changing money (various bills and coins)
• Practicing regrouping in preparation for multidigit addition

Object of the Game: To be the first player to collect a $1,000 bill

Players: Two or three

MATERIALS

Place markers

Cube

five pennies
two nickels
five dimes
two quarters
two half dollars

Per player:
ten $1 bills
two $5 bills
five $10 bills
two $20 bills
two $50 bills
ten $100 bills
one $1,000 bill

HARDER RUMMAGE SALE GAME

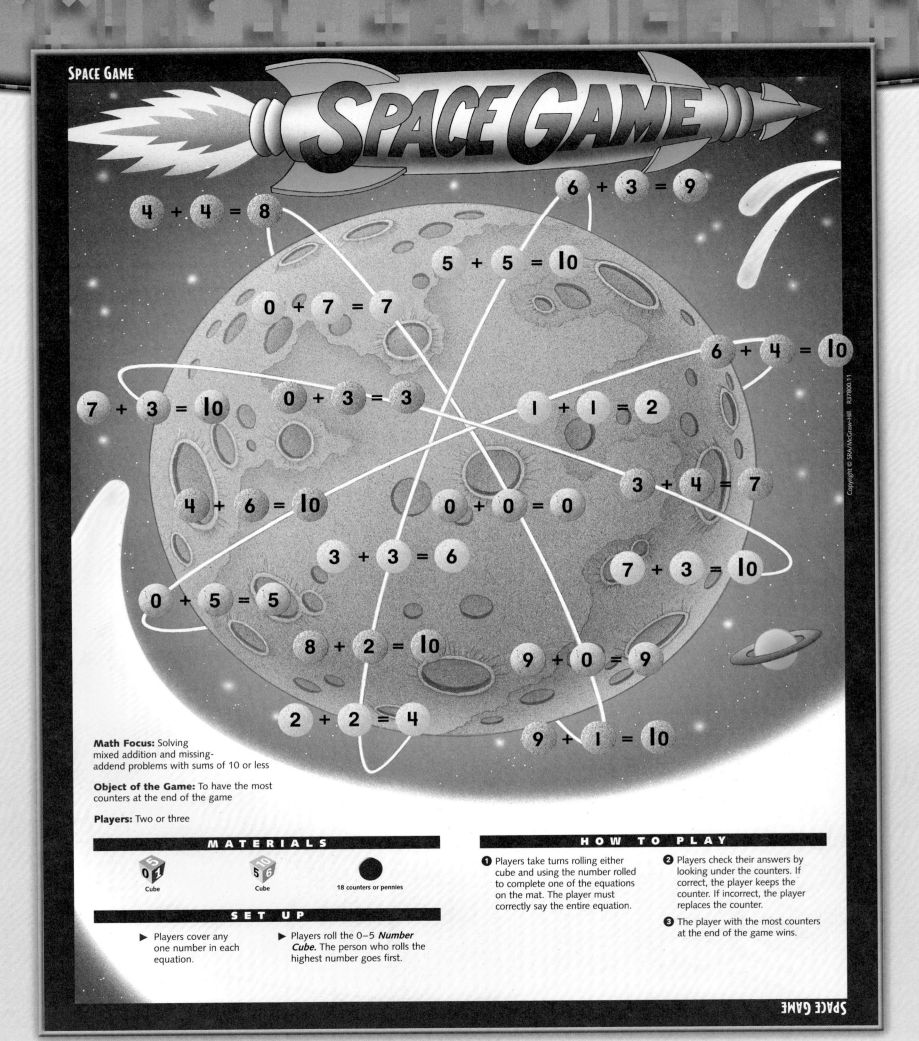

SPACE GAME

6 + 3 = 9

4 + 4 = 8

5 + 5 = 10

0 + 7 = 7

6 + 4 = 10

7 + 3 = 10

0 + 3 = 3

1 + 1 = 2

3 + 4 = 7

4 + 6 = 10

0 + 0 = 0

3 + 3 = 6

7 + 3 = 10

0 + 5 = 5

8 + 2 = 10

9 + 0 = 9

2 + 2 = 4

9 + 1 = 10

Math Focus: Solving mixed addition and missing-addend problems with sums of 10 or less

Object of the Game: To have the most counters at the end of the game

Players: Two or three

MATERIALS

Cube

Cube

18 counters or pennies

SET UP

▶ Players cover any one number in each equation.

▶ Players roll the 0–5 **Number Cube.** The person who rolls the highest number goes first.

HOW TO PLAY

❶ Players take turns rolling either cube and using the number rolled to complete one of the equations on the mat. The player must correctly say the entire equation.

❷ Players check their answers by looking under the counters. If correct, the player keeps the counter. If incorrect, the player replaces the counter.

❸ The player with the most counters at the end of the game wins.

SPACE GAME

HARDER SPACE GAME

$10 - 7 = 3$

$7 - 2 = 5$

$0 + 0 = 0$

$3 + 6 = 9$

$6 - 1 = 5$

$6 - 5 = 1$

$1 + 9 = 10$

$3 + 6 = 9$

$3 + 6 = 9$

$5 + 5 = 10$

$1 - 0 = 1$

$1 + 8 = 9$

$5 - 3 = 2$

$8 - 4 = 4$

$6 + 4 = 10$

$2 + 1 = 3$

$4 + 2 = 6$

$8 - 3 = 5$

Math Focus: Solving mixed addition, subtraction, missing-addend, -minuend, and -subtrahend problems with numbers of 10 or less

Object of the Game: To have the most counters at the end of the game

Players: Two or three

MATERIALS

Cube

Cube

18 counters or pennies

SET UP

▶ Players cover any one number in each equation.

▶ Players roll the 0–5 **Number Cube.** The person who rolls the highest number goes first.

HOW TO PLAY

❶ Players take turns rolling either cube and using the number rolled to complete one of the equations on the mat. The player must correctly say the entire equation.

❷ Players check their answers by looking under the counters. If correct, the player keeps the counter. If incorrect, the player replaces the counter.

❸ The player with the most counters at the end of the game wins.

HARDER SPACE GAME

Go

9:15

2:40

8:40

12:10

Time Game

1:25

2:05

9:25

12:50

3:35

11:05

6:50

Math Focus: Telling time to five-minute intervals

Object of the Game: To have the most counters at the end of the game

Players: Two or three

MATERIALS

Place markers   Cube   16 counters or pennies

SET UP

▶ The red answer circles in each space must be covered by a counter.

▶ Players put their place markers on the space marked GO.

▶ Players roll the 0–5 **Number Cube.** The person who rolls the highest number goes first.

HOW TO PLAY

❶ Players take turns rolling the cube and moving their place markers the number of spaces indicated. Players must correctly state the time indicated on the clock in each space where they land.

❷ Players check their answers by looking under the counter. If correct, the player keeps the counter; if incorrect, the player replaces the counter.

❸ A player who gives an incorrect answer and then rolls a 0 on the next turn may try again to win the counter.

❹ Players who land on empty circles cannot win a counter and must wait until the next turn to roll again.

❺ Players who land on the space marked PENALTY must, if possible, place one of their own counters on an empty circle.

❻ The player with the most counters at the end of the game wins.

4:45

4:10

5:55

10:20

7:05

Penalty
COVER AN ANSWER

HARDER TIME GAME

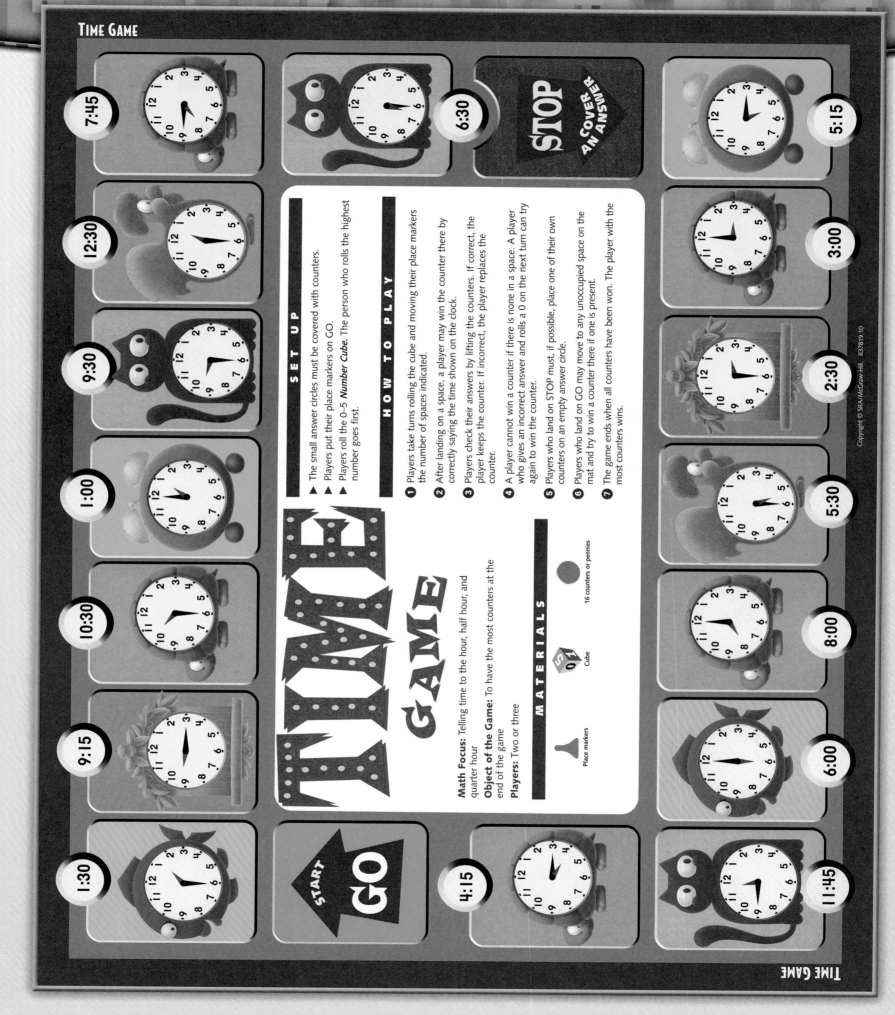

TIME GAME

7:45 · **12:30** · **9:30** · **1:00** · **10:30** · **9:15** · **1:30**

6:30 · STOP COVER AN ANSWER

5:15 · **3:00** · **2:30** · **5:30** · **8:00** · **6:00** · **11:45**

4:15

GO START

TIME GAME

Math Focus: Telling time to the hour, half hour, and quarter hour

Object of the Game: To have the most counters at the end of the game

Players: Two or three

MATERIALS

Place markers

Cube

16 counters or pennies

SET UP

▲ The small answer circles must be covered with counters.

▲ Players put their place markers on GO.

▲ Players roll the 0–5 *Number Cube.* The person who rolls the highest number goes first.

HOW TO PLAY

1 Players take turns rolling the cube and moving their place markers the number of spaces indicated.

2 After landing on a space, a player may win the counter there by correctly saying the time shown on the clock.

3 Players check their answers by lifting the counters. If correct, the player keeps the counter. If incorrect, the player replaces the counter.

4 A player cannot win a counter if there is none in a space. A player who gives an incorrect answer and rolls a 0 on the next turn can try again to win the counter.

5 Players who land on STOP must, if possible, place one of their own counters on an empty answer circle.

6 Players who land on GO may move to any unoccupied space on the mat and try to win a counter there if one is present.

7 The game ends when all counters have been won. The player with the most counters wins.

Copyright © SRA/McGraw-Hill. R37819.10

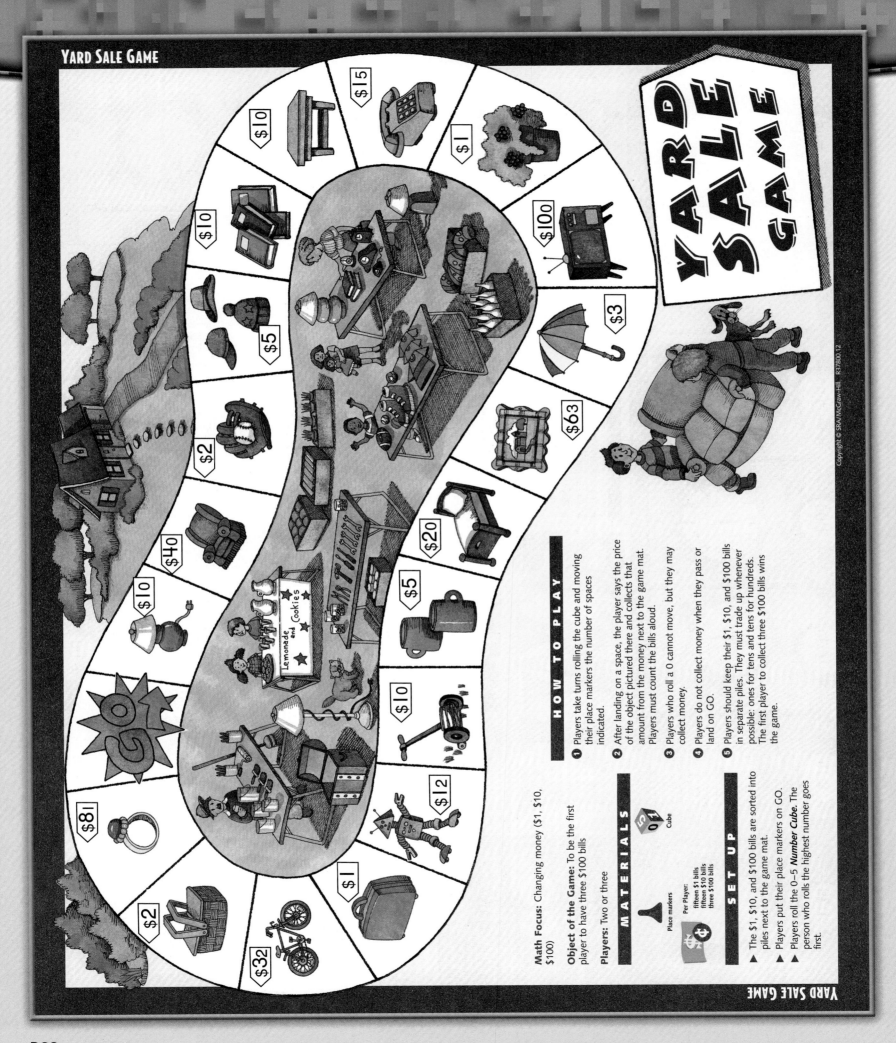

Math Focus: Changing money ($1, $10, $100)

Object of the Game: To be the first player to have three $100 bills

Players: Two or three

MATERIALS

Cube

Place markers

Per Player:
fifteen $1 bills
fifteen $10 bills
three $100 bills

SET UP

▲ The $1, $10, and $100 bills are sorted into piles next to the game mat.

▲ Players put their place markers on GO.

▲ Players roll the 0–5 *Number Cube.* The person who rolls the highest number goes first.

HOW TO PLAY

① Players take turns rolling the cube and moving their place markers the number of spaces indicated.

② After landing on a space, the player says the price of the object pictured there and collects that amount from the money next to the game mat. Players must count the bills aloud.

③ Players who roll a 0 cannot move, but they may collect money.

④ Players do not collect money when they pass or land on GO.

⑤ Players should keep their $1, $10, and $100 bills in separate piles. They must trade up whenever possible: ones for tens and tens for hundreds. The first player to collect three $100 bills wins the game.

Copyright © SRA/McGraw-Hill. R37800.12

HARDER YARD SALE GAME

$35 $18 $55 $60 $14 $7 $20 $15 $12 $37 $25 $10 $9 $65 $50 $15 $21 $20 $20

Lemonade and Cookies

Math Focus: Changing money ($1, $5, $10, $20, $50, $100)

Object of the Game: To be the first player to have three $100 bills

Players: Two or three

HOW TO PLAY

1. Players take turns rolling the cube and moving their place markers the number of spaces indicated.

2. After landing on a space, the player says the price of the object pictured there and collects that amount from the money next to the game mat. Players must use the fewest number of bills possible and count them aloud, largest bills first.

3. Players who roll a 0 cannot move, but they may collect money.

4. Players do not collect money when they pass or land on GO.

5. Players should keep their bills in separate piles. They must trade up whenever possible: ones for fives, tens for twenties, and so on. The first player to collect three $100 bills wins the game.

MATERIALS

Place markers

Cube

Per player:
seven $1 bills
three $5 bills
five $10 bills

five $20 bills
three $50 bills
three $100 bills

SET UP

▲ The money is sorted into piles next to the game mat.

▲ Players put their place markers on GO.

▲ Players roll the 0–5 **Number Cube.** The person who rolls the highest number goes first.

HARDER YARD SALE GAME

Index

Index

Index

Index

Index

Index